W9-CSA-877

Viscoelastic Fluids

CHEMICAL PROCESSING AND ENGINEERING

An International Series of Monographs and Textbooks

EDITORS

Lyle F. Albright
Purdue University
West Lafayette, Indiana

R. N. Maddox
Oklahoma State University
Stillwater, Oklahoma

John J. McKetta
University of Texas
at Austin
Austin, Texas

IN PREPARATION

Viscoelastic Fluids

AN INTRODUCTION TO
THEIR PROPERTIES AND BEHAVIOR

Ronald Darby

Department of Chemical Engineering
Texas A & M University
College Station, Texas

MARCEL DEKKER, INC.   New York and Basel

TA
418
.22
D37
CHEM

CHEMISTRY

6129 6302

COPYRIGHT © 1976 by MARCEL DEKKER, INC. ALL RIGHTS RESERVED.

Neither this book nor any part may be reproduced or transmitted
in any form or by any means, electronic or mechanical, including
photocopying, microfilming, and recording, or by any information
storage and retrieval system, without permission in writing from
the publisher.

MARCEL DEKKER, INC.

270 Madison Avenue, New York, New York 10016

LIBRARY OF CONGRESS CATALOG CARD NUMBER: 75-39437

ISBN: 0-8247-6412-9

Current printing (last digit):
10 9 8 7 6 5 4 3 2 1

PRINTED IN THE UNITED STATES OF AMERICA

PREFACE

The objective of this book is to provide the student with the background in the concepts and principles of continuum mechanics which are necessary to an understanding and a proper description of the very complex flow properties of viscoelastic materials. The need for such knowledge has been greatly intensified by the explosive nature of the world-wide polymer industry, and the recognition of the fact that polymeric materials exhibit complex and unusual flow characteristics when processed in the molten or solution state.

The material is intended for those who have little or no previous knowledge of the subject, and represents a conscientious attempt to "bridge the gap" between the oversimplified one-dimensional approach to linear viscoelasticity and the highly mathematical generalized approach of tensor calculus. The book evolved over a number of years from notes prepared for an introductory interdisciplinary engineering course in continuum mechanics and rheology. Continuous interaction with the students, who represented essentially the entire spectrum of engineering disciplines, provided the primary stimulus for development and constant revision of the material. As a result, a conscious attempt has been made to write from the viewpoint of the student as well as the teacher. Because of this, the

7589

material is presented in ascending sequence of difficulty, with concepts introduced and illustrated in terms of simple one-dimensional deformations before generalizing to more complex systems. Consequently, as much material as possible is presented without recourse to the mathematical properties of general tensors until a familiarity with the physical concepts is developed. Indeed, it is strongly felt that the previously unexposed student develops a "feel" for the material much more quickly if the emphasis is placed on the physical rather than the mathematical details. It is for this reason that the elegant formulations of continuum mechanics have been delayed until after the physical and phenomenological aspects have been discussed.

The objective which has been set with regard to mathematical rigor is that which has been so aptly stated by Margenau and Murphy:*

> The degree of rigor to which we have aspired is that customary in careful scientific demonstrations, not the lofty heights accessible to the pure mathematician. For this we make no apology; if the history of the exact sciences teaches anything it is that emphasis on extreme rigor often engenders sterility, and that the successful pioneer depends more on brilliant hunches than on the results of existence theorems. We trust, of course, that our effort to avoid rigor mortis has not brought us dangerously close to the opposite extreme of sloppy reasoning.

While an effort has been made to ensure that the material is as current as possible, the emphasis is primarily on fundamental concepts many of which are classical in nature. Thus the references cited are not intended to comprise a complete survey of the latest "state-of-the-art," but are intended only to be illustrative. Indeed, any attempt at a comprehensive survey of the latest developments would be essentially futile because of the rapid development of the field of rheology and the controversy surrounding the tentative nature of many of the latest results.

---

*Preface from H. Margenau and G. M. Murphy, *The Mathematics of Physics and Chemistry*, Van Nostrand, New York, 1957.

The scope of the book has been limited to the continuum properties of materials and has not included the so-called "molecular
theories" of rheology. This is primarily because the book is written
by an engineer for students of engineering or others interested primarily in relating measurable properties of a complex material to its
mechanical behavior. There are many who feel that a description of
material properties is insufficient unless these properties can be
related to molecular parameters. Indeed, a most extensive literature has built up around attempts to do just that, but the results
have generally been disappointing. There is as yet no theory which
has been successful in accurately predicting rheological properties
of complex (e.g., polymeric) materials from purely molecular characteristics. This differentiation between "continuum" and "molecular"
rheology was addressed by Truesdell in his classical treatise* with
the following comment:

> I hope that what little I can present will encourage
> the reader to question the all too common assumption
> that because physical matter is composed of molecules,
> a theory based on the crudest and most unrealistic
> molecular hypothesis is automatically preferable to
> any continuum theory. Indeed, I contend that gross
> phenomena are most naturally, accurately, and elegantly
> represented by gross hypotheses alone.

Rather than being mutually exclusive, the molecular and continuum
approaches are indeed complementary. The mechanical properties of
materials which govern their deformation behavior can only be properly defined with reference to continuum concepts of stress and
strain, whereas the ultimate goal would be an understanding of
how these properties relate to molecular structure. However, inasmuch as even the simplest rheological property of an ideal viscous
liquid, its viscosity, cannot as yet be calculated from molecular
parameters only, this goal must be considered to be unattainable
for complex materials in context of the present state-of-the-art.

---

*C. Truesdell, *Continuum Mechanics I, The Foundations of Elas-
ticity and Fluid Dynamics*, App. 1, Gordon and Breach, New York, 1966.

The author has been influenced by the writings of so many workers in the fields of fluid mechanics and rheology, that it has been impossible to give adequate credit to all. Of particular influence, however, have been the enlightening works of J. G. Oldroyd and, especially, R. B. Bird, his coworkers, and students. Sincere apologies are offered to those who may have contributed, indirectly or otherwise, but have not been acknowledged.

Special gratitude is due to my wife and children, and to the Chemical Engineering Department, Texas A&M University, for making this work possible.

Ronald Darby
College Station, Texas

INTRODUCTION

In 1970, the worldwide production of polymeric plastic materials was on the order of 150 billion pounds. Based on the rate of growth at that time, it has been estimated that the total volume of polymers used for all purposes will exceed that of metals by the early 1980's. We need only to look briefly around us to identify hundreds of items made of polymeric materials that we encounter every day.

Essentially all of these materials were produced and processed in the liquid (molten or solution) state. These polymeric liquids, because of their very complex structure, exhibit complicated and unusual flow behavior. Not only do they exhibit widely varying and nonlinear viscous properties, but they also exhibit very marked elastic properties which are, in turn, responsible for some rather remarkable effects. For example a molten polymer extruded from a die will swell to a size considerably larger than the die, in contrast to a linear inelastic fluid which may contract instead. The elastic properties of these fluids create "extra" forces under flow conditions which may cause circulation patterns in equipment which are exactly opposite to those exhibited by inelastic fluids, or may cause the polymer to climb up the shaft of a rotating stirrer instead of being thrown away from it. In flows through pipes and vessels, these fluids may exhibit much larger pressure drops across orifices,

fittings, or in the entrance region of tubes, than an inelastic
fluid. Conversely, some very dilute solutions of high polymers in
turbulent flow in straight tubes may exhibit as much as 80% less
pressure drop than the solvent alone at the same flow rate.

These effects, as well as many other equally remarkable phenomena, cannot be explained on the basis of classical Newtonian
fluid mechanics. While the fundamental principles of the conservation of mass, energy, and momentum, and the basic laws of mechanics
still apply, the properties of the materials to which they must be
applied are very complex and must be properly and carefully defined
in order to permit realistic and consistent predictions of material
behavior. Our objective is, therefore, to present those fundamental
concepts and principles which are necessary to the proper description of the mechanical behavior of complex materials, with special
emphasis on nonlinear viscoelastic fluids. These principles are
applied to the problems of properly determining and describing the
mechanical properties of such materials which are responsible for
their unusual behavior, as well as the utilization of the resulting
information to determine the flow behavior of a specific material.

Although the primary stimulus and need for such information
derives mainly from the explosive polymer industry, the concepts,
principles and methods apply equally to other complex materials
such as slurries, suspensions, etc., under appropriate conditions.
Inasmuch as our emphasis is on fundamental principles and methods,
and their application, no attempt has been made to provide a collection of data for specific materials. Indeed, such a collection of
data would rapidly become obsolete because of the immense variation in possible materials and the relatively small amount of reliable and comprehensive data available. On the other hand, the
principles and methods required to obtain, describe, and utilize
such data are much more permanent.

As usual, space limitations have governed the scope of material
which could be presented. Consequently the treatment has been
limited to the continuum mechanical properties of isothermal laminar systems. Thus the consideration of temperature effects,

relations between molecular and mechanical properties, and turbulent flow systems has been omitted despite the fact that a large volume of literature and many interesting results have been developed relative to these topics.

CONTENTS

Viscoelastic Fluids

Chapter 1

BASIC CONCEPTS

1.1. INTRODUCTION

This chapter presents a qualitative introduction to the basic concepts which constitute the foundations of continuum mechanics, upon which all of the material in this book is based. Classical definitions of basic terms and variables are presented, with an attempt to emphasize their physical rather than their mathematical significance. Cartesian tensor index notation is explained and utilized, but the mathematics of tensor analysis is deferred until considerably later until the reader has developed more of a familiarity with the physical significance of the quantities involved. This will be done in subsequent chapters by consideration of special cases involving simple deformations, and simple materials, with more general relations being deferred until after the mathematics are developed.

1.2. WHAT IS RHEOLOGY?

The classical definition of rheology is "the science of deformation and flow of matter." Specifically, it is concerned with those properties of matter which determine how it will deform or flow when subjected to an external force or systems of forces.

Hence, rheology could be considered a "material science," since it is concerned with material properties, i.e., rheological or mechanical properties.

However, rheology is more commonly classified as a branch of mechanics, for it is by application of the basic laws of mechanics that rheological properties are determined. Application of these laws to determine the physical forces which cause motion comprises the subject of *dynamics*. The mathematical quantity which represents these forces is stress, which may be considered the *primary dynamic variable*. Stress represents a "force concentration," with dimensions of force per unit area. Since both force and area have directional as well as magnitude characteristics, there will, in general, be a number of directional components of stress. The general representation which includes or implies all of these components is called the *stress tensor*.

When subjected to a stress, all real materials will deform to a greater or lesser extent. If the material is a fluid, it may deform continuously or flow. A description of the state of deformation or motion is the subject of *kinematics*, the *primary kinematic variables* being *strain* and *strain rate*. Strain is a measure of deformation, being essentially a "relative displacement" (no dimensions). Thus strain is determined by displacement gradients, and strain rate by velocity gradients. These are also tensor quantities having a number of components, represented by the *strain* and *rate of strain tensors*.

The specific relationship between an applied stress and the resulting deformation of a material is a unique function of the material. This function defines the *rheological properties* of the material. These can be expressed either empirically in terms of material functions, which relate specific components of stress and strain or strain rate, or in terms of a *rheological equation of state* (sometimes called a *constitutive equation*), which is an analytical relation between the complete stress and strain (strain rate) tensors. Rheological equations of state are usually formulated by

inductive reasoning, and hence represent idealized models for material response. These models, along with the values of the parameters
or material properties incorporated into them, must predict material
behavior consistent with the experimentally determined material
functions if they are to be valid.

Figure 1.1 illustrates the correspondence between the physical
forces and deformations and the mathematical quantities stress and

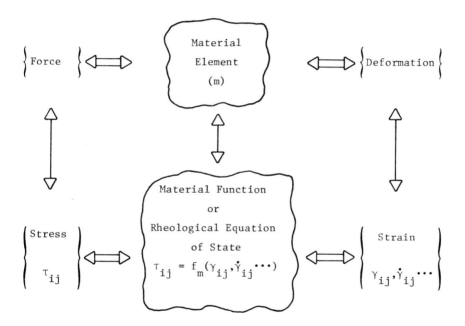

FIG. 1.1 Physical and mathematical relation between force,
deformation, and material properties.

strain. It also indicates that the functional relation between
stress and strain, represented by the material function or rheological equation of state, is a unique property of the material.

1.3. CAUSE AND EFFECT

We have implied that the rheological properties of a material
determine the manner in which it will deform or flow when subjected
to an imposed force or system of forces (stress). In principle, it
is immaterial whether the stress or the deformation is taken to be
cause or effect. However, in practice, it is usually impossible to
determine unambiguously the detailed state of deformation or flow of
a material from a specification of only the external forces which
act upon the system. It is almost always necessary to assume a
priori that the possible deformation (or flow) configuration may be
restricted on physical or geometrical grounds (for example, elements
of a material are generally constrained by boundaries which permit
motion only in certain specific directions). Thus, once the general
nature of the deformation (or flow) is specified, the rheological
properties of the material determine the internal stresses which are
generated within the material as a function of the specified deformation. These stresses are exerted on confining boundaries (or
against gravity in the case of a free surface) and the reaction to
them can be considered to be the external system of forces which
must be imposed upon the material in order to achieve or sustain the
initially specified state of deformation or flow. This is simply a
manifestation of Newton's third law of motion, namely:

$$\{Action\} = \{Reaction\}$$

Hence it is customary to consider a specified imposed deformation
(strain or strain rate) to be the "cause" factor, and the resulting
internal stresses developed within the material to be the "effect,"
which depend upon the specific deformation and the particular nature
and the mechanical (rheological) properties of the material.

1.4. ASSUMPTIONS AND RESTRICTIONS

Before continuing our discussion of basic concepts, it might be appropriate to pause at this point and enumerate some of the inherent assumptions which will constitute restrictions on the systems and materials which will be considered.

One of the primary assumptions involved in the formulation of rheological equations of state and their applications to the solution of deformation and flow problems is that the material is a continuum, and hence subject to the rules of continuum mechanics. That is, it is assumed that all material properties are continuous at every point within the material, with no discontinuities from point to point. This is obviously incorrect for many materials, such as suspensions and emulsions, wherein the properties of the suspended matter are considerably different from those of the suspending medium. However, the assumption of a continuum may be quite adequate if the smallest region of practical interest is large compared to the size of the particles or molecules, or the distance between them, whichever is greater. For example, blood, which is a suspension of cells, may be treated as a continuum in large vessels and arteries which are many times larger than the blood cells, but such treatment is wholly inadequate for analysis of flow in capillaries, which may be of about the same diameter as the cells. The same conclusion applies in the case of a low pressure gas in a channel or pore, the width of which may be of the same order as the mean free path between the gas molecules.

Another assumption is that of *homogeneity*. That is, the material properties are assumed the same in all parts of the system. A suspension, for example, in which the particles are not uniformly distributed (or had partially settled) would violate this assumption.

One very important assumption we will make is that all material properties are *isotropic*. An isotropic quantity is the same in any direction from a given point in the system. Anisotropy, on the other hand, implies a dependence upon direction or orientation. Water, for example, is an isotropic material since its properties are independent of direction or orientation (i.e., its viscosity does not depend upon the direction of shear). Wood, however, is anisotropic since its properties (yield stress, thermal conductivity, etc.) are quite different in the direction along the grain than against it. The consideration of anisotropic materials is outside the scope of this treatment.

(4)   Our considerations will be directed toward flow systems in the *laminar* regime. When the intermolecular forces (manifested as viscous forces) between molecules in a flowing fluid are substantial relative to inertial forces, adjacent fluid elements slip smoothly past one another and a given fluid element will move in a smooth path called a "pathline" (see note 1). This is called laminar flow, and occurs in all fluids flowing sufficiently slowly. At sufficiently high velocities, however, inertia forces will eventually overwhelm these viscous forces and instabilities develop. These are manifested by statistical fluctuations in the fluid motion, which increase in intensity as the velocity increases. In this regime viscosity still plays an important role in dissipating energy, but inertial forces predominate (see note 2).

For the types of materials of greatest interest to the rheologist, the viscous forces are so great that laminar flow generally persists to velocities larger than normally encountered in handling them, so that it is the regime of greatest interest. Furthermore, only laminar flows can be analyzed precisely, so that they are employed exclusively for the measurement of fluid rheological properties.

(5)   Finally, we will limit our considerations to isothermal systems. It should be recognized that all material properties vary with temperature, and the determination of this temperature dependence is an important aspect of a complete characterization of rheological or mechanical properties. However, space limitations preclude considerations of these effects in an introductory work of this nature.

1.5. SIMPLE SHEAR

Before considering general relations between stress and strain
(tensors), a great deal can be learned about the rheological properties of a material by considering its behavior in a particular
simplified deformation called *simple shear*. The distinguishing
characteristic of this deformation is that an imposed shearing strain
or strain rate (tensor) has only one nonzero component, which is uniform throughout the material (i.e., homogeneous). Because of the
unique relation between stress and deformation, the resulting nonzero components of stress are also uniform throughout the material.
This is in contrast to other configurations commonly employed for
determining rheological properties (e.g., viscometers) in which the
nonzero stress and/or strain (rate) components are inhomogeneous.

Consider a material contained between two parallel plates, one
of which is stationary, the other being constrained to move in its
own plane subject to a force F acting parallel to the plate
(Fig. 1.2). The force F acting on the plate, which has an area A,
produces a *shear stress* $\tau = F/A$. This stress is uniform throughout
the material at steady state, as can be seen by making a force balance on any horizontal slice of material, one surface of which is in .
contact with the upper plate.

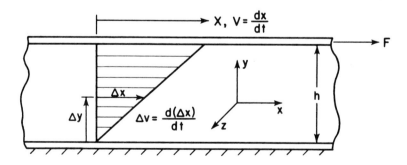

FIG. 1.2 Simple shear.

Displacement of the top plate results in relative displacement of all elements of the material in the x direction as shown in Fig. 1.2, resulting in a *deformation*. If the displacement of a given element located at Δy is Δx, the shear strain is given by

$$\gamma = \frac{\Delta x}{\Delta y} \qquad\qquad (1.5\text{-}1)$$

The mechanical properties of the material define a unique relationship between stress and strain. Thus, if these properties are independent of position (i.e., the material is homogeneous), the steady-state homogeneous stress distribution requires that the strain also be homogeneous at steady state.

　　If the material is a fluid, a constant stress on the plate will result in a constant velocity, V, of the plate at steady state. This deformation can be described by the time rate of change of the shear strain, referred to variously as the rate of strain or shear rate (see note 3). If the velocity at the position Δy is Δv, the shear rate is

$$\dot\gamma = \frac{d\gamma}{dt} = \frac{d}{dt}\left(\frac{\Delta x}{\Delta y}\right) = \frac{1}{\Delta y}\frac{d\Delta x}{dt} = \frac{\Delta v}{\Delta y} = \frac{V}{h} \qquad\qquad (1.5\text{-}2)$$

With one plate moving at a constant velocity, the velocity gradient in simple shear is also constant (uniform), and is identical to Eq. (1.5-2). Thus the shear strain, Eq. (1.5-1), is identical to the *displacement gradient* and the shear rate is the *velocity gradient*, both being homogeneous for a homogeneous material in simple shear at steady state.

　　These concepts of shear strain and shear rate may be extended directly to any (one-dimensional) deformation, whether it is homogeneous or not. That is, the expressions (1.5-1) and (1.5-2) reduce identically to (1.5-3) and (1.5-4) in the limit as Δy (e.g., the separation between two points within the medium) approaches zero:

Shear strain: $\quad \gamma = \dfrac{dx}{dy}$ $\qquad\qquad$ (1.5-3)

Shear rate $\quad : \quad \dot{\gamma} = \dfrac{dv}{dy}$ $\qquad\qquad$ (1.5-4)

Thus, shear strain or shear rate may be defined at any point within a continuous medium in terms of the displacement or velocity gradients evaluated at that point.

1.6. CLASSIFICATION OF MATERIALS

Materials may be classified rheologically with respect to their shear stress-shear strain behavior in simple shear. Various expressions relating shear stress and shear strain have been developed, which are characteristic of certain classes of materials. These expressions represent idealized "models" which define these materials, but do not guarantee exact reproduction of the behavior of real materials. Many of them, however, provide quite adequate representation of the flow or deformation behavior of a large number of materials in many practical applications. A portion of the total classification spectrum is shown in Fig. 1.3. Additional classes, such as linear viscoelastic and nonlinear viscoelastic, may be added under both solid and fluid categories.

While many materials may be obviously classed as solid or fluid, there are many others in the midregion of the spectrum which are neither obviously liquid nor solid, but have certain properties characteristic of both. It is these materials which are of greatest interest to the rheologist. Indeed, it is difficult to formulate an adequate definition of liquids and solids which will differentiate between these materials. In general, a fluid will undergo a continuous deformation without rupture when subjected to a constant anisotropic stress, whereas a solid will generally assume a static equilibrium configuration under such conditions. However, this type of behavior is relative, and depends upon the characteristic time required for the material to respond to a change in stress or strain

Rigid Solid (Euclidean)

$$\gamma = 0$$

Linear Elastic Solid (Hookean)

$$\tau = G\ \gamma \qquad (G = const)$$

Nonlinear Elastic Solid

$$\tau = G(\gamma)\ \gamma$$

Solid

Viscoelastic

$$\tau = f(\gamma,\ \dot{\gamma},\ t\cdots)$$

Nonlinear Viscous Fluid (non-Newtonian)

$$\tau = \eta(\dot{\gamma})\ \dot{\gamma}$$

Linear Viscous Fluid (Newtonian)

$$\tau = \mu\ \dot{\gamma} \quad (\mu = const)$$

Fluid

Inviscid Fluid (Pascalian)

$$\tau = 0$$

FIG. 1.3 Spectrum of material classification in simple shear deformations.

relative to the time scale of observation, as well as the magnitude
of the stress or strain. For instance, some materials such as "silly
putty" (a silicone) will fracture cleanly as a solid if subjected to
a large suddenly applied stress, while they will flow freely as a
liquid when subjected to a constant stress of low or moderate magnitude. Granite, normally considered a solid, will flow measurably
in large formations over a period of geologic time under the influence of gravity alone. In fact, a basic axiom of rheology, attributed to the Greek philosopher Heraclitus, is that "everything flows."

We will be concerned primarily with those materials which will
flow under the proper conditions, and hence exhibit some type of
(complex) fluid-like behavior. A few examples of commonly encountered materials with complex rheological properties are:

Paint

Toothpaste

Crude oil

Grease

Asphalt

Foodstuffs, such as cookie and cake dough and batters, con-
 densed milk, cream cheese, tomato juice, mustard, catsup,
 etc.

Biological fluids, such as blood, synovial fluid, protein
 solutions, etc.

Soaps and soap solutions

Polymers and polymer solutions

Drilling mud

Paper pulp and other slurries

Cosmetics

These materials exhibit flow characteristics which are markedly
different from those of simple Newtonian fluids (such as water).
Such characteristics may include (a) nonlinear shear stress-shear
rate relations in steady flow, (b) shear-dependent "extra" normal
stresses developed in directions other than the flow direction, and

(c) time-dependent material characteristics, which are most evident in time-dependent deformations. It is these properties with which we will be most directly concerned.

1.7. MECHANICS AND NEWTON'S LAWS

Only in the case of steady simple shear is it possible to measure forces and displacements which may be used directly to calculate stress and strain (or strain rate) at some point within the material. In general, it is necessary to introduce the material into a system (e.g., a viscometer) for which measurable forces and displacements do not correspond directly to stress and strain (or strain rate) at a specific point in the system. In a like manner, these forces and displacements (such as pressure drop and flow rate in a tube) cannot be determined solely from the rheological properties of the material. In each case, it is necessary to apply the laws of mechanics to the system in order to relate rheological properties to measurable forces and displacements. These laws are basically an expression of Newton's laws of motion, which may be stated as follows [1.3]:

> *First Law*: A body remains in its state of rest or of uniform motion in a straight line unless it is acted upon by an external force.
>
> *Second Law*: The rate of change of momentum of a body is proportional to the resultant of the applied force, the change being in the direction of the force.
>
> *Third Law*: For every action there is an equal and opposite reaction.

We have already made use of the second and third laws in Secs. 1.4 and 1.2, respectively.

For materials which flow, the application of the second law to an element of fluid results in the general momentum *equations of motion*, which we will derive subsequently. It is important to emphasize that Newton's laws, including the general equations of motion, *apply to any system regardless of the material comprising the system*. For example, the equation of motion for laminar flow in a circular pipe is the same whether the material in the pipe is acetone or cream cheese. In order to determine how a specific material will behave in a given system (e.g., determine flow rate for given pressure gradient), the rheological properties (e.g., rheological equation of state or material function) must be known, and used simultaneously with the equations of motion as they apply to the system. The determination of these rheological properties is the objective of the rheologist, whereas the application of the equations to the determination of the behavior of a given fluid in a given system is the objective of the fluid mechanic.

1.8. RHEOLOGY AND FLUID MECHANICS

Since most of our concern will be with fluid materials, it is important to distinguish between the fields of rheology and fluid mechanics.

To begin with, the two fields are intimately interrelated. Both employ the same measurable quantities and the same basic laws and equations. The primary difference is one of objective. To illustrate, let us consider the laminar flow of a fluid in a circular tube. Both the rheologist and the fluid "mechanic" must consider the following:

1. Newton's laws of motion, i.e., the equations of motion, which apply to the *system* (laminar flow in circular tube), together with the appropriate boundary conditions.
2. The rheological properties of the *material*, e.g., a rheological equation of state or material function.
3. Measurable *data* representing forces and displacements characteristic of the system, e.g., pressure drop and flow rate of the fluid in the tube.

It should be clear that the *data* are characteristic of both the *material* and the *system*.

Now the objective of the "fluid mechanic" is the prediction of relations between the characteristic forces and displacements from a knowledge of the general equations of motion and the rheological properties of fluid. This can be illustrated as follows:

Fluid Mechanic

$$\left\{\begin{array}{c} \text{Equations of}\\ \text{motion for the}\\ \text{system} \end{array}\right\} + \left\{\begin{array}{c} \text{Rheological}\\ \text{properties}\\ \text{of the fluid} \end{array}\right\} \rightarrow \left\{\begin{array}{c} \text{Predicted pressure}\\ \text{drop vs. flow rate}\\ \text{for the fluid in}\\ \text{the system} \end{array}\right\}$$

The objective of the rheologist, on the other hand, is the determination of the rheological properties of the material from the fundamental equations of motion and measured values of characteristic forces and displacements:

Rheologist

$$\left\{\begin{array}{c} \text{Equations of}\\ \text{motion for the}\\ \text{system} \end{array}\right\} + \left\{\begin{array}{c} \text{Measured}\\ \text{pressure drop}\\ \text{and flow rate}\\ \text{for the fluid}\\ \text{in the system} \end{array}\right\} \rightarrow \left\{\begin{array}{c} \text{Rheological}\\ \text{properties of}\\ \text{the fluid} \end{array}\right\}$$

Hence the fluid mechanic cannot achieve his objective without utilizing the results of rheology, and the rheologist cannot achieve his objective without making use of the principles of fluid mechanics. We will illustrate both procedures, of course, but will be more concerned with the problems of the rheologist.

1.9. THE CONCEPT OF TENSORS

The rheological properties of a material are a function only of the material, and are defined by a relation between the stress and deformation (e.g., strain) associated with a specific element of the material. Stress and strain are quantities which are often referred to as *tensors*, although the more precise term would be

second-order tensor or dyad. The general term tensor includes a
wide range of mathematical quantities of various orders, such as
scalars, vectors, dyads, etc. Hence, a thorough and general description of rheological properties must, of necessity, depend upon the
characteristics and properties of tensors. We will discuss the
mathematical nature of tensors in some detail later, but will give
here a more qualitative discussion for benefit of those readers who
are unfamiliar with the concepts. It will be assumed in this chapter that all tensor components are referred to a rectangular
(Cartesian) set of coordinates (see Fig. 1.4).

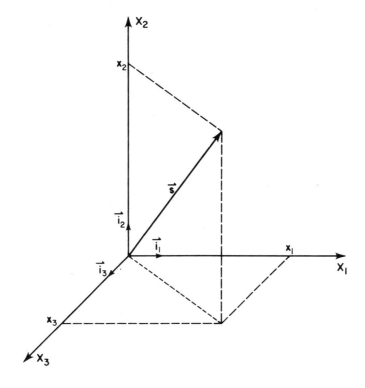

FIG. 1.4 Cartesian components of the position vector.

Essentially all mathematical entities are tensors of one sort or another, and they are best introduced by considering some quantities with which we are all familiar.

1. *Scalars*: A scalar is a quantity which can be described by a single magnitude. Hence it is independent of the specific coordinate system used as a reference frame for describing the system; i.e., it has no directional characteristics. A scalar can thus be defined in terms of a *single component* (i.e., its magnitude). Typical scalar quantities are temperature, pressure, density, etc.

2. *Vectors*: A quantity which must be defined in terms of a direction or orientation as well as a magnitude is a vector. In three-dimensional space, a vector can be completely specified by *three components*, each of which is conveniently taken to lie in the direction parallel to one of the coordinate axes which serve as a frame of reference for describing the system. One example is the position or location of a point in space (Fig. 1.4). The position vector $\vec{S}$ may be designated by various methods of notation:

(a) *Vector notation*, implying both magnitude and direction from a given reference point: $\vec{S}$.

(b) ·*A sum of vector components*, each represented by the product of a scalar magnitude ($\vec{x}$) and a unit direction vector ($\vec{i}$), the latter being defined as a unit vector which lies in the direction of one axis of the reference coordinate system:

$$\vec{S} = x_1\vec{i}_1 + x_2\vec{i}_2 + x_3\vec{i}_3 \qquad (1.9\text{-}2)$$

(c) *The matrix of the components* (magnitudes), which may be taken relative to any arbitrary coordinate system:

$$\vec{S} = (x_1, x_2, x_3) \qquad (1.9\text{-}3)$$

This notation implies the existence of a coordinate system (three components implying three coordinates, as required for three-dimensional space), to which the components are referred. However, no specific coordinate system is implied by the notation, but of course one must be specified in order to determine the magnitudes of the components.

(d) *Generalized index notation*, in which an index (either subscript or superscript) is used to imply any or all of the vector components:

$$\vec{S} = x_i \qquad (i = 1,2,3) \qquad\qquad (1.9\text{-}4)$$

The "range" of the index is equal to the dimensionality of the space required to define the vector (a range of three for three-dimensional space). Thus Eq. (1.9-4) implies the existence of three components, (x_i), corresponding to the range of the index. Unless otherwise specified, all indices are understood to have a range of three. Hence the notation x_i may represent the entire array of components (x_1, x_2, x_3), or any one (the ith) component.

It should be noted that a given vector always implies a specific magnitude and direction in space, regardless of the reference frame (coordinates) used to describe the space. The vector can be uniquely described in three-dimensional space by specifying three components. However, these components have meaning (i.e., their magnitudes can be determined) only with respect to a specific coordinate reference frame. There is, of course, an endless variety of coordinate frames which can serve this purpose, the most common being the linear orthogonal (Cartesian) system. Unless otherwise noted, all vector and tensor components in this chapter will be assumed to be determined relative to Cartesian coordinates, although we will later generalize these relations to apply to any system, orthogonal or nonorthogonal, linear or curvilinear.

It should also be emphasized that the notation of Eqs. (1.9-1), (1.9-3), and (1.9-4) is perfectly general, in that it is completely independent of the particular coordinate system to which the components of the vector are referred. Of course the coordinate system must be specified before the magnitude of the components can be determined. However, the notation of Eq. (1.9-2) implies a specific coordinate system, which is defined by the base vectors $\vec{i}_1, \vec{i}_2, \vec{i}_3$.

Another familiar example of a vector is the *velocity vector*

$$\vec{v} = \frac{d\vec{S}}{dt} = v_1\vec{i}_1 + v_2\vec{i}_2 + v_3\vec{i}_3 = (v_1, v_2, v_3) = v_i \qquad (1.9-5)$$

Also the *gradient of a scalar* is a vector, since there are three possible directions in which the magnitude of the scalar may vary, thus defining the three components of the gradient vector:

$$\vec{\nabla T} = \frac{dT}{d\vec{S}} = \frac{\partial T}{\partial x_1}\vec{i}_1 + \frac{\partial T}{\partial x_2}\vec{i}_2 + \frac{\partial T}{\partial x_3}\vec{i}_3 = \left(\frac{\partial T}{\partial x_1}, \frac{\partial T}{\partial x_2}, \frac{\partial T}{\partial x_3}\right) = \frac{\partial T}{\partial x_i} \quad (1.9-6)$$

3. *Dyads*: If we consider the gradient of a vector quantity, we note that there are three components of the vector, each of which may vary in any or all of three possible directions (relative to any coordinate system in three-dimensional space). Thus there are nine possible components of the gradient of a vector. Each of these components is associated with a *magnitude* and *two directions*: the direction associated with the vector component, and the direction in which it varies. Such a quantity is termed *dyad*, an example being the *velocity gradient* $d\vec{v}/d\vec{S}$. The velocity $\vec{v}$ is a vector, having magnitude and direction, and the magnitudes of each of its three components may vary in any or all of the three coordinate directions. The three principle methods of notation for a dyad are:

(a) *Vector notation*

$$\frac{d\vec{v}}{d\vec{S}} \qquad \text{or} \qquad \frac{d\vec{v}}{dS} \qquad \text{or} \qquad \nabla\vec{v} \qquad (1.9-7)$$

(b) *Matrix of components*

$$\frac{d\vec{v}}{d\vec{S}} = \begin{bmatrix} \dfrac{\partial v_1}{\partial x_1} & \dfrac{\partial v_1}{\partial x_2} & \dfrac{\partial v_1}{\partial x_3} \\[2ex] \dfrac{\partial v_2}{\partial x_1} & \dfrac{\partial v_2}{\partial x_2} & \dfrac{\partial v_2}{\partial x_3} \\[2ex] \dfrac{\partial v_3}{\partial x_1} & \dfrac{\partial v_3}{\partial x_2} & \dfrac{\partial v_3}{\partial x_3} \end{bmatrix} \qquad (1.9\text{-}8)$$

(c) *Index notation*

$$\frac{d\vec{v}}{d\vec{S}} = \frac{\partial v_i}{\partial x_j} \qquad (i,j = 1,2,3) \qquad (1.9\text{-}9)$$

Note that two independent indices are required to specify a dyad, representing the two directions associated with each component. Since each index has a range of three, $(i,j = 1,2,3)$, there are nine possible combinations of the numbers represented by i and j, representing the nine dyad components. Other dyads (second-order tensors) will be illustrated when we discuss stress and strain.

These concepts may be extended directly to higher order quantites if we so desire (e.g., the gradient of a dyad, etc.); however, these examples should be sufficient to illustrate the concepts.

All of the above quantites are *tensors*, i.e.:

A scalar is a zero-order tensor

A vector is a first-order tensor

A dyad is a second-order tensor

The number of components required to specify a given tensor quantity is directly related to the order of the tensor and the dimensionality of the space (i.e., number of coordinates) as follows:

Number of components = (number of coordinates)^{Order}

$$= (3)^{\text{Order}} \text{ (usually)}$$

The index notation for specifying tensors and their components is very useful. The number of different (independent) (see note 4) indices required to specify the tensor is the same as the order of the tensor, and hence the total number of components is immediately discernible from the number of independent indices.

4. *Note in Regard to Indices:* The general convention which will be followed with regard to symbolic index notation, unless otherwise specified, will be as follows:

General letter indices (i,j,k, ... α,β,γ) will indicate a set or matrix of components relative to any general (arbitrary) three-dimensional coordinate space. The coordinates to which tensor components are referred may be linear or curvilinear, orthogonal, or nonorthogonal.

Numbered indices (1,2,3) will refer to a specific tensor component with respect to an ordered set of general (arbitrary) three-dimensional coordinates.

Coordinate lettered indices (x,y,z or r,θ,z, etc.) will refer to a specific tensor component relative to a specific coordinate system (Cartesian, cylindrical, etc.). The coordinate systems most commonly used are defined and described in Appendix C.

The only exception to the above is that all tensor components referred to in Chaps. 1 and 2 are assumed to be defined relative to Cartesian coordinates. The tensor relations in these chapters will be generalized in later sections to apply to any coordinate reference system.

This discussion is intended merely to introduce the reader to the concept of tensors and the notation used to represent them. The

great utility of tensor notation lies in its generality which permits description and manipulation of such quantities independently
of any specific coordinate system to which the components may be
referred. That is, a general tensor relation, if formulated properly, is the same no matter if the physical system is described with
respect to a Cartesian, an orthogonal curvilinear, or a nonorthogonal coordinate system.

The mathematical principles and properties of tensors which
enable the proper formulation of such generalized relations will be
discussed in detail in a later chapter. At that time a more rigorous
mathematical definition of a tensor will be given.

1.10 STRESS AND DEFORMATION

We have defined shear stress and shear strain in terms of simple
shear, for which only one nonzero component of each was of interest.
However, we have alluded to the stress and strain tensors, which
include a total of nine components each. Furthermore, we shall
have occasions to refer to certain of these additional components
before proceeding to more general considerations, so it is appropriate at this point to present a more comprehensive description of
stress and deformation.

1.10.1. Stress

Stress is defined as force per unit area, and is distributed
continuously throughout any continuous medium which is subjected to
external forces.

Force is a vector, having in general three components in three-
dimensional space. Surface area can also be considered a vector,
since it has a magnitude as well as a direction or orientation.
This direction is indicated by a unit vector which is normal to the
surface. Any element of a surface can be expressed as the sum of

three components in three-dimensional space, each component having
a normal vector which is parallel to one of the coordinate axes.
A given surface area component is identified with the coordinate
direction of its normal vector. Hence stress is a second-order tensor, or dyad, having in general nine components representing the nine
combinations of three force components acting on three surface components at a given point. These components are illustrated in
Fig. 1.5, in which the force vector and hence all nine stress components act at the point of intersection of the three planes. The
three planes represent unit components of a surface which passes
through the point. It follows that as many as nine stress components
may be associated with every point in a continuous material subjected
to external forces.

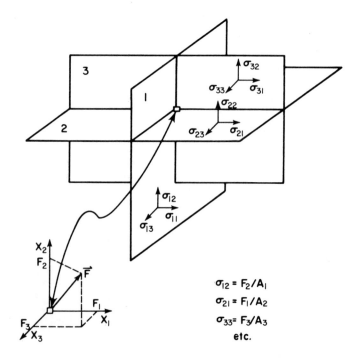

FIG. 1.5 Stress components at a point.

The stress tensor can be specified by index notation or by the matrix of its components:

$$
\sigma_{ij} = \begin{bmatrix} \sigma_{11} & \sigma_{12} & \sigma_{13} \\ \sigma_{21} & \sigma_{22} & \sigma_{23} \\ \sigma_{31} & \sigma_{32} & \sigma_{33} \end{bmatrix} \tag{1.10-1}
$$

As we shall show later, the stress tensor is symmetric ($\sigma_{ij} = \sigma_{ji}$) so that only six of the nine possible stress components are independent.

1.10.2. Classical Strain

Although there is no ambiguity in the definition of stress, there are various ways to define strain. The description which we will present here corresponds to the *classical* definition of *infinitesimal* strain, and is strictly valid only for small amplitude deformations. A more general definition, appropriate for continuous, as well as large-amplitude deformations, will be presented later.

Strain is a quantitative measure of the deformation of a material body or element. A deformation can be said to occur whenever any two points in a material are displaced from their initial positions such that a change in the separation between them results. The magnitude of the deformation is determined by the relative displacements of the points. Thus, we must first establish a measure of *relative displacement*, or the *displacement gradient*.

In our description of simple shear, we indicated that a measure of shear strain is given by the displacement of the movable plate relative to the distance between the plates. In essence, we were referring to the relative displacement in the x_1 direction between two points in the material in contact with the upper and lower plates, respectively, divided by their initial separation (in the x_2 direction). This defines the displacement gradient in simple shear. This concept may be applied on a differential scale to any continuous medium.

Consider a point (1) located at position $\vec{S}_1 = (x_1, x_2, x_3)$ in a continuous medium (Fig. 1.6). If the medium is deformed, this point may be displaced from its original position by an amount $\vec{u}_1$ to (1'). Now consider another point (2) in the same material, which is initially located at point $\vec{S}_2$. Since the material is continuous, the deformation which resulted in the displacement of (1) to (1') will also result in a displacement of (2) to (2'), which we will denote by $\vec{u}_2$.

The *displacement gradient* at point (1) is the relative displacement of the two points, divided by their initial separation, in the limit as point (2) approaches point (1):

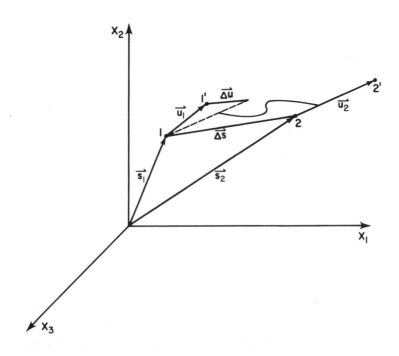

FIG. 1.6 Displacement and separation.

$$
\begin{array}{c}
\text{Displacement} \\
\text{gradient} \\
\text{at point 1}
\end{array}
= \lim_{\vec{S}_2 \to \vec{S}_1} \left[\frac{\vec{u}_2 - \vec{u}_1}{\vec{S}_2 - \vec{S}_1} \right] = \lim_{\Delta\vec{S} \to 0} \left(\frac{\Delta\vec{u}}{\Delta\vec{S}} \right) = \left(\frac{d\vec{u}}{d\vec{S}} \right)_1
\qquad (1.10\text{-}2)
$$

Now $d\vec{u}$ and $d\vec{s}$ are both vectors, with three components. Thus the displacement gradient is a second-order tensor (dyad) with nine possible components:

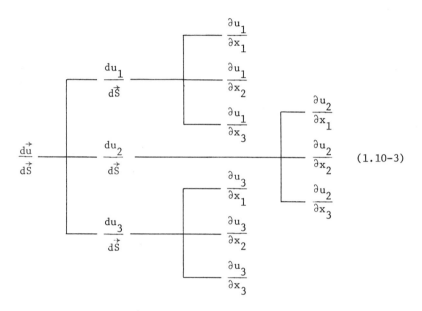

$$(1.10\text{-}3)$$

$$
\frac{d\vec{u}}{d\vec{S}} = \frac{\partial u_i}{\partial x_j} =
\begin{bmatrix}
\dfrac{\partial u_1}{\partial x_1} & \dfrac{\partial u_1}{\partial x_2} & \dfrac{\partial u_1}{\partial x_3} \\[2ex]
\dfrac{\partial u_2}{\partial x_1} & \dfrac{\partial u_2}{\partial x_2} & \dfrac{\partial u_2}{\partial x_3} \\[2ex]
\dfrac{\partial u_3}{\partial x_1} & \dfrac{\partial u_3}{\partial x_2} & \dfrac{\partial u_3}{\partial x_3}
\end{bmatrix}
\qquad (1.10\text{-}4)
$$

(See note 5.) Note that each component, $\partial u_i / \partial x_j$, represents the relative displacement in the i direction per unit separation in the j direction between two points initially separated by dx_j in the j direction.

—————————————————————————— 0 ——————————————————————————

Example 1.1 For a simple shear deformation, as illustrated in Fig. 1.2, determine the components of the displacement gradient tensor.

First of all, we assign a numerical order to the coordinates, as follows:

$$x = x_1 \qquad\qquad y = x_2 \qquad\qquad z = x_3$$

This ordering is arbitrary, although we will establish a convention for this later. However, it is necessary in order to keep proper track of tensor components relative to their matrix position.

The only displacement is in the x (x_1) direction, and this varies in the y (x_2) direction only. Thus, by Eq. (1.10-4) the displacement gradient is:

$$\frac{\partial u_i}{\partial x_j} = \begin{bmatrix} 0 & \dfrac{du_x}{dx_2} & 0 \\ 0 & 0 & 0 \\ 0 & 0 & 0 \end{bmatrix} = \frac{du_x}{dy} \begin{bmatrix} 0 & 1 & 0 \\ 0 & 0 & 0 \\ 0 & 0 & 0 \end{bmatrix}$$

The partial derivative becomes a total derivative, since there is only one independent variable (x_2).

—————————————————————————— 0 ——————————————————————————

Now it would seem that the displacement gradient should be an adequate measure of deformation, since it is a measure of the relative displacement between two material points separated by an infinitesimal distance. This is not necessarily so, however, as illustrated by the following.

Consider point (1) of an arbitrarily small (infinitesimal) rectangular element to be held fixed, and the material subjected to a two-dimensional deformation such that $\partial u_1/\partial x_2 = -\partial u_2/\partial x_1 = \alpha$ (Fig. 1.7A). The components of the displacement gradient tensor are

$$\frac{\partial u_i}{\partial x_j} = \alpha \begin{bmatrix} 0 & 1 & 0 \\ -1 & 0 & 0 \\ 0 & 0 & 0 \end{bmatrix} \qquad (1.10-5)$$

Note that each displacement gradient component represents a rotation of the side of the element by an angle α. If both components are of equal magnitude but of opposite sign, their sum represents twice the rotation of the separation vector $\vec{ds}$ through the same angle in the same direction. The net result is a pure rotation and no deformation, since the length of the separation vector has not changed. Thus it is possible to have nonzero displacement gradient components with no deformation (strain).

In general, a measure of the net rotation of an infinitesimal material element at a point is given by the average rotation of the sides of the element, as determined by the displacement gradient components at the point:

$$\alpha = \frac{1}{2} \left(\frac{\partial u_1}{\partial x_2} - \frac{\partial u_2}{\partial x_1} \right) \qquad (1.10-6)$$

If the material is subjected to a displacement such that $\alpha = \partial u_1/\partial x_2 = \partial u_2/\partial x_1$, the situation is as depicted in Fig. 1.7B. In this case, the components of the displacement gradient tensor are

$$\frac{\partial u_i}{\partial x_j} = \alpha \begin{bmatrix} 0 & 1 & 0 \\ 1 & 0 & 0 \\ 0 & 0 & 0 \end{bmatrix} \qquad (1.10-7)$$

This situation obviously results in a pure deformation but no rotation, since the separation vector $\vec{ds}$ has changed in magnitude but not direction.

Thus a nonzero displacement gradient tensor may represent pure rotation, pure deformation, or both. Each displacement gradient component may thus be separated into two parts, as follows:

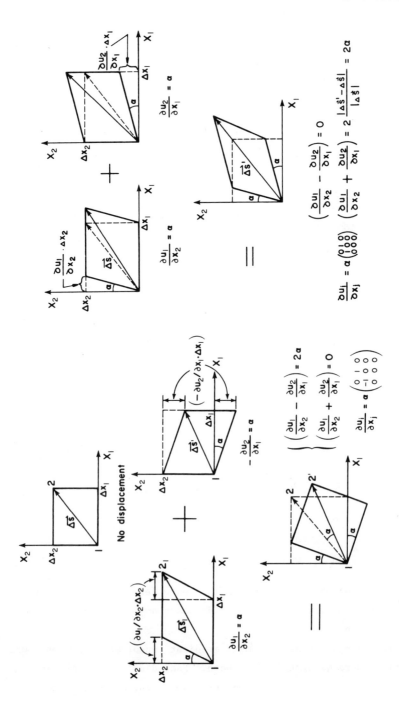

FIG. 1.7B Pure shear.

FIG. 1.7A Pure rotation.

$$\frac{\partial u_i}{\partial x_j} = \frac{1}{2}\left(\frac{\partial u_i}{\partial x_j} + \frac{\partial u_j}{\partial x_i}\right) + \frac{1}{2}\left(\frac{\partial u_i}{\partial x_j} - \frac{\partial u_j}{\partial x_i}\right) \tag{1.10-8}$$

Pure deformation   Pure rotation

The second term represents the net rotation, which is zero for a pure deformation, while the first term represents the relative separation between material points (a pure deformation), and thus is the proper measure of infinitesimal deformation or strain. The (classical infinitesimal) *strain tensor*, e_{ij} is therefore defined as

$$e_{ij} = \left(\frac{\partial u_i}{\partial x_j} + \frac{\partial u_j}{\partial x_i}\right) \tag{1.10-9}$$

(See note 6.) Similarly, a *rotation tensor* may be defined as

$$r_{ij} = \left(\frac{\partial u_j}{\partial x_i} - \frac{\partial u_i}{\partial x_j}\right) \tag{1.10-10}$$

The order of the indices is chosen to conform with a positive rotation being counterclockwise.

Equation (1.10-8) is equivalent to separating the displacement gradient into symmetric and antisymmetric parts. Thus the strain tensor is symmetric ($e_{ij} = e_{ji}$), whereas the rotation tensor is antisymmetric ($r_{ij} = -r_{ji}$).

It should be noted that the components of a symmetric second-order tensor (dyad) are of the form

$$S_{ij} = \begin{bmatrix} S_{11} & S_{12} & S_{13} \\ S_{12} & S_{22} & S_{23} \\ S_{13} & S_{23} & S_{33} \end{bmatrix} \tag{1.10-11}$$

Because of symmetry, only three of the six off-diagonal components are independent, so that only six of the nine total components are

independent. An antisymmetric tensor (sometimes called skew symmetric) has components of the form

$$
A_{ij} = \begin{bmatrix} 0 & A_{12} & A_{13} \\ -A_{12} & 0 & A_{23} \\ -A_{13} & -A_{23} & 0 \end{bmatrix} = -A_{ji} \tag{1.10-12}
$$

Antisymmetry requires that all diagonal components be zero, so that
only three of the nine total components of an antisymmetric tensor
are independent. Consequently, any second-order tensor may be
written as the sum of a symmetric and an antisymmetric tensor:

$$
T_{ij} = \frac{1}{2} (T_{ij} + T_{ji}) + \frac{1}{2} (T_{ij} - T_{ji}) = S_{ij} + A_{ij} \tag{1.10-13}
$$

This is just what has been done in Eq. (1.10-8).

Note also that *simple shear*, for which there is only one nonzero displacement gradient component, is not a pure deformation,
since this component contributes to both the symmetric (strain)
and antisymmetric (rotation) tensors. Thus simple shear comprises
both a deformation and a rotation, which can be illustrated by im-
printing a set of orthogonal axes upon the material (Fig. 1.8).

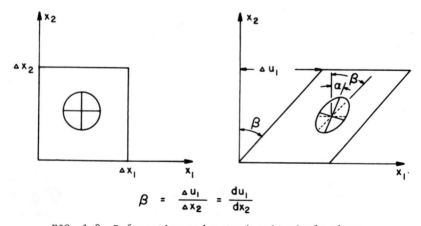

$$
\beta = \frac{\Delta u_1}{\Delta x_2} = \frac{du_1}{dx_2}
$$

FIG. 1.8   Deformation and rotation in simple shear.

——————————————————————— 0 ———————————————————————

Example 1.2 For simple shear deformation, determine the components of the strain and rotation tensors.

From Example 1.1 the displacement gradient tensor is

$$\frac{\partial u_i}{\partial x_j} = \frac{du_x}{dy} \begin{bmatrix} 0 & 1 & 0 \\ 0 & 0 & 0 \\ 0 & 0 & 0 \end{bmatrix}$$

Thus, from Eq. (1.9-9) the strain tensor is

The Transpose of →

$$e_{ij} = \left(\frac{\partial u_i}{\partial x_j} + \frac{\partial u_i}{\partial x_i}\right) = \begin{bmatrix} 0 & \dfrac{du_1}{dx_2} & 0 \\ 0 & 0 & 0 \\ 0 & 0 & 0 \end{bmatrix} + \begin{bmatrix} 0 & 0 & 0 \\ \dfrac{du_1}{dx_2} & 0 & 0 \\ 0 & 0 & 0 \end{bmatrix}$$

$$= \frac{du_x}{dy} \left\{ \begin{bmatrix} 0 & 1 & 0 \\ 0 & 0 & 0 \\ 0 & 0 & 0 \end{bmatrix} + \begin{bmatrix} 0 & 0 & 0 \\ 1 & 0 & 0 \\ 0 & 0 & 0 \end{bmatrix} \right\} = \frac{du_x}{dy} \begin{bmatrix} 0 & 1 & 0 \\ 1 & 0 & 0 \\ 0 & 0 & 0 \end{bmatrix}$$

From (1.10-10) the rotation tensor is

$$r_{ij} = \left(\frac{\partial u_i}{\partial x_i} - \frac{\partial u_i}{\partial x_j}\right) = \begin{bmatrix} 0 & 0 & 0 \\ \dfrac{du_1}{dx_2} & 0 & 0 \\ 0 & 0 & 0 \end{bmatrix} - \begin{bmatrix} 0 & \dfrac{du_1}{dx_2} & 0 \\ 0 & 0 & 0 \\ 0 & 0 & 0 \end{bmatrix}$$

$$= \frac{du_x}{dy} \begin{bmatrix} 0 & -1 & 0 \\ 1 & 0 & 0 \\ 0 & 0 & 0 \end{bmatrix}$$

Note the symmetry of e_{ij} and the antisymmetry of r_{ij}.

——————————————————————— 0 ———————————————————————

The *rate of strain tensor*, Δ_{ij}, follows directly from the previous analysis, with the displacement components replaced by velocity components:

$$\Delta_{ij} = \frac{\partial}{\partial t}(e_{ij}) = \frac{\partial}{\partial t}\left(\frac{\partial u_i}{\partial x_j} + \frac{\partial u_j}{\partial x_i}\right)$$

$$= \frac{\partial}{\partial x_j}\left(\frac{\partial u_i}{\partial t}\right) + \frac{\partial}{\partial x_i}\left(\frac{\partial u_j}{\partial t}\right) \qquad (1.10\text{-}14)$$

$$= \left(\frac{\partial v_i}{\partial x_j} + \frac{\partial v_j}{\partial x_i}\right) = \Delta_{ji}$$

In a similar fashion, a *vorticity tensor* (whose components are also components of the angular velocity vector) can be defined from the antisymmetric (rotation) tensor components, and represents twice the local rate of rotation of the fluid element:

$$\Omega_{ij} = \left(\frac{\partial v_j}{\partial x_i} - \frac{\partial v_i}{\partial x_j}\right) = -\Omega_{ji} \qquad (1.10\text{-}15)$$

Thus, a given nonzero velocity gradient component contributes to both a deformation rate (rate of strain) and a rotation rate:

$$\frac{\partial v_i}{\partial x_j} = \frac{1}{2}(\Delta_{ij} + \Omega_{ji}) \qquad (1.10\text{-}16)$$

1.10.3. Isotropic and Anisotropic Stress and Strain

The total stress and strain tensors (indeed, any symmetric second-order tensor) can be expressed as the sum of an isotropic tensor and an anisotropic tensor.

An *isotropic stress*, such as static pressure (which is independent of direction), acting on an isotropic material element will result in, at most, a change in volume but no change in shape of the element. This volume change constitutes an *isotropic strain*, which is also referred to as a *volumetric strain* (Fig. 1.9). (A compressive stress such as pressure is taken to be negative, while a tensile stress is positive.) An isotropic decrease in volume is a *compression*, while an increase in volume is referred to as a *dilation*. Since isotropic stress and strain are independent of direction, they are scalar quantities, having one component (magnitude) only.

Conversely, when a purely anisotropic (directionally dependent) stress acts on an isotropic material element, the result is a change in shape but no change in volume. This is referred to as a *shear strain* (Fig. 1.10).

The resultant of an isotropic stress acts normal to all surfaces of the material element, and is equal in all directions. The

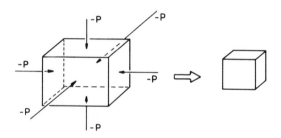

FIG. 1.9 Isotropic (volumetric) stress and strain.

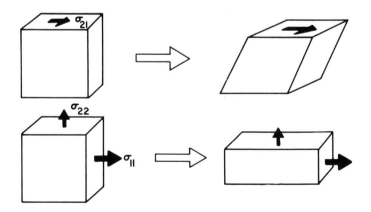

FIG. 1.10 Anisotropic (shear) stress and strain.

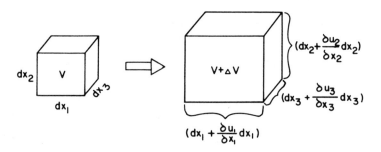

FIG. 1.11 Volumetric strain.

anisotropic (shear) stress, on the other hand, may have components which act normal as well as tangential to various surfaces of the element. Thus a shear strain may result from anisotropic normal and/or shear (tangential) stresses.

In order to resolve the isotropic and anisotropic components of strain, consider a differential element of material subjected to a small change in volume (dilation) by extension of all sides in a direction normal to themselves (Fig. 1.11).

The *relative* change in volume is

$$\frac{\Delta V}{V} = \frac{\left[\left(dx_1 + \frac{\partial u_1}{\partial x_1}\right)\left(dx_2 + \frac{\partial u_2}{\partial x_2}dx_2\right)\left(dx_3 + \frac{\partial u_3}{\partial x_3}dx_3\right) - dx_1 dx_2 dx_3\right]}{dx_1 dx_2 dx_3}$$

$$= \left(\frac{\partial u_1}{\partial x_1} + \frac{\partial u_2}{\partial x_2} + \frac{\partial u_3}{\partial x_3}\right) + \left(\frac{\partial u_1}{\partial x_1}\frac{\partial u_2}{\partial x_2} + \frac{\partial u_1}{\partial x_1}\frac{\partial u_3}{\partial x_3} + \frac{\partial u_2}{\partial x_2}\frac{\partial u_3}{\partial x_3} + \frac{\partial u_1}{\partial x_1}\frac{\partial u_2}{\partial x_2}\frac{\partial u_3}{\partial x_3}\right)$$

$$\cong \frac{\partial u_1}{\partial x_1} + \frac{\partial u_2}{\partial x_2} + \frac{\partial u_3}{\partial x_3} = \frac{1}{2}(e_{11} + e_{22} + e_{33}) = e_v \qquad (1.10\text{-}17)$$

or

$$e_v = \frac{3}{2}\bar{e}$$

where

$$\bar{e} = \frac{1}{3} (e_{11} + e_{22} + e_{33}) = \frac{1}{3} \text{ tr } (e_{ij}) \tag{1.10-18}$$

(See note 7.) Here e_v is the *total volumetric strain* (i.e., relative increase in volume), and $\bar{e}$ is the *mean normal strain*. This result is valid only for small (infinitesimal) strain, for which multiples of deformation gradient components are of second-order smallness and can be neglected.

We may thus write the strain tensor as the sum of its isotropic (scalar) part and the remaining anisotropic part, γ_{ij}:

$$e_{ij} = \bar{e} \, \delta_{ij} + \gamma_{ij} \tag{1.10-19}$$

where δ_{ij} is the *unit tensor* or *Kronecker delta*, with components

$$\delta_{ij} = \begin{bmatrix} 1 & 0 & 0 \\ 0 & 1 & 0 \\ 0 & 0 & 1 \end{bmatrix} = \begin{cases} 1 \text{ if } i = j \\ 0 \text{ if } i \neq j \end{cases} \tag{1.10-20}$$

The tensor e_{ij} represents a measure of *total strain* or deformation, including both changes in volume and changes in shape. The tensor γ_{ij} is a measure of shear deformation or change in shape only, and is thus referred to as the *shear strain* tensor.

———————————————— 0 ————————————————

Example 1.3 Determine the mean normal strain and components of the shear strain tensor for simple shear deformation.

From Example 1.2 the strain tensor is:

$$e_{ij} = \frac{du_x}{dy} \begin{bmatrix} 0 & 1 & 0 \\ 1 & 0 & 0 \\ 0 & 0 & 0 \end{bmatrix}$$

The mean normal strain is

$$\bar{e} = \frac{1}{3} (e_{11} + e_{22} + e_{33}) = 0$$

Therefore, from Eq. (1.10-18):

$$\gamma_{ij} = e_{ij} = \frac{du_x}{dy} \begin{bmatrix} 0 & 1 & 0 \\ 1 & 0 & 0 \\ 0 & 0 & 0 \end{bmatrix}$$

Thus there is no change of volume associated with a simple shear deformation. This is also known as an *isochoric* deformation.

——————————————— 0 ———————————————

The mean normal strain ($\bar{e}$) thus represents a change in volume but not shape, while the tensor γ_{ij} represents a change in shape but not volume. Thus the total tensor (e_{ij}) may be resolved into a *volumetric (isotropic) strain* ($e_v = 3/2\ \bar{e}$) and a *shear (anisotropic) strain*, (γ_{ij}). The tensor γ_{ij} is sometimes called the *deviatoric strain*, since it represents the deviation from isotropy, but we will favor the term *shear strain*.

For an *incompressible* (isochoric) *material* (which is not subject to volume changes):

$$\bar{e} = \frac{1}{3} (e_{11} + e_{22} + e_{33}) = \frac{1}{3}\ \text{tr}\ (e_{ij}) = 0$$

and

$$e_{ij} = \gamma_{ij} \qquad\qquad (1.10-21)$$

Note also that the rate of strain tensor, given by Eq. (1.10-14) can be written as the sum of isotropic and anisotropic components:

$$\Delta_{ij} = \bar{\Delta}\ \delta_{ij} + \dot{\gamma}_{ij} \qquad\qquad (1.10-22)$$

where

$$\bar{\Delta} = \frac{1}{3} (\dot{e}_{11} + \dot{e}_{22} + \dot{e}_{33}) = \frac{2}{3} \left(\frac{\partial v_1}{\partial x_1} + \frac{\partial v_2}{\partial x_2} + \frac{\partial v_3}{\partial x_3} \right) = \frac{2}{3} \dot{e}_v$$

and

$$\dot{\gamma}_{ij} = \left(\frac{\partial v_i}{\partial x_j} + \frac{\partial v_j}{\partial x_i} \right) - \bar{\Delta} \, \delta_{ij} \qquad (1.10\text{-}23)$$

Here $\bar{\Delta} = d\bar{e}/dt = 2/3 \; \dot{e}_v$ is the mean normal strain rate and is equal to two-thirds of the rate of volumetric change. For an incompressible material, we have

$$\bar{\Delta} = \frac{1}{3} \; \text{tr} \, (\dot{e}_{ij}) = 0$$

$$\Delta_{ij} = \dot{\gamma}_{ij} = \left(\frac{\partial v_i}{\partial x_j} + \frac{\partial v_j}{\partial x_i} \right) \qquad (1.10\text{-}24)$$

As with the strain tensor, the total rate of strain tensor, Δ_{ij}, may thus be resolved into a volumetric (isotropic) strain rate, $\dot{e}_v = 3/2 \; \bar{\Delta}$, and a shear (anisotropic) strain rate, $\dot{\gamma}_{ij}$.

It is evident that any second-order tensor may be written as the sum of an isotropic and an anisotropic (deviatoric) component, the isotropic component being conveniently represented by the mean normal value, or one-third of the trace, of the tensor. Inasmuch as the isotropic component is a scalar, having no directional properties, it can be combined with other second-order anisotropic tensor components only when multiplied by the unit tensor (e.g., δ_{ij}).

––––––––––––––––––––––––––– 0 –––––––––––––––––––––––––––

Example 1.4 Determine the nonzero components of the stress tensor in simple shear.

The definition of simple shear implies a specified deformation. In accordance with the concepts of Sec. 1.1, the rheological properties of the material must be known in order to determine those stresses which result in a given deformation. Of course it is

evident that, in order to displace the upper surface of the material, a force would have to be applied in the direction of the displacement. Since the surface upon which it acts is a y (i.e., x_2)
surface, the corresponding stress component is

$$\tau_{yx} = \frac{F_x}{A_y} \qquad \text{or} \qquad \tau_{21} = \frac{F_1}{A_2}$$

Because of symmetry, $\tau_{21} = \tau_{12}$. Thus the stress tensor has, at
least, the nonzero components

$$\tau_{ij} = \begin{bmatrix} 0 & \tau_{12} & 0 \\ \tau_{12} & 0 & 0 \\ 0 & 0 & 0 \end{bmatrix}$$

However, unless the rheological nature of the material is specified,
no conclusions can be drawn at this point with regard to the other
stress components. Indeed, there are many materials for which additional stress components are nonzero in this deformation.

———————————————————— 0 ————————————————————

The stress tensor may likewise be separated into an isotropic
and an anisotropic component:

$$\sigma_{ij} = \bar{\sigma} \, \delta_{ij} + \tau_{ij} \tag{1.10-25}$$

where

$$\bar{\sigma} = \frac{1}{3}\left(\sigma_{11} + \sigma_{22} + \sigma_{33}\right) = \text{tr}(\sigma_{ij}) \tag{1.10-26}$$

is the mean normal stress and τ_{ij} is the deviatoric stress. Now
for a fluid in a state of equilibrium (i.e., at rest), the only
stress which may exist is pressure, which is isotropic. It is
therefore usual to associate the mean normal stress with isotropic

pressure, and the deviatoric stress with those stresses which reduce to zero in a state of equilibrium.

For a compressible material, we have seen that the mean normal (isotropic) strain is associated with a change in volume ($\bar{e} = 2e_v/3$). Likewise, the mean normal stress may be associated with the change in pressure which accompanies a change of volume at equilibrium:

$$\bar{\sigma} = -\bar{P} = -(P_o + P_v) \qquad\qquad (1.10\text{-}27)$$

or

$$\bar{P} - P_o = P_v \qquad\qquad (1.10\text{-}28)$$

Here P_o represents the pressure existing in the *reference* or *undeformed state*. P_v therefore represents the change in equilibrium pressure relative to P_o, associated with a volumetric strain e_v (measured relative to the reference state). Since this pressure is defined in terms of equilibrium states, it is identical to the *thermodynamic pressure*, which is a measure of the change in internal energy with volume at constant entropy for a unit mass:

$$-P_v(e_v) = \left(\frac{\partial E}{\partial V}\right)_S \qquad\qquad (1.10\text{-}29)$$

and is determined only by the temperature and density. For an incompressible material $P_v = 0$, so that

$$\sigma_{ij} = -P_o \delta_{ij} + \tau_{ij} \qquad\qquad (1.10\text{-}30)$$

which at equilibrium becomes

$$\sigma_{ij} = -P_o \delta_{ij} \qquad\qquad \tau_{ij} = 0 \qquad\qquad (1.10\text{-}31)$$

In a dynamic (i.e., nonequilibrium) state, however, both isotropic and anisotropic stresses may exist in a fluid. Furthermore, a definition of the isotropic stress in terms of equilibrium states is no longer adequate, so that the "pressure" becomes another dynamic variable being a function of the state of deformation or flow. For compressible fluids, it is usual to assume that volume changes during flow are reversible, so that the thermodynamic pressure, Eq. (1.10-29), can still be used to define this contribution to pressure, and P_o is the isotropic stress which varies with flow conditions. For an incompressible fluid, however, the dynamic variable P_o is determinable only to within an arbitrary constant, since a uniform change in the total pressure level does not affect the dynamic flow behavior. That is, the flow of an incompressible fluid is affected only by changes in pressure (i.e., the pressure gradient), and not by the magnitude of the pressure.

The deviatoric stress tensor, τ_{ij}, is sometimes referred to as the dynamic stress tensor or the shear stress tensor, since it vanishes in a fluid in a state of equilibrium and is a function only of the shear or change in shape of a material element. We will favor the latter designation for this quantity. Note that a consequence of Eq. (1.10-25) and the definition of pressure is

$$-\bar{P} = \frac{1}{3} (-\bar{P} + \tau_{11} - \bar{P} + \tau_{22} - \bar{P} + \tau_{33}) \qquad (1.10\text{-}32)$$

or

$$\tau_{11} + \tau_{22} + \tau_{33} = tr(\tau_{ij}) = 0 \qquad (1.10\text{-}33)$$

That is, the trace of the shear stress tensor must vanish.

All of the above definitions of stress components may also be applied to solids as well as fluids, with the exception that a solid may support an anisotropic stress in a state of equilibrium. Thus, for a solid τ_{ij} does not vanish at equilibrium, and all stresses and strains must be measured relative to those existing in some (arbitrary) reference state. The physical significance of pressure (in particular P_o) as a dynamic variable is therefore not so important for a solid as for a fluid.

1.11. MATERIAL PROPERTIES

As stated in Sec. 1.2, the mechanical or rheological properties
of a material are those which determine how the material will deform
when subjected to a stress or, conversely, the internal stresses
which develop within the material when it is deformed. Since the
state of stress and deformation is described by the components of
the stress and strain tensors, respectively, the material properties
determine a specific relation between stress and strain which is a
characteristic only of the material. Since this relation is unique
for a given material, it is called the *rheological equation of state*
or sometimes the *constitutive* equation for the material (since it is
determined only by the nature or constitution of the material).

It is usual to distinguish between the volumetric and shear
properties of a material, as these are considered a consequence of
different material characteristics. The volumetric properties are
defined by a relation between the volumetric (isotropic) components
of stress and strain:

$$P_v = P_v(e_v) \tag{1.11-1}$$

or

$$e_v = e_v(P_v) \tag{1.11-2}$$

Since both e_v and P_v are normally defined (and measured) in terms of
equilibrium states of the material [e.g., Eq. (1.10-28)], they are
related to thermodynamic behavior, so that Eq. (1.11-1) or (1.11-2)
thus becomes identical to the thermodynamic equation of state (at a
given temperature).

The shear properties define a constitutive equation relating
the (anisotropic) stress and strain tensors associated with changes
of shape but not volume, i.e., τ_{ij} and γ_{ij}:

$$\tau_{ij} = \tau_{ij}(\gamma_{ij}) \tag{1.11-3}$$

or

$$\gamma_{ij} = \gamma_{ij}(\tau_{ij}) \tag{1.11-4}$$

The constitutive equations also reflect the time-dependent characteristics of the material by inclusion of derivative or integral functions of stress and/or strain (i.e., strain rate) with respect to time. Specifically, the manner in which time dependence must be introduced into the constitutive equation to describe stress-deformation properties serves as a basis for classifying materials, as pointed out in Sec. 1.6. That is, a material which can be described by a constitutive equation relating stress and strain only (i.e., all stress components are determined only by the instantaneous values of the strain components) is defined as *purely elastic*:

$$\tau_{ij} = \tau_{ij}(\gamma_{ij} \text{ only}) \tag{1.11-5}$$

A material for which all stress components are determined uniquely by only the rate of strain components is defined as *purely viscous*:

$$\tau_{ij} = \tau_{ij}(\dot{\gamma}_{ij} \text{ only}) \tag{1.11-6}$$

If neither (1.11-5) nor (1.11-6) is adequate to describe observed behavior of a given material, but a more complex time dependence is necessary, the material is said to be *viscoelastic*. Such materials have characteristics which are a combination of those of purely elastic and purely viscous materials, so that the constitutive equation may be represented symbolically by

$$\tau_{ij} = \tau_{ij}(\gamma_{ij}, \dot{\gamma}_{ij}, \ \dots \ ) \tag{1.11-7}$$

However, additional terms involving higher order derivatives of strain and/or stress with respect to time (or integral functions of time) are usually required in Eq. (1.11-7) to describe the observed behavior of real materials.

Note that all stresses and strains are measured relative to an undeformed reference state in which the only stress is the isotropic pressure P_o. Also, constitutive equations similar to Eqs. (1.11-3) to (1.11-7) could also be defined relating volumetric stress and strain, strain rate, etc. However, from our previous discussion of pressure and the conventional practice of defining volumetric relations in terms of equilibrium states, volumetric properties are normally considered to be purely elastic so that a relation of the form of Eq. (1.11-1) or (1.11-2) is sufficient to describe these. Thus, properties such as bulk viscosity (which will be elaborated on in the following chapter, and which define the isotropic stress which resists a rate of volume change) are consequently considered to be included in a constitutive equation of the form of Eq. (1.11-6) by including $\dot{e}_v$ in the argument. This is still consistent with the interpretation of τ_{ij} as a "dynamic" stress, which vanishes when the fluid is at rest, however.

Although we will include some further discussion of volumetric properties, most of the materials which exhibit the most interesting rheological behavior are, for practical purposes, incompressible. Hence, we will be concerned primarily with such materials.

The constitutive equations implied by Eqs. (1.11-1) to (1.11-7) may be linear or nonlinear relations between stress and strain, as necessary to represent the behavior of a specified material. The form of the equation is a characteristic of the nature of the material behavior, and the values of all constants or parameters which must be incorporated in order to specify the equation become the mechanical or rheological properties of the material. In this regard, it is important to distinguish between the following:

1. *Constitutive equation*: As defined above, the constitutive equation relates all components of (volumetric or shear) stress and strain. As it is a characteristic only of the material, it

describes that material in any type of configuration of deformation or flow, regardless of its complexity and the number of
stress and strain components which may be of concern. It represents the most general description of material behavior, and
as such must be carefully formulated with due regard to the geometrical properties of the variables involved so as to be independent of the geometry of any specific configuration. All
other representations of the mechanical behavior of a material
may be considered a special case of the constitutive equation.

2. *Material functions:* A material function for a given material is
a relation between certain specific components of stress and
strain, and hence is a special case of the constitutive equation.
For example, the functions implied in Fig. 1.3 are material
functions, in that they relate only those specific shear components of stress and strain defined in Fig. 1, relative to a
simple shear deformation. Material functions may be determined
directly from laboratory measurements of specific components of
force and displacement, and are often expressed in terms of
empirical equations relating the corresponding components of
stress and strain. The number of material functions which may
be determined for a given material is limited basically by the
variables which can be measured on the material in a state of
deformation, the range of conditions which can be achieved while
making the measurements, and the degree to which measured physical variables may be related to actual stress and strain components at some point in the material. The limitations of a
constitutive equation for a material are determined by the degree
to which the equation will predict material functions which describe the observable behavior of the material in a wide variety
of deformations.

3. *Material properties:* As mentioned above, the mechanical or
rheological properties of a material are the values of the
scalar parameters which are required to define the relation between stress and strain. Thus, they are defined by a "model,"

which comprises the specific equation chosen to represent this
relation. Since a "model" may be deduced to represent any measurable material function, the material properties are often
defined in terms of such models. If a constitutive equation can
be found which represents all measurable material functions, it
comprises the most general "model" of the material. In this
case, all material properties may be expressed in terms of the
parameters needed to define the constitutive "model," which, in
turn, comprise the fundamental material properties.

In the succeeding several chapters, we will be concerned only
with material functions, models for representing them, using them
to determine flow behavior, and methods for determining them from
measurable data. Then, after establishing the mathematical properties of tensor transformations which govern their manipulation,
we shall illustrate various types of constitutive equations which
have been proposed to describe complex materials together with
their respective advantages and disadvantages.

PROBLEMS

1-1. Simple shear, defined in Sec. 1.5, involves material between
parallel plates one of which is deflected parallel to itself
in response to the application of a parallel constant force.
At steady state, both stress and deformation (i.e., strain or
strain rate) are uniform throughout the material (homogeneous).
What are the implied conditions or restrictions which must be
satisfied for this situation to exist?

1-2. (a) Prove that the shear stress, shear strain, and shear
rate are homogeneous in simple shear.

(b) Is this conclusion valid if the stress or deformation
varies with time? Explain.

(c) Is the deformation distribution shown below possible in
simple shear? Why?

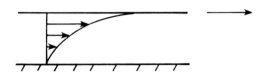

1-3. How would you classify the following materials as to solid
      or fluid? Carefully explain the criteria you use as a basis
      for your decision, and any qualifications which apply to your
      answer.

                    Shaving cream   Asphalt
                    Toothpaste   Rubber
                    Chewing gum   Jello
                    Cream cheese   Mud
                    Paint

1-4. (a) How many tensor components would be required to describe
           the stress gradient?
      (b) How many indices would be required to indicate this quan-
           tity in tensor (index) notation?
      (c) How would you represent it in matrix form?

1-5. It was illustrated in Sec. 1.10-2 (Fig. 1.8) that simple shear
      comprises both a rotation and a deformation. If β is the
      angle of inclination of the imbedded axis with the vertical
      for the element in Fig. 1.8, and α is the angle through which
      the rigid orthogonal axes have rotated at any time, show that:

          $$\alpha = \tfrac{1}{2}\,\beta$$

1-6. Red blood cells are disc-like in shape, with a diameter of
      approximately 8 μm, and occupy about 45% of normal blood by
      volume. What would be the limitations on applying the laws
      of continuum mechanics to determine the flow properties of
      blood in the vascular system?

1-7. The components of a given second-order tensor, A_{ij}, are as
      follows:

$$A_{ij} = \begin{bmatrix} 3 & 6 & 3 \\ 1 & 1 & 7 \\ 3 & 4 & 5 \end{bmatrix}$$

(a) Write this tensor as the sum of a symmetric and an anti-
     symmetric tensor, giving the matrix of the components
     of each.

(b) Write the symmetric tensor as the sum of an isotropic
     and an anisotropic tensor, in matrix form.

1-8. For the shear deformation illustrated in the figure, deter-
      mine all components of the (1) strain, (2) rate of strain,
      (3) displacement gradient, and (4) vorticity tensors in
      terms of the quantities shown in the figure. Write the
      results in matrix form.

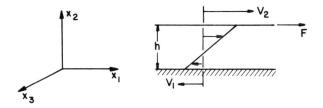

1-9. Repeat Prob. 1-8 for the deformation known as simple tension,
      shown in the figure.

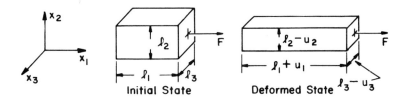

1-10.   Repeat Prob. 1-8 for the case of steady flow through a rec-
        tangular duct, illustrated in the figure.

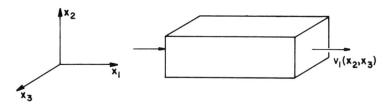

1-11.   With reference to the two-dimensional illustration of pure
        shear in Fig. 1.7B, show that:

$$
e_{ij} = \begin{bmatrix} 0 & e_{12} & 0 \\ e_{12} & 0 & 0 \\ 0 & 0 & 0 \end{bmatrix} = 2\alpha \begin{bmatrix} 0 & 1 & 0 \\ 1 & 0 & 0 \\ 0 & 0 & 0 \end{bmatrix}
$$

where

$$
e_{12} = \left(\frac{\partial u_1}{\partial x_2} + \frac{\partial u_2}{\partial x_1} \right) = 2 \frac{|\Delta \vec{S}' - \Delta \vec{S}|}{|\Delta \vec{S}|} = 2\alpha
$$

NOTES

1. For steady flows, the "pathlines" are identical to "streamlines,"
    both of which follow the path of a given fluid particle.

2. "Larger swirls give smaller swirls, which feed on their veloc-
    ity. Smaller swirls give lesser swirls, and so on to viscos-
    ity" (Ref. [1.2]).

3. We will later make a distinction between the rate of strain and
    shear rate, with respect to more general deformations.

4. The term "independent" indices is intended to exclude any dummy
    indices, which always appear as repeated (paired) indices in
    terms in which they arise. This will be elaborated upon in
    Chap. 6.

5. The expression for the displacement gradient components, as well as all other gradients of tensor quantities referred to in this chapter, which is valid for any coordinate system, will be presented later.

6. The factor $\frac{1}{2}$ in Eq. (1.10-8) is sometimes included in the definition of the strain tensor, but is omitted here for the sake of conformity with the majority of the literature on fluid mechanics, and the usual definition of viscosity. This definition coincides with what is sometimes called the *engineering strain*.

7. The sum of the diagonal elements of a tensor is called its *trace* indicated by tr. It is a scalar quantity (e.g., a volumetric change is isotropic, and hence has a magnitude, but no directional properties), and hence is called an *invariant*. It is one of three scalar invariants which can be formed from the components of any symmetrical second-order tensor. These will be considered in detail later.

Chapter 2

MATERIAL RESPONSE

2.1. INTRODUCTION

This chapter is concerned with the response of various classes
of materials to certain specific imposed conditions in simple deformations (such as simple shear) in which the nonzero components of
stress and strain are uniform throughout the material (i.e., homogeneous). We shall consider purely viscous (linear and nonlinear),
linear elastic, and linear viscoelastic materials, with emphasis
upon materials capable of continuous deformation (i.e., fluids).
The response of such materials constitutes the various applied
stress components required to sustain a given deformation (or,
what is equivalent, the internal stresses developed within the
material) as a function of the deformation, or vice versa. The
relation between a specific component of stress and deformation
(strain, strain rate, and/or time) serves to define a *material
function*. If these material functions can be expressed mathematically, by empirical means or otherwise, the constant parameters
which are required to define the mathematical function then constitute the rheological or mechanical properties of the material.

We will distinguish between a material function and a *rheological equation of state* (constitutive equation). For our purposes, a material function is a relation between specific

components of stress and strain, relative to a particular set of
imposed conditions. Such functions may be determined experimentally,
and can be represented by empirical data or a mathematical function
which represents the data. A rheological equation of state, on the
other hand, is an analytical relation between the total stress and
strain tensors and is applicable to any and all conceivable imposed
conditions or deformations. Since it involves all possible components of stress and strain, the general rheological equation includes
all possible material functions as special cases for specific deformations. The emphasis in this chapter will be on material functions,
with a detailed consideration of the properties of general constitutive equations being deferred until later.

2.2. PURELY VISCOUS FLUIDS

In Sec. 1.11, we deduced that the general rheological description of an incompressible material may be represented by the implied
function

$$\tau_{ij} = \tau_{ij}(\gamma_{ij}, \dot{\gamma}_{ij}, \ldots) \tag{2.2-1}$$

A purely viscous material is defined as one for which the
shear stress is a function only of the instantaneous rate of deformation. This is a special case of (2.2-1), then, for which

$$\tau_{ij} = \tau_{ij}(\dot{\gamma}_{ij}) \tag{2.2-2}$$

Such a material is a fluid, since it will deform continuously or
"flow" i.e., it will support a nonzero rate of deformation) in
response to an applied anisotropic stress.

In this section we will consider certain special cases of
Eq. (2.2-2), including linear (Newtonian) and nonlinear (non-
Newtonian) fluids. The material functions which relate stress and
strain (strain rate) are characteristic of the fluid, and are therefore valid at any given point within the material, regardless of

the distribution of the stress and strain components. For flow fields in general, these quantities vary from point to point (i.e., are inhomogeneous). However, for simple shear deformation (Fig. 1.2), stress and strain are homogeneously distributed (in a homogeneous material). Thus, the stress and strain components are simply related to directly measurable external forces and displacements only for simple shear. A later chapter will be devoted to establishing such relations for more complex (inhomogeneous) flow fields.

For the most part, the material functions described in this chapter will be defined in terms of the τ_{21} and $\dot{\gamma}_{21}$ components of shear stress and shear rate, which may be considered relative to a simple shear deformation for which $\dot{\gamma}_{21}$ is the only nonzero shear rate component (we shall later define a class of deformations called "viscometric flows" for which $\dot{\gamma}_{12}$ is the only nonzero shear rate component). In this case, we shall omit the indices on τ and $\dot{\gamma}$, with the understanding that the 21 components are implied. Thus, for simple shear, Eq. (2.2-2) may be expressed as

$$\tau = \tau(\dot{\gamma}) \tag{2.2-3}$$

where the shear rate ($\dot{\gamma}$) is directly related to the distance between the plates (h) and the velocity of the moving plate (V):

$$\gamma = \dot{\gamma}_{12} = \frac{dv_1}{dx_2} = \frac{v}{h} \tag{2.2-4}$$

and

$$\dot{\gamma}_{ij} = \begin{bmatrix} 0 & 1 & 0 \\ 1 & 0 & 0 \\ 0 & 0 & 0 \end{bmatrix} \tag{2.2-5}$$

For a purely viscous fluid, the internal shear stress developed within the material is a unique functiononly of the material and the instantaneous shear rate ($\dot{\gamma}$). This implies that, immediately upon cessation of any relative motion (i.e., when $\dot{\gamma} = 0$), the shear stress instantly becomes zero. That is, the response of shear

stress to changes in shear rate (and vice versa) is instantaneous,
if inertial effects are neglected. Conversely, the sudden removal
of all forces or stress will result in instantaneous cessation of
all relative motion (i.e., $\dot{\gamma} = 0$), again neglecting inertial
effects

Of course inertial forces will not be negligible in unsteady
motion if either the mass of material or its acceleration is sufficiently large. If such is the case, the application of Newton's
laws of motion to the continuously deforming material gives rise to
the momentum equations of motion which account for inertial forces
arising from mass or momentum effects. These equations must be satisfied by all materials in any system, regardless of their rheological properties, and hence provide a basis for determining the
stress distribution in an inhomogeneous deformation. These equations
and methods of using them will be discussed in subsequent chapters.
Thus, material rheological or constitutive relations involve only
those stresses required to deform the material, exclusive of any
additional stresses or forces associated with mass or inertial
effects.

2.2.1. Newtonian Fluids

For many fluids, measurements of shear stress and shear rate
(at various magnitudes of both) indicate a direct proportionality
between the two:

$$\tau = \mu\dot{\gamma} \qquad\qquad\qquad (2.2\text{-}6)$$

where μ is the coefficient of proportionality. It is therefore a
rheological property of the material, and is called the *viscosity*.
Equation (2.2-6), in fact, constitutes the definition of viscosity:

$$\mu = \frac{\tau}{\dot{\gamma}} \left(\frac{dyne\text{-}sec}{cm^2}\right) = poise \qquad\qquad (2.2\text{-}7)$$

Such materials for which the ratio of shear stress to shear rate, or
viscosity, is constant (i.e., independent of the magnitude of shear

stress or shear rate) are called *Newtonian*. Most fluids of simple
structure, composed of relatively simple molecules in a single
phase, behave as Newtonian fluids.

The formation of a general constitutive equation for the
Newtonian fluid simply involves generalizing Eq. (2.2-6) by replacing the shearing stress component τ by the shear (anisotropic) stress
tensor τ_{ij} and the shear rate component $\dot{\gamma}$ by the (anisotropic) shear
rate tensor $\dot{\gamma}_{ij}$:

$$\tau_{ij} = \mu \dot{\gamma}_{ij} \tag{2.2-8}$$

or

$$\begin{bmatrix} \tau_{11} & \tau_{12} & \tau_{13} \\ \tau_{21} & \tau_{22} & \tau_{23} \\ \tau_{31} & \tau_{32} & \tau_{33} \end{bmatrix} = \mu \begin{bmatrix} \dot{\gamma}_{11} & \dot{\gamma}_{12} & \dot{\gamma}_{13} \\ \dot{\gamma}_{21} & \dot{\gamma}_{22} & \dot{\gamma}_{23} \\ \dot{\gamma}_{31} & \dot{\gamma}_{32} & \dot{\gamma}_{33} \end{bmatrix} \tag{2.2-9}$$

It is important to note that this constitutes a hypothetical model
of fluid behavior, and can only be confirmed by comparison of predicted behavior with observed behavior. It is possible that a given
fluid may appear to be Newtonian with regard to the relation between
τ_{12} and $\dot{\gamma}_{12}$, but not with regard to other stress components in a
given flow situation. However, a general conclusion as to the
suitability of a given constitutive equation must consider which
stress components can be measured and the corresponding possible
range of measurements (i.e., range of shear rates), as well as the
conditions under which it is desired to apply the equation.

Equation (2.2-8) relates the anisotropic components of stress
and strain associated with shear deformation or changes in shape.
If the fluid is incompressible, no other deformation is possible
(e.g., liquids, for practical purposes, can be considered incompressible under all but very unusual conditions). However, for compressible fluids, an additional rheological relation between isotropic components of stress is required to describe volumetric deformations. Although essentially all fluids which are interesting

from a rheological point of view may be considered incompressible, many materials (including gases, which are invariably Newtonian) are compressible, so that a volumetric relation is required. Therefore, for the sake of completeness, we shall briefly discuss compressible or volumetric properties.

2.2.2. Volumetric Properties

In Sec. 1.10, we observed that the stress and strain tensors could be resolved into normal (isotropic) and shear (anisotropic) components, and indicated that two categories of material properties could be defined which relate these two types of components, respectively. We have also seen that the isotropic (mean normal) stress component $(-\bar{P})$ may be associated with the total static pressure in the system. For an incompressible fluid, this static pressure does not influence the deformation of the material, and is hence an arbitrary constant component $(-P_o)$ of the total stress. However, for a compressible material, any change in the isotropic stress is accompanied by a corresponding change in volume; i.e., isotropic strain. If the isotropic pressure corresponding to the (arbitrary) reference undeformed state is P_o, and P_v is the deviation in pressure from this value which produces a volumetric deformation (e_v), the relation between these can be expressed as

$$\bar{P} - P_o = -Ke_v = -K\left(\frac{3\bar{e}}{2}\right) \qquad (2.2\text{-}10)$$

or

$$P_v(\bar{e}) = -Ke_v \qquad (2.2\text{-}11)$$

where

$$\bar{P} = P_o + P_v(\bar{e})$$

Equation (2.2-11) defines the bulk modulus, K, which is a characteristic material (rheological) property of any compressible material (solid or fluid). A constant bulk modulus implies purely

elastic volumetric properties. It is emphasized that this property
is defined in terms of the deviation of pressure from the (arbitrary)
reference pressure, P_o, which is assumed to correspond to an (arbitrary) undeformed or reference state. Thus, the pressure P_o still
represents an arbitrary constant component of isotropic stress,
whether the material is compressible or incompressible.

The bulk modulus is equivalent to the compressibility of the
material, which may be defined by expanding P_v as a function of
density about the reference point, P_o:

$$P_v = \bar{P} - P_o = \left(\frac{\partial \bar{P}}{\partial \rho}\right)_{T, \rho_o} (\rho - \rho_o) + \cdots = \beta_o \left(\frac{\rho - \rho_o}{\rho_o}\right) + \cdots \qquad (2.2\text{-}12)$$

The compressibility β_o, at the reference temperature and density
$(T_o,\ \rho_o)$ is thus defined as:

$$\beta_o = \rho_o \left(\frac{\partial \bar{P}}{\partial \rho}\right)_{T_o, \rho_o} \qquad (2.2\text{-}13)$$

(See note 1.) Written in terms of volume instead of density, Eq.
(2.2-13) is equivalent to:

$$\beta_o = -V_o \left(\frac{\partial \bar{P}}{\partial V}\right)_{T_o, V_o} \qquad (2.2\text{-}14)$$

These volumetric properties are normally referred to states of
static equilibrium, and hence may also be defined as thermodynamic
properties of the material.

───────────────────────────────── 0 ─────────────────────────────────

Example 2.1 Show that the compressibility, β_o, defined by Eq.
(2.2-14) and the bulk modulus, K, defined by Eq. (2.2-11) are
equivalent.

From Eq. (2.2-11):

$$K = -\frac{2P_v}{3\bar{e}} = -\frac{P_v}{e_v}$$

For infinitesimal volumetric strain:

$$\frac{P_v}{e_v} = \lim_{V \to V_o} \left[\frac{\bar{P} - P_o}{(V - V_o)/V_o} \right]$$

$$= \lim_{\Delta V \to 0} \left(\frac{V_o \Delta P}{\Delta V} \right) = V_o \left(\frac{\partial P}{\partial V} \right)_{V_o}$$

So that

$$K = -\frac{P_v}{e_v} = -V_o \left(\frac{\partial P}{\partial V} \right)_{V_o}$$

which is identical to β_o by (2.2-14) at temperature T_o.

————————————————— 0 —————————————————

Equation (2.2-11) implies that the equilibrium isotropic properties of the material are purely elastic; that is, the volumetric
stress (P_v) is a function only of the volumetric strain (e_v). Indeed, if K (or β_o) is constant (independent of pressure), then the
volumetric properties are linearly elastic. However, changes in
volume may also be resisted by viscous forces. That is, the
stress required to produce a change in volume may also depend upon
the rate of volumetric strain. This contribution to stress is
usually assumed to be a component of the shear (deviatoric) tensor
τ_{ij}, since it disappears when the material is in an equilibrium
state. Of course, only the normal (diagonal) components of this
tensor are affected, since only the volumetric (isotropic) strain

rate components are involved. Thus, the total shear tensor for a
purely viscous fluid may be written:

$$(\tau_{ij})_{Total} = \bar{\tau}(\dot{e}_v)\,\delta_{ij} + \tau_{ij}(\dot{\gamma}_{ij}) \tag{2.2-15}$$

where $\bar{\tau}$ represents the isotropic contribution to τ_{ij} which is associated with a finite rate of volumetric strain.

For a Newtonian fluid, for example, this expression becomes:

$$\tau_{ij} = \kappa\dot{e}_v\,\delta_{ij} + \mu\dot{\gamma}_{ij} \tag{2.2-16}$$

where κ is called the *bulk viscosity*. Substituting for $\dot{\gamma}_{ij}$ in
terms of Δ_{ij}, Eq. (2.2-16) becomes:

$$\tau_{ij} = \kappa\left(\frac{3}{2}\bar{\Delta}\right)\delta_{ij} + \mu(\Delta_{ij} - \bar{\Delta}\delta_{ij})$$

$$= \left(\frac{3}{2}\kappa - \mu\right)\bar{\Delta}\delta_{ij} + \mu\Delta_{ij}$$

$$= \left(\kappa - \frac{2}{3}\mu\right)\dot{e}_v\,\delta_{ij} + \mu\Delta_{ij} \tag{2.2-17}$$

Equation (2.2-17) is a form of the general constitutive for a
Newtonian fluid which is frequently quoted, although the form of
Eq. (2.2-16) is more descriptive of the significance of the terms.
Both indicate that the Newtonian fluid is purely viscous with regard
to the deviatoric stress, τ_{ij}, although equilibrium volumetric
properties are purely elastic (e.g., Eq. (2.2-11). The definition
of a Newtonian fluid implies a direct proportionality between corresponding stress and strain rate components, hence constant fluid
properties (μ, κ) at a given temperature. However, there are many
fluids for which these components of stress and strain rate are
not directly proportional, so that the Newtonian model does not
apply.

2.2.3. Generalized Newtonian
(Non-Newtonian) Fluids [2.1-2.3]

Any fluid for which the relation between shear stress and
shear rate cannot be described by Eq. (2.2-6) [or the more general
equivalent, Eq. (2.2-16)] is referred to as *non-Newtonian*. A great
many complex fluids, including those containing very large molecules
(polymers), suspensions or slurries of rigid or deformable solid
matter, and pastes or emulsions are non-Newtonian.

Many complex non-Newtonian fluids are not purely viscous (especially polymeric fluids). However, measurements of shear stress
and shear rate may be made for these materials in steady shearing
flows, and the ratio of these quantities may be defined as a rheological characteristic analogous to the Newtonian viscosity. Since
this ratio of shear stress to shear rate is not a constant (i.e.,
doubling the shear stress will not result in twice the shear rate,
or vice versa), it defines a function which is called the *apparent
viscosity* or sometimes the *viscosity function:*

$$\eta(\dot{\gamma}) = \frac{\tau}{\dot{\gamma}} \qquad\qquad\qquad (2.2-18)$$

Since the apparent viscosity is defined by a relation between
shear stress and shear rate identical to the definition of the
Newtonian viscosity [Eq. (2.2-7)], materials which are characterized
in this manner are often referred to as *generalized Newtonian fluids*.
[Extension of (2.2-18) to a more general constitutive equation involving the complete shear stress and shear rate tensors requires
special considerations, and will be discussed in Chap. 3.] Although
we have indicated the apparent viscosity to be a function of shear
rate, it may just as well be specified as a function of shear stress
because of the unique relation which exists between the two.

It will be illustrated later, however, that the generalized
Newtonian fluid model does not provide the most general description
of the steady shear properties of a purely viscous fluid.

A. Classification of Non-Newtonian Behavior [2.1]

These fluids may be classified by the way in which the shear stress varies with shear rate, or in terms of the variation of apparent viscosity with shear stress or shear rate. Some of the most common classifications are as follows.

1. Plastic (Viscoplastic or Bingham Plastic)

This material behaves as an ideal rigid solid (no deformation) when subjected to a shear stress smaller than a certain (yield) value (τ_o). For stresses above the yield value, the Bingham plastic flows as a fluid, with the shear stress being a linear function of shear rate. This behavior is illustrated in Fig. 2.1. Although it is doubtful that any real material actually behaves precisely in this manner, the behavior of many materials, notable pastes, suspensions, slurries, paints, etc., may often be adequately approximated by this model over a suitable range of conditions.

2. Pseudoplastic (Shear Thinning)

These materials exhibit a decrease in apparent viscosity as the shear rate increases. Thus, the apparent viscosity curve is qualitatively similar to that of the Bingham plastic, as seen in Fig. 2.1B (hence the term pseudoplastic). However, there is no actual yield stress (e.g., Fig. 2.1A), as the shear stress-shear rate curve passes through the origin. If the material is such that this curve rises rapidly and then flattens out at a relatively low shear rate, it may be extremely difficult to differentiate between a Bingham plastic and a pseudoplastic material, and very accurate data at quite low shear rates would be required to prove or disprove the existence of a yield stress. Many materials exhibit pseudoplastic behavior in varying degrees, and it is probably the most common type of observed non-Newtonian behavior. Polymers and polymer solutions, most notably, fit this category over much of the observed shear rate range.

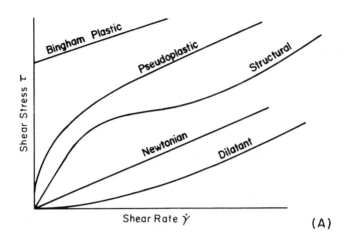

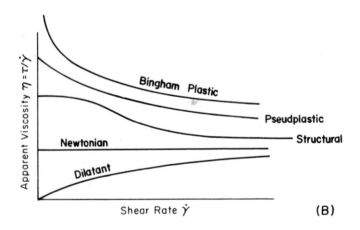

FIG. 2.1   Classes of non-Newtonian behavior.

3. *Dilatant (Shear Thickening)*

There are some materials which appear to expand or "dilate"
when subjected to shear stresses. These materials also tend to
exhibit an increase in apparent viscosity with shear rate because
of this dilation. This is illustrated in Fig. 2.1. This type of
behavior is relatively rare compared with pseudoplastic behavior,
but is exhibited by some concentrated suspensions of solids, slurries,
proteins, and certain polymer solutions. Since dilation refers to a
volumetric effect and shear thickening to a shear or flow effect, the
two phenomena are actually distinct. However, since a material which
exhibits one effect will generally exhibit both, the terms are often
used interchangeably.

4. *Structural Viscosity (Strukturviskosität) [2.4]*

This is a more general type of shear thinning behavior characterized by three different and distinct regions: a Newtonian region
at low shear rates (characterized by a zero shear rate limiting viscosity); a nonlinear region at intermediate shear rates; and another
Newtonian region at high shear rates (characterized by a high shear
rate-limiting viscosity). The zero shear viscosity is usually
greater than the high shear limiting value, as illustrated in Fig.
2.1. The converse, in which the zero shear viscosity is lower, can
also occur but is much less common. The different regions were
originally thought to be due to a basic change in the structure of
the material as a function of shear rate, hence the term "structural
viscosity." This effect is very common in solutions of macromole-
cules (particularly coiled polymers), many slurries and suspensions,
and some lubricating oils. Many materials which appear to be pseudoplastic or dilatant over a limited range of shear rate will actually
exhibit this more general type of behavior over a much wider range
of shear rate.

5. *Thixotropy*

Thixotropy is often confused with shear thinning behavior, inasmuch as they both refer to a decrease in apparent viscosity. However, thixotropy is a time-dependent effect, rather than a shear-dependent effect, and refers to a reversible decrease in apparent viscosity with time at a constant shear rate. This is generally due to a reversible change in structure of the material with time under shear, with a limiting viscosity ultimately being approached. The result is a series of hysteresis curves of τ vs. $\dot{\gamma}$, when $\dot{\gamma}$ is repeatedly cycled, as seen in Fig. 2.2. The criteria of reversibility is a necessary condition of this definition (the structure recovers upon setting), since an irreversible decrease in viscosity is termed *shear degradation*. Certain clay suspensions, gels, colloidal sols, and polymers may exhibit thixotropic behavior.

6. *Rheopexy*

Rheopexy is essentially the reverse of thixotropy in that it represents an increase of apparent viscosity with time at a constant shear rate. One difference is that the term rheopexy is often used in reference to an irreversible change rather than a reversible

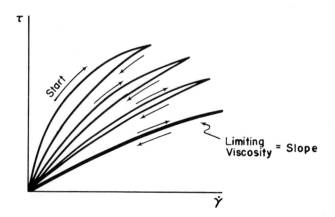

FIG. 2.2 Thixotropy.

change, which would then be called *negative thixotropy*. Hysteresis
curves are also observed upon cycling the shear rate, but in the
opposite direction from those in Fig. 2.2. Pastes of gypsum powder
exhibit this type of behavior, and it is often associated with a
metastable system which reverts to a permanent gel upon shearing.

B. Empirical Models for Non-Newtonian Behavior

The most successful attempts at describing the steady shear
stress-shear rate behavior of non-Newtonian fluids have been largely
empirical. It would be much more satisfying if one could derive
these functions from theories based upon molecular structure, but
most of the materials of greatest interest are extremely complex
and presently available molecular theories are largely oversimplified and generally inadequate for describing real behavior. Hence,
at present, empirical observations represent the most reliable source
of rheological information. The following represents some of the
more common empirical models which have been utilized to represent
the various classes of observed non-Newtonian behavior.

1. *Bingham Plastic*

$$\text{If } |\tau| > |\tau_o|: \quad \tau = \pm \tau_o + \mu_o \dot{\gamma} \left\{ \begin{array}{l} + \text{ if } \tau \text{ and } \dot{\gamma} \text{ are } + \\[6pt] - \text{ if } \tau \text{ and } \dot{\gamma} \text{ are } - \end{array} \right\} \quad (2.2\text{-}19)$$

$$\text{If } |\tau| < |\tau_o|: \quad \dot{\gamma} = 0$$

This is a two-parameter model, the parameters being

$$\tau_o = \text{yield stress}$$

$$\mu_o = \text{plastic viscosity}$$

The apparent viscosity function becomes

$$|\tau| > \tau_o: \quad \eta = \mu_o + \left| \frac{\tau_o}{\dot{\gamma}} \right| \qquad (2.2\text{-}21)$$

$$|\tau| < \tau_o \; : \; \eta = \infty \tag{2.2-22}$$

2. *Power Law (Ostwald-deWaele)*

$$\tau = m|\dot{\gamma}|^{n-1}\dot{\gamma} \tag{2.2-23}$$

This is also a two-parameter model:

n = flow index

m = consistency

For n = 1, the model is Newtonian (m = μ)

n < 1, the model os pseudoplastic (shear thinning)

n > 1, the model is dilatant (shear thickening)

Because the dimensions of m will depend upon the value of n, it is more satisfying to introduce a standard or reference shear rate ($\dot{\gamma}_p$, usually taken to be 1 sec^{-1}) so that the Power law model can be written:

$$\tau = \eta_p \left|\frac{\dot{\gamma}}{\dot{\gamma}_p}\right|^{n-1}\dot{\gamma} \tag{2.2-24}$$

Thus, η_p always has dimensions of viscosity (e.g., poise), and is in fact the value of the apparent viscosity at the reference shear rate. The apparent viscosity function for this model is

$$\eta = \eta_p \left|\frac{\dot{\gamma}}{\dot{\gamma}_p}\right|^{n-1} \tag{2.2-25}$$

The Power law model is the most widely used of any model, since it is relatively easy to incorporate into analytical solutions to flow problems, and it can be made to fit almost any data over a limited range of shear rate. However, it has two serious drawbacks: for constant values of n and η_p, it predicts unlimited increasing or decreasing apparent viscosity with shear rate; and it predicts either zero or infinite values of the limiting zero shear viscosity for n greater or less than 1, respectively.

3. *Eyring*

$$\tau = \eta_o \, B \, \text{arcsinh} \, \frac{\dot{\gamma}}{B} \tag{2.2-26}$$

The two parameters which characterize this model are η_o and B. The model becomes Newtonian with $\mu = \eta_o$ as $\dot{\gamma} \to 0$; otherwise, it is pseudoplastic. The apparent viscosity function is

$$\eta = \eta_o \, \frac{\text{arcsinh} \, (\dot{\gamma}/B)}{(\dot{\gamma}/B)} \tag{2.2-27}$$

4. *Reiner-Philippoff*

$$\tau = \left[\eta_\infty + \frac{\eta_o - \eta_\infty}{1 + (\tau/\tau_s)^2} \right] \dot{\gamma} \tag{2.2-28}$$

This is a three-parameter model, the parameters being η_o, η_∞, τ_s with an apparent viscosity function:

$$\eta = \eta_\infty + \frac{\eta_o - \eta_\infty}{1 + (\tau/\tau_s)^2} \tag{2.2-29}$$

The τ vs. $\dot{\gamma}$ curve has an inflection point at

$$\tau = \pm\tau_s \sqrt{\frac{3\eta_o}{\eta_\infty}}$$

and exhibits high and low shear rate-limiting viscosities as follows:

As $\tau \to \infty$ the model becomes Newtonian with $\mu = \eta_\infty$

$\tau \to 0$ the model becomes Newtonian with $\mu = \eta_o$

5. Truncated Power Law

For $|\dot\gamma| < |\dot\gamma_1|$: $\tau = \eta_p \dot\gamma$ (2.2-30)

$|\dot\gamma| > |\dot\gamma_1|$: $\tau = \eta_p \left|\dfrac{\dot\gamma}{\dot\gamma_1}\right|^{n-1} \dot\gamma$ (2.2-31)

This is also a three-parameter model, with η_p, n, and $\dot\gamma_1$ being the parameters. Here $\dot\gamma_1$ is a parameter which determines the transition point from Newtonian to Power law behavior, and should not be confused with $\dot\gamma_p$ of Eq. (2.2-24), which is not a parameter, but simply an arbitrary reference point. This model removes the second major objection to the Power law model, mentioned above.

6. Ellis

$$\tau = \left(\frac{\eta_o}{1 + |\tau/\tau_{\frac{1}{2}}|^{\alpha-1}}\right)\dot\gamma \tag{2.2-32}$$

where η_o, $\tau_{\frac{1}{2}}$, and α are the three material parameters, and the apparent viscosity function is:

$$\eta = \frac{\eta_o}{1 + |\tau/\tau_{\frac{1}{2}}|^{\alpha-1}} \tag{2.2-33}$$

Here $\tau_{\frac{1}{2}}$ is the value of τ at which $\eta = \frac{1}{2}\eta_o$. This model exhibits the following characteristics:

As $\tau \to 0$, the model becomes Newtonian with $\mu = \eta_o$, and for $\eta \ll \eta_o$, it reduces to the Power law with $n = 1/\alpha$

7. Meter

$$\eta = \eta_o\left[\frac{1 + |\tau/\tau_m|^{\alpha-1}\ (\eta_\infty/\eta_o)}{1 + |\tau/\tau_m|^{\alpha-1}}\right] \tag{2.2-34}$$

This model has four parameters: η_0, η_∞, τ_m, α, and exhibits high and low limiting viscosities:

As $\tau \to 0$ the model becomes Newtonian with $\mu = \eta_0$

$\tau \to \infty$ the model becomes Newtonian with $\mu = \eta_\infty$

Here τ_m is the value of τ at which η has a value equal to $(\eta_0 + \eta_\infty)/2$. For an intermediate range of τ, the model reduces to the Power law model, with $n = 1/\alpha$. If $\eta_\infty \ll \eta_0$, this model is equivalent to the Ellis model.

There are a wide variety of models which can be written in the general form:

$$\frac{\eta - \eta_\infty}{\eta_0 - \eta_\infty} = f(\dot{\gamma}) \tag{2.2-35}$$

where $f(\dot{\gamma})$ is a decreasing function of $\dot{\gamma}$. Such models exhibit the general characteristics of structural viscosity, as do a great many real complex fluids. Specifically, if the function $f(\dot{\gamma})$ is such that:

$$f(0) = 1 \quad \text{and} \quad f(\infty) = 0 \tag{2.2-36}$$

then η_0 and η_∞ represent the low and high shear rate-liming viscosities, respectively. A few examples of this type of model follow:

8. Cross [2.6]

$$\eta = \eta_\infty + \frac{\eta_0 - \eta_\infty}{1 + (\dot{\gamma} t_1)^P} \tag{2.2-37}$$

which has four parameters: η_0, η_∞, t_1, P. For $\eta_0 \gg \eta \gg \eta_\infty$ this model reduces to the Power law, with $n = (1 - P)$ and $m = \eta_0 (t_1)^{-P}$. The parameter t_1 is a characteristic time constant, and is equal to the reciprocal of the value of $\dot{\gamma}$ at which

$$\eta = \frac{\eta_o + \eta_\infty}{2}$$

9. *Williams [2.7]*

$$\eta = \eta_\infty + \frac{\eta_o - \eta_\infty}{(1 + 2t_1^2 \dot\gamma^2)^P} \qquad\qquad (2.2\text{-}38)$$

The four material parameters are: η_o, η_∞, t_1, P. For $\eta_o \gg \eta \gg \eta_\infty$ and $\eta_o^{1/P} \gg \eta^{1/P}$, this model reduces to Power law, with $n = (1 - 2P)$ and $m = \eta_o(2t_1^2)^{-P}$. The general characteristics of these models are shown in Fig. 2.3.

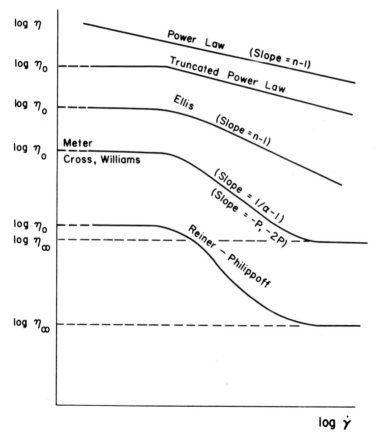

FIG. 2.3 Characteristics of various non-Newtonian fluid models.

2.3. PURELY ELASTIC SOLIDS [2.8]

A purely elastic material is one for which all internal stresses are a function only of the instantaneous magnitude of deformation, or strain. Equivocally, when subjected to a constant shear stress in simple shear an elastic material will respond instantly with an equilibrium shear strain or displacement. Such a material is a solid since, in response to a constant applied stress, continuous flow is not possible short of rupture. A linear elastic solid, for which stress is directly proportional to strain, is called a *Hooke solid*. Materials which do not obey this linear relation may be appropriately termed non-Hookean, although such materials have not been classified to the degree that the corresponding nonlinear (non-Newtonian) fluids have.

In simple shear, the linear relation between shear stress and shear strain for a Hooke solid is a direct proportionality:

$$\tau = G\gamma \tag{2.3-1}$$

where the constant of proportionality, G, is called the *elastic modulus* or *shear modulus*. Note the analogy between Eqs. (2.2-6) and (2.3-1) (the latter being the defining equation for the shear modulus, G). The generalized equivalent constitutive equation, analogous to Eq. (2.2-8), is

$$\tau_{ij} = G\gamma_{ij} \tag{2.3-2}$$

For an incompressible linear elastic (Hookean) solid, Eq. (2.3-2) provides a relation between all components of stress and strain. For a linear compressible material Eq. (2.2-11) relating volumetric stress and strain in terms of the bulk modulus, is also necessary.

$$P_v = -Ke_v = \frac{-3\bar{K}\bar{e}}{2} \tag{2.2-11}$$

Since we are primarily interested in fluids, we will not now attempt to discuss nonlinear effects in elastic solids. However,

it is informative to illustrate how the fundamental elastic properties G and K are related to certain other material constants which
are commonly used to characterize the deformation response of a
linear elastic solid.

In order to do this, let us consider a rod of an isotropic
elastic material subjected to a uniaxial force (stress), as in
Fig. 2.4. This particular deformation is referred to as *simple tension*. The force F produces a stress which has only one nonzero
normal component (in the x_1 direction) and is uniform throughout the
rod:

Homogeneous: $\sigma_n = \sigma_{11} = \dfrac{F}{A}$ (2.3-3)

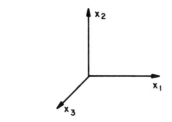

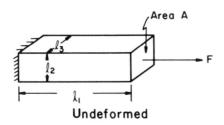

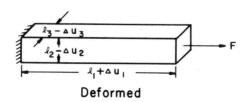

FIG. 2.4 Simple tension.

The components of the total stress tensor are therefore

$$\sigma_{ij} = \sigma_n \begin{bmatrix} 1 & 0 & 0 \\ 0 & 0 & 0 \\ 0 & 0 & 0 \end{bmatrix} \qquad (2.3\text{-}4)$$

The mean normal (isotropic) stress component is

$$-P = \frac{1}{3} \, \text{tr}(\sigma_{ij}) = \frac{\sigma_{11}}{3} \qquad (2.3\text{-}5)$$

and the shear (anisotropic) components of the stress tensor follow by definition:

$$\tau_{ij} = \sigma_{ij} + P\delta_{ij}$$

$$= \begin{bmatrix} \sigma_{11} - \dfrac{\sigma_{11}}{3} & 0 & 0 \\ 0 & \dfrac{-\sigma_{11}}{3} & 0 \\ 0 & 0 & \dfrac{-\sigma_{11}}{3} \end{bmatrix} = \frac{\sigma_{11}}{3} \begin{bmatrix} 2 & 0 & 0 \\ 0 & -1 & 0 \\ 0 & 0 & -1 \end{bmatrix} \qquad (2.3\text{-}6)$$

Let us now determine the deformation which a compressible elastic solid would exhibit in response to these imposed conditions. The normal (isotropic) strain follows from Eqs. (2.2-11) and (2.3-5) with a constant bulk modulus. Taking P to be the gage pressure (i.e., $P = \bar{P} - P_o = P_v$), these equations become:

$$e_v = \frac{3\bar{e}}{2} = -\frac{P}{K} = \frac{\sigma_{11}}{3K} \qquad (2.3\text{-}7)$$

From Eqs. (2.3-2) and (2.3-6), the shear (anisotropic) strain components are:

$$\gamma_{ij} = \frac{1}{G} \tau_{ij} = \frac{\sigma_{11}}{3G} \begin{bmatrix} 2 & 0 & 0 \\ 0 & -1 & 0 \\ 0 & 0 & -1 \end{bmatrix} \qquad (2.3\text{-}8)$$

Equations (2.3-7) and (2.3-8) thus define the strain components:

$$e_{ij} = \frac{2e_v}{3} \delta_{ij} + \gamma_{ij}$$

$$= \frac{2\sigma_{11}}{9K} \begin{bmatrix} 1 & 0 & 0 \\ 0 & 1 & 0 \\ 0 & 0 & 1 \end{bmatrix} + \frac{\sigma_{11}}{3G} \begin{bmatrix} 2 & 0 & 0 \\ 0 & -1 & 0 \\ 0 & 0 & -1 \end{bmatrix} \qquad (2.3\text{-}9)$$

which, in turn, determine the displacement gradient components:

$$e_{11} = 2 \frac{\partial u_1}{\partial x_1} = 2\sigma_{11}\left(\frac{1}{9K} + \frac{1}{3G}\right) \qquad (2.3\text{-}10)$$

$$e_{22} = 2 \frac{\partial u_2}{\partial x_2} = \sigma_{11}\left(\frac{2}{9K} - \frac{1}{3G}\right) = e_{33} \qquad (2.3\text{-}11)$$

It is evident that the lateral displacement gradients are equal $(\partial u_3/\partial x_3 = \partial u_2/\partial x_2)$. Assuming σ_{11} and the material properties are constant, these equations can be integrated to give the displacement components:

$$\Delta u_1 = \frac{\sigma_{11}}{3}\left(\frac{1}{G} + \frac{1}{3K}\right)\ell_1 \qquad (2.3\text{-}12)$$

$$\Delta u_2 = -\frac{\sigma_{11}}{3}\left(\frac{1}{2G} - \frac{1}{3K}\right)\ell_2 \qquad (2.3\text{-}13)$$

$$\Delta u_3 = -\frac{\sigma_{11}}{3}\left(\frac{1}{2G} - \frac{1}{3K}\right)\ell_3 \qquad (2.3\text{-}14)$$

Since these last three expressions assume $\sigma_{11} = F/A$ is independent of x_i, they are strictly valid only for infinitesimal displacements, for which A is essentially constant.

The deformation of an elastic solid in simple tension is often described by two alternate parameters, Young's modulus, E, and Poisson's ratio, ν, defined in terms of specific stress and displacement gradient components as follows:

$$E = \frac{\sigma_{11}}{\partial u_1/\partial x_1} \qquad (2.3\text{-}15)$$

$$\nu = \frac{\partial u_2/\partial x_2}{\partial u_1/\partial x_1} = -\frac{\partial u_3/\partial x_3}{\partial u_1/\partial x_1} \qquad (2.3\text{-}16)$$

These parameters are related to the shear modulus, G, and bulk modulus, K, by rearrangement of Eqs. (2.3-10) and (2.3-11):

$$E = \frac{9KG}{3K + G} \qquad (2.3\text{-}17)$$

$$\nu = -\left(\frac{3K - 2G}{6K + 2G}\right) \qquad (2.3\text{-}18)$$

For an incompressible material $e_v = 0$, which requires $K = \infty$. For this condition, Eqs. (2.3-17) and (2.3-18) become:

$$E = 3G \qquad \nu = \frac{1}{2} \qquad (2.3\text{-}19)$$

The shear modulus, G, and bulk modulus, K, are fundamental material properties in contrast to Young's modulus and Poisson's ratio, since they are defined in a more general sense in terms of the complete stress and strain tensors [Eqs. (2.3-2) and 2.2-11)]. That is, they relate all components of stress and strain regardless of the nature of the deformation, whereas Young's modulus and Poisson's ratio are strictly defined only for a simple tension or equivalent deformation.

It is of interest to compare the form of the general stress-strain relation for a Hookean solid with that of a Newtonian fluid. For the former

$$\sigma_{ij} = -P\delta_{ij} + \tau_{ij} = -P_o\delta_{ij} + Ke_v\delta_{ij} + G\gamma_{ij} \qquad (2.3\text{-}20)$$

This may be written in terms of the total strain tensor as

$$\sigma_{ij} = -P_o \delta_{ij} + \left(K - \frac{2G}{3}\right) e_v \delta_{ij} + G e_{ij} \qquad (2.3-21)$$

The equivalent expression for a Newtonial fluid follows from Eq. (2.2-17):

$$\sigma_{ij} = -P_o \delta_{ij} + K e_v \delta_{ij} + \tau_{ij}$$

$$= (-P_o + K e_v) \delta_{ij} + \left(\kappa - \frac{2\mu}{3}\right) \dot{e}_v \delta_{ij} + \mu \Delta_{ij} \qquad (2.3-22)$$

The analogy is most evident when comparing the total stress in excess of the reference pressure $(\sigma_{ij} + P_o \delta_{ij})$ for the solid with the anisotropic stress (τ_{ij}) for the fluid.

2.4. LINEAR VISCOELASTIC MATERIALS

As implied by the name, viscoelastic materials possess both viscous and elastic properties in varying degrees. These may vary from *viscous solids*, such as rubber, which are more elastic than viscous, to *elastic liquids*, such as molten polymers and polymer solutions, which are more viscous than elastic. Although we have seen that a compressible fluid may be viscous in shear and elastic in volumetric deformations, the term viscoelastic is reserved for materials which exhibit both viscous and elastic properties in either shear and/or volumetric deformation.

The term *elasticoviscous* has been used by some with reference to elastic liquids, to distinguish them from viscoelastic solids. However, this nomenclature has not been widely accepted, and the term viscoelastic is commonly used for both types of materials. This is probably just as well, since solid or fluid behavior is largely relative, and there are many materials in an intermediate category which are difficult to classify distinctly as either solid or fluid (e.g., silly putty).

Because of this apparent overlap between viscoelastic solids and fluids, most of the discussion concerning the properties of viscoelastic materials and the methods for characterizing them are applicable to both. Hence, although we are primarily interested in fluids, the material properties and functions described in this section are generally applicable to both fluids and solids. For our purpose, the distinction between a fluid and a solid is that a fluid is capable of sustaining a continuous deformation at a finite rate when subjected to a constant anisotropic stress, whereas a solid is not. This distinction is somewhat artificial, since a given material may behave as either a fluid or a solid, depending upon the magnitude of the applied stress and the time spent observing it (i.e., granite will flow under its own weight, albeit at an extremely low rate, whereas putty and even water will rupture as a solid when subjected to sufficiently large stress applied rapidly). A corollary of the distinction between fluids and solids is that, in response to an anisotropic stress, a solid will achieve an equilibrium deformed state, whereas there is no such equilibrium state for a fluid.

2.4.1. Relative Response of Viscous, Elastic, and Viscoelastic Materials

As previously noted, for a purely viscous material all internal stresses are a function only of the instantaneous rate of strain. Conversely, a purely elastic material develops stresses which are a function only of the instantaneous strain. For a viscoelastic material, on the other hand, internal stresses are a function not only of the instantaneous deformation (strain, rate of strain, etc.) but also depend upon the entire past history of deformation. For this reason, viscoelastic fluids are often called memory fluids, since previous deformations influence the present state of stress. For real materials, the most recent past history is more important than the more distant history, so that they may be described as having

a fading memory. As we shall see, this influence of time upon the
relation between stress and strain can be described either by a
differential equation involving derivatives of stress and/or strain
with respect to time, or by an integral equation with time as the
variable.

It is not surprising, then, that differences in the mechanical
behavior of viscous, elastic, and viscoelastic materials are most
evident in unsteady or time-dependent situations. For fluids, this
includes flows which are unsteady in either the Eulerian or
Lagrangian sense (see note 2). A comparison of the response characteristics of ideal viscous (Newtonian), ideal elastic (Hookean), and
typical viscoelastic materials in unsteady shear is shown in Fig. 2.5.
The solid and dashed lines for the viscoelastic material represent
the idealized response of "solid" and "fluid" materials, respectively, although it would not be unusual to have material which
showed a response intermediate to these. Figure 2.5 illustrates
response to four different time-dependent situations, as follows.

1. *Creep and recoil*: A constant stress is applied at time t_o and
    removed at time t_1. The various materials respond as follows.
    a. *Newtonian fluid* responds with a constant rate of strain from
        t_o to t_1, with a constant strain (displacement) maintained
        after t_1 (no strain recovery or rebound).
    b. *Hooke solid* responds with a constant strain from t_o to t_1,
        with complete and instant strain recovery (rebound) at t_1.
    c. *Viscoelastic material* responds with a nonlinear strain
        which approaches a constant rate for the fluid and a con-
        stant magnitude for the solid. At t_1 rebound or strain re-
        covery occurs at a finite rate, being complete for the solid
        and incomplete for the fluid.
2. *Stress relaxation*: An instantaneous strain (displacement) is
    applied at t_o, and maintained constant. The various materials
    respond as follows.
    a. *Newtonian fluid* responds with an instantaneous infinite im-
        pulsive stress, corresponding to instantaneous infinite rate

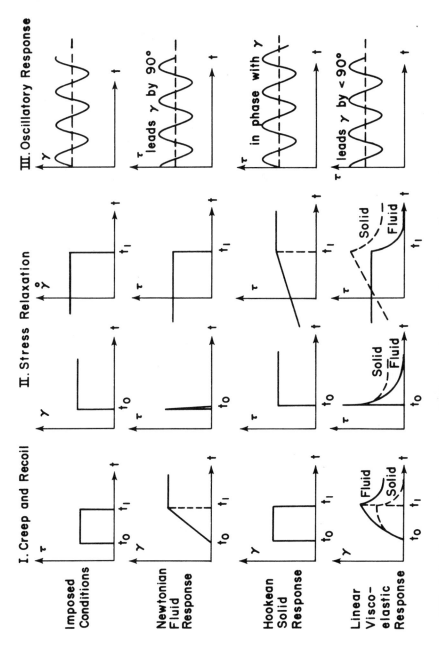

FIG. 2.5 Comparative response of linear viscous, elastic, and viscoelastic materials.

of strain (i.e., an infinite stress is required to produce
an infinite strain rate in a Newtonian fluid).

   b. *Hooke solid* responds with instantaneous constant stress.

   c. *Viscoelastic material* responds with an instantaneous stress
   which is infinite for the fluid, but finite for the solid,
   and relaxes at a finite rate. Relaxation is complete for
   the fluid, but incomplete for the solid.

3. *Oscillatory response*: A sinusoidal strain is applied to the
   material.

   a. *Newtonian fluid*--oscillatory stress is developed which leads
   the strain by 90° (stress is in phase with strain rate).

   b. *Hooke solid*--oscillatory stress is in phase with strain.

   c. *Viscoelastic material*--stress leads strain by less than 90°
   giving both "in-phase" and "out-of-phase" stress components.

The effects described above are a consequence only of the mechanical (rheological) properties of the materials, and have neglected
inertial effects. For example, an instantaneous strain (displacement) would require an infinite force for any body of finite mass,
since this corresponds to an infinite acceleration. However, if
the mass of the system or accelerations are sufficiently small that
inertial forces are much smaller than viscous and elastic forces,
the actual response will closely resemble the behavior described
above.

Figure 2.6 illustrates some additional consequences of elasticity in liquids in various flow situations, as contrasted with the
behavior of purely viscous liquids. In Fig. 2.6A, a line is drawn
within the fluid in a tube by injection of a charcoal slurry, and
flow is initiated by application of a pressure gradient. When the
pressure gradient is removed, the inelastic liquid will stop flowing
immediately (if inertial forces are small). However, in the case
of an elastic liquid, the fluid stops, but then rebounds to a position upstream from its position at the time of removal of the
pressure gradient.

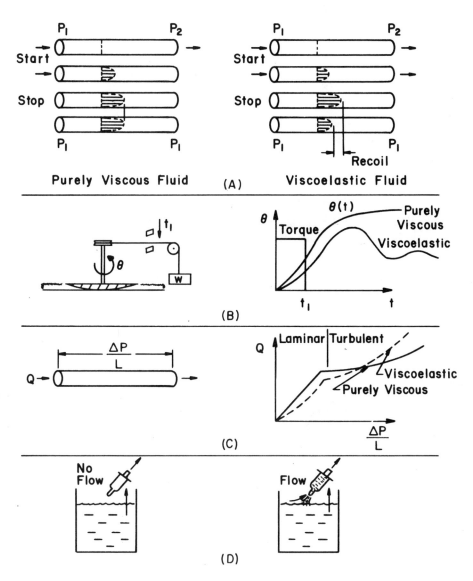

FIG. 2.6 Comparison of purely viscous and viscoelastic fluid behavior.

In Fig. 2.6B, the fluid is contained between a shallow cone and a flat plate. A torque is applied to the fluid by means of a weight attached to the cone over a pulley, which is released after a given time, resulting in a square pulse torque function. For an inelastic fluid, the cone will gradually coast to a stop, but if the fluid is elastic, one or more rebound oscillations may be observed.

Figure 2.6C illustrates the drag reduction effect observed in turbulent flow when a very small percentage (several parts per million) of certain high molecular weight soluble polymers are added to water. The result can be a rather drastic reduction in friction loss (pressure drop) at a given flow rate in the turbulent regime at sufficiently high flow rates.

The last effect, Fig. 2.6D, can be observed when transferring dilute polymer solutions with a syringe. When drawing a purely viscous fluid into the syringe, if the syringe tip is raised above the level of the liquid, the flow, of course, stops. However, in the case of the elastic polymer solution, the tip of the syringe can be raised an inch or more above the surface without interrupting the flow. The liquid continues to flow in a free jet from the beaker into the syringe. Thus these fluids not only exhibit a *memory* of past states, but it could be said that the fluid thinks ahead or anticipates succeeding states.

Still another class of unusual flow behavior exhibited by viscoelastic fluids in steady flow is a consequence of the extra normal stresses which are developed in directions normal to the direction of flow when the fluid is sheared. These stresses will be discussed in more detail in a later section, and further discussion of these effects will be deferred until then.

2.4.2. Rate or Derivative Models

A classical approach to the description of the response of materials which exhibit combined viscous and elastic properties is based upon an analogy with the response of certain mechanical elements. This involves construction of viscoelastic models by combination of

mechanical elements which represent purely viscous and purely elastic
properties. Such models are, of course, idealized and purely hypothetical, and are useful for representing the behavior of real materials only to the extent that the observed response of the real
material can be approximated by that of the model.

Analog models constructed from linear viscous (Newtonian) and
linear elastic (Hookean) elements represent linear viscoelastic behavior. Since real materials generally exhibit nonlinear behavior
under large deformations, such models are appropriate only for small
amplitude displacements, and hence are not generally adequate for
predicting continuous deformation or flow behavior of real materials.
This problem can be alleviated to some degree by redefining strain
in a manner which describes the deformation of a material element as
it moves with time from place to place. These factors will be considered in detail later.

The conventional mechanical elements representing linear viscous
and elastic behavior are the *spring* and *dashpot* (Fig. 2.7). The
force applied to a linear spring is directly proportional to its
displacement, the spring constant being the constant of proportionality. If the force is assumed analogous to shear stress and displacement analogous to shear strain, the spring becomes analogous to
a Hookean elastic material in shear, with the spring constant

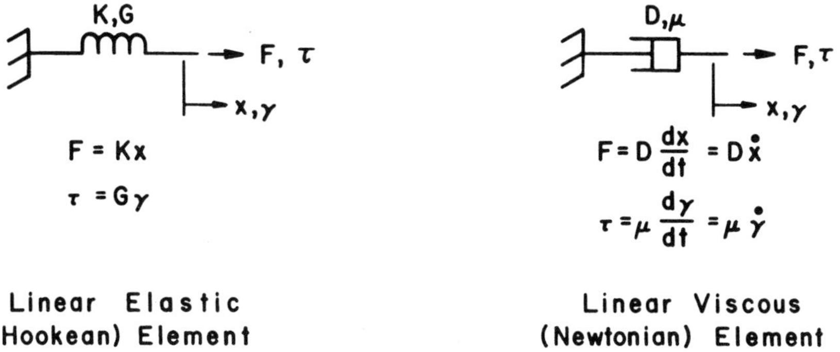

$$F = Kx$$
$$\tau = G\gamma$$

**Linear Elastic
(Hookean) Element**

$$F = D\frac{dx}{dt} = D\dot{x}$$
$$\tau = \mu\frac{d\gamma}{dt} = \mu\dot{\gamma}$$

**Linear Viscous
(Newtonian) Element**

FIG. 2.7 Linear elastic and viscous mechanical elements.

representing the shear modulus. In a similar fashion the force
acting on a linear dashpot is proportional to the resulting rate of
extension, which may be assumed analogous to the shear stress and
shear rate for a Newtonian fluid in shear, respectively. The proportionality factor in this case represents the Newtonian viscosity.
The dashpot is assumed to be unrestrained and infinite in extent,
so that continuous displacement (flow) is possible. Various combinations of springs and dashpots thus represent linear viscoelastic
behavior, and may serve as idealized models for the rheological
behavior of viscoelastic materials.

A. Maxwell Fluid

One of the simplest models which can be constructed is one
spring and one dashpot in series, and is known as the Maxwell model
(Fig. 2.8). This is a fluid model, since a constant applied stress
will result in a continuous deformation due to unrestrained extension of the dashpot.

The total strain (displacement of the model is the sum of
elastic strain (γ_s) of the spring and the fluid strain (γ_d) of
the dashpot:

$$\gamma = \gamma_s + \gamma_d \tag{2.4-1}$$

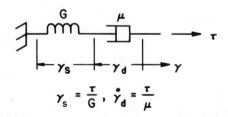

FIG. 2.8 Mechanical model of a Maxwell fluid.

Differentiating this with respect to time:

$$\dot{\gamma} = \dot{\gamma}_s + \dot{\gamma}_d = \frac{\dot{\tau}}{G} + \frac{\tau}{\mu} \tag{2.4-2}$$

or

$$\tau + \lambda\dot{\tau} = \mu\dot{\gamma} \tag{2.4-3}$$

where

$$\lambda = \frac{\mu}{G} \tag{2.4-4}$$

Equation (2.4-3) is the rheological equation relating shear stress and shear rate for the Maxwell fluid. Note that if $G = \infty$ (i.e., $\lambda = 0$), the spring becomes a rigid connection, and the model reduces to that of a Newtonian fluid. Conversely, if $\mu = \infty$ (i.e., $\lambda = \infty$), the dashpot becomes rigid and the model becomes that of a Hookean solid. These conclusions also follow directly from a consideration of Eq. (2.4-2) or (2.4-3).

1. *Stress Relaxation*

To get a feel for the behavior of the Maxwell fluid, let us consider its response to a stress relaxation test in simple shear, in which a shear strain of magnitude γ_o is suddenly applied at time zero (i.e., a sudden displacement of the plate), and is then held constant (Fig. 2.9). If the initial extension were infinitely fast

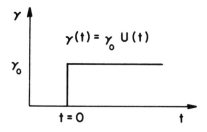

FIG. 2.9 Applied strain for stress relaxation test.

the dashpot would remain rigid, since an infinite strain rate would require an infinite stress to extend it. Hence only the spring will extend initially. If the extension is then maintained constant, however, the spring contraction force will react on the dashpot, causing it to extend as the spring relaxes. The stress required to maintain the constant strain may be calculated from Eq. (2.4-3) as follows.

The imposed strain function may be represented as

$$\gamma(t) = \gamma_o U(t) \tag{2.4-5}$$

where $U(t)$ is the *unit step function*, defined as

$$U(t) = \begin{cases} 0 & \text{for } t \leq 0 \\ 1 & \text{for } t > 0 \end{cases} \tag{2.4-6}$$

The resulting stress as a function of time is given by the solution of Eqs. (2.4-3) and (2.4-5). These equations are readily solved by means of the Laplace transform which, in effect, involves a change of independent variable (from t to the Laplace variable, s) enabling the reduction of linear differential or integral equations to algebraic equations. A short table of transform pairs is given in Appendix A, which we will consult for solution of such problems.

The transform of Eq. (2.4.3), from Appendix A.I.3, is seen to be

$$\bar{\tau}(s)[1 + \lambda s] - \lambda\tau(0) = \mu[s\bar{\gamma}(s) - \gamma(0)] \tag{2.4-7}$$

where the overbars represent the transforms of the variables, which are functions of s. The quantities $\tau(0)$ and $\gamma(0)$ are the initial values of these variables at zero time. For our purposes, it is most convenient to define zero time to correspond to the reference or undeformed state of the material. This would then be the instant before application of the imposed step strain (at t = 0−), so that

$$\tau(0) = \gamma(0) = 0 \tag{2.4-8}$$

The transform of the strain function, Eq. (2.4-5), is, from A.II.3:

$$\bar{\gamma}(s) = \frac{\gamma_o}{s} \qquad (2.4\text{-}9)$$

Combining Eqs. (2.4-7), (2.4-8), and (2.4-9), and solving for $\bar{\tau}$ gives

$$\bar{\tau}(s) = \frac{\mu\gamma_o}{1 + \lambda s} = \frac{G\gamma_o}{s + 1/\lambda} \qquad (2.4\text{-}10)$$

The inverse transform of (2.4-10) is, from A.II.8:

$$\tau(t) = G\gamma_o\, e^{-t/\lambda} = \tau_o\, e^{-t/\lambda} \qquad (2.4\text{-}11)$$

It is seen that the initial stress response, ($\tau_o \rightarrow G\gamma_o$ as $t \rightarrow 0+$) is purely elastic. It then decays exponentially with time, reaching 37% of its initial value at a time equal to λ. Thus, the material property λ is a characteristic time constant of the material, representative of the time scale for stress relaxation, and is therefore called the *relaxation time*.

If the material were a purely viscous fluid, then $G = \infty$ and $\lambda = 0$. Thus from Eq. (2.4-11) the stress would relax infinitely fast. Actually, if the deformation were applied instantaneously, the infinite strain rate would require an infinite stress which, however, would instantly disappear. In reality, inertia effects would preclude the application of a truly instantaneous displacement. If the material were purely elastic, then $\mu = \infty$ and $\lambda = \infty$, and the stress would not relax at all. The relative response of these three materials is shown in Fig. 2.10.

All real materials exhibit both viscous and elastic properties in varying degrees. The relative viscous or elastic nature of a given material may be indicated by the magnitude of a characteristic time constant of the material (equivalent to the relaxation time) relative to a characteristic time of observation. For example, a formation of granite may have a characteristic time of many years.

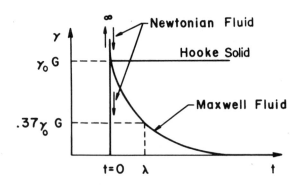

FIG. 2.10   Response to stress relaxation test.

Thus if it were subjected to a stress relaxation test lasting for several hours or days, or even weeks, it would appear to be an elastic solid. However, if it were observed for many decades, the stress would probably relax completely, and it would appear to be a fluid. Conversely, a stress relaxation test on water in which the time of observation was measured to a precision of, say, 0.1 sec, would indicate a purely viscous fluid. However, if the observations were limited to within, say, 10^{-12} sec, the test would probably indicate solid behavior. Obviously, inertial effects would have to be accounted for in this test.

The ratio of the characteristic material relaxation time to the characteristic time of observation has been called the *Deborah number* (N_{De}) by Reiner [2.9]:

$$N_{De} = \frac{\lambda}{t_e} \tag{2.4-12}$$

In a physical system, t_e represents the time scale over which significant changes occur, and can be anything from the residence time in a pipe or tank to a statistical time scale for turbulence fluctuations. Evidently $N_{De} \ll 1$ represents predominantly viscous (fluid) behavior, $N_{De} \gg 1$ predominantly elastic (solid) behavior, and $N_{De} \cong 1$ viscoelastic behavior, for a viscoelastic fluid.

2. *Creep*

Another test which distinguishes relative viscous and elastic behavior is the *creep test*, in which a constant shear stress of magnitude, τ_o, is instantly applied at time zero and maintained indefinitely, and resulting deformation is observed as a function of time. It is also informative to observe the strain response after removal of the stress after a finite time, this being referred to as *creep recovery*, or *recoil*. The imposed stress condition is illustrated in Fig. 2.11, and may be represented as

$$\tau(t) = \tau_o[U(t) - U(t - t_1)] = \tau_o G_o(t_1) \qquad (2.4\text{-}13)$$

where $G_o(t_1)$ is called the *gate function*. It represents a square pulse of unit magnitude which starts at $t = 0$ and ends at $t = t_1$.

Again we employ the Laplace transform to solve Eqs. (2.4-3) and (2.4-13) for the strain response. As before, we define our reference condition as the undeformed state, so that all initial conditions are zero. The transform of (2.4-13) is, therefore,

$$\bar{\tau}(s) = \frac{\tau_o}{s}(1 - e^{-t_1 s}) \qquad (2.4\text{-}14)$$

Combining (2.4-7) and (2.4-14), and solving for $\bar{\gamma}$ results in

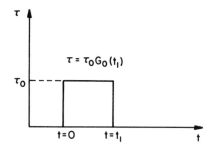

FIG. 2.11 Applied stress for creep test.

$$\bar{\gamma}(s) = \frac{\tau_o}{s} \left[\frac{1 + \lambda s}{\mu s}\right]\left(1 - e^{-t_1 s}\right) = \frac{\tau_o}{\mu}\left[\frac{1}{s^2} + \frac{\lambda}{s}\right]\left(1 - e^{-t_1 s}\right) \quad (2.4\text{-}15)$$

The inverse transform of (2.4-15) may be obtained from Appendix A.II.3 and A.II.9, and by noting that the exponential has the effect of shifting the t axis (Appendix A.I.9).   the result is

$$\gamma(t) = \frac{\tau_o}{\mu}\left\{t + \lambda - \left[(t - t_1) + \lambda\right] U(t - t_1)\right\} \quad (2.4\text{-}16)$$

Note that the step function is identically zero for $t < t_1$. For $t > t_1$, the time variable cancels out, and the strain is constant at a value of ($\tau_o t_1/\mu$). The complete response is shown in Fig. 2.12. It is seen that the initial response is elastic, followed by a purely viscous flow response. When the stress is removed, the response again ie elastic, showing a recoverable strain, recoil, rebound, or memory effect. This type of behavior is qualitatively representative of elastic fluids, although no real fluid has been found to correspond quantitatively to the Maxwell model.

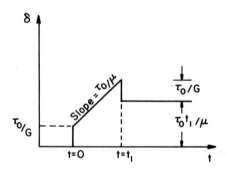

FIG. 2.12   Creep and creep recovery for a Maxwell fluid.

B. Voigt Solid

One spring and one dashpot in parallel represents the simplest possible model for a viscoelastic solid, and is called the Voigt, or sometimes the Kelvin, solid (Fig. 2.13). Since continuous deformation in response to a constant stress is impossible because of the constraint of the spring, the model represents a viscoelastic solid.

To derive the rheological equation for this material, note that the total stress is the sum of the elastic (solid) and viscous (fluid) stresses:

$$\tau = \tau_s + \tau_d = G\gamma + \mu\dot{\gamma} \qquad (2.4\text{--}17)$$

which can also be written

$$\frac{\tau}{G} = \lambda'\dot{\gamma} + \gamma \qquad (2.4\text{--}18)$$

where

$$\lambda' = \frac{\mu}{G} \qquad (2.4\text{--}19)$$

Equation (2.4-18) is the rheological equation relating shear stress and shear rate for the Voigt solid. Note that this model reduces to a Newtonian fluid if $G = 0$ (or $\lambda' = \infty$), and to a Hooke solid if $\mu = 0$ (or $\lambda' = 0$).

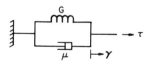

FIG. 2.13 Mechanical analog of Voigt solid.

1. Creep and Recoil

We can calculate the strain response of a Voigt solid to creep
and recovery test (Fig. 2.11) by using the Laplace transform as we
did for the Maxwell fluid. The transform of the imposed stress
function is given by Eq. (2.4-14), and the transform of Eq. (2.4-18)
is

$$\bar{\tau}(s) = G\lambda'[s\bar{\gamma}(s) - \gamma(0)] + G\bar{\gamma}(s) \qquad (2.4-20)$$

where the undeformed state again corresponds to the reference or
initial condition, so that $\gamma(0) = 0$.

Solving (2.4-13) and (2.4-20) for $\bar{\gamma}(s)$ gives

$$\bar{\gamma}(s) = \frac{\tau_o}{\lambda'G} \frac{1}{s(s + 1/\lambda')} \left[1 - e^{-t_1 s} \right] \qquad (2.4-21)$$

Comparison of this with A.II.12 and A.I.9 shows that the inverse
transform is

$$\gamma(t) = \frac{\tau_o}{G} \left[\left(1 - e^{-t/\lambda'} \right) - \left(1 - e^{-(t-t_1)/\lambda'} \right) U(t - t_1) \right] \qquad (2.4-22)$$

which is illustrated in Fig. 2.14.

If the stress was not removed at time t_1 but held constant, the
response (2.4-22) would be simply

$$\gamma(t) = \frac{\tau_o}{G} \left(1 - e^{-t/\lambda'} \right) \qquad (2.4-23)$$

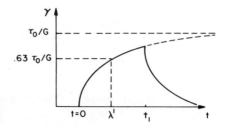

FIG. 2.14   Creep and recoil of a Voigt solid.

It is evident that the strain initially increases exponentially, ultimately approaching an asymptotic value of τ_o/G. If the material were a Hooke solid ($\mu = 0$), it would displace instantly by this amount. The viscosity thus serves to retard the rate at which this equilibrium strain is approached. Again the quantity λ' represents a characteristic time of the material, being the time required for the strain to attain 63% of its final equilibrium value. For this reason, λ' is called the *retardation time* of the viscoelastic solid.

Note that if the time of observation is large compared with λ' (i.e., $\lambda' \ll t$, or $N_{De}' \ll 1$), Eq. (2.4-23) reduces to

$$\gamma \cong \frac{\tau_o}{G} \qquad\qquad (2.4\text{-}24)$$

i.e., the behavior appears to be a purely elastic (Hookean) solid. Differentiating (2.4-23) with respect to time gives

$$\dot{\gamma} = \frac{\tau_o}{\mu} e^{-t/\lambda'} \qquad\qquad (2.4\text{-}25)$$

which, for $t \ll \lambda'$ (or $N_{De}' \gg 1$), becomes

$$\dot{\gamma} \cong \frac{\tau_o}{\mu} \qquad\qquad (2.4\text{-}26)$$

i.e., the material appears to be a purely viscous (Newtonian) fluid.

This qualitative significance of the retardation time is opposite to that of the relaxation time, defined in terms of the Maxwell fluid. It is important to remember, however, that the retardation time applies to viscoelastic solids, that is, materials which will not deform continuously in a creep test, but instead approach an equilibrium deformed state.

2. Stress Relaxation

The stress required to maintain an imposed step strain (Fig. 2.9) may be determined in a similar manner. Combining the

transformed Voigt equation (2.4-20) with the transform of the imposed
strain function (2.4-9) and solving for $\bar{\tau}$, we get

$$\bar{\tau}(s) = G\gamma_o\left(\frac{1}{s} + \lambda'\right) \qquad\qquad (2.4\text{-}27)$$

The inverse of (2.4-27) is obtained by comparison with Appendix
A.II.1 and A.II.3, and is

$$\tau(t) = \gamma_o[G + \mu\delta(t)] \qquad\qquad (2.4\text{-}28)$$

where $\delta(t)$ represents the *Dirac delta* or *impulse function*. It has
an infinite magnitude at $t = 0$, but is zero for all other time.
However, it must have unit area, since it also represents the derivative of the unit step function (i.e., the integral of $\delta(t)$ must be
unity):

$$\delta(t) = \begin{cases} \infty & \text{at } t = 0 \\ 0 & \text{for } t \neq 0 \end{cases} \qquad\qquad (2.4\text{-}29)$$

$$\int_{-\infty}^{t} \delta(t)\ dt = U(t) \qquad\qquad (2.4\text{-}30)$$

A useful property of the Dirac delta is that of a *sampling function*:

$$\int_{-\infty}^{t} f(x)\delta(x - \tau)\ dx = f(\tau)U(t - \tau) \qquad\qquad (2.4\text{-}31)$$

This result follows directly from the fact that the product in the
integrand is a constant, being equal to the value of $f(x)$ at the
point $x = \tau$; i.e., $f(\tau)$.

   Equation (2.4-28) shows that the inclusion of viscous properties
in an otherwise elastic solid requires that an infinite stress be
applied to the material (for an infinitesimal time) to achieve an
imposed step strain. Again, it is evident from Eq. (2.4-28) that

viscous stresses relax infinitely fast in a solid, whereas the elastic stresses do not relax at all. This is in contrast with the stress relaxation properties of the Maxwell fluid illustrated in Fig. 2.10.

Perhaps it is appropriate at this point to summarize the differences between the Maxwell fluid and Voigt solid. Table 2.1 compares the qualitative behavior of the two materials with reference to the tests described so far.

TABLE 2.1

Qualitative Comparison of Maxwell Fluid
and Voigt Solid Response Characteristics

	Maxwell fluid	Voigt solid
Stress relaxation	Complete relaxation at exponential rate	Incomplete instantaneous relaxation
Creep	Initial instantaneous elastic strain followed by steady flow	Approaches constant equilibrium strain at an exponential rate
Creep recovery (recoil or rebound)	Incomplete instantaneous recovery	Complete recovery at exponential rate
Deborah number $N_{De} = \lambda/t_e$ or λ'/t_e	Viscous fluid if $N_{De} \ll 1$ Elastic solid if $N_{De} \gg 1$	Elastic solid if $N_{De} \ll 1$ Viscous fluid if $N_{De} \gg 1$

In reality, no actual materials have been found which are true
Maxwell fluids or Voigt solids. Many actual viscoelastic materials
may exhibit some type of behavior intermediate to these extremes,
which makes them difficult to classify as to solids or fluids. For
example a creep test might show rapid initial deformation followed
by a continuous deformation which does not, however, become linear.
A stress relaxation test might show initial rapid relaxation followed
by a slower but continuing relaxation. Inertial forces are important
in these unsteady situations and should be evaluated and, when necessary, corrected for. These factors will be considered later.

Our primary concern will be with materials which are more-or-
less obviously fluid, in that they will flow continuously when subjected to an anisotropic stress. Hence, we will concentrate here-
after upon such materials.

C. Generalized Maxwell Model

There are a great many models which can be formulated by hook-
ing different numbers springs and dashpots together in various ways,
in order to simulate a system which has a response which may be used
to approximate the behavior of a specific viscoelastic material.
One of the most useful for viscoelastic fluids is the generalized
Maxwell model which, in essence, assumes that instead of a single
relaxation time the fluid has a response characteristic of a whole
series or distribution of relaxation times. This model can be made
to fit data for many real fluids if a suitable distribution of relaxation times is used.

The physical model is simply a parallel arrangement of many
individual Maxwell elements, each with a different relaxation time
(Fig. 2.15). This also implies a distribution of shear and/or viscous moduli. To derive the rheological equation for this model,
consider first only two elements in parallel. The equations for
each of these may be written

$$\tau_1 + \lambda_1 \dot{\tau}_1 = \mu_1 \dot{\gamma} \qquad\qquad (2.4\text{-}32)$$

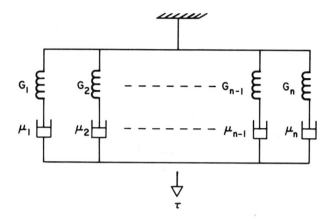

FIG. 2.15 Mechanical analog of generalized Maxwell model.

$$\tau_2 + \lambda_2 \dot{\tau}_2 = \mu_2 \dot{\gamma} \qquad (2.4\text{-}33)$$

where

$$\lambda_1 = \frac{\mu_1}{G_1} \qquad \lambda_2 = \frac{\mu_2}{G_2}$$

Also, the total force (stress) applied to the system is the sum of the forces (stresses) in each element

$$\tau = \tau_1 + \tau_2 \qquad (2.4\text{-}34)$$

By eliminating τ_1 and τ_2 from the above three equations, we get one equation relating τ and γ. This is most easily done with the aid of the Laplace transform, since the equations are linear. The result is

$$\lambda_1 \lambda_2 \ddot{\tau} + (\lambda_1 + \lambda_2)\dot{\tau} + \tau = \lambda_1 \lambda_2 (G_1 + G_2)\ddot{\gamma}$$

$$+ (\lambda_1 G_1 + \lambda_2 G_2)\dot{\gamma} \qquad (2.4\text{-}35)$$

Note that in steady shear flow, all terms are identically zero,

$$ss$$

$$\tau = (\eta_1 + \eta_2)\dot{\gamma}$$

$$= [\eta_0 P + \eta_0 (1-P)]\dot{\gamma} = \eta_0 \dot{\gamma}$$

except those involving τ and $\dot{\gamma}$. Thus it is evident that the material behaves as a Newtonian fluid in steady flow, with a viscosity given by

$$\mu_o = \frac{\tau}{\dot{\gamma}} = \lambda_1 G_1 + \lambda_2 G_2 \tag{2.4-36}$$

or

$$\mu_o = \mu_1 + \mu_2$$

For N Maxwell elements in parallel, a direct extension of the above leads to

$$\tau_i + \lambda_i \dot{\tau}_i = \mu_i \dot{\gamma} \tag{2.4-37}$$

$$\tau = \sum_{i=1}^{N} \tau_i \qquad \mu_o = \sum_{i=1}^{N} \mu_i = \sum_{i=1}^{N} \lambda_i G_i \tag{2.4-38}$$

The corresponding differential equation relating τ and $\dot{\gamma}$ can be written in terms of the linear differential operators P and R

$$P\tau = R\dot{\gamma} \tag{2.4-39}$$

where

$$P \equiv 1 + p_1 \frac{d}{dt} + p_2 \frac{d^2}{dt^2} + \cdots + p_N \frac{d^N}{dt^N} \tag{2.4-40}$$

$$R = \mu_o \left(1 + r_1 \frac{d}{dt} + r_2 \frac{d^2}{dt^2} + \cdots + r_M \frac{d^M}{dt^M} \right) \tag{2.4-41}$$

$$(M = N - 1)$$

The parameters μ_o, p_i, and r_i are material properties, and are uniquely related to the λ_i and μ_i (or G_i) of Eq. (2.4-37).

For any possible series and/or parallel combination of Maxwell and Voigt elements, the corresponding differential equation can be written in the operator form of Eq. (2.5-39), or the more general form:

$$P\tau = Q\gamma \tag{2.4-42}$$

where

$$P = \sum_{j=0}^{N} p_j \frac{d^j}{dt^j} \qquad Q = \sum_{j=0}^{N} q_i \frac{d^j}{dt^j} \tag{2.4-43}$$

[Since Eq. (2.4-42) can be divided through by any constant without loss of generality, we can set $p_o = 1$.] Note that any one or more of the constants (material properties) p_j or q_j may be zero. In particular, if the material is a fluid (with no equilibrium deformation under stress), q_o must be zero. The result is then equivalent to Eq. (2.4-39).

---------------------- 0 ----------------------

Example 2.2 Determine the differential equation and the parameters p_j and q_j of Eq. (2.4-43) for a model composed of a Maxwell and Voigt element in series:

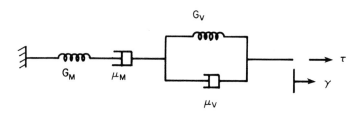

Note that the total stress is common to both Maxwell and Voigt elements, but the total strain is the sum of the Maxwell and Voigt strain.

Maxwell:

$$\tau + \frac{\mu_M}{G_M} \dot{\tau} = \mu_M \dot{\gamma}_M$$

Transform:

$$\bar{\tau}\left(1 + \frac{\mu_M s}{G_M}\right) = \mu_M s \bar{\gamma}_M$$

or

$$\bar{\gamma}_M = \bar{\tau}\left(\frac{1}{\mu_M s} + \frac{1}{G_M}\right)$$

Voigt:

$$\tau = G_V \gamma_V + \mu_V \dot{\gamma}_V$$

Transform:

$$\bar{\tau} = \bar{\gamma}_V (G_V + \mu_V s)$$

or

$$\bar{\gamma}_V = \frac{\bar{\tau}}{G_V + \mu_V s}$$

Total strain:

$$\gamma = \gamma_M + \gamma_V$$

Transform:

$$\bar{\gamma} = \bar{\gamma}_M + \gamma_V$$

From above:

$$\bar{\gamma} = \bar{\tau}\left(\frac{1}{\mu_M s} + \frac{1}{G_M} + \frac{1}{G_V + \mu_V s}\right)$$

Clear of fractions:

$$\mu_M G_M s(G_V + \mu_V s)\bar{\gamma} = (G_V G_M + \mu_V G_M s + G_V \mu_M s + \mu_M G_M s + \mu_M \mu_V s^2)\bar{\tau}$$

Invert:

$$\mu_M G_M \left(\mu_V \frac{d^2\gamma}{dt^2} + G_V \frac{d\gamma}{dt} \right) = \mu_M \mu_V \frac{d^2\tau}{dt^2} + (\mu_V G_M + \mu_M G_V + \mu_M G_M) \frac{d\tau}{dt} + G_M G_V \tau$$

Divide by coefficient of τ:

$$\tau + \left(\frac{\mu_V}{G_V} + \frac{\mu_M}{G_M} + \frac{\mu_M}{G_V} \right) \frac{d\tau}{dt} + \frac{\mu_M \mu_V}{G_M G_V} \frac{d^2\tau}{dt^2} = \mu_M \left(\frac{\mu_V}{G_V} \frac{d^2\gamma}{dt^2} + \frac{d\gamma}{dt} \right)$$

Compare Eq. (2.4-43):

$$P_o = 1 \qquad P_1 = \left(\frac{\mu_V}{G_V} + \frac{\mu_M}{G_M} + \frac{\mu_M}{G_V} \right) \qquad P_2 = \frac{\mu_M \mu_V}{G_M G_V}$$

$$q_o = 0 \qquad q_1 = \mu_M \qquad q_2 = \mu_M \frac{\mu_V}{G_V}$$

If the model is expressed in terms of the operator Eq. (2.4-39), the right-hand side of the above equation would be written:

$$\mu_M \left(\frac{\mu_V}{G_V} \frac{d\dot{\gamma}}{dt} + \dot{\gamma} \right)$$

Comparing (2.4-41) gives the equivalent parameters r_j:

$$\mu_o = \mu_M \qquad\qquad r_1 = \frac{\mu_V}{G_V}$$

Note that initial conditions are ignored in the above process. They would have to be considered, of course, if it were desired to determine the response of the model to a specified stress or strain input history. The result is then equivalent to Eq. (2.4-39).

D.   Other Analogs

The use of mechanical springs and dashpots to represent elasticity and viscosity, with the corresponding forces and displacements
being analogs of shear stress and shear strain, is not the only analog system which can be used to represent the behavior of linear
viscoelastic materials.   Others, such as electrical analogs, may
actually be more useful, if it is desired to construct a physical
analog or model of a material in order to, say, adjust the values
of the parameters in the model to achieve the best fit of data.

Table 2.2 presents some electrical analogs which could be used
to model linear viscoelastic materials.   The table shows the elements
analogous to Newtonian and Hookean components, the physical analogs
of stress, strain, viscosity, and elasticity, and the corresponding
Maxwell and Voigt models, for three different analog systems.

2.4.3.   Linear Viscoelastic Material Functions

The models described in the previous section (based upon spring-
dashpot analogs) effectively illustrate the general characteristics
of linear viscoelastic materials.   However, as previously noted,
these simple models (such as the Maxwell and Voigt) do not accurately
represent the observed behavior of real materials.   Indeed, it is not
usually possible, or even desirable, to postulate an appropriate
model for an unknown material a priori.   It is much more satisfactory to describe the material by certain material response functions,
defined in terms of readily measurable quantities with respect to
specific deformations or imposed conditions, which are independent
of any specific model.   These material functions may be evaluated
experimentally, and the results may then be modeled by determining
the analytical function or model which best fits the data.   This,
of course, is the procedure by which the purely viscous empirical
models for non-Newtonian behavior in Sec. 2.2.3 were determined.
In that case, it was assumed that the corresponding values of shear
stress and shear rate can be measured directly for an unknown fluid

TABLE 2.2

Some Electrical Analogs

Analog Variables	Hooke Solid	Newtonian Fluid	Maxwell Fluid	Voigt Solid
$i = \tau$ $e = \gamma$ (I)	$R = 1/G$ $i = (1/R)e$	$c = \mu$ $i = c\,de/dt$	$R = 1/G$, $c = \mu$ $\frac{1}{R}\,de/dt = di/dt + i/Rc$	$c = \mu$, $R = 1/G$ $i = c\,de/dt + e/R$
$e = \tau$ $Q = \gamma$ (II)	$C = 1/G$ $e = (1/C)Q$	$R = \mu$ $e = Ri = R\,dQ/dt$	$c = 1/G$, $R = \mu$ $\frac{1}{c}\,dQ/dt = de/dt + e/Rc$	$R = \mu$, $c = 1/G$ $e = R\,dQ/dt + Q/c$
$e = \tau$ $i = \gamma$ (III)	$R = G$ $e = Ri$	$L = \mu$ $e = L\,di/dt$	$R = G$, $L = \mu$ $R\,di/dt = de/dt + e\,R/L$	$R = G$, $L = \mu$ $e = L\,di/dt + Ri$

in an appropriate steady flow system. These measurable values in
turn serve to define the apparent viscosity *material function*. Once
sufficient data for the apparent viscosity as a function of shear
rate (or stress) are obtained, an appropriate "model" can be sought
which fits the data.

In the case of viscoelastic materials, we have seen that one
of their most significant characteristics is the time dependence of
response to certain imposed stresses or deformations. Consequently,
the inclusion of time as an independent variable is necessary to
adequately define viscoelastic properties. Indeed, the material
functions which serve to characterize linear viscoelastic behavior
are functions only of time. Various such material functions may be
defined, each with respect to a specific imposed test condition or
deformation. Such tests include stress relaxation, creep, and oscillatory response. The independent variable for the first two is
time, while for the third it is frequency. However, inasmuch as all
of these functions are different measures of the same properties,
they are not independent, but are all interrelated, as will be
shown. Hence, for linear viscoelastic materials, any one of the
material functions defined in this section is sufficient in principle
to completely describe the time response (or "memory") properties
of the material. However, as a practical matter they are often used
in combination to supplement one another due to experimental limitations for a given test.

We have indicated that the viscoelastic material functions to
be discussed are sufficient to define the properties of linear materials. A linear viscoelastic material may be defined as one for
which the material function is a function only of time, and is
independent of the magnitude of imposed stress or strain. Hence, a
direct test of the linearity of response would involve subjecting
the material to one or more of the tests described herein, under
various magnitudes of imposed stress or strain. The response of a
truly linear material would be the same function of time, for all
magnitudes of stress or strain. With regard to models for viscoelastic response, a consequence of linearity is that the differential or

integral equation representing the model is mathematically linear, as illustrated in the preceding section. Consequently, all viscous and elastic parameters in the model would be constants, so that such materials behave as Newtonian fluids in flow or as Hookean solids under equilibrium deformation.

Essentially all real materials which exhibit viscoelastic properties are also nonlinear in general. That is, they are non-Newtonian in steady shear or non-Hookean in equilibrium deformation if a sufficiently wide range of strain or strain rate is considered. This would seem to negate the use of linear viscoelastic functions for such materials. However, any material, even the most nonlinear, will exhibit essentially linear behavior when subjected to a sufficiently small magnitude deformation (strain or strain rate). Thus the linear material functions defined herein may be considered characteristic of even nonlinear materials if the deformation is restricted to a sufficiently small magnitude.

There is another objection to the extension of linear material functions to viscoelastic materials under large deformations, based on our previous definition of strain. This is a consequence of the time dependence of such material properties, which requires that the relation between the stresses and strains associated with a given element of material be determined over a period of time. If strain is defined in terms of the displacements of the fixed coordinates of a given material point (as in Chap. 1), such definition is valid only if the position (fixed coordinates) of the point remains essentially fixed in space with time. Thus, if the material undergoes a large amplitude deformation, the element of material which is located at a given point at a given time will not be the same element at that location at a later time. That is, time varying stresses and strains evaluated at a fixed point in space will have no meaning with respect to a specific material element which moves from point to point with time. This problem can be alleviated by defining strain with reference to a moving reference frame, and will be addressed in a later chapter.

In this section, we will define quantitatively various time-dependent linear viscoelastic material functions. Methods of experimentally evaluating these functions will be discussed in a subsequent chapter.

A. Creep Compliance

As defined by the creep test, a constant stress is instantly applied to the material at time zero and the resulting deformation is determined as a function of time. The applied stress, of magnitude τ_o, can be represented by

$$\tau(t) = \tau_o U(t) \tag{2.4-44}$$

The resulting strain or deformation as a function of time $\gamma(t)$, which results from this stress can then be expressed as

$$\gamma(t) = \tau(t) \cdot J(t) = \tau_o U(t) \cdot J(t) \tag{2.4-45}$$

where $J(t)$ is called the *creep compliance*. The creep compliance may thus be defined by

$$J(t) \equiv \frac{\gamma(t)}{\tau_o} \tag{2.4-46}$$

where it is understood that the strain is measured relative to the undeformed state at time zero and τ_o is the magnitude of the imposed step stress (Fig. 2.16). It is a function which is clearly characteristic only of the viscoelastic properties of the material under test, and is thus a *material function*.

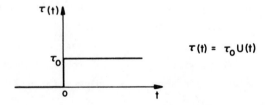

FIG. 2.16 Imposed conditions for creep test.

It is emphasized that J(t) represents a measurable function of time, and as such may be purely empirical. It may or may not be readily represented by an analytical function or mathematical "model." If, for example, this function could be represented by a linear function of time with a nonzero intercept, comparison with Eq. (2.4-16) (the first two terms) would indicate that the material is a Maxwell fluid. If, however, the response exponentially approached a constant value, it could be represented by an expression of the form of Eq. (2.4-23) and the material would be a Voigt solid. In any case, if the material is linearly viscoelastic, the magnitude of strain will be proportional to the magnitude of the applied stress (or vice versa) so that the creep compliance would be independent of both.

B. Relaxation Modulus

In the stress relaxation test, a constant deformation or strain of magnitude γ_0 is applied instantly at time zero (Fig. 2.9) and the resulting stress as a function of time is measured. The relation between stress and strain can be expressed as

$$\tau(t) = \gamma_0 U(t) \cdot G(t) \tag{2.4-47}$$

which serves to define the relaxation modulus, G(t):

$$G(t) \equiv \frac{\tau(t)}{\gamma_0} \tag{2.4-48}$$

As before, the observed stress is understood to be relative to the unstressed state at time zero, and γ_0 is the magnitude of the imposed step strain. This function is also characteristic of the viscoelastic properties of the material, and hence is a material function.

A material which behaves as a Maxwell fluid would exhibit stress relaxation which decreases exponentially with time and hence could be represented by a function of the form of Eq. (2.4-11), the relaxation modulus being G exp $(-t/\lambda)$. If the material behaved as a Voight

solid, the stress relaxation would be given by a function of the
form of Eq. (2.4-29) and the relaxation function would be $G + \mu\delta(t)$.

It is noted that elastic properties give rise to a constant
equilibrium term in the relaxation modulus for the Voigt solid and
in the creep compliance for both the Maxwell fluid and the Voigt
solid. For this reason, the relaxation modulus is sometimes separated into two parts:

$$G(t) = G_e + G_1(t) \tag{2.4-49}$$

where the equilibrium modulus, G_e, is zero for a viscoelastic fluid,
since stresses relax completely for such materials. Similarly, the
creep compliance may also be separated into two parts:

$$J(t) = J_e + J_1(t) \tag{2.4-50}$$

where J_e represents an equilibrium compliance for a solid, and a
steady-state compliance (instantaneous elastic response) for a viscoelastic fluid. Note that for a viscoelastic fluid G_e must be zero,
although J_e may or may not be zero. However, for a viscoelastic
solid neither G_e nor J_e is zero. Specifically, $J_e G_e = 1$ for a solid.
Also for real materials, $G(t)$ is a decreasing function of time,
whereas $J(t)$ is an increasing function of time.

C. Oscillatory Response

A commonly employed testing procedure, which has been previously
mentioned but not discussed in detail, involves the application of
a sinusoidal shearing strain to the material, which may be represented by either a sine or cosine function, e.g.,

$$\gamma = \gamma(\omega) = \gamma_o \cos \omega t \tag{2.4-51}$$

If the material is linearly elastic (i.e., Hookean), the shear
stress will be in phase with the shear strain:

Hooke solid:

$$\tau(\omega) = G\gamma(\omega) = G\gamma_o \cos \omega t \tag{2.4-52}$$

On the other hand, if the material is linearly viscous (or Newtonian) the stress will lead the strain by 90°, since stress is proportional to (in phase with) the rate of strain:

Newtonian fluid:

$$\tau(\omega) = \mu\dot{\gamma}(\omega) = \mu\omega\gamma_o \cos (\omega t + \varepsilon) \tag{2.4-53}$$

where $\varepsilon = \pi/2$.

For viscoelastic materials, it would be expected that the phase difference between stress and strain would be between 0° and 90°. Hence the viscoelastic properties of the material may be characterized by the emplitude and phase relations between oscillatory stress and strain (see Fig. 2.5).

A convenient means of manipulating oscillatory quantities is in terms of their complex equivalents, which is based upon the Euler identity

$$e^{j\theta} = \cos \theta + j \sin \theta \tag{2.4-54}$$

where

$$j \equiv \sqrt{-1} \quad \text{(imaginary)}$$

Thus the cosine and sine terms represent the real (Re) and imaginary (Im) components of a complex number, respectively:

$$\cos \theta = \text{Re } e^{j\theta} \qquad \sin \theta = \text{Im } e^{j\theta} \tag{2.4-55}$$

Any complex number can therefore be represented either in terms of its real and imaginary parts, or in exponential form, e.g.,

$$z(\omega t) = x(\omega) + jy(\omega) = z_o[\cos \omega t + j \sin \omega t] \qquad (2.4\text{-}56)$$

$$= z_o e^{j\omega t}$$

where

$$z_o^2 = x^2 + y^2, \ \tan \omega t = \frac{y}{x}$$

These expressions illustrate the equivalence between an oscillatory motion and a rotation. Thus, any complex quantity can be represented by a vector in a complex (Im vs. Re) plane, as illustrated in Fig. 2.17, in which the vector is rotating counterclockwise at an angular rate of ω rad/sec. Hence oscillatory strain and stress become

$$\gamma(\omega t) = \gamma_o e^{j\omega t} = \gamma_o[\cos \omega t + j \sin \omega t]$$

$$= \gamma'(\omega) + j\gamma''(\omega) \qquad (2.4\text{-}57)$$

$$\tau(\omega t) = \tau_o e^{j(\omega t+\varepsilon)} = \tau_o[\cos (\omega t + \varepsilon) + j \sin (\omega t + \varepsilon)]$$

$$= \tau'(\omega) + j\tau''(\omega) \qquad (2.4\text{-}58)$$

where τ_o and γ_o are the amplitudes of stress and strain, ε is the phase angle between them, the primes represent the real part, and the double primes represent the imaginary part of the complex quantities.

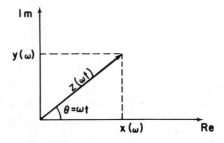

FIG. 2.17 Complex plane representation.

Of primary interest is the relation between stress and strain, i.e., the relative position of the τ and γ vectors in the complex plane at any instant. If we consider the instant when the strain vector coincides with the real axis (i.e., taking strain to be the reference with a real part only), the relation between stress and strain can be represented diagrammatically, as in Fig. 2.18. Thus τ' $(= \tau_o \cos \varepsilon)$ represents the component of stress in phase with strain (elastic component) and τ'' $(= \tau_o \sin \varepsilon)$ is the component which is 90° out of phase (viscous component).

Relations between these components of oscillatory stress and strain are the basis for the definitions of several different material functions. The most common of those is the complex shear modulus G^*, defined as the ratio of oscillatory stress to oscillatory strain:

$$G^*(j\omega) = \frac{\tau(\omega t)}{\gamma(\omega t)} = \frac{\tau_o}{\gamma_o} e^{j\varepsilon} = \frac{\tau_o}{\gamma_o} (\cos \varepsilon + j \sin \varepsilon)$$

or

$$G'(\omega) + jG''(\omega) = \frac{1}{\gamma_o} [\tau'(\omega) + j\tau''(\omega)] \tag{2.4-59}$$

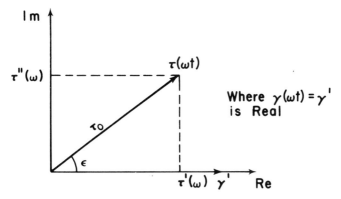

FIG. 2.18 Oscillatory stress and strain components.

The "in-phase" component, G', represents the elastic character of the material and hence is called the *storage modulus* (since elastic energy is stored and can be recovered). The "out-of-phase" component, G'', represents the viscous character, and is called the loss modulus (since viscous energy is dissipated or lost). The tangent of the phase angle ε is sometimes called the *loss tangent*, since $\tan \varepsilon = \tau''/\tau' = G''/G'$.

For a linear viscous (Newtonian) fluid, Eqs. (2.4-53) and (2.4-57) show that

Newtonian:

$$G^* = \frac{\tau(\omega t)}{\gamma(\omega t)} = \frac{\mu \dot{\gamma}}{\gamma} = j\omega\mu \frac{\gamma}{\gamma} = j\omega\mu \qquad (2.4\text{-}60$$

or

$$G' = 0 \qquad\qquad G'' = \omega\mu \qquad\qquad \varepsilon = 90° \qquad (2.4\text{-}61)$$

For a linear elastic solid, Eqs. (2.4-52) and (2.4-57) give

Hookean:

$$G^* = \frac{\tau(\omega t)}{\gamma(\omega t)} = \frac{G \gamma}{\gamma} = G \qquad\qquad (2.4\text{-}62)$$

or

$$G' = G(\text{const}) \qquad\qquad G'' = 0 \qquad\qquad \varepsilon = 0 \qquad (2.4\text{-}63)$$

For viscoelastic materials, both G' and G'' will be nonzero, and will also be in general functions of frequency. For example, the complex modulus for the Maxwell fluid can be determined from its rheological equation (2.4-3), by substituting (2.4-57) and (2.4-58) for γ and τ, respectively. The result is

$$\tau_o e^{j\varepsilon}(1 + j\omega\lambda) = j\omega G\lambda\gamma_o \qquad\qquad (2.4\text{-}64)$$

from which the complex modulus follows directly:

Maxwell:

$$G^*(j\omega) = \frac{\tau_o e^{j\varepsilon}}{\gamma_o} = \frac{j\omega G\lambda}{1 + j\omega\lambda} \tag{2.4-65}$$

or

$$G'(\omega) = \frac{G\omega^2\lambda^2}{1 + \omega^2\lambda^2} \qquad G''(\omega) = \frac{G\omega\lambda}{1 + \omega^2\lambda^2} \tag{2.4-66}$$

$$\tan \varepsilon = \frac{1}{\omega\lambda}$$

Note that G', G'', and ε are all functions of frequence (or "time").

───────────────────────── 0 ─────────────────────────

Example 2.3 Use the Maxwell model to illustrate that the complex modulus can be determined directly from the differential equation for the model by applying the Laplace transform, and then replacing the transform variable s by the imaginary frequency $j\omega$, and then determining the ratio of stress to strain transforms.

Maxwell model:

$$\tau + \lambda\dot{\tau} = \mu\dot{\gamma}$$

Transform:

$$\bar{\tau}(1 + \lambda s) = \mu s\bar{\gamma}$$

$s \to j\omega$:

$$\bar{\tau}(1 + j\omega\lambda) = j\omega\mu\bar{\gamma}$$

Modulus:

$$G^*(j\omega) = \frac{\bar{\tau}}{\bar{\gamma}} = \frac{j\omega\mu}{1 + j\omega\lambda} = \frac{j\omega G\lambda}{1 + j\omega\lambda}$$

Comparison with Eq. (2.4-65) proves the result.

───────────────────────── 0 ─────────────────────────

———————————————— 0 ————————————————

Example 2.4 Use the method of Example 2.3 to determine the complex modulus for a Voigt solid.

Voigt:

$$\tau = G\gamma + \mu\dot{\gamma}$$

Transform:

$$\bar{\tau} = (G + \mu s)\bar{\gamma}$$

$s \rightarrow j\omega$:

$$\bar{\tau} = G(1 + j\omega\lambda')\bar{\gamma}$$

Modulus:

$$G^*(j\omega) = \frac{\bar{\tau}}{\bar{\gamma}} = G(1 + j\omega\lambda')$$

$$G' = G \qquad\qquad G'' = (\omega\lambda'G) = \omega\mu$$

———————————————— 0 ————————————————

The reciprocal of the complex modulus is sometimes defined as an additional oscillatory material function. It is called the *complex compliance*, J^*:

$$J^*(j\omega) = \frac{1}{G^*(j\omega)} = \frac{\gamma(j\omega)}{\tau(j\omega)} = J'(\omega) + jJ''(\omega) \qquad (2.4\text{-}67)$$

The real and imaginary components of the complex compliance are related to those of the complex modulus by:

$$J'(\omega) = \frac{G'}{G'^2 + G''^2}$$

$$(2.4\text{-}68)$$

$$J''(\omega) = -\frac{G''}{G'^2 + G''^2}$$

Since G^* and J^* are defined in terms of stress and strain components they are mostly used to characterize essentially solid-like viscoelastic materials (although not exclusively so). An equivalent parameter, which is more appropriate for fluids in that it is defined in terms of strain rate instead of strain, is the *complex viscosity* $\eta^*(j\omega)$.

$$\eta^*(j\omega) \equiv \frac{\tau(\omega t)}{\dot{\gamma}(\omega t)} = \frac{\tau}{j\omega\gamma} = \eta'(\omega) - j\eta''(\omega) \qquad (2.4\text{-}69)$$

Note that the imaginary part of the complex viscosity is defined as that portion multiplied by $-j$ as opposed to the usual definition. These material function components are related to those of the complex modulus by:

$$\eta^* = \frac{G^*}{j\omega} \qquad \eta' = \frac{G''}{\omega} \qquad \eta'' = \frac{G'}{\omega} \qquad (2.4\text{-}70)$$

It is evident that η' represents the viscous or "in-phase" component between stress and strain rate, while η'' represents the elastic or "out-of-phase" component.

The complex material functions G^*, J^*, and η^* all provide the same information about a given material, and the choice as to which to use is purely a matter of preference. It is not unusual to characterize viscous properties by η' and elastic properties by G', for example. Note that both real and imaginary components of these quantities are, in general, functions of frequency, and hence the nature of this frequency dependence serves to distinguish the viscoelastic nature of the material.

D. Integral or Hereditary Functions

In Secs. 2.4.A and 2.4.B we defined certain material functions in terms of the response to a single step change in stress or strain. In this section we will show that these same functions may serve to describe material response to any arbitrary time variation in stress or strain.

1. *Boltzmann Superposition*

Consider the function $\gamma(t)$ to be representative of some cause acting upon a system, and $\tau(t)$ the effect resulting from this cause. Initially, we suppose that both γ and τ are zero. Now a variation in the cause ($\Delta\gamma$) occurring at time t_1 may produce a corresponding effect ($\Delta\tau$) at some later time t, which may be expressed as

$$\Delta\tau(t) = \psi(t - t_1)\,\Delta\gamma(t_1) \qquad\qquad (2.4-71)$$

Here $\psi(t - t_1)$ is an *influence function*, which is a property of the system and relates cause and effect. It is a function of the time delay $(t - t_1)$ between cause and effect, since, in general, the magnitude of the effect will depend upon the time elapsed since the cause occurred. An influence function which is a decreasing function of $(t - t_1)$ represents a "fading memory," that is, the influence of the cause upon the effect decreases with the time elapsed since the cause occurred.

A series of changes in the cause, each occurring at a different time, will all contribute cumulatively to the effect at some later time (t). If the system is linear, the total effect will be a linear combination of these separate contributions:

$$\tau(t) = \sum_i \Delta\tau_i = \psi(t - t_1)\,\Delta\gamma(t_1) + \psi(t - t_2)\,\Delta\gamma(t_2) + \cdots$$

$$= \sum_i^{\infty} \psi(t - t_i)\,\Delta\gamma(t_i) \qquad\qquad 2.4-72)$$

This linear addition or superposition of causes is known as the Boltzmann superposition principle, and is a general property of linear systems. Most systems (materials) will behave in a linear manner for sufficiently small displacement from equilibrium (i.e., small strains, or strain rates).

If the change in cause occurs continuously rather than in discrete steps, the sum may be replaced by an integral:

$$\tau(t) = \int_{\gamma(-\infty)}^{\gamma(t)} \psi(t-t') \, d\gamma(t') = \int_{-\infty}^{t} \psi(t-t')\dot{\gamma}(t') \, dt' \qquad (2.4\text{-}73)$$

The lower limit implies that all causes that have occurred anytime in the past will contribute to the effect at the present time, t. For a system with a fading memory, there will be some time prior to which all causes which have previously occurred will have a negligible contribution to the effect at the present time t. If time is measured from this instant, the result is the same as if the cause were zero for all time less than zero. In this case, (2.4-73) can be written:

$$\tau(t) = \gamma(0)\psi(t) + \int_{0}^{t} \psi(t-t')\dot{\gamma}(t') \, dt' \qquad (2.4\text{-}74)$$

If the material is in an undeformed state for $t \leq 0$, then $\gamma(0) = 0$ by definition, and only the integral term remains.

2. Relaxation and Memory Functions

If the "cause," $\gamma(t')$, is taken to be the shear strain and the "effect," $\tau(t)$, to be shear stress, the influence function, $\psi(t-t')$, is referred to as the *relaxation function*. Equation (2.4-73) thus implies that the stress at any time (t) depends upon the entire past history of deformation. For this reason, such an expression is referred to as a *hereditary integral*.

Equation (2.4-73) can be written in an alternate form by integrating by parts:

$$\tau(t) = \psi(0)\gamma(t) + \int_{-\infty}^{t} \phi(t-t')\gamma(t') \, dt' \qquad (2.4\text{-}75)$$

where

$$\phi(t - t') = -\frac{d\psi(t - t')}{dt'} = \frac{d\psi(t - t')}{d(t - t')} \qquad (2.4\text{-}76)$$

or

$$\phi(t) = \frac{d\psi(t)}{dt}$$

is called the *memory function*. Since, for a fading memory, strains occurring at time $t' = -\infty$ have no influence on stress at the present time t, the function $\psi(\infty)$ must be zero. Hence the first term from the integration by parts reduces to $\psi(0)\gamma(t)$. Furthermore, if the configuration at the present time t is taken to be the reference (undeformed) state, then $\gamma(t) = 0$ by definition, and this term becomes identically zero. Equation (2.4-75), with the time origin chosen so that $\gamma = 0$ for $t \leq 0$, also follows from (2.4-74) by integration by parts.

3. Creep Function

If we consider the "cause" to be shear stress and the "effect" to be shear strain, then a process analogous to that above results in a hereditary integral expression relating strain at any time, t, to the entire stress history at all prior times, t':

$$\gamma(t) = \int_{\tau(-\infty)}^{\tau(t)} J(t - t') \, d\tau(t') = \int_{-\infty}^{t} J(t - t')\dot{\tau}(t') \, dt' \qquad (2.4\text{-}77)$$

$$= J(t)\tau(0) + \int_{0}^{t} J(t - t')\dot{\tau}(t') \, dt' \qquad (2.4\text{-}78)$$

where the influence function J(t) is called the *creep function*.

It should be evident that specification of either the relaxation (memory) or creep function uniquely defines the time-dependent rheological properties of the material, and hence these are material functions. They are difficult to measure directly, and the usual

procedure is to postulate mathematical models for them on physical
or other grounds, and test the postulated functions by comparison
of observed and predicted response.

4. *Integral Functions from Differential Models*

Since the derivative (differential equation) and integral expressions should both provide a complete description of the time-
dependent stress-strain history of a viscoelastic material (subject
to certain restrictions to be discussed subsequently), they should
be equivalent and derivable from one another. To illustrate, let
us consider the Maxwell fluid, defined by the differential equation
(2.4-3):

$$\tau + \lambda \dot{\tau} = \mu \dot{\gamma} \tag{2.4-3}$$

This can best be converted to integral form by means of the
Laplace transform. Using a bar to denote transformed quantities,
the transform of (2.4-3) is:

$$\bar{\tau}(s)(1 + \lambda s) - \lambda \tau(0) = \mu \bar{\dot{\gamma}}(s) \tag{2.4-79}$$

or

$$\bar{\tau}(s) = \frac{\mu}{\lambda} \frac{1}{s + (1/\lambda)} \bar{\dot{\gamma}}(s) + \frac{\tau(0)}{s + (1/\lambda)} \tag{2.4-80}$$

By making use of the convolution theorem, the inverse transform of
(2.4-80) is readily found to be

$$\tau(t) = \tau(0) e^{-t/\lambda} + \int_{o}^{t} G e^{-(t-t')/\lambda} \dot{\gamma}(t') \, dt' \tag{2.4-81}$$

where

$$\tau(0) = G\gamma(0) \qquad \text{and} \qquad G = \frac{\mu}{\lambda}$$

Comparing (2.4-81) and (2.4-74) shows that, for the Maxwell model:

$$\psi(t - t') = Ge^{-(t-t')/\lambda}$$

or

$$\psi(t) = Ge^{-t/\lambda} \tag{2.4-82}$$

Comparison of (2.4-82) with (2.4-11) also shows that $G(t)$, the relaxation modulus, and $\psi(t)$, the relaxation function are identical. Note that for steady flow (constant $\dot{\gamma}$), Eq. (2.4-73) becomes

$$\tau = \dot{\gamma} \int_{-\infty}^{t} \psi(t - t') \ dt' = \dot{\gamma} \int_{0}^{\infty} \psi(t) \ dt \tag{2.4-83}$$

The fluid viscosity is thus related to the relaxation function by

$$\mu = \frac{\tau}{\dot{\gamma}} = \int_{0}^{\infty} \psi(t) \ dt \tag{2.4-84}$$

Example 2.5 Using the relaxation function form of the integral model of the Maxwell fluid, determine an expression for the response to a creep and creep recovery (recoil) test.

Imposed condition:

$$\tau(t) = \tau_o G_o(t_1)$$

Transform:

$$\bar{\tau} = \frac{\tau_o}{s} (1 - e^{-t_1 s})$$

Integral equation:

$$\tau(t) = \int_{0}^{t} \psi(t - t')\dot{\gamma}(t') \ dt' = \int_{0}^{t} Ge^{-(t-t')/\lambda}\dot{\gamma}(t') \ dt'$$

Transform:

$$\bar{\tau} = \bar{\psi} \, \bar{\dot{\gamma}} = \frac{s\lambda G\bar{\gamma}}{(1 + \lambda s)}$$

Equate expressions for $\bar{\tau}$ and solve for $\bar{\gamma}$:

$$\bar{\gamma} = \frac{\tau_o(1 + \lambda s)(1 - e^{-t_1 s})}{s^2 \lambda G} = \frac{\tau_o}{\lambda G}\left[\left(\frac{1}{s^2} + \frac{\lambda}{s}\right)\left(1 - e^{-t_1 s}\right)\right]$$

Invert:

$$\gamma(t) = \frac{\tau_o}{\lambda G}\left[\left(t + \lambda U(t)\right) - \left(t - t_1 + \lambda U(t - t_1)\right)\right]$$

Comparing this with Eq. (2.4-16) proves result.

──────────────── 0 ────────────────

5. *Relaxation Spectra*

A consideration of the generalized Maxwell model, Eqs. (2.4-37) and (2.4-38), shows that the appropriate relaxation function corresponding to an infinite series of relaxation times is

$$G(t) = \psi(t) = \sum_{i=1}^{\infty} G_i e^{-t/\lambda_i} \tag{2.4-85}$$

So that (2.4-73) becomes:

$$\tau(t) = \sum_{i=1}^{\infty} G_i \int_{-\infty}^{t} e^{-(t-t')/\lambda_i} \, \dot{\gamma}(t') \, dt' \tag{2.4-86}$$

Now if the spectrum of relaxation times is continuous instead of discrete, (2.4-85) may be written

$$\psi(t) = \int_{0}^{\infty} F(\lambda) e^{-t/\lambda} \, d\lambda \tag{2.4-87}$$

and (2.4-86) becomes

$$\tau(t) = \int_{-\infty}^{t} \int_{0}^{\infty} F(\lambda)e^{-(t-t')/\lambda} \, \dot{\gamma}(t') \, d\lambda \, dt' \qquad (2.4\text{-}88)$$

Here $F(\lambda) \, d\lambda$ can be interpreted as the shear modulus corresponding
to a relaxation time having a value between λ and $(\lambda + d\lambda)$. Thus
$F(\lambda)$ is actually the spectrum of the distribution of shear moduli.
(It is sometimes incorrectly referred to as the distribution of
relaxation times.) In general, a given material will exhibit a
distribution or spectrum of relaxation times, which in turn gives
rise to a distribution of shear moduli, although the two distribution functions may be markedly different, as illustrated in Fig. 2.19.
(The difference may be due, e.g., to a distribution of viscous moduli as well as a distribution of shear moduli in the material, since
$\mu = \lambda G$).

An alternative distribution function, $H(\lambda)$, is sometimes used
in place of $F(\lambda)$, and is defined as

$$H(\lambda) = \lambda F(\lambda) \qquad (2.4\text{-}89)$$

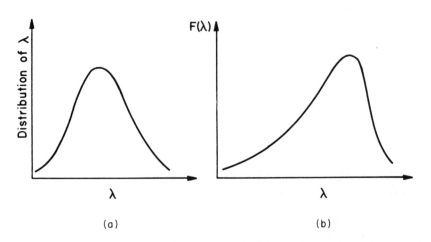

FIG. 2.19 Spectrum of relaxation times and distribution of
shear moduli for a hypothetical material.

It should be evident that, if $F(\lambda)$ represents a distribution function
for shear moduli, the function $H(\lambda)$ is a corresponding distribution
function or spectrum of viscous moduli or viscosities. The implication of these functions is that a naturally occurring distribution
of relaxation times, arising from, say, a distribution of molecular
weights or chain lengths, or particle sizes, is responsible for a
corresponding distribution of shear moduli or viscosities. Of
course, only two of these three distributions may be independent.
Thus, an alternate expression for the relaxation function, (2.4-87),
in terms of $H(\lambda)$ is

$$\psi(t) = \int_0^\infty \frac{H(\lambda)}{\lambda} e^{-t/\lambda} \, d\lambda = \int_{-\infty}^\infty H(\lambda) e^{-t/\lambda} \, d\ln\lambda \qquad (2.4\text{-}90)$$

Changing the order of integration in Eq. (2.4-88) gives

$$\tau(t) = \int_0^\infty F(\lambda) \int_{-\infty}^t e^{-(t-t')/\lambda} \dot{\gamma}(t') \, dt' \, d\lambda \qquad (2.4\text{-}91)$$

For steady flow (constant $\dot{\gamma}$), this becomes

$$\tau = \dot{\gamma} \int_0^\infty F(\lambda) \int_{-\infty}^t e^{-(t-t')/\lambda} \, dt' \, d\lambda$$

$$= \dot{\gamma} \int_0^\infty F(\lambda) \int_0^\infty \left(e^{-s/\lambda} \right) ds \, d\lambda = \dot{\gamma} \int_0^\infty \lambda F(\lambda) \, d\lambda \qquad (2.4\text{-}92)$$

The fluid viscosity is thus related to the distribution function by:

$$\mu = \frac{\tau}{\dot{\gamma}} = \int_0^\infty \lambda F(\lambda) \, d\lambda \qquad (2.4\text{-}93)$$

or

$$\mu = \int_0^\infty H(\lambda) \; d\lambda = \int_{-\infty}^\infty \lambda H(\lambda) \; d \ln \lambda \qquad\qquad (2.4\text{-}94)$$

———————————————————— 0 ————————————————————

Example 2.6 Show that the relaxation function $\psi(t)$, for a visco-elastic fluid, can be obtained from the derivative of the stress-strain curve resulting from an instantly imposed constant shear rate of magnitude $\dot{\gamma}_o$, starting from an initial stress-free state.

Imposed condition:

$$\dot{\gamma} = \dot{\gamma}_o U(t) \qquad\qquad \dot{\gamma}_o = \text{constant}$$

$$\tau(0) = 0 \qquad\qquad \gamma = \dot{\gamma}_o \, t$$

Integral equation:

$$\tau(t) = \int_0^t \psi(t - t')\dot{\gamma}(t') \; dt' = \dot{\gamma}_o \int_0^t \psi(t - t') \; dt'$$

Change variable to $s = t - t'$:

$$\tau(t) = -\dot{\gamma}_o \int_t^0 \psi(s) \; ds = \dot{\gamma}_o \int_0^t \psi(s) \; ds$$

Differentiate with respect to t using Leibnitz' rule (see note 3).

$$\frac{d\tau}{dt} = \dot{\gamma}_o \frac{d}{dt} \int_0^t \psi(s) \; ds = \dot{\gamma}_o \psi(t)$$

Thus:

$$\psi(t) = \frac{1}{\dot{\gamma}_o} \frac{d\tau}{dt} = \frac{d\tau(t)}{d\gamma(t)}$$

———————————————————— 0 ————————————————————

The relaxation function $\psi(t)$ can, in principle, be measured or determined directly from experimental data (see Example 2.6 and Prob. 2-29) or can be calculated directly from Eq. (2.4-87) if the function $F(\lambda)$ is known. The determination of the distribution function $F(\lambda)$ from a known relaxation function is not as direct, however, but can be done by noting the similarity between (2.4-87) and the definition of the Laplace transform $[\bar{G}(s)]$:

$$\bar{G}(s) = \mathscr{L}[g(t)] = \int_0^\infty g(t)e^{-st}\,dt \qquad (2.4-95)$$

The function $g(t)$ can thus be obtained from a knowledge of $\bar{G}(s)$ by the process of inverse transformation, with the aid of a table of transform pairs:

$$g(t) = \mathscr{L}^{-1}[\bar{G}(s)] \qquad (2.4-96)$$

Now a change of variables in Eq. (2.4-87), in which t is replaced by s, and $1/\lambda$ by t, results in

$$\psi(s) = \int_\infty^0 F\left(\frac{1}{t}\right) e^{-st}\left(-\frac{dt}{t^2}\right) = \int_0^\infty \frac{F(1/t)}{t^2}\,e^{-st}\,dt \qquad (2.4-97)$$

Comparison of (2.4-97) and (2.4-95) shows that the distribution function may be obtained from the relaxation function as follows:

$$F(\lambda) = \frac{1}{\lambda^2}\left\{\mathscr{L}^{-1}[\psi(s)]\right\}_{t \to 1/\lambda} \qquad (2.4-98)$$

Note that $\psi(s)$ is not the Laplace transform of $\psi(t)$, but is $\psi(t)$ with the variable t replaced by the transform variable s.

If the form of the function $\psi(t)$ is such that the inverse transform in (2.4-98) is not easily obtained, or is in the form of empirical data which are not easily represented by a suitable function, approximate methods can be used to estimate $F(\lambda)$.

A first approximation to the distribution function can be obtained from a known relaxation function as follows [2.10]. If, in Eq. (2.4-87), the approximation

$$e^{-t/\lambda} \sim U(\lambda - t) \tag{2.4-99}$$

is made, the integral equation becomes

$$\psi(t) = \int_t^\infty F(\lambda) \, d\lambda \tag{2.4-100}$$

The approximation (2.4-99) involves replacing a function of λ which varies exponentially from zero (at $\lambda = 0$) to unity (at $\lambda = \infty$) by a step function which goes from zero to unity instantly at $\lambda = t$. The exponential function has a value of 0.37 at $\lambda = t$. Differentiation of (2.4-100) by Leibnitz' rule gives:

$$\frac{d\psi}{dt} = -F(t) \tag{2.4-101}$$

or

$$-\left(\frac{d\psi}{dt}\right)_{t=\lambda} = F(\lambda) \tag{2.4-102}$$

which can also be written

$$-\left(\frac{d\psi}{d \ln t}\right)_{t=\lambda} = H(\lambda) \tag{2.4-103}$$

by virtue of (2.4-89). Thus the distribution function can be determined from the (negative) point slope of the relaxation function versus time. This method is due to Alfrey [2.10]. Higher order approximations as well as other approximate methods have been discussed by Gross [2.11], Ferry and Williams [2.12], Ferry [2.13], and Smith [2.14].

An analogous procedure can be followed involving the creep function, $J(t)$, in place of the relaxation function. The analysis could be based upon a generalized Voigt model, derived by generalizing Eq. (2.4-23) in the same manner that (2.4-11) was generalized to give (2.4-85). A corresponding continuous spectrum of shear compliance moduli may thus be defined by a distribution modulus, $L(\lambda)$, analogous to the spectrum of shear moduli $F(\lambda)$. This function would be related to the creep function by an expression analogous to Eq. (2.4-87). This development is left as an exercise for the reader.

Empirical expressions for $\psi(t)$ based upon an analogy with the generalized Maxwell model [Eq. (2.4-85)] are often useful due to the versatile nature of the expression. The series as written involves an infinite number of terms, and a corresponding infinite number of parameters or material properties. However, the molecular theory of polymer solutions developed by Zimm [2.15] and Rouse [2.16] has suggested a form for the distribution of relaxation times, which can be used to reduce the number of parameters in the series. This can be expressed in general terms as [2.17, 2.18]:

$$\lambda_i = \frac{\lambda_o}{i^\alpha} \qquad G_i = \frac{\mu_i}{\lambda_i} = \frac{\mu_o}{\sum\limits_{k=1}^{\infty} \lambda_k} = \frac{\mu_o}{\lambda_o \sum\limits_{k=1}^{\infty} 1/k^\alpha} = \frac{G_o}{Z(\alpha)} \qquad (2.4\text{-}104)$$

Where $Z(\alpha)$ is the Riemann zeta function. The number of parameters in (2.4-85) has thus been reduced from infinite to three: μ_o, λ_o, and α:

μ_o = zero-shear-rate limiting viscosity

λ_o = longest relaxation time

α = dimensionless index

The Rouse-Zimm theory for dilute polymer solutions predicts $\alpha = 2$. However, it has been found that data for η' and η'' from oscillatory tests on concentrated polymer solutions can be described better with α ranging from 2 to 4.

Equation (2.4-104) implies a single elastic modulus, $G_o/Z(\alpha)$, where $G_o = \mu_o/\lambda_o$ is a constant. This, in turn, with the indicated discrete distribution of relaxation times, implies a corresponding distribution of viscosities (or viscous moduli):

$$\mu_i = \lambda_i G_i = \frac{G_o \lambda_o}{i^\alpha Z(\alpha)} \tag{2.4-105}$$

The corresponding relaxation function is given by Eq. (2.4-85).

E. Interrelations Between Viscoelastic Material Functions

Any one of the linear viscoelastic material functions discussed so far should provide a unique characterization of the time dependent stress-deformation characteristics of a given linear viscoelastic material in small amplitude shear deformation. Hence they all represent different measures of the same material properties, and should therefore all be interrelated. In this section we will review these material functions and show how they are related.

Since all of the functions relate to a time-dependent linear system, they can best be compared in terms of the Laplace transform of their defining expressions. The transform operation replaces derivative and integral functions of time by algebraic functions of the transform variable s.

Initially, we illustrated that viscoelastic response could be described in terms of a differential equation relating stress (and its various time derivatives) to strain (and its various time derivatives). The coefficients of the terms in the differential equation thus constitute the characteristic parameters or material properties which are necessary to describe the rheological or mechanical response of a given material. A generalized expression representing this equation was written in terms of the differential operators P and R or Q [Eqs. (2.4-39) and (2.4-42)]. If the material is at rest in the undeformed state, corresponding to t = 0, the Laplace transform of Eqs. (2.4-39) and (2.4-42) can be written:

$$P(s)\bar{\tau}(s) = Q(s)\gamma(s) = R(s)\bar{\dot{\gamma}}(s) \qquad (2.4-106)$$

where

$$P(s) = \sum_{k=0}^{N} p_k s^k \qquad Q(s) = \sum_{k=0}^{N} q_k s^k$$

$$(2.4-107)$$

$$R(s) = \mu \sum_{k=0}^{M} r_k s^k$$

The ratio of the transforms of stress to strain is thus

$$\frac{\bar{\tau}(s)}{\bar{\gamma}(s)} = \frac{Q(s)}{P(s)} = \frac{sR(s)}{P(s)} \qquad (2.4-108)$$

or, for the ratio of the transforms of stress to strain rate:

$$\frac{\bar{\tau}(s)}{\bar{\dot{\gamma}}(s)} = \frac{R(s)}{P(s)} \qquad (2.4-109$$

The polynomials $P(s)$, $Q(s)$, and $R(s)$ are defined by the coefficients p_k, q_k, and r_k of Eq. (2.4-107), which constitute the material properties.

The creep compliance for a material was defined in terms of its strain response to a step stress by Eq. (2.4-46) (for $t \geq 0$);

$$J(t) = \frac{\gamma(t)}{\tau_o} \qquad (2.4-46)$$

where the applied stress is of the form

$$\tau(t) = \tau_o U(t) \qquad 2.4-44)$$

Transforming (2.4-46) and (2.4-44), and solving for the ratio of the transforms of stress to strain, we get

$$\frac{\bar{\tau}(s)}{\bar{\gamma}(s)} = \frac{\tau_o/s}{\tau_o \bar{J}(s)} = \frac{1}{s\bar{J}(s)} \qquad (2.4-110)$$

Comparing (2.4-110) and (2.4-108) shows that the transforms of the creep compliance and the differential operators are related by:

$$\bar{J}(s) = \frac{P(s)}{sQ(s)} \quad \frac{P(s)}{s^2 R(s)} \tag{2.4-111}$$

Likewise, the relaxation modulus was defined in terms of stress response to a step strain by Eq. (2.4-48):

$$G(t) = \frac{\tau(t)}{\gamma_o} \tag{2.4-48}$$

where γ_o is the magnitude of the applied step strain function:

$$\gamma(t) = \gamma_o U(t) \tag{2.4-112}$$

Transforming (2.4-48) and (2.4-112) and solving for the ratio of the transforms of stress to strain:

$$\frac{\bar{\tau}(s)}{\bar{\gamma}(s)} = \frac{\gamma_o \bar{G}(s)}{\gamma_o/s} = s\bar{G}(s) \tag{2.4-113}$$

Comparing (2.4-113) and (2.4-108) provides a relation between the transforms of the relaxation modulus and the differential operators:

$$\bar{G}(s) = \frac{Q(s)}{sP(s)} = \frac{R(s)}{P(s)} \tag{2.4-114}$$

Note that, by (2.4-114), the relaxation modulus $G(t)$ is related to the operator Eq. (2.4-106) as the inverse transform of the ratio of the rate of strain differential operator, $R(s)$, to the stress operator, $P(s)$, and not the ratio of strain to stress operators as might be implied from the original definition of the relaxation modulus.

Now a comparison of (2.4-111) and (2.4-114) shows that the transforms of the creep compliance and relaxation modulus are related by:

$$\bar{G}(s)\bar{J}(s) = \frac{1}{s^2} \qquad (2.4\text{-}115)$$

Hence the operator equation, the creep compliance, and relaxation modulus are all simply related through their transforms. Thus if, for example, $J(t)$ is determined from creep measurements and can be represented by a suitable expression in time, the relaxation modulus can then be determined from:

$$G(t) = \mathcal{L}^{-1} \frac{1}{s^2 \bar{J}(s)} \qquad (2.4\text{-}116)$$

where

$$\bar{J}(s) = \mathcal{L}\left[J(t)\right] = \int_0^\infty J(t)e^{-st}\, dt \qquad (2.4\text{-}117)$$

A similar procedure would permit the determination of $J(t)$ from a knowledge of $G(t)$. This assumes, of course, that the measured functions in the time domain can be adequately represented by a function which is readily transformable, and that the inverse transform (2.4-116) is determinable.

The oscillatory response functions (G^*, J^*, η^*) were all defined in terms of small amplitude steady oscillatory or sinusoidal deformation. When subjected to oscillatory deformation, the resulting stress also oscillates at the same frequency (after the transients have relaxed), but will in general be out of phase with the strain:

$$\gamma = \gamma_o e^{j\omega t} \qquad \tau = \tau_o e^{j(\omega t + \varepsilon)} \qquad (2.4\text{-}118)$$

Substituting (2.4-118) into the operator Eq. (2.4-106) gives

$$\tau_o e^{j(\omega t + \varepsilon)} \sum_{k=0}^{N} [P_k(j\omega)]^k = \gamma_o e^{j\omega t} \sum_{k=0}^{N} [q_k(j\omega)]^k \qquad (2.4\text{-}119)$$

or

$$P(j\omega)\tau_o e^{j\varepsilon} = Q(j\omega)\gamma_o \qquad\qquad (2.4\text{-}120)$$

This shows that the oscillatory stress and strain are related by an
equation identical to that which relates their Laplace transforms
(2.4-106), with the variable s replaced by $j\omega$. This is a general
consequence of linear systems which permits direct determination of
the frequency response characteristics from the Laplace transform
of the differential equation describing the system.

From the definition of the complex modulus, Eqs. (2.4-59) and
(2.4-120), we see that

$$G^*(j\omega) = \frac{\tau_o e^{j\varepsilon}}{\gamma_o} = \frac{Q(j\omega)}{P(j\omega)} \qquad\qquad (2.4\text{-}121)$$

Comparing (2.4-121) and (2.4-114) shows that

$$G^*(j\omega) = j\omega\bar{G}(j\omega) \qquad\qquad (2.4\text{-}122)$$

where

$$\bar{G}(j\omega) = \left[\mathcal{L}G(t) = \bar{G}(s)\right]_{s=j\omega}$$

by which the complex modulus can be determined from the relaxation
modulus, if the latter can be represented by a transformable function.

It is possible, in principle, to convert data directly from the
time domain [e.g., $G(t)$] to the frequency domain [$G*(j\omega)$], or vice
versa, without the necessity of curve fitting to find an analytical
transformable function which accurately represents the data. The
conversion may be performed by direct numerical integration, as
follows.

Introducing the definition of the Laplace transform into
Eq. (2.4-122), it becomes:

$$G^*(j\omega) = G'(\omega) + jG''(\omega) = j\omega \int_0^\infty G(t)e^{-j\omega t}\, dt \qquad (2.4\text{-}123)$$

Now the right-hand side of (2.4-123) may be separated into real and imaginary parts to give

$$G'(\omega) = \omega \int_0^\infty G(t)\, \sin \omega t\, dt \qquad (2.4\text{-}124)$$

and

$$G''(\omega) = \omega \int_0^\infty G(t)\, \cos \omega t\, dt \qquad (2.4\text{-}125)$$

Comparing (2.4-124) with the definition of the Fourier sine transform:

$$F_s(\omega) = \int_0^\infty f(t)\, \sin \omega t\, dt \qquad (2.4\text{-}126)$$

for which the inverse is:

$$f(t) = \frac{2}{\pi} \int_0^\infty F_s(\omega)\, \sin \omega t\, d\omega \qquad (2.4\text{-}127)$$

and comparing (2.4-125) with the Fourier cosine transform:

$$F_c(\omega) = \int_0^\infty f(t)\, \cos \omega t\, dt \qquad (2.4\text{-}128)$$

and its inverse:

$$f(t) = \frac{2}{\pi} \int_0^\infty F_c(\omega) \cos \omega t \, d\omega \qquad\qquad (2.4-129)$$

shows that $G(t)$ can be determined from either G' or G'' as follows:

$$G(t) = \frac{2}{\pi} \int_0^\infty \frac{G'(\omega)}{\omega} \sin \omega t \, d\omega \qquad\qquad (2.4-130)$$

or

$$G(t) = \frac{2}{\pi} \int_0^\infty \frac{G''(\omega)}{\omega} \cos \omega t \, d\omega \qquad\qquad (2.4-131)$$

A similar process can be followed to relate the creep compliance, $J(t)$, to the complex compliance, $J^*(j\omega)$. These relations are only valid, of course, for functions whose Fourier transforms exist, i.e., only when the above integrals converge.

A relation between the complex viscosity or complex modulus and the relaxation modulus also follows from the definition:

$$\eta^*(j\omega) = \frac{\tau(\omega t)}{\dot{\gamma}(\omega t)} = \frac{\tau}{j\omega\gamma} = \frac{G^*(j\omega)}{j\omega} = [\bar{G}(s)]_{s=j\omega} \qquad\qquad (2.4-132)$$

where $\bar{G}(s)$ is the transform of the relaxation modulus.

The relaxation function, defined by the integral or hereditary equation of state, may also be related to the foregoing functions. This function is defined by Eq. (2.4-73):

$$\tau(t) = \int_0^t \psi(t - t')\dot{\gamma}(t') \, dt' \qquad\qquad (2.4-73)$$

where the lower limit, $t' = 0$, represents the reference time corresponding to the "unstressed" (undeformed) state.

Making use of the convolution theorem, the Laplace transform of (2.4-73) is

$$\bar{\tau}(s) = \bar{\psi}(s) \cdot \bar{\dot{\gamma}}(s) = \bar{\psi}(s) \cdot s\bar{\gamma}(s) \qquad (2.4-133)$$

or

$$\bar{\psi}(s) = \frac{\bar{\tau}(s)}{s\bar{\gamma}(s)} = \frac{\bar{\tau}(s)}{\bar{\dot{\gamma}}(s)} \qquad (2.4-134)$$

which is identical to Eq. (2.4-113). Hence the relaxation function, $\psi(t)$ is identical to the relaxation modulus, $G(t)$.

A similar result for $J(t)$ follows from a consideration of Eqs. (2.4-78) and (2.4-110).

2.4.4. Restrictions of Linearity

The assumption of linear material response is inherent in all of the models discussed in Sec. 2.4.2 as well as in the definition of each of the viscoelastic material functions in Sec. 2.4.3. The models based upon mechanical analogs (e.g., Maxwell, Voigt, etc.) are inherently linear since they are formulated by combining linear elastic (Hookean) and linear viscous (Newtonian) elements, with the resulting behavior being described by linear differential (or integral) equations in time as the dependent variable.

The viscoelastic material functions (e.g., creep and relaxation moduli) which have been considered are also linear, since they are assumed to be functions of time only, independent of the magnitude of stress or strain. Likewise the complex moduli are inherently linear, not only because of the assumed absence of amplitude dependence, but also because of the assumed sinusoidal nature of both input and response. For a nonlinear material, a sinusoidal input will not produce a truly sinusoidal response.

One of the consequences of linearity for a fluid is that of Newtonian behavior in steady flow. Now from a practical standpoint

all fluids which exhibit elasticity are also non-Newtonian in steady
flow, if a sufficiently wide range of shear rate or flow conditions
is considered. This would seem to provide a serious restriction on
the description of the properties of such materials by linear viscoelastic functions. However, several points must be made clear in
order to place this in proper perspective.

First of all, a description of the time-dependent properties of
viscoelastic materials requires a relation of stress and strain components which are associated with a given material element over a
finite period of time. Thus, if strain is defined in terms of displacement gradients relative to a fixed frame of reference, such
time-dependent properties can be defined only if all material elements remain (essentially) at a fixed location with time relative
to this same reference frame. In other words, since a viscoelastic
material possesses "memory" for prior states, if material elements
are displaced over appreciable distances with time, it is necessary
to define a measure of deformation which "follows" each element with
time as it moves in order to relate the stresses on the element at
a given time to its state of deformation at prior times. As we
shall see later, this can be achieved by employing a different definition of the time derivative which follows a given material element
as it translates, rotates, and deforms in the system.

We are thus led to the conclusion that the viscoelastic material
functions which we have presented so far cannot be completely adequate, in general, for materials undergoing large or continuous deformation (flow). This, therefore, automatically precludes the prediction of non-Newtonian viscosities. Hence the validity of linear
time-dependent viscoelastic material functions should be considered
to be restricted to deformations and/or deformation rates of small
magnitude. The extent of this restriction depends upon the actual
degree of nonlinearity present in the material. On the other hand,
no matter how nonlinear the material might inherently be, it should
respond in a linear fashion if subjected to deformations and/or
deformation rates of sufficiently small magnitude. Hence these

functions may be considered valid for any viscoelastic material, under suitable conditions. We will be concerned with the principles necessary for removing these restrictions in later chapters.

The apparent viscosity material function is not subject to such restrictions, since it is defined in terms of a constant shear rate (continuously deforming) system. As such, it is a measure only of purely viscous properties of a fluid, that is, those which are a function only of the instantaneous rate of strain, but not dependent on the history of deformation. There are, of course, no linearity assumptions, implied or otherwise, associated with this function.

The material functions discussed so far have been defined for various time-dependent imposed conditions in terms of one component of stress and of strain, which are the components usually associated with simple shear deformation. However, similar functions may be defined in terms of any component of stress and strain relative to any deformation for which these components may be related to measurable quantities (e.g., isotropic or volumetric stress and strain, anisotropic normal components relative to simple tension deformation, etc.). Of course all of these material functions are not independent, but may be different manifestations of the same material properties (in varying degrees and combinations) and may all be described, in principle, by a single general rheological constitutive equation.

In the next section, we will consider some material functions defined in terms of anisotropic normal stress components.

2.5. NORMAL STRESS EFFECTS

There are a number of unusual, and rather remarkable, effects exhibited by viscoelastic fluids in steady flow which cannot be attributable to viscous (shear stress) effects. Some of these are illustrated in Fig. 2.20.

In Fig. 2.20a, the shape of the free surface of a liquid in a vessel is depicted when it is subjected to an angular deformation by a rotating rod or cylinder. For fluids without elasticity,

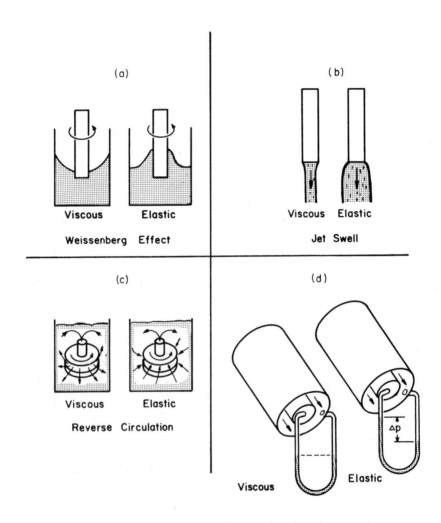

FIG. 2.20 Normal stress effects in elastic liquids.

centrifugal force creates a concave vortex in the liquid. However, elastic liquids develop stresses which oppose that of centrifugal force and cause the fluid to climb up the rotating shaft. This is known as the Weissenberg effect.

Figure 2.20b illustrates the shape of a free jet issuing from the end of a tube. The jet of an inelastic liquid contracts slightly from the diameter of the tube, while that of the elastic liquid may swell to a diameter considerably larger than that of the tube.

In Fig. 2.20c, two parallel discs are immersed in a fluid. One of them has a hole in the center, and one disc is rotating. In an inelastic fluid, centrifugal force causes the fluid to flow in through the hole and out at the edge, while in the elastic fluid the flow is in at the periphery and out through the hole in the center.

Figure 2.20d illustrates steady axial flow in an annulus. For an inelastic fluid, the pressure on the inner and outer walls of the annulus is the same, while the elastic liquid causes a larger pressure to develop at the outer wall than at the inner.

Now these phenomena can be attributed to "extra" stresses which are developed in elastic fluids under shear, in directions normal to the plane of shear. These normal stresses, which are not isotropic, are a function of the rate of shear and thus disappear when the fluid is at rest. They are illustrated in Fig. 2.21 for the case of simple shear, and are attributed to elasticity inasmuch as they are absent in purely viscous (inelastic) fluids in this type of deformation. The three anisotropic normal stress components are designated τ_{11}, τ_{22}, and τ_{33}. The standard convention with regard to numbering of the coordinate axes is that x_1 is taken to coincide with the direction of motion or flow, x_2 is the direction of the displacement gradient, and x_3 is the "neutral" direction, in which the flow is unchanged.

The exact molecular origin of these normal stresses is not entirely understood. However, a qualitative, albeit considerably oversimplified, explanation is possible in terms of elastic

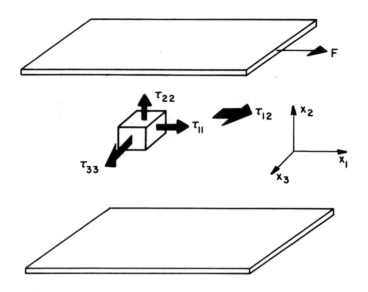

FIG. 2.21 Anisotropic normal stresses in simple shear.

properties. If the fluid (e.g., a polymer solution) is envisioned
to be comprised of elastic segments or lengths of "rubber bands"
which are stretched or extended in the direction of shear, the resulting "tensile" forces can explain many of the observed phenomena.
For example, if the fluid is sheared in rotational flow between concentric cylinders, the contraction force due to the stretched elements acts inward toward the axis of rotation like a "strangulation,"
which forces the fluid in toward the axis. This results in the fluid
climbing up the inner cylinder, or the Weissenberg effect. Likewise,
relaxation of the elastic forces when the fluid exits from the open
end of a tube in a free jet causes the elastic elements to contract,
or "pile up." This would cause the jet to swell when the stresses
relax. Thus, one effect of these normal stresses is an additional
tensile force in the direction of shearing.

     As we shall see later, properly generalized forms of the visco-
elastic equations of state indeed predict the existence of these
anisotropic normal stress effects in simple shear, even for fluids

with Newtonian viscosities. Hence these effects are generally considered to be a manifestation of the elastic properties of the fluid in steady shear. It should be noted that anisotropic normal stresses can also be predicted by a generalized purely viscous equation of state. (This is the Stokesian or Reiner-Rivlin fluid and will be considered in detail later.) However, the character of these predicted stresses is not consistent with observations which have been made on actual fluids, so that such a fluid must be considered as purely hypothetical.

2.5.1. Normal Stress Material Functions

The anisotropic normal stress components, illustrated in Fig. 2.21, cannot be measured directly in a fluid system. Measurements can be made, however, of total normal stress components. As discussed in Sec. 1.10.3, the total stress (σ_{ij}) includes a contribution from both (isotropic) pressure as well as the fluid shear (anisotropic) stress:

$$\sigma_{ij} = -\bar{P}\delta_{ij} + \tau_{ij} = \begin{bmatrix} -\bar{P} + \tau_{11} & \tau_{12} & \tau_{13} \\ \tau_{21} & -\bar{P} + \tau_{22} & \tau_{23} \\ \tau_{31} & \tau_{32} & -\bar{P} + \tau_{33} \end{bmatrix} \quad (2.5-1)$$

In addition, we have seen that for an incompressible fluid the static pressure (P_o) and the mean normal stress are identical:

$$P_o = \bar{P} = -\frac{1}{3} \sum_i \sigma_{ii} \quad (2.5-2)$$

Therefore, in order to eliminate the contribution of static pressure on the total normal stress components, resulting in stresses which are characteristic only of the deformation properties of the fluid, only the differences in normal stresses are considered:

$$\sigma_{11} - \sigma_{22} = (-\bar{P} + \tau_{11}) - (-P + \tau_{22}) = \tau_{11} - \tau_{22} \quad (2.5-3)$$

Thus, the normal stress character may be completely defined by a
knowledge of two normal stress differences as a function of deformation (e.g., shear rate), plus the consequence of the definition of
pressure (Eq. 1.10-33):

$$\text{First normal stress difference} = (\tau_{11} - \tau_{22}) = N_1 \qquad (2.5\text{-}4)$$

$$\text{Second normal stress difference} = (\tau_{22} - \tau_{33}) = N_2 \qquad (2.5\text{-}5)$$

$$\text{Pressure definition:} \quad (\tau_{11} + \tau_{22} + \tau_{33}) = 0 \qquad (2.5\text{-}6)$$

The normal stress differences are independent of the sign
(direction) of shear, and so are assumed to be proportional to the
square of the shear rate. Thus two normal stress material functions (θs) may be defined in a manner similar to the definition
of the apparent viscosity function:

$$\theta_1(\dot{\gamma}) = \frac{N_1}{\dot{\gamma}^2} \qquad (2.5\text{-}7)$$

$$\theta_2(\dot{\gamma}) = \frac{N_2}{\dot{\gamma}^2} \qquad (2.5\text{-}8)$$

The degree to which these functions are shear rate-dependent is also
an indication of the nonlinear character of a viscoelastic fluid.

It has only been in the last 10 years or so that reliable measurements of these normal stresses have been made. Data for N_1 for
polymeric fluids are fairly abundant, due primarily to the availa-
bility of the Weissenberg rheogoniometer (various methods of measuring normal stresses will be discussed in Chap. 5). However, only
in the last few years have reliable measurements of N_2 been made.
A postulate, attributed initially to Weissenberg, that N_2 should be
zero, was widely accepted for many years. After methods were developed for making these measurements, a considerable amount of data
was generated which was later discounted because of extraneous
effects which were not accounted for, or faulty analysis.

A survey and critical analysis of available normal stress data
for polyisobutylene solutions (usually in decalin or cetane) has
been made by Ginn and Metzner [2.19] and also by Tanner [2.20].
Such solutions are by far the most widely studied from a rheological
standpoint, and have almost reached the point of becoming standards
for viscoelastic fluid properties. A qualitative comparison of the
viscosity and two normal stress functions versus shear rate, indicating relative orders of magnitude, for typical solutions is shown in
Fig. 2.22. Note that N_2 is negative and typically 10-20% of the

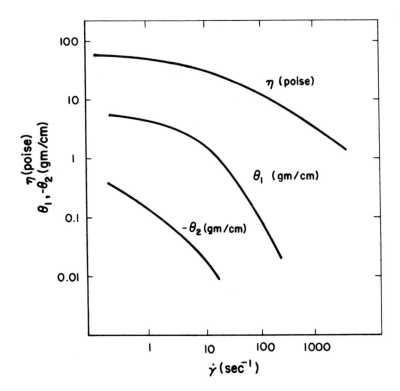

FIG. 2.22 Relative values of viscous and normal stress functions for polymer solutions.

magnitude of N_1. This ratio varies with shear rate, however, generally decreasing with increasing shear rate. The relative positions of these curves are typical of other polymer solutions as well. However, the relative magnitudes of the elastic properties (including normal stresses) generally increases with the viscosity of the solvent. For polymer melts, the relative magnitudes of the normal stress functions are considerably greater, and it is not uncommon for the magnitude of the normal stresses to exceed that of the shear stresses. It is also possible for the magnitude of N_2 to exceed that of N_1 for melts, especially at lower shear rates.

2.6. COMBINED BEHAVIOR

Each of the material functions which have been defined in this chapter, as well as others which may be conceived, can be measured for any given material by suitable experimental methods. Some of these experimental methods will be discussed in detail in later chapters. These measurements may be presented in tabular or graphical form, and may in turn be fitted by analytical functions by empirical methods. Examples of the result of this process have been given for the apparent viscosity function.

Although such empirical material functions each represent accurately the mechanical or rheological response characteristics of a given material in a deformation situation similar to that of the test in which the function was determined, they may not be sufficient to determine the deformation or flow properties in a more complex situation. This can only be done if a truly general rheological equation of state (or constitutive equation) which is characteristic of the material, is known. Such an equation, formulated in terms of the complete stress and strain/strain rate tensors is capable of predicting, in principle, the stress-deformation properties of the material in any given system, no matter how complex. Thus, all of the measurable material functions must be "contained within" or predictable by such a general rheological equation. It is thus the ultimate objective of the rheologist to determine such an equation for

a given material which constitutes a complete description of the
mechanical properties of that material. We will discuss the principles required for formulating such an equation in later chapters.

Once the rheological properties of material are known in a general form, the flow or deformation properties of that material can,
in principle, be calculated under any circumstances. This is the
objective of the fluid mechanic. However, it is not, in general,
possible to measure directly the appropriate stress and strain components in a deformed material (particularly a fluid), which can
be used to formulate or confirm the rheological equation of state.
The measurements generally consist, instead, of forces and displacements or velocities which are characteristic not only of the material, but the system in which it is contained as well. Such measurements can be related to the desired components of stress and strain
by suitable application of conservation principles or the laws of
mechanics which apply to all materials in any system.

Thus it is appropriate at this point to discuss these fundamentals which constitute the basic "tools" of both the rheologist
and the fluid mechanic. This will be the subject of the following
chapter.

PROBLEMS

2-1. A "time constant" can be defined for various non-Newtonian
      fluids from their steady shear stress-shear rate behavior, by
      combining the parameters in their apparent viscosity function
      such that the result has dimensions of time. Determine this
      characteristic "time" for the following fluid models:
      (a) Bingham plastic
      (b) Power law
      (c) Eyring
      (d) Ellis
      (e) Reiner-Philippoff
      (f) Meter

2-2.   The viscous properties of blood may be represented by the
       "Casson equation": $\tau^{1/2} = \tau_o^{1/2} + (\mu_o \dot{\gamma})^{1/2}$. For
       $\tau_o = 3 \times 10^{-2}$ dyn/cm^2 and $\mu_o = 4$ CP, plot the apparent viscos-
       ity versus shear rate for this model for $0.01 \leq \dot{\gamma} \leq 100$. Can
       you think of any fundamental objections to this model?

2-3.   The accompanying plot of apparent viscosity versus shear rate
       represents data for three concentrations (100, 250, and 500 ppm)
       of a high molecular weight polymer in distilled water. These
       solutions exhibit some remarkable flow properties, including
       reduced drag in turbulent flow (as much as 80% less than pure
       water at the same flow rate). Determine the apparent viscos-
       ity model which best fits these data. Determine appropriate
       numerical values of the parameters in the model for each of
       the three curves shown, and plot the predicted curves from the
       model on the same plot as the data for comparison.

2-4.   Sketch a plot of the apparent viscosity versus shear rate for
       the Eyring model. For what magnitude of shear rate would you
       expect this model to be most useful? Can you think of any
       fundamental objections to this model on physical grounds?

2-5.   Starting with the definition of compressibility (Eq. 2.2-13),
       derive an expression for the compressibility of a perfect gas.

2-6.   Consider a fiber of a very viscous liquid (or "soft solid"),
       subjected to a constant longitudinal stress σ_{11} (or simple
       tension) (Fig. 2.4), which has a Newtonian viscosity, μ_o. If
       the material extends at a constant rate (velocity) $v_1 = \Delta \ell_1 / t$,
       and its length at any time t is $\ell_o + \Delta \ell_1(t)$, its longitudinal
       strain rate is given by:

$$\Delta_{11} = 2 \frac{\partial v_1}{\partial \ell_1} = 2 \frac{v_1}{\Delta \ell_1} = 2 \dot{e}_n$$

       If the *extensional viscosity* is defined as

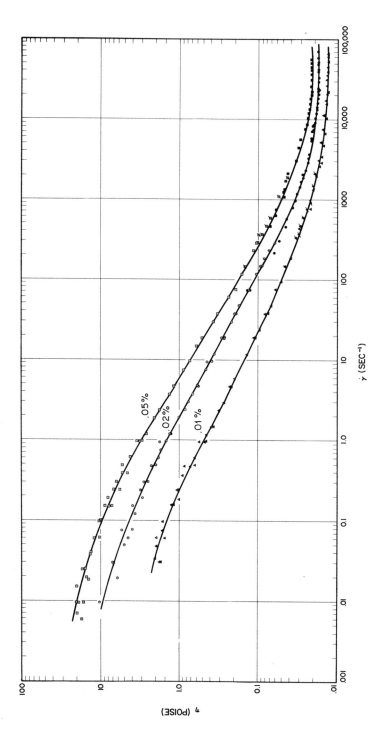

PROB. 2-3 Apparent viscosity of three polyacrilamide solutions.
(Reprinted from Ref. 2.21, p. 190, by courtesy of John Wiley & Sons.)

$$\mu_e = \frac{\sigma_{11}}{\dot{e}_n}$$

show that

$$\mu_e = 3\mu_o$$

2-7. Calculate the response of a Maxwell fluid subjected to an im-
      posed stress of the following form:

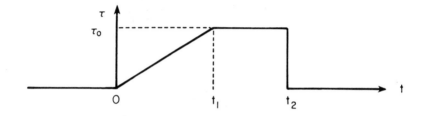

Start with the differential Eq. (2.4-3), and use Laplace transforms to derive the strain as a function of time. Sketch a
plot of your solution.

2-8. Two independent investigators studying the same material have
      concluded, respectively, that it can be represented by models
      (a) and (b) below. Are these two models equivalent? If so,
      determine the relationships between the parameters of the two
      models.

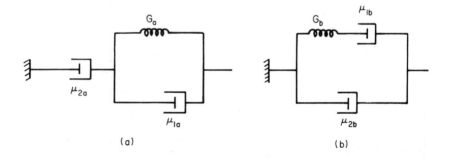

(a)   (b)

2-9. The following three-parameter fluid model is sometimes re-
      ferred to as the Jeffreys model:

$$\tau + \lambda_1 \dot{\tau} = \mu(\dot{\gamma} + \lambda_2 \ddot{\gamma})$$

What is the spring-dashpot analog of this model? Evaluate
the "spring constants" and "viscosities" in the analog in
terms of the parameters μ, λ_1, λ_2.

2-10. Show quantitatively that the Maxwell fluid behaves as a
      Hooke solid in a stress relaxation test, if the Deborah num-
      ber is sufficiently large.

2-11. Show that the material parameters p_i and r_i, defined by the
      general differential operators P and R of Eqs. (2.4-41) and
      (2.4-42) are related to the relaxation times and shear moduli
      of the generalized Maxwell model by:

$$p_i = \sum_{\alpha=1}^{N} \sum_{\beta=\alpha+1}^{N} \sum_{\gamma=\beta+1}^{N} \sum_{\kappa=i}^{N} \lambda_\alpha \lambda_\beta \lambda_\gamma \cdots \lambda_\kappa$$

$$r_i = \frac{1}{\mu_o} \left[\sum_{\alpha=1}^{N} \sum_{\beta=\alpha+1}^{N} \sum_{\gamma=\beta+1}^{N} \cdots \sum_{\kappa=i+1}^{N} \lambda_\alpha \lambda_\beta \lambda_\gamma \cdots \right.$$

$$\left. \lambda_\kappa (G_\alpha + G_\beta + \cdots + G_\kappa) \right]$$

2-12. Derive the electrical analog circuits corresponding to ana-
      logs I, II, and III of Table 2.2, for each of the following
      spring-dashpot models:

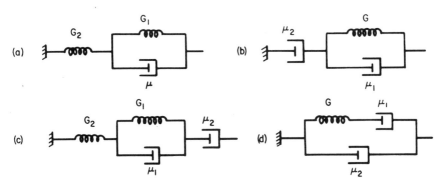

2-13. Derive the equation for the creep compliance of a Voigt solid from preceding relations.

2-14. Derive the relaxation modulus and creep compliance for each of the models in Prob. 2-12.

2-15. Derive the differential rheological equation relating shear stress and shear strain, the complex shear modulus, and the complex viscosity for each of the models in Prob. 2-12.

2-16. The local rate at which work must be done to deform a material, per unit volume, is simply $\tau\dot{\gamma}$. In steady shear flow, all of this work (or energy) is dissipated, eventually appearing as heat. In an oscillatory deformation, that portion of the power supplied which is dissipated is given by the real (in-phase) product of stress and strain rate, i.e., $Re(\tau)Re(\dot{\gamma})$. Note that this may also be written as $\frac{1}{2}[Re(\tau\dot{\gamma}) + Re(\tau\dot{\gamma}_c)]$ where $\dot{\gamma}_c$ is the complex conjugate of $\dot{\gamma}$. Use this to derive an expression for the instantaneous rate of energy dissipation in terms of the complex viscosity components η' and η''.

2-17. Show that the average power dissipated per unit volume over the period of one cycle may be expressed as

$$\bar{P} = \tfrac{1}{2}\,\omega^2\eta'\gamma_o^2 \qquad \text{or} \qquad \bar{P} = \tfrac{1}{2}\,\omega G''\gamma_o^2$$

2-18. Use the result of Prob. 2-16 to determine an expression for the average rate of energy dissipation per unit volume per cycle for a (a) Newtonian fluid, (b) Maxwell fluid, (c) Voigt solid, (d) Jeffreys fluid (Prob. 2-9).

2-19. A rod of material which can be characterized as a Voigt solid is subjected to an oscillatory longitudinal stress σ_{11} in simple tension. Derive expressions for the longitudinal strain, e_{11}, and the phase angle between e_{11} and σ_{11} as a function of frequency. If the same sample were subjected to oscillatory stress in simple shear, determine the expression for the shear strain and phase angle as a function of frequency.

2-20. Derive the creep function (Eq. 2.4-77) for model (c) in Prob. 2-12. Calculate and plot the displacement versus time curve for this model if a shear stress of magnitude 2 dyn/cm^2 is applied for a period of 1 sec, for $G_1 = 2$, $\mu_1 = 1$, $G_2 = 0.3$, and $\mu_2 = 4$.

2-21. Show that, for the generalized Maxwell fluid defined by Eq. (2.4-85):

$$\psi(t) = \sum_{i=1}^{\infty} G_i e^{-t/\lambda_i}$$

the real and imaginary parts of the complex viscosity are given by:

$$\eta'(\omega) = \sum_{i=1}^{\infty} \frac{\lambda_i G_i}{1 + (\lambda_i \omega)^2} \qquad \eta''(\omega) = \sum_{i=1}^{\infty} \frac{\omega \lambda_i^2 G_i}{1 + (\lambda_i \omega)^2}$$

2-22. Repeat Prob. 2-7, starting with the creep function for the Maxwell fluid and the integral Eq. (2.4-78).

2-23. Derive the distribution function for shear moduli (density of the distribution) for a Maxwell fluid, from the relaxation function [Eq. (2.4-82)]. Check your result by using it in Eq. (2.4-87) to regenerate the relaxation function.

2-24. A certain viscoelastic material is subjected to a step strain (stress relaxation test) of magnitude γ_o. The stress required to maintain this strain was measured as a function of time and could be accurately represented by a function of the form:

$$\tau(t) = \frac{a}{t} + \frac{b}{t^2} + \frac{c}{t^3}$$

(a) Is the material a fluid or a solid? Explain.

(b) What is the relaxation modulus and relaxation function for this material?

(c) Determine the functional form of the density of the distribution of shear moduli $(F(\lambda))$ for this material. Sketch the function $F(\lambda)$.

2-25. A distribution of retardation times can be defined in terms of an appropriate distribution density, $L(\lambda)$, by an expression analogous to Eq. (2.4-87), relating $L(\lambda)$ to the creep function $J(t)$.

(a) Derive this expression, starting with the concept of a generalized Voigt solid.

(b) Derive the inverse relation, giving $L(\lambda)$ as a function of $J(t)$.

2-26. Determine the creep function, $J(t)$, for a generalized Maxwell fluid starting with the expression for the relaxation function, Eq. (2.4-85).

2-27. Derive expressions for determining the complex compliance, $J*(j\omega)$, directly from a measurement of the creep function, $J(t)$, and vice versa.

2-28. Show that the real and imaginary components of the complex viscosity are related to the distribution function $H(\lambda)$ by:

$$\eta'(\omega) = \int_0^\infty \frac{H(\lambda)\ d\lambda}{1 + (\lambda\omega)^2} \qquad \eta''(\omega) = \omega \int_0^\infty \frac{H(\lambda)\lambda\ d\lambda}{1 + (\lambda\omega)^2}$$

2-29. Show that the relaxation function, $\psi(t)$, can be obtained from the derivative of the stress relaxation curve after sudden cessation of steady flow $[\dot{\gamma} = \dot{\gamma}_o(1 - U(t))]$ as follows:

$$\psi(t) = -\frac{1}{\dot{\gamma}_0}\frac{d\tau(t)}{dt}$$

2-30. Show that the relaxation function, $\psi(t)$, can be obtained from the derivative of the stress growth curve after sudden application of a constant shear rate $[\dot{\gamma} = \dot{\gamma}_0 U(t)]$ as follows:

$$\psi(t) = \frac{1}{\dot{\gamma}_0}\frac{d\tau(t)}{dt}$$

2-31. Show that, for a linear viscoelastic material subjected to a steady oscillatory shear deformation, a plot of shear stress versus shear strain is an ellipse oriented with its major axis at a 45° angle, and that the ratio of the minor to major axes of the ellipse is tan $(\varepsilon/2)$. Thus show that the complex modulus of the material may be determined directly from the ellipse geometry, since the peak values of stress and strain define the magnitude of the modulus:

$$|G| = \frac{\tau_0}{\gamma_0} = \sqrt{(G')^2 + (G'')^2}$$

and the phase angle defines the ratio of the loss to storage modulus:

$$\tan \varepsilon = \frac{G''}{G'}$$

NOTES

1. The compressibility is sometimes defined as the reciprocal of this quantity, i.e.,

$$\frac{1}{\rho_0}\left(\frac{\partial\rho}{\partial\bar{P}}\right)_{T_0,P_0}$$

2. The Lagrangian method describes what happens to a given fluid element in the course of time, as it moves through the system,

while the Eulerian method describes what happens at a fixed
point in space within the fluid as a function of time. Clearly
a given flow situation may be steady in the Eulerian sense and,
at the same time, unsteady in the Lagrangian sense, or vice
versa.

3. Leibnitz' rule for differentiating an integral with respect to
a parameter has been used here:

$$\frac{\partial}{\partial x} \int_{A(x)}^{B(x)} I(x, y) \, dy = \int_{A(x)}^{B(x)} \frac{\partial I}{\partial x} \, dy + I(x, B) \frac{\partial B}{\partial x}$$

$$- I(x, A) \frac{\partial A}{\partial x}$$

Chapter 3

MECHANICS AND
CONSERVATION PRINCIPLES

3.1. INTRODUCTION

In this chapter, we review the description of the forces which
may act upon or within a material medium to produce motion, and present the dual concept of stress and momentum flux. We then apply
the principles of conservation of mass and momentum, the latter
being equivalent to Newton's second law of motion, to derive the
general equations of motion. These equations must be satisfied in
any continuously deforming medium, and are therefore independent of
the rheological properties of the material. In order to determine
the flow behavior of a given material, these equations must be
solved simultaneously with the rheological equations of the material,
which relate the forces at all points in the material to the local
deformation. The resulting relations, then, constitute the fundamental principles or "tools" by which the flow or deformation characteristics of a given material in a given system may be determined.
Conversely, these same "tools" may be used to determine the basic
rheological properties of a given material from observations of its
flow or deformation behavior in a given system.

3.2. STRESS AND MOMENTUM

The subject of dynamics is concerned with the description of
all of the forces which act on or within a system to produce motion.
The quantitative measure of these forces for a continuous medium is
provided by the stress tensor, which may thus be described as the
primary dynamic variable.

3.2.1. Concentration of Force

In Sec. 1.10.2, stress was introduced as a "force concentration," that is, a force per unit area. Since both force and area
(surface) are vector quantities, it was deduced that stress must be
a dyad (second-order tensor) with nine possible components acting
at every point in the medium, as illustrated in Fig. 1.5. An alternate illustration of these components, in terms of the forces
acting on a small cubical element of material is shown in Fig. 3.1.
In the limit as the size of the cube shrinks to zero, all nine of
the stress components act at a single point. The stress tensor and
its components may thus be represented as

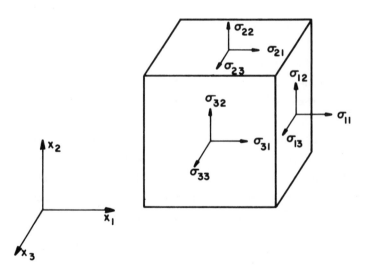

FIG. 3.1 Stress components.

$$\sigma_{ij} = \begin{bmatrix} \sigma_{11} & \sigma_{12} & \sigma_{13} \\ \sigma_{21} & \sigma_{22} & \sigma_{23} \\ \sigma_{31} & \sigma_{32} & \sigma_{33} \end{bmatrix} = \begin{bmatrix} -p + \tau_{11} & \tau_{12} & \tau_{13} \\ \tau_{21} & -p + \tau_{22} & \tau_{23} \\ \tau_{31} & \tau_{32} & -p + \tau_{33} \end{bmatrix} \quad (3.2-1)$$

Now the two indices associated with each stress component have a special significance. As pointed out in Chap. 1, many second-order tensors (dyads) represent quantities which have not only magnitude, but two directional properties. In the case of stress, these directions are the direction in which the force vector acts, and the direction or orientation of the material surface upon which it acts. The latter is specified by the direction of a unit vector which is normal to the surface. A given surface has two sides, so that its normal vector may point in either of two directions. However, the surface of interest is that associated with a specific material element, such as the cube of Fig. 3.1. It is therefore conventional to define the positive direction of the surface vector as that of the outward normal with reference to the volume element contained within the surface. Thus, referring to Fig. 3.1, a surface whose outward normal is in the $+x_1$ direction would be referred to as the +1 surface, whereas the surface with outward normal in the $-x_1$ direction would be a −1 surface, etc. With this convention in mind, then, the indices on each stress component have the following significance:

$$\sigma_{ij} = \left\{\begin{matrix} \text{Force in the j direction acting on a} \\ \text{unit area of i surface} \end{matrix}\right\} \quad (3.2-2)$$

Note that a positive stress will result from a positive force acting on a positive surface, or a negative force on a negative surface. A negative stress will result whenever the force and surface are of opposite sign. This is consistent with the standard convention of mechanics whereby tensile stresses are taken to be positive and compressive stresses are negative.

It was shown in Sec. 1.10.3 that the stress tensor can be written as the sum of an isotropic component ($-\bar{P}$), equal to the negative
of the mean normal stress, and an anisotropic shear tensor (τ_{ij}),
which is a function only of shear deformation:

$$\sigma_{ij} = -\bar{P} \, \delta_{ij} + \tau_{ij} \qquad\qquad (3.2\text{-}3)$$

For incompressible materials, $-\bar{P}$ is identical to the static pressure
($-P_o$), while for compressible materials it includes the isotropic
stress associated with changes in volume, as discussed in Sec. 2.2.2.

In Chap. 1, it was stated that the stress tensor is symmetric
(that is, corresponding components on either side of the diagonal are
equal, or $\sigma_{ij} = \sigma_{ji}$). This can readily be demonstrated by applying
the principle of conservation of angular momentum (sometimes called
moment of momentum) to a cubical element of material. This involves
evaluating the moments (or torques) about an axis through the center
of the element resulting from the shear forces acting on the surfaces,
and equating the result to the product of the moment of inertia and
angular momentum about the center. By taking the limit as the size
of the element approaches zero, the moment of inertia becomes vanishingly small and the result is the desired relation. The details of
this procedure are left to the reader (see Prob. 3-5).

The principle of conservation of angular momentum has been
applied in the above argument. It has been suggested [3.1] that
there are circumstances in which angular momentum is not conserved,
and hence the stress tensor would not be symmetric under these circumstances. These conditions are rather unique, however, and will
not be of concern to us so that we shall assume symmetry holds for
all cases of practical interest.

3.2.2. Momentum Flux

Newton's second law of motion (Sec. 1.7) provides an equivalence
between force and rate of change of momentum. This relation can be
utilized to provide an alternative interpretation of the stress tensor.

surface direct.
force direct.

Consider the simple shear situation, introduced in Sec. 1.5, and
illustrated again in Fig. 3.2. The force F acting on the upper surface results in a shear stress τ_{21} at all points in the fluid, being
the force in the x_1 direction acting on a unit area of x_2 surface.
By Newton's second law of motion, a force corresponds to a rate of
change or transport of momentum:

$$F_1 = \frac{d}{dt}(mv_1) \tag{3.2-4}$$

Momentum is obviously a vector quantity, which in this case has a
component only in the x_1 direction (i.e., "x_1 momentum"). Under
steady-state conditions, this momentum varies only in the x_2 direction. That is, the x_1 velocity (v_1) varies from a maximum at the
top plate to zero at the bottom, and the corresponding x_1 momentum
is transported by the "drag force" from the faster to the slower
moving fluid, in the negative x_2 direction. Hence a force in the
positive x_1 direction acting on unit area of positive x_2 surface is
equivalent to a flux of x_1 momentum in the negative x_2 direction

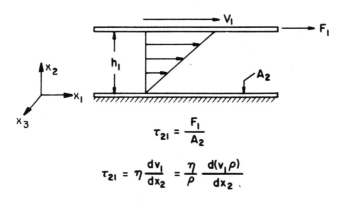

$$\tau_{21} = \frac{F_1}{A_2}$$

$$\tau_{21} = \eta \frac{dv_1}{dx_2} = \frac{\eta}{\rho}\frac{d(v_1\rho)}{dx_2}$$

$$\left\{\begin{array}{c}\text{Flux of } x_1 \text{ momentum}\\ \text{in } -x_2 \text{ direction}\end{array}\right\} = \frac{\eta}{\rho}\left\{\begin{array}{c}\text{Gradient of the concentration}\\ \text{of } x_1 \text{ momentum in } x_2 \text{ direction}\end{array}\right\}$$

FIG. 3.2 Simple shear.

("flux" being defined as a rate of transport per unit area normal to the direction of transport).

We are thus led to the two equivalent interpretations of the quantity τ_{ij}:

$$\tau_{ij} = \begin{Bmatrix} \text{Force in the} \\ \text{j direction acting} \\ \text{on unit area of} \\ \text{i surface} \end{Bmatrix} = \begin{Bmatrix} \text{Flux of j} \\ \text{momentum in the} \\ \text{negative i direction} \end{Bmatrix} \qquad (3.2\text{-}5)$$

Note that both interpretations involve a magnitude and two directions, characteristic of the dyadic nature of τ_{ij}. The difference in sign arises from the fact that a shear force acting along a positive surface of a material element transports momentum into the element, in the direction of the negative surface vector.

The reader should verify that the dimensions of stress are identical to those of momentum flux.

Before proceeding to a development of the general equations of motion which are valid for any continuous medium, it should be noted that the equations governing certain flow problems may be formulated by direct application of Newton's second law or the conservation of momentum. The problems which are susceptible to direct formulation by this approach are subject to certain restrictions, namely,

1. Steady, laminar flow
2. Straight flow streamlines
3. Fully developed flow (i.e., no change of velocity in the direction of flow)
4. Constant fluid properties
5. The fluid behaves as a continuum

Note that (3) above is also implied by (1), if "steady" is interpreted in both the Eulerian and Lagrangian sense. Certain of these restrictions may be relaxed by exercise of sufficient ingenuity; however, in such cases it is generally easier to apply the general equations of motion (to be derived subsequently), tailored for the specific problem. This process will be illustrated in the following chapter.

Various steady flow problems which meet these restrictions may be formulated by the application of Newton's second law to the fluid in a thin "shell" in the system, in the following form:

$$
\left\{\begin{array}{l} \text{Sum of forces} \\ \text{acting on} \\ \text{the element} \end{array}\right\} = \left\{\begin{array}{l} \text{Rate of momentum} \\ \text{transport out of} \\ \text{the element} \end{array}\right\} - \left\{\begin{array}{l} \text{Rate of momentum} \\ \text{transport into} \\ \text{the element} \end{array}\right\} \quad (3.2\text{-}6)
$$

This may also be interpreted as a statement of the principle of *conservation of momentum*. Since momentum (or force) is a vector quantity, Eq. (3.2-6) may be applied to each component of the vector. Hence, for the general case, three such expressions may result, one for each component. However, most of the problems for which this simple approach is useful are those in which only one velocity (or momentum) component is nonzero, so that only one equation will be required.

The usual approach is to apply Eq. (3.2-6) to the fluid contained in a thin "shell," whose boundaries are parallel to those of the restraining boundaries of the system. By taking the limit as the thickness of the shell approaches zero, a differential equation for the stress components as a function of position results. In order to obtain a solution of the flow problem (i.e., velocity as a function of position), this differential equation must be solved simultaneously with the rheological equation of state for the specific material or fluid, which relates the stress components to the deformation variables in terms of, e.g., velocity or displacement gradients. This method is illustrated by many examples in Ref. 3.2.

Note that inasmuch as stress may be interpreted as either a force per unit area or as a momentum flux, the stress components may enter into Eq. (3.2-6) on the left- or right-hand side, respectively, with proper attention to algebraic sign and Eq. (3.2-5).

———————————————————————— 0 ————————————————————————

Example 3.1 Determine the stress distribution within any fluid in Poiseuille flow in a tube, and use the result to calculate the velocity distribution and volumetric flow rate for a Newtonian fluid in Poiseuille flow.

   Poiseuille flow is the name given to steady, laminar, fully developed flow of an homogeneous incompressible fluid in a circular tube (not restricted to Newtonian fluids). These conditions are seen to satisfy all of the above stated restrictions, provided the fluid contains no particulate structure which is not small compared with the tube diameter. The situation is illustrated in Fig. 3.3, wherein the tube is inclined to the vertical by an angle β, and the flow is in the axial (z) direction. There will be a drop in pressure over a distance L in the flow direction, given by $(P_o - P_L)$.

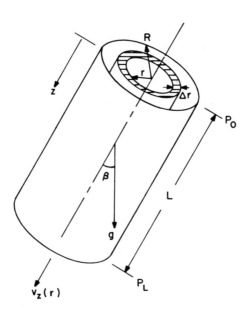

FIG. 3.3 Poiseuille flow.

We apply Eq. (3.2-13) to the fluid in a cylindrical shell of thickness Δr and located at a radius r. Since the flow is in the z direction only, we consider only the z component of momentum and the forces in the z direction acting on all surfaces of the shell and on the fluid as a whole in it, as well as the transport of z momentum through each surface.

End surface at z = 0. The rate of transport of z momentum through this surface into the element is just the rate of mass flow times the velocity:

$$(wv_z)\Big|_{z=0} = (2\pi r\ \Delta r \rho v_z^{\ 2})\Big|_{z=0} \tag{1}$$

Also acting on this surface is the force in z direction due to fluid pressure:

$$(P_o \cdot 2\pi r\ \Delta r)\Big|_{z=0} \tag{2}$$

End surface at z = L. The rate of transport of z momentum out of the element through this surface is

$$(wv_z)\Big|_{z=L} = (2\pi r\ \Delta r \rho v_z^{\ 2})\Big|_{z=L} \tag{3}$$

The force in z direction on this surface due to fluid pressure is

$$-(P_L \cdot 2\pi r\ \Delta r)\Big|_{z=L} \tag{4}$$

Outer cylindrical surface at r + Δr. The stress component τ_{rz} at this surface can be interpreted as either a force in the z direction acting on an r surface, or as a flux of z momentum in the −r direction (into the element), by Eq. (3.2-12):

$$\left\{\begin{array}{l}\text{Rate of transport of}\\ \text{z momentum } \textit{into}\ \text{ the}\\ \text{element}\end{array}\right\} = \left\{\begin{array}{l}\text{Force in z}\\ \text{direction acting}\\ \text{on the element}\end{array}\right\} = (\tau_{rz} \cdot 2\pi r L)\Big|_{r+\Delta r} \tag{5}$$

Inner cylindrical surface at $r = r$. Since this is a $-r$ surface of the shell, the force in the z direction acting on the fluid in the shell through this surface is represented by the $-\tau_{rz}$ stress component. Likewise, this stress component may be considered a flux of z momentum in the $+r$ direction; i.e., into the element:

$$\left\{\begin{array}{l} \text{Rate of z} \\ \text{momentum } into \\ \text{the element} \end{array}\right\} = \left\{\begin{array}{l} \text{Force in z} \\ \text{direction acting} \\ on \text{ the element} \end{array}\right\} = -(\tau_{rz} \cdot 2\pi rL)\Big|_{r} \qquad (6)$$

The gravitational force acting on the entire fluid in the element (total body force) in the z direction is

$$2\pi r \, \Delta rL\rho g \cos \beta \qquad (7)$$

When all of these terms are substituted into Eq. (3.2-6), the momentum transport terms through the ends cancel, since $v_z\big|_{z=0} = v_z\big|_{z=L}$. Also, the stress terms may be interpreted as either forces (on the left side) or as momentum transport terms (on the right side), so that either way the conservation equation becomes:

$$(2\pi rL\tau_{rz})\Big|_{r+\Delta r} - (2\pi rL\tau_{rz})\Big|_{r} + 2\pi r \, \Delta r(P_o - P_L)$$

$$+ 2\pi r \, \Delta rL\rho g \cos \beta = 0 \qquad (8)$$

Dividing by $2\pi L \, \Delta r$ and taking the limit as $\Delta r \to 0$, this becomes

$$\frac{d(r\tau_{rz})}{dr} = r \frac{\Delta P}{L} \qquad (9)$$

where

$$\Delta P = (P_L + \rho gh_L) - (P_o + \rho gh_o) = P_L - P_o \qquad (10)$$

and

$$h = -z \cos \beta \qquad (11)$$

is the vertical elevation *above* an arbitrary horizontal reference plane (i.e., z = 0). The term P thus represents the fluid pressure in excess of the hydrostatic pressure existing at rest. Equation (9) is the differential equation for the radial distribution of the stress component τ_{rz}. It can be integrated to give:

$$\tau_{rz} = \frac{\Delta P r}{2L} + \frac{C_1}{r} \tag{12}$$

The constant C_1 must be zero, since otherwise the stress in the center (r = 0) would be infinite, and no material (other than a perfectly rigid solid) can support an infinite stress. Therefore

$$\tau_{rz} = \frac{\Delta P r}{2L} \tag{13}$$

Note that this equation could also be derived directly by a force balance on a cylindrical plug of fluid of radius r concentric with the tube.

At the tube wall (r = R) the stress exerted by the fluid on the tube (τ_w) is:

$$\tau_w = -(\tau_{rz})_{r=R} = -\frac{\Delta P R}{2L} \tag{14}$$

so that (13) can also be written as:

$$\tau_{rz} = -\tau_w \left(\frac{r}{R}\right) \tag{15}$$

This shows that the stress varies linearly with radius, from zero at the center to a maximum at the wall. Note that ΔP is negative and τ_w is positive. Equations (13) to (15) are perfectly valid for any material in the tube, for any orientation of the tube, and for any flow regime (i.e., laminar or turbulent). In order to determine the flow properties of a specific material, its rheological equation must be introduced. For example, if the material is a Newtonian fluid in laminar flow:

$$\tau_{ij} = \mu \dot{\gamma}_{ij}$$

or

$$\tau_{rz} = \mu \frac{dv_z}{dr} \tag{16}$$

since

$$\dot{\gamma}_{ij} = \begin{bmatrix} 0 & \dfrac{dv_z}{dr} & 0 \\[2ex] \dfrac{dv_z}{dr} & 0 & 0 \\[2ex] 0 & 0 & 0 \end{bmatrix} \tag{17}$$

Eliminating τ_{rz} from (5) and (16):

$$\frac{dv_z}{dr} = \frac{\Delta P r}{2L\mu} = -\frac{\tau_w r}{\mu R} \tag{18}$$

Integrating, and making use of the boundary condition:

$$\text{B.C.: } v_z = 0 \text{ at } r = R \tag{19}$$

gives the velocity distribution

$$\begin{aligned} v_z &= \frac{\Delta P R^2}{4L\mu}\left[1 - \left(\frac{r^2}{R^2}\right)\right] \\[2ex] &= \frac{\tau_w R}{2\mu}\left[1 - \left(\frac{r^2}{R^2}\right)\right] \end{aligned} \tag{20}$$

which is parabolic. All pertinent flow characteristics of a Newtonian fluid in Poiseuille flow can be calculated from this equation. For example, the volumetric flow rate is given by:

$$Q = \int_A v_z \, dA = \int_o^R 2\pi r v_z \, dr = -\frac{\pi \, \Delta P R^4}{8\mu L} \tag{21}$$

which is known as the Hagen-Poiseuille equation.

Equation (21) can also be written:

$$\tau_w = \mu\Gamma \tag{22}$$

where

$$\Gamma = \frac{4Q}{\pi R^3} \tag{23}$$

Comparison of (22) with (16) evaluated at the tube wall, shows that the shear rate at the wall is given by:

$$-\dot{\gamma}_w = -\left.\left(\frac{dv_z}{dr}\right)\right|_{r=R} = \Gamma = \frac{4Q}{\pi R^3} \tag{24}$$

Thus the shear stress at the wall, Eq. (14), and the shear rate at the wall, Eq. (24), for a Newtonian fluid can be evaluated directly from measurements of the pressure gradient and flow rate, respectively.

For a non-Newtonian fluid, the wall shear stress is still given by Eq. (14), which follows directly from Eq. (13), which is valid for any fluid. However, the expression for the wall shear rate, Eq. (24), was derived from the assumption of Newtonian behavior and so is not valid for a non-Newtonian fluid. The calculation of the flow rate for a non-Newtonian fluid would require the introduction of the appropriate nonlinear rheological equation in place of Eq. (16). The procedure from that point would then be parallel to that followed for the Newtonian fluid.

Axial flow in other cylindrical geometries (e.g., annular flow between concentric tubes) would be handled in an identical fashion, with only a change in the boundary conditions for Eq. (12) being required. Other geometries with straight streamlines (e.g., flow between flat plates) would require a "shell" with a geometry similar to that of the flow boundaries.

--------------------------- 0 ---------------------------

It should now be evident that the solution of flow problems involves the simultaneous solution of three sets of equations:

1. The continuity equation or the conservation of mass
2. The equations of motion, representing the conservation of momen-
    tum (or Newton's second law). There will be one equation for
    each nonzero momentum component (i.e., velocity component)
3. The rheological equation of state for the material relating the
    internal fluid stress (or momentum flux) components to the fluid
    deformation, in terms of displacement or velocity gradient compo-
    nents

The direct application of the momentum balance (Newton's law)
method is relatively easy and straightforward for flows with straight
streamlines, such as axial flows in tubes, slits, channels, etc. However, for systems involving curved streamlines (such as angular flow
between concentric cylinders, around spheres, etc.) additional forces
are present which must be accounted for (such as centrifugal, Coriolis,
etc.). With respect to a momentum balance, the consequence of these
forces is that the conservation of angular as well as linear momentum
must be considered. This complicates the procedure considerably, and
it has been found much easier to derive a completely general set of
equations of motion or conservation equations which include all of
these effects, and can be written for any coordinate system. The
specific equations to be solved for any problem may then be obtained
from these general equations by discarding those terms which must be
zero on physical or geometrical grounds. These general equations
will be developed in the next section.

3.3. EQUATIONS OF MOTION

The laws of mechanics or conservation of momentum apply to all
systems and, for a deforming medium which is large compared with
molecular dimensions, can be interpreted as an application of Newton's

laws of motion at all points in the continuous medium. From the dual
nature of the second law (i.e., the equivalence between force and
momentum change), the equations can be derived from application of
either a conservation of momentum or from a consideration of the
forces acting at a point. In this section, we will employ the latter approach, but will first discuss various mathematical descrip-
tions of time rates of change.

3.3.1. Time Derivatives

The fluid mechanical equations of change involve quantities
which may vary with time as well as position within a system. Thus,
before proceeding with these equations, it is desirable to consider
a description of various ways of specifying time derivatives.

A. Partial Derivative

Let us consider some quantity, such as the point velocity of
water in a flowing stream. In general, this velocity may vary with
position and time:

$$\vec{v} = \vec{v}(x_1, x_2, x_3 \; t) \tag{3.3-1}$$

where x_1, x_2, and x_3 are the Cartesian coordinates of the point relative to a fixed reference frame. The partial time derivative of $\vec{v}$
is a measure of the time rate of change of the velocity with all
other independent variables held constant; i.e., at a fixed position
in the stream:

$$\left(\frac{\partial \vec{v}}{\partial t}\right)_{x_1, x_2, x_3} \tag{3.3-2}$$

This is also referred to as the "Eulerian" time derivative.

B. Total Derivative

Now suppose an observer were to wander about the stream at random, recording the observed velocity with time as he goes. If
$\vec{s} = (x_1, x_2, x_3)$ is the position vector of the observer relative to
a fixed point in space, and hence the instantaneous position of the
observed point, this will vary with time as the observer wanders.
Thus the recorded velocities may vary with time because (a) the total
flow in the stream may be varying with time at any given point [as
in (3.3-2)], or (b) the velocity of the stream varies with position,
and the position of the observed point varies with time as the observer wanders. Hence the total variation of the observed velocity
with time can be expressed as:

$$\frac{d\vec{v}}{dt} = \frac{\partial\vec{v}}{\partial t} + \frac{\partial\vec{v}}{\partial\vec{s}} \cdot \frac{d\vec{s}}{dt} \qquad\qquad (3.3\text{-}3)$$

or

$$\frac{d\vec{v}}{dt} = \frac{\partial\vec{v}}{\partial t} + \frac{\partial\vec{v}}{\partial x_1}\frac{dx_1}{dt} + \frac{\partial\vec{v}}{\partial x_2}\frac{dx_2}{dt} + \frac{\partial\vec{v}}{\partial x_3}\frac{dx_3}{dt} \qquad\qquad (3.3\text{-}4)$$

or

$$\frac{dv_i}{dt} = \frac{\partial v_i}{\partial t} + \sum_{k=1}^{3}\frac{\partial v_i}{\partial x_k}\frac{dx_k}{dt} \qquad\qquad (3.3\text{-}5)$$

where $\vec{v}$ is the velocity in the stream at the position $\vec{s} = (x_1, x_2, x_3)$,
relative to the fixed reference frame. Likewise, v_i is the component
of velocity in the x_i direction at this point.

C. Material Derivative

Now if the observer, instead of wandering at random, attaches
himself to an element of the fluid and floats downstream with it, the
rate at which his position changes is identical to the rate of change

of the position of the material element; i.e., its point velocity.
This, then, is just a special case of the total derivative in which
the rate at which the observer's position changes is the same as the
local point velocity of the stream. It is called the *material derivative*, and is written:

$$\frac{D\vec{v}}{Dt} = \frac{\partial\vec{v}}{\partial t} + \vec{v} \cdot \frac{\partial\vec{v}}{\partial\vec{s}} \qquad (3.3\text{-}6)$$

or

$$\frac{D\vec{v}}{Dt} = \frac{\partial\vec{v}}{\partial t} + v_1 \frac{\partial\vec{v}}{\partial x_1} + v_2 \frac{\partial\vec{v}}{\partial x_2} + v_3 \frac{\partial\vec{v}}{\partial x_3} \qquad (3.3\text{-}7)$$

or

$$\frac{Dv_i}{Dt} = \frac{\partial v_i}{\partial t} + \sum_{k=1}^{3} v_k \frac{\partial v_i}{\partial x_k} \qquad (3.3\text{-}8)$$

The material derivative is sometimes called the *substantial
derivative*, *intrinsic derivative*, or the *derivative following the
motion*. The term material derivative is descriptive, in that it is
relative to an observer who is attached to and follows an element of
the material as it moves continuously. This is also known as a
"Lagrangian" point of view.

It is important to realize that all quantities in the above expressions are specified relative to a coordinate system that is fixed
in space. (Cartesian coordinates being implied by the use of x_1, x_2
x_3.) Hence, even though the material derivative represents the
change with time as a given material element is followed through the
system, all position and velocity components in Eq. (3.3-8) are
relative to a fixed frame of reference, and hence the coordinates of
the element relative to this frame change continuously with time (see
note 1).

This is in contrast to a convected derivative, which we will
consider later, which is a type of time derivative following the

motion of the fluid, but in which all quantities (velocities, etc.)
are taken relative to a set of coordinate axes which move and deform
with the material as it flows (i.e., the axes are convected). In
this system, the coordinates of a given element of material moving
through the system are always the same relative to the convected
axes.

The above illustrations of time derivatives have been written
for a tensor quantity with several components (e.g., the velocity
with three components). The equations (3.3-2) through (3.3-8) apply
to each component of the tensor, so that they each represent three
equations, one for each component of the tensor (v_1, v_2, v_3).

The use of the coordinate axes (x_1, x_2, x_3) implies a Cartesian
or rectangular frame of reference. However, it is often convenient
to utilize some other coordinate frame, such as cylindrical, spherical, etc. The material derivative can be written in general vector
notation applicable to any coordinate system as follows:

$$\frac{D\vec{v}}{Dt} = \frac{\partial \vec{v}}{\partial t} + \vec{v} \cdot (\vec{\nabla}\vec{v}) \tag{3.3-9}$$

(see note 2) where $(\vec{\nabla}\vec{v})$ represents the gradient of the vector $\vec{v}$
[Eqs. (1.9-7) and (1.9-9)]. However, instead of this notation we
will use the more general and more descriptive tensor index notation,
which was introduced in Chap. 1 and will be discussed in detail in
Chap. 6. In index notation, the material derivative becomes:

$$\frac{Dv^i}{Dt} = \frac{\partial v^i}{\partial t} + \sum_{k=1}^{3} v^k v^i_{,k} \tag{3.3-10}$$

where $v^i_{,k}$ is the notation for a generalized equivalent of the gradient (or spatial derivative) called the *covariant derivative*. This
operation is defined in general terms which are valid for any coordinate system, and is defined explicitly and discussed in Chap. 6.
Specific component forms of the covariant and material derivatives
relative to Cartesian, cylindrical, and spherical coordinates are
tabulated in Appendix D.

In the following section, we present derivations of general equations expressing the conservation of mass and momentum. These derivations will be developed in terms of Cartesian coordinates, and the general tensor equivalent of the resulting equations, valid for any coordinate system, will be presented without proof. Specific forms of these equations will be tabulated for components relative to Cartesian, cylindrical, and spherical coordinates, and will be used in the following chapters to set up and solve specific problems. The reader is asked to accept the curvilinear forms of these equations without proof until the principles for deriving them are presented in Chap. 6. At that time the reader will acquire the facility for deriving these forms.

3.3.2. Conservation of Mass

Let us consider a cubical region within a continuous medium (Fig. 3.4). A mass balance on material entering and leaving the cube may be written

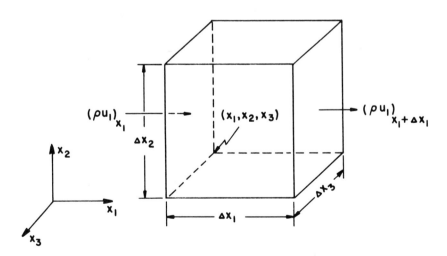

FIG. 3.4 Conservation of mass (x_1 component only).

$$\begin{Bmatrix} \text{Rate of} \\ \text{mass flow} \\ \text{in} \end{Bmatrix} - \begin{Bmatrix} \text{Rate of} \\ \text{mass flow} \\ \text{out} \end{Bmatrix} = \begin{Bmatrix} \text{Rate of} \\ \text{accumulation} \\ \text{of mass in cube} \end{Bmatrix} \qquad (3.3\text{--}11)$$

or

$$[(\rho v_1)\Big|_{x_1} \Delta x_2 \Delta x_3 + (\rho v_2)\Big|_{x_2} \Delta x_1 \Delta x_3 + (\rho v_3)\Big|_{x_3} \Delta x_1 \Delta x_2]$$

$$- [(\rho v_1)\Big|_{x_1+\Delta x_1} \Delta x_2 \Delta x_3 + (\rho v_2)\Big|_{x_2+\Delta x_2} \Delta x_1 \Delta x_3 \qquad (3.3\text{--}12)$$

$$+ (\rho v_3)\Big|_{x_3+\Delta x_3} \Delta x_1 \Delta x_2] = \frac{\partial \rho}{\partial t} \Delta x_1 \Delta x_2 \Delta x_3$$

Dividing by $(\Delta x_1 \Delta x_2 \Delta x_3)$, and taking the limit as the cube dimensions approach zero, results in the *continuity equation*:

$$\frac{\partial \rho}{\partial t} = - \frac{\partial (\rho v_1)}{\partial x_1} + \frac{\partial (\rho v_2)}{\partial x_2} + \frac{\partial (\rho v_3)}{\partial x_3} \qquad (3.3\text{--}13)$$

which is an expression of the conservation of mass, and must be satisfied at all points within the medium. In general vector notation, this equation is

$$\frac{\partial \rho}{\partial t} = -\vec{\nabla} \cdot (\rho \vec{v}) \qquad (3.3\text{--}14)$$

which, in general index or tensor notation, is equivalent to:

$$\frac{\partial \rho}{\partial t} = -\sum_i^3 (\rho v^i),_i \qquad (3.3\text{--}15)$$

By expanding the right side of (3.3--13), (3.3--14) or (3.3--15), and combining the terms involving derivatives of ρ with the left side, an equivalent form of the continuity equation results:

$$\frac{D\rho}{Dt} = -\rho \left(\frac{\partial v_1}{\partial x_1} + \frac{\partial v_2}{\partial x_2} + \frac{\partial v_3}{\partial x_3} \right) \tag{3.3-16}$$

or

$$\frac{D\rho}{Dt} = -\rho \, \vec{\nabla} \cdot \vec{v} \tag{3.3-17}$$

or

$$\frac{D\rho}{Dt} = -\rho \sum_{i}^{3} v^i,_i \tag{3.3-18}$$

For an incompressible (isochoric) fluid (for which ρ is constant; see note 3), these equations reduce to:

$$\frac{\partial v_1}{\partial x_1} + \frac{\partial v_2}{\partial x_2} + \frac{\partial v_3}{\partial x_3} = 0 \tag{3.3-19}$$

or

$$\vec{\nabla} \cdot \vec{v} = \sum_{i} v^i,_i = 0 \tag{3.3-20}$$

The specific component forms of Eq. (3.3-15) for cylindrical and spherical as well as Cartesian coordinates are tabulated in Table 3.1A.

All continuous systems for which mass is conserved must satisfy the continuity equation.

TABLE 3.1

A. Continuity Equation
(Conservation of Mass)

Rectangular coordinates (Cartesian):

1. $\frac{\partial \rho}{\partial t} + \frac{\partial}{\partial x} (\rho v_x) + \frac{\partial}{\partial y} (\rho v_y) + \frac{\partial}{\partial z} (\rho v_z) = 0$

TABLE 3.1 (Continued)

Cylindrical coordinates;

2. $\dfrac{\partial \rho}{\partial t} + \dfrac{1}{r}\dfrac{\partial}{\partial r}(\rho r v_r) + \dfrac{1}{r}\dfrac{\partial}{\partial \theta}(\rho v_\theta) + \dfrac{\partial}{\partial z}(\rho v_z) = 0$

Spherical coordinates:

3. $\dfrac{\partial \rho}{\partial t} + \dfrac{1}{r^2}\dfrac{\partial}{\partial r}(\rho r^2 v_r) + \dfrac{1}{r\sin\theta}\dfrac{\partial}{\partial \theta}(\rho v_\theta \sin\theta) + \dfrac{1}{r\sin\theta}\dfrac{\partial}{\partial \phi}(\rho v_\phi) = 0$

B. Equations of Motion
(Conservation of Momentum)

Cartesian coordinates:

4.   x comp: $\rho\left(\dfrac{\partial v_x}{\partial t} + v_x\dfrac{\partial v_x}{\partial x} + v_y\dfrac{\partial v_x}{\partial y} + v_z\dfrac{\partial v_x}{\partial z}\right)$

$= -\dfrac{\partial P}{\partial x} + \left(\dfrac{\partial \tau_{xx}}{\partial x} + \dfrac{\partial \tau_{yx}}{\partial y} + \dfrac{\partial \tau_{zx}}{\partial z}\right) + \rho g_x$

5.   y comp: $\rho\left(\dfrac{\partial v_y}{\partial t} + v_x\dfrac{\partial v_y}{\partial x} + v_y\dfrac{\partial v_y}{\partial y} + v_z\dfrac{\partial v_y}{\partial z}\right)$

$= -\dfrac{\partial P}{\partial y} + \left(\dfrac{\partial \tau_{xy}}{\partial x} + \dfrac{\partial \tau_{yy}}{\partial y} + \dfrac{\partial \tau_{zy}}{\partial z}\right) + \rho g_y$

6.   z comp: $\rho\left(\dfrac{\partial v_z}{\partial t} + v_x\dfrac{\partial v_z}{\partial x} + v_y\dfrac{\partial v_z}{\partial y} + v_z\dfrac{\partial v_z}{\partial z}\right)$

$= -\dfrac{\partial P}{\partial z} + \left(\dfrac{\partial \tau_{xz}}{\partial x} + \dfrac{\partial \tau_{yz}}{\partial y} + \dfrac{\partial \tau_{zz}}{\partial z}\right) + \rho g_r$

Cylindrical coordinates:

7.   r comp: $\rho\left(\dfrac{\partial v_r}{\partial t} + v_r\dfrac{\partial v_r}{\partial r} + \dfrac{v_\theta}{r}\dfrac{\partial v_r}{\partial \theta} - \dfrac{v_\theta^{\,2}}{r} + v_z\dfrac{\partial v_r}{\partial z}\right)$

$= -\dfrac{\partial P}{\partial r} + \left[\dfrac{1}{r}\dfrac{\partial}{\partial r}(r\tau_{rr}) + \dfrac{1}{r}\dfrac{\partial \tau_r}{\partial \theta} - \dfrac{\tau_{\theta\theta}}{r} + \dfrac{\partial \tau_{rz}}{\partial z}\right] + \rho g_r$

TABLE 3.1 (Continued)

8. θ comp: $\rho\left(\dfrac{\partial v_\theta}{\partial t} + v_r\dfrac{\partial v_\theta}{\partial r} + \dfrac{v_\theta}{r}\dfrac{\partial v_\theta}{\partial \theta} + \dfrac{v_r v_\theta}{r} + v_z\dfrac{\partial v_\theta}{\partial z}\right)$

$$= -\frac{1}{r}\frac{\partial P}{\partial \theta} + \left(\frac{1}{r^2}\frac{\partial}{\partial r}(r^2\tau_{r\theta}) + \frac{1}{r}\frac{\partial \tau_{\theta\theta}}{\partial \theta} + \frac{\partial \tau_{\theta z}}{\partial z}\right) + \rho g_\theta$$

9. z comp: $\rho\left(\dfrac{\partial v_z}{\partial t} + v_r\dfrac{\partial v_z}{\partial r} + \dfrac{v_\theta}{r}\dfrac{\partial v_z}{\partial \theta} + v_z\dfrac{\partial v_z}{\partial z}\right)$

$$= -\frac{\partial P}{\partial z} + \left(\frac{1}{r}\frac{\partial}{\partial r}(r\,\tau_{rz}) + \frac{1}{r}\frac{\partial \tau_{\theta z}}{\partial \theta} + \frac{\partial \tau_{zz}}{\partial z}\right) + \rho g_z$$

Spherical coordinates:

10. r comp: $\rho\left(\dfrac{\partial v_r}{\partial t} + v_r\dfrac{\partial v_r}{\partial r} + \dfrac{v_\theta}{r}\dfrac{\partial v_r}{\partial \theta} + \dfrac{v_\phi}{r\sin\theta}\dfrac{\partial v_r}{\partial \phi} - \dfrac{v_\theta^2 + v_\phi^2}{r}\right)$

$$= -\frac{\partial P}{\partial r} + \left(\frac{1}{r^2}\frac{\partial}{\partial r}(r^2\tau_{rr}) + \frac{1}{r\sin\theta}\frac{\partial}{\partial \theta}(\tau_{r\theta}\sin\theta)\right.$$

$$\left. + \frac{1}{r\sin\theta}\frac{\partial \tau_{r\phi}}{\partial \phi} - \frac{\tau_{\theta\theta} + \tau_{\phi\phi}}{r}\right) + \rho g_r$$

11. θ comp: $\rho\left(\dfrac{\partial v_\theta}{\partial t} + v_r\dfrac{\partial v_\theta}{\partial r} + \dfrac{v_\theta}{r}\dfrac{\partial v_r}{\partial \theta} + \dfrac{v_\phi}{r\sin\theta}\dfrac{\partial v_\theta}{\partial \phi} + \dfrac{v_r v_\theta}{r} - \dfrac{v_\phi^2\cot\theta}{r}\right)$

$$= -\frac{1}{r}\frac{\partial P}{\partial \theta} + \left(\frac{1}{r^2}\frac{\partial}{\partial r}(r^2\tau_{r\theta}) + \frac{1}{r\sin\theta}\frac{\partial}{\partial \theta}(\tau_{\theta\theta}\sin\theta)\right.$$

$$\left. + \frac{1}{r\sin\theta}\frac{\partial \tau_{\theta\phi}}{\partial \phi} + \frac{\tau_{r\theta}}{r} - \frac{\cot\theta}{r}\tau_{\phi\phi}\right) + \rho g_\theta$$

TABLE 3.1 (Continued)

12. ϕ comp: $\rho \left(\dfrac{\partial v_\phi}{\partial t} + v_r \dfrac{\partial v_\phi}{\partial r} + \dfrac{v_\theta}{r} \dfrac{\partial v_\phi}{\partial \theta} + \dfrac{v_\phi}{r \sin \theta} \dfrac{\partial v_\phi}{\partial \phi} + \dfrac{v_\phi v_r}{r} + \dfrac{v_\theta v_\phi}{r} \cot \theta \right)$

$$= - \frac{1}{r \sin \theta} \frac{\partial P}{\partial \phi} + \left(\frac{1}{r^2} \frac{\partial}{\partial r} (r^2 \tau_{r\phi}) \right.$$

$$+ \frac{1}{r} \frac{\partial \tau_{\theta\phi}}{\partial \theta} + \frac{1}{r \sin \theta} \frac{\partial \tau_{\phi\phi}}{\partial \phi} + \frac{\tau_{r\phi}}{r} + \frac{2 \cot \theta}{r} \tau_{\theta\phi} \bigg) + \rho g_\phi$$

3.3.3. Conservation of Momentum

As we have seen, Newton's second law of motion is equivalent to a conservation of momentum. Now let us consider all of the forces which can act on the fluid which, at any given time, is contained within a fixed cubical region in the medium (Fig. 3.5). The lower rear corner

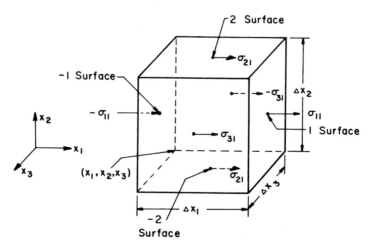

FIG. 3.5   Forces (in x_1 direction) acting on surfaces of a cubicle volume.

of the cube is located at the point (x_1, x_2, x_3), and the lengths of the sides are $(\Delta x_1, \Delta x_2, \Delta x_3)$. The forces acting in the x_1 direction, in terms of the stress components acting on each face of the cube, are:

On $-x_1$ surface: $(-\sigma_{11} \Delta x_2 \Delta x_3)\Big|_{x_1}$

On $-x_2$ surface: $(-\sigma_{21} \Delta x_1 \Delta x_3)\Big|_{x_2}$

On $-x_3$ surface: $(-\sigma_{31} \Delta x_1 \Delta x_2)\Big|_{x_3}$

On x_1 surface: $(\sigma_{11} \Delta x_2 \Delta x_3)\Big|_{x_1+\Delta x_1}$

On x_2 surface: $(\sigma_{21} \Delta x_1 \Delta x_3)\Big|_{x_2+\Delta x_2}$

On x_3 surface: $(\sigma_{31} \Delta x_1 \Delta x_2)\Big|_{x_3+\Delta x_3}$

In addition, we must include the x_1 component of any external forces which act on the body of material as a whole, such as gravity, etc.:

Body force:

$$\rho g_1 \Delta x_1 \Delta x_2 \Delta x_3 \tag{3.3-22}$$

By Newton's second law, the sum of all the forces acting in a given direction on a mass of material equals the product of the mass and the component of acceleration (i.e., the inertial force) in the same direction. Now the acceleration is that which is experienced by the fluid as it is passing through the cubical region. This is simply the material derivative of the velocity:

Mass:

$$\rho \Delta x_1 \Delta x_2 \Delta x_3 \tag{3.3-23}$$

Acceleration in x_1 direction:

$$\frac{Dv_1}{Dt} \tag{3.3-24}$$

Summing all of these forces, dividing by the volume $(\Delta x_1, \Delta x_2, \Delta x_3)$, and taking the limit as the size of the cube approaches zero results in the following differential equation:

$$\rho \frac{Dv_1}{Dt} = \frac{\partial \sigma_{11}}{\partial x_1} + \frac{\partial \sigma_{21}}{\partial x_2} + \frac{\partial \sigma_{31}}{\partial x_3} + \rho g_1 \tag{3.3-25}$$

This is the x_1 component of the momentum equation of motion. By an identical procedure, involving a force balance in the x_2 or x_3 directions, the other two component equations of motion can be derived. These equations may also be considered general expressions of the conservation of momentum. Note that no assumption has been made with regard to the nature of the material, other than that it deforms continuously or "flows," and has continuous properties (i.e., it is a continuum). Thus these equations are valid, and must be satisfied, at all points within any deforming continuous material.

The derivation has been presented with respect to Cartesian coordinates (see note 4). Using general vector notation, Eq. (3.3-25) may be written

$$\rho \frac{D\vec{v}}{Dt} = \vec{\nabla} \cdot \overset{\leftrightarrow}{\sigma} + \rho \vec{g} \tag{3.3-26}$$

while the tensor index notation equivalent is

$$\frac{Dv^i}{Dt} = \sum_{k=1}^{3} \sigma^{ik}{}_{,k} + \rho g^i \tag{3.3-27}$$

Again, the comma notation represents the operation of covariant differentiation, which is a generalized directional derivative. The specific component forms of these equations for rectangular Cartesian, cylindrical, and spherical coordinate systems are tabulated in

Table 3.1. In this table, the stress tensor has been separated into its isotropic (pressure) and anisotropic (shear) components:

$$\sigma_{ij} = -P\,\delta_{ij} + \tau_{ij} \qquad\qquad (3.3\text{-}28)$$

Various illustrations of the use of these equations will be presented in the following chapter.

These equations are perfectly general, and apply to any continuous material in any system. However, they merely express relations between stress components which are required in order to satisfy the conservation of momentum and are insufficient to determine the behavior of a given material until additional expressions relating these stresses to the deformation of the material are specified. The 4 equations (3 equations of motion plus continuity) involve 13 dependent unknowns [3 displacement or velocity components, 9 stress components, plus the pressure (gradient)]. The 9 additional relations required for a complete solution are provided by the deformation properties of the material, in the form of a constitutive equation or rheological equation of state for the 9 stress components as a function of the state of deformation (strain, strain rate, etc.) such as the implied function of Eq. (1.11-7):

$$\tau_{ij} = \tau_{ij}(\gamma_{ij}, \dot{\gamma}_{ij}, \ldots) \qquad\qquad (1.11\text{-}7)$$

The deformation variables $(\gamma_{ij}, \dot{\gamma}_{ij}, \ldots)$ are expressible in terms of displacement and/or velocity gradient components, and hence do not introduce any additional unknowns. For a compressible material, the pressure in addition becomes a function of the volumetric deformation, and another relation of the form implied by Eq. (1.11-1) is required.

Actually, because of symmetry, only 6 of the 9 components of stress are independent, thus reducing the total number of unknowns and equations from 13 to 10. Furthermore, many systems of practical interest involve physical restraints which further limit the number of nonzero unknowns to a manageable number. This will be illustrated

in Chap. 4, wherein the solution of various types of flow problems
will be presented.

To summarize, the solution of flow problems to determine the
behavior of a given material (fluid) in a given system requires the
simultaneous solution of two sets of equations:

1. The component equations of change, which are unique for a given
    flow system, but independent of the material in the system.
    These are the continuity equations plus the momentum equations
    of motion.
2. The rheological equation of state (constitutive equation), which
    is unique for a given material, but independent of the system in
    which the material is contained.

3.4. KINEMATICS OF VISCOUS FLUIDS

The subject of kinematics is concerned with a quantitative description of the detailed state of deformation of all points within
a material, without regard to the forces which produce the deformation. Once suitable definitions of stress and deformation are established, the mechanical (i.e., rheological) properties of the material
may be defined in terms of a functional dependence of stress upon deformation (or vice versa), which is a unique characteristic of the
material.

The stress tensor provides an unambiguous description of the
forces which may act at all points in a material. However, a suitable
description of deformation is not as unambiguous. In Sec. 1.10.2,
the classical (infinitesimal) strain tensor was defined in terms of
displacement gradients relative to a fixed reference frame. This
quantity is adequate for describing the deformation of continuous
media only under conditions of small displacements from a reference
or equilibrium state, since the definition is valid only for small
displacements. It is suitable for describing the instantaneous rate
of deformation in any medium, however. It is thus a suitable measure
of deformation for purely viscous fluids in any state since, by

definition, stresses in such materials are a function only of their instantaneous rate of strain.

For materials with both viscous and elastic properties, however, it was illustrated in Sec. 2.4.3 that the instantaneous state of stress depends not only upon the instantaneous strain or rate of strain, but upon the entire past history of deformation. This memory property requires that deformation be defined in a manner such that it is always valid for a given material element regardless of the displacement history of the element with time. If all points of the material medium undergo only small (or "infinitesimal") displacements during this period, then the classical strain tensor is suitable for this purpose. However, for a memory material undergoing a large or continuous deformation (i.e., flow), then such a strain measure is clearly inadequate.

This difficulty can be alleviated by defining strain terms of displacements relative to a reference frame which moves and deforms with the material. This is known as a Lagrangian reference, and such a strain measure will always refer to the same material point or element. For a full understanding and appreciation of the signifi-cance of this approach, however, an understanding of the general properties of coordinate transformations and tensor components is nec-essary. Hence, we will defer a consideration of Lagrangian or con-vected strain and the kinematics of viscoelastic (memory) materials until after we have established the proper generalization principles in Chap. 6.

Thus, for the present, we will limit our consideration of kine-matics to the description of deformation provided by the classical strain (and rate of strain) tensors. This, then, restricts us to materials which are not time-dependent (i.e., purely viscous fluids) in large or continuous, steady or unsteady, deformations or to time-dependent (memory) materials in small amplitude deformations or in steady (see note 5) flow. It will be shown later, however, that the general kinematic description of memory fluids reduces to that derived from the classical strain tensor for sufficiently small rates of strain, so that present considerations may be extended to include such cases.

3.4.1. Rate of Strain

In Sec. 1.10.2, the classical strain tensor e_{ij} was defined in terms of the displacement gradients at a point in a continuous medium relative to Cartesian axes as

$$e_{ij} = \left(\frac{\partial u_i}{\partial x_j} + \frac{\partial u_j}{\partial x_i} \right) \qquad (3.4\text{-}1)$$

and the corresponding rate of strain being

$$\Delta_{ij} = \frac{\partial e_{ij}}{\partial t} = \left(\frac{\partial v_i}{\partial x_j} + \frac{\partial v_j}{\partial x_i} \right) \qquad (3.4\text{-}2)$$

The notation of Eqs. (3.4-1) and (3.4-2) implies, and is strictly valid only for, rectangular (Cartesian) coordinates. The general expression, which is valid for any coordinate system, involves replacing the partial derivative by the covariant derivative:

$$e_{ij} = u_{i,j} + u_{j,i} \qquad (3.4\text{-}3)$$

and

$$\Delta_{ij} = v_{i,j} + v_{j,i} \qquad (3.4\text{-}4)$$

An equivalent expression in terms of vector notation can be written in the form

$$\vec{\vec{\Delta}} = \vec{\nabla}\vec{v} + (\vec{\nabla}\vec{v})^T \qquad (3.4\text{-}5)$$

where $\vec{\nabla}\vec{v}$ is the gradient of the velocity vector and $(\vec{\nabla}\vec{v})^T$ is the transpose of this quantity (i.e., the matrix of components of $\vec{\nabla}\vec{v}$ in which rows and columns have been interchanged). The definition of the transpose is obvious from the index notation of Eq. (3.4-3) or (3.4-4), which is generally more descriptive of the nature of tensor quantities. The specific definition of the covariant derivative will be presented in Chap. 6, along with methods for evaluating it for any coordinate system. For the present, however, the specific components of the rate of strain tensor are tabulated in Table 3.2 in terms of physical velocity components for Cartesian, cylindrical, and spherical coordinate systems without proof.

TABLE 3.2

Components of the Rate of Strain Tensor

1. Cartesian coordinates: $(x = z^1, y = z^2, z = z^3)$

$$
\Delta_{ij} = \begin{bmatrix}
\left[2\dfrac{\partial v_x}{\partial x} \right] & \left[\dfrac{\partial v_x}{\partial y} + \dfrac{\partial v_y}{\partial x} \right] & \left[\dfrac{\partial v_x}{\partial z} + \dfrac{\partial v_z}{\partial x} \right] \\[3mm]
\left[\text{sym} \right] & \left[2\dfrac{\partial v_y}{\partial y} \right] & \left[\dfrac{\partial v_y}{\partial z} + \dfrac{\partial v_z}{\partial y} \right] \\[3mm]
\left[\text{sym} \right] & \left[\text{sym} \right] & \left[2\dfrac{\partial v_z}{\partial z} \right]
\end{bmatrix}
$$

$$
\dot{e}_v = \vec{\nabla} \cdot \vec{v} = \frac{1}{2}\,\text{tr}\,\Delta_{ij} = \left(\frac{\partial v_x}{\partial x} + \frac{\partial v_y}{\partial y} + \frac{\partial v_z}{\partial z} \right)
$$

2. Cylindrical coordinates: $(r = z^1, \theta = z^2, z = z^3)$

$$
\Delta_{ij} = \begin{bmatrix}
\left[2\dfrac{\partial v_r}{\partial r} \right] & \left[\dfrac{1}{r}\dfrac{\partial v_r}{\partial \theta} + r\dfrac{\partial}{\partial r}\left(\dfrac{v_\theta}{r} \right) \right] & \left[\dfrac{\partial v_r}{\partial z} + \dfrac{\partial v_z}{\partial r} \right] \\[3mm]
\left[\text{sym} \right] & 2\left[\dfrac{1}{r}\dfrac{\partial v_\theta}{\partial \theta} + \dfrac{v_r}{r} \right] & \left[\dfrac{\partial v_\theta}{\partial z} + \dfrac{1}{r}\dfrac{\partial v_z}{\partial \theta} \right] \\[3mm]
\left[\text{sym} \right] & \left[\text{sym} \right] & \left[2\dfrac{\partial v_z}{\partial z} \right]
\end{bmatrix}
$$

$$
\dot{e}_v = \vec{\nabla} \cdot \vec{v} = \frac{1}{2}\,\text{tr}\,\Delta_{ij} = \left(\frac{1}{r}\frac{\partial}{\partial r}(rv_r) + \frac{1}{r}\frac{\partial v_\theta}{\partial \theta} + \frac{\partial v_z}{\partial z} \right)
$$

TABLE 3.2 (Continued)

3.   Spherical coordinates: $(r = z^1, \theta = z^2, \phi = z^3)$

$$\Delta_{ij} = \begin{bmatrix} \left[2\dfrac{\partial v_r}{\partial r}\right] & \left[\dfrac{1}{r}\dfrac{\partial v_r}{\partial \theta} + r\dfrac{\partial}{\partial r}\left(\dfrac{v_\theta}{r}\right)\right] & \left[\dfrac{1}{r\sin\theta}\dfrac{\partial v_r}{\partial \phi} + r\dfrac{\partial}{\partial r}\left(\dfrac{v_\phi}{r}\right)\right] \\[3mm] \left[\text{sym}\right] & 2\left[\dfrac{1}{r}\dfrac{\partial v_\theta}{\partial \theta} + \dfrac{v_r}{r}\right] & \left[\dfrac{1}{r\sin\theta}\dfrac{\partial v_\theta}{\partial \phi} + \dfrac{\sin\theta}{r}\dfrac{\partial}{\partial \theta}\left(\dfrac{v_\phi}{\sin\theta}\right)\right] \\[3mm] \left[\text{sym}\right] & \left[\text{sym}\right] & 2\left[\dfrac{1}{r\sin\theta}\dfrac{\partial v_\phi}{\partial \phi} + \dfrac{v_r}{r} + \dfrac{v_\theta\cot\theta}{r}\right] \end{bmatrix}$$

$$\dot{e}_v = \vec{\nabla}\cdot\vec{v} = \frac{1}{2}\,\text{tr}\,\Delta_{ij} = \left[\frac{1}{r^2}\frac{\partial}{\partial r}(v_r r^2) + \frac{1}{r\sin\theta}\frac{\partial}{\partial \theta}(v_\theta \sin\theta)\right.$$

$$\left. + \frac{1}{r\sin\theta}\frac{\partial v_\phi}{\partial \phi}\right]$$

————————————————— 0 —————————————————

Example 3.2   Determine the nonzero components of the rate of strain tensor for Poiseuille flow.

Poiseuille flow, defined in Example 3.1, implies a particular deformation in which only certain components are nonzero. This is seen as follows.

With respect to cylindrical coordinates, symmetry requires that

$$v_\theta = 0$$

Thus the continuity equation 2 from Table 3.1A, for steady, incompressible flow, reduces to

$$\frac{1}{r}\frac{\partial}{\partial r}(rv_r) + \frac{\partial v_z}{\partial z} = 0$$

However, fully developed flow (i.e., steady flow in the Eulerian sense) requires that v_z not vary in the z direction. Thus this equation becomes

$$\frac{\partial (rv_r)}{\partial r} = 0$$

or

$$v_r = \frac{const}{r}$$

However, since $v_r \neq \infty$ at $r = 0$, the value of the constant must be zero. (Also, $v_r = 0$ at the tube wall, $r = R$.) Thus

$$v_r = 0$$

and the continuity equation is automatically satisfied. Thus v_z must be the only nonzero velocity component. Since symmetry requires that it be independent of θ, we are led to

$$v_z(r)$$

i.e., v_z is a function only of r, and is the only nonzero velocity component.

Applying these results to Eq. 2 of Table 3.2 shows that the rate of strain tensor reduces to

$$\Delta_{ij} = \begin{bmatrix} 0 & 0 & \dfrac{dv_z}{dr} \\ 0 & 0 & 0 \\ \dfrac{dv_z}{dr} & 0 & 0 \end{bmatrix}$$

The result is independent of the rheological nature of the fluid in the tube.

—————————————————————— 0 ——————————————————————

3.4.2. Purely Viscous Fluids

As we have seen, a purely viscous fluid is a material for which
all shear (anisotropic) stress components at any point in the material
are a function only of the instantaneous rate of strain at that point.
Two special cases of this class of materials are the Newtonian and
Generalized Newtonian fluids. A more general description of a purely
viscous fluid (known as the Reiner-Rivlin fluid) will also be discussed in Chap. 7.

The Newtonian fluid was defined in Sec. 2.2.1 as a material for
which each stress component is directly proportional to the corresponding rate of strain component. The general rheological or constitutive equation was given in Eq. (2.2-16) or (2.2-17).

$$\tau_{ij} = \mu \dot{\gamma}_{ij} + \kappa \dot{e}_v \, \delta_{ij} \qquad\qquad (2.1\text{-}16)$$

or

$$\tau_{ij} = \mu \, \Delta_{ij} + \left[\kappa - \frac{2}{3} \mu \right] \dot{e}_v \, \delta_{ij} \qquad\qquad (2.1\text{-}17)$$

where κ is the bulk viscosity, which characterizes the stresses which
resist the rate of change of volume, and μ is the shear viscosity
which determines the stresses which resist a rate of change of shape.
Both κ and μ are isotropic (scalar) material properties. For incompressible fluids, Eqs. (2.2-16) and (2.2-17) reduce to

$$\tau_{ij} = \mu \, \Delta_{ij} = \mu \dot{\gamma}_{ij} \qquad\qquad (3.4\text{-}6)$$

Thus for a given deformation, in which the nonzero velocity and
velocity gradient components are specified, the corresponding nonzero
components of the rate of strain tensor may be determined by reference
to Table 3.2 (for Cartesian, cylindrical or spherical coordinates).
The corresponding nonzero stress components for an incompressible
Newtonian fluid follow from Eq. (3.4-6), or from Eq. (2.2-16) or
(2.2-17) if the fluid is compressible. It should be pointed out
that, even for relatively simple deformations, there may be several

nonzero rate of strain and corresponding stress components, as
illustrated in Example 3.3.

—————————————————————— 0 ——————————————————————

Example 3.3 Determine the nonzero stress components for an incompressible Newtonian fluid in radial flow in the annulus between two
concentric porous cylinders (Fig. 3.6).

It is evident from Fig. 3.6 that the only nonzero velocity component relative to cylindrical coordinates, is v_r. Furthermore,
because of symmetry, the velocity will vary only in the r direction.
The velocity components are therefore

$$v_r(r) \quad v_\theta = v_z = 0$$

It follows that, from Table 3.2 Eq. 2, the rate of strain components
reduce to

$$\Delta_{ij} = \begin{bmatrix} 2\dfrac{dv_r}{dr} & 0 & 0 \\[2ex] 0 & 2\dfrac{v_r}{r} & 0 \\[2ex] 0 & 0 & 0 \end{bmatrix}$$

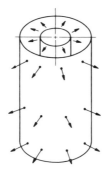

FIG. 3.6   Radial flow between concentric porous cylinders.

Now the continuity equation (Table 3.1A, Eq. 2) reduces to:

$$\frac{\partial(rv_r)}{\partial r} = 0$$

or

$$\frac{v_r}{r} = \frac{const}{r^2} \qquad \frac{dv_r}{dr} = \frac{-const}{r^2}$$

Thus from Eq. (3.4-6), the nonzero stress components become

$$\tau_{ij} = \begin{bmatrix} \tau_{rr} & 0 & 0 \\ 0 & \tau_{\theta\theta} & 0 \\ 0 & 0 & 0 \end{bmatrix} = \frac{2\mu(const)}{r^2} \begin{bmatrix} -1 & 0 & 0 \\ 0 & 1 & 0 \\ 0 & 0 & 0 \end{bmatrix}$$

In this example there are two nonzero stress components, even though there is only one nonzero velocity component and one velocity gradient component. Note, also, that $\tau_{\theta\theta}$ stress component is not zero even though there is no velocity component in the θ direction, and there is no variation of velocity in the θ direction.

――――――――――――――――――――――― 0 ―――――――――――――――――――――――

The generalized Newtonial fluid was introduced in Sec. 2.2.3 under the heading of non-Newtonian fluids. With respect to simple shear deformation, there are many materials for which the ratio of shear stress to shear rate is not constant, but varies with the magnitude of stress or shear rate. This ratio, which defines the viscosity of a Newtonian fluid, may still serve to characterize the shear behavior of such nonlinear materials, and is called the viscosity function or apparent viscosity:

$$\eta = \frac{\tau}{\dot{\gamma}} = \eta(\dot{\gamma}) \qquad or \qquad \eta(\tau) \qquad\qquad (3.4\text{-}7)$$

This function has no fundamental basis other than as a convenient means for the empirical description of non-Newtonian fluid shear properties in a manner analogous to the Newtonian viscosity.

For more complex deformations, it would seem reasonable to generalize Eq. (3.4-7) in a manner similar to Eq. (3.4-6), by replacing τ by τ_{ij} and $\dot{\gamma}$ by $\dot{\gamma}_{ij}$. However, the result would give rise to an apparent viscosity which depends upon the tensor Δ_{ij} in a complex manner, and which would therefore be expected to have the characteristics of a tensor, i.e., multiple components which depend on the reference frame or geometry used to define them.

However, we have stated that $\eta(\dot{\gamma})$ is a material function, being uniquely characteristic only of the particular material it represents. Now if the material is isotropic, all material functions must also be isotropic; that is, they must not be dependent upon the system in which the material is deformed, its geometry, or the particular coordinate axes used to describe the geometry or flow field. In other words, they must have no directional characteristics, and hence must be scalars. The question is how, then, can the apparent viscosity be a function of the rate of strain tensor, yet be a scalar with none of the direction properties of a tensor?

The answer is that there are certain real combinations of the components of every symmetric second-order tensor which are invariant to transformation of coordinates, and hence are scalar quantities. There are three such combinations of components, and they are known as the *scalar invariants* of the tensor. These will be derived and discussed in detail in Chap. 6, but for now will be presented without proof. In Cartesian tensor notation, they are:

First invariant:

$$I = \operatorname{tr} \Delta_{ij} = \sum_{m}^{3} \Delta_{mm} = \Delta_{11} + \Delta_{22} + \Delta_{33} = 2\vec{\nabla} \cdot \vec{v} = 2\dot{e}_{v} \qquad (3.4\text{-}8)$$

Second invariant:

$$II = \frac{1}{2}\left[I^2 - \sum_{m}^{3}\sum_{n}^{3} \Delta_{mn}\Delta_{nm}\right] = \frac{1}{2}[I^2 - \mathrm{tr}\,(\Delta_{im}\Delta_{mj})] \tag{3.4-9}$$

$$= \frac{1}{2}(I^2 - \vec{\vec{\Delta}}:\vec{\vec{\Delta}})$$

$$= \begin{vmatrix} \Delta_{22} & \Delta_{23} \\ \Delta_{32} & \Delta_{33} \end{vmatrix} + \begin{vmatrix} \Delta_{11} & \Delta_{13} \\ \Delta_{31} & \Delta_{33} \end{vmatrix} + \begin{vmatrix} \Delta_{11} & \Delta_{12} \\ \Delta_{21} & \Delta_{22} \end{vmatrix} \tag{3.4-10}$$

Third invariant:

$$III = \left|\Delta_{ij}\right| \text{ (determinant of components of } \Delta_{ij}) \tag{3.4-11}$$

Note that the first invariant (I) is simply the sum of the diagonal components (i.e., the trace) of the tensor. For the rate of strain tensor, this is proportional to the isotropic volumetric rate of strain, and is thus identically zero for incompressible materials.

The three ways of expressing the second invariant (II) are all equivalent. The $\vec{\vec{\Delta}}:\vec{\vec{\Delta}}$ notation for the double summation is sometimes referred to as the tensor "double dot" or scalar product. Equation (3.4-10) shows that the second invariant is the sum of the minors of the diagonal elements of the matrix of the rate of strain components.

The third invariant (III) is simply the determinant of the components of the tensor. It has, of course, only a magnitude and no direction, and hence is a scalar just as I and II are scalars.

Thus we must conclude that if the apparent viscosity is to be a function of the rate of strain, it can be at most a function of those combinations of components of Δ_{ij} which are scalars; i.e., η can be a function only of the invariants of Δ_{ij}. For incompressible fluids, for which the first invariant is zero, this reduces to $\eta(II, III)$, where II is then $-\frac{1}{2}\vec{\vec{\Delta}}:\vec{\vec{\Delta}}$.

Furthermore, many of the flow deformations of common interest
(which are subject to exact analysis) belong to a class called
viscometric flows. These are defined as flows for which there is
only one nonzero velocity component, and this varies only in one coordinate direction normal to the direction of flow (see note 6).
That is,

$$v_1 = v_1(x_2) \qquad \text{all others} = 0 \qquad (3.4-12)$$

Some of these flows will be described in detail in Chap. 5. For
now, we only note that the rate of strain tensor for such cases
reduces to:

$$\Delta_{ij} = \begin{bmatrix} 0 & \Delta_{12} & 0 \\ \Delta_{21} & 0 & 0 \\ 0 & 0 & 0 \end{bmatrix} = \dot{\gamma} \begin{bmatrix} 0 & 1 & 0 \\ 1 & 0 & 0 \\ 0 & 0 & 0 \end{bmatrix} \qquad (3.4-13)$$

and the three invariants become

$$I = 0 \qquad II = -\dot{\gamma}^2 \qquad III = 0 \qquad (3.4-14)$$

As a result, the apparent viscosity function for a viscometric flow
depends only upon the second invariant of the rate of strain tensor.
For nonviscometric flows, because of a general lack of knowledge to
the contrary, it is usually assumed that the influence of the third
invariant on the apparent viscosity function may be neglected. Furthermore, since most complex materials of interest are essentially
incompressible, the final conclusion is that the apparent viscosity
is assumed to be a function only of the second invariant of the rate
of strain tensor. Since this invariant involves only squares of rate
of strain components, the appropriate generalization of the viscosity
function $\eta(\dot{\gamma})$ from the simple shear forms of Sec. 2.2.3 to any flow
system would involve the substitution

$$\dot{\gamma} \rightarrow (\tfrac{1}{2} \vec{\Delta} : \vec{\Delta})^{\tfrac{1}{2}} = \sqrt{-II} \qquad (3.4-15)$$

TABLE 3.3

The Second Invariant of Δ_{ij} for Incompressible Materials

1. Cartesian

$$\tfrac{1}{2}(\vec{\Delta}:\vec{\Delta}) = -II = \left\{ 2\left[\left(\frac{\partial v_x}{\partial x}\right)^2 + \left(\frac{\partial v_y}{\partial y}\right)^2 + \left(\frac{\partial v_z}{\partial z}\right)^2\right] + \left[\frac{\partial v_y}{\partial x} + \frac{\partial v_x}{\partial y}\right]^2 \right.$$

$$\left. + \left[\frac{\partial v_z}{\partial y} + \frac{\partial v_y}{\partial z}\right]^2 + \left[\frac{\partial v_x}{\partial z} + \frac{\partial v_z}{\partial x}\right]^2 \right\}$$

2. Cylindrical

$$\tfrac{1}{2}(\vec{\Delta}:\vec{\Delta}) = -II = \left\{ 2\left[\left(\frac{\partial v_r}{\partial r}\right)^2 + \left(\frac{1}{r}\frac{\partial v_\theta}{\partial \theta} + \frac{v_r}{r}\right)^2 + \left(\frac{\partial v_z}{\partial z}\right)^2\right] \right.$$

$$\left. + \left[r\frac{\partial}{\partial r}\left(\frac{v_\theta}{r}\right) + \frac{1}{r}\frac{\partial v_r}{\partial \theta}\right]^2 + \left[\frac{1}{r}\frac{\partial v_z}{\partial \theta} + \frac{\partial v_\theta}{\partial z}\right]^2 + \left[\frac{\partial v_r}{\partial z} + \frac{\partial v_z}{\partial r}\right]^2 \right\}$$

3. Spherical

$$\tfrac{1}{2}(\vec{\Delta}:\vec{\Delta}) = -II = \left\{ 2\left[\left(\frac{\partial v_r}{\partial r}\right)^2 + \left(\frac{1}{r}\frac{\partial v_\theta}{\partial \theta} + \frac{v_r}{r}\right)^2 \right.\right.$$

$$\left.\left. + \left(\frac{1}{r \sin \theta}\frac{\partial v_\phi}{\partial \phi} + \frac{v_r}{r} + \frac{v_\theta \cot \theta}{r}\right)^2\right] \right.$$

$$\left. + \left[r\frac{\partial}{\partial r}\left(\frac{v_\theta}{r}\right) + \frac{1}{r}\frac{\partial v_r}{\partial \theta}\right]^2 \right.$$

$$\left. + \left[\frac{\sin \theta}{r}\frac{\partial}{\partial \theta}\left(\frac{v_\phi}{\sin \theta}\right) + \frac{1}{r \sin \theta}\frac{\partial v_\theta}{\partial \phi}\right]^2 \right.$$

$$\left. + \left[\frac{1}{r \sin \theta}\frac{\partial v_r}{\partial \phi} + r\frac{\partial}{\partial r}\left(\frac{v_\phi}{r}\right)\right]^2 \right\}$$

That is, an apparent viscosity function, given in terms of the single shear rate component $\dot\gamma$ which is valid for any viscometric flow, should be applicable to a more complex (nonviscometric) flow if $\dot\gamma$ is replaced by $\sqrt{-II}$:

$$\eta(\dot\gamma) \rightarrow \eta(\sqrt{-II}) \qquad\qquad (3.4\text{-}16)$$

The proper general tensor form of Eq. (3.4-7) for the incompressible generalized Newtonian fluid may therefore be written:

$$\tau_{ij} = \eta(\sqrt{-II})\, \Delta_{ij} \qquad\qquad (3.4\text{-}17)$$

To simplify the evaluation of the second invariant of Δ_{ij}, the quantity $(\tfrac{1}{2}\, \overset{\leftrightarrow}{\Delta}:\overset{\leftrightarrow}{\Delta})$ is tabulated in Table 3.3 for all possible nonzero velocity gradient components in three major orthogonal coordinate systems.

———————————————— 0 ————————————————

Example 3.4 Determine expressions for the nonzero stress components in a Power law fluid in the radial flow field of Fig. 3.6.

As in Example 3.3, the velocity and rate of strain components are

$$v_r(r) \qquad v_\theta = v_z = 0$$

$$\Delta_{ij} = 2\begin{bmatrix} \dfrac{dv_r}{dr} & 0 & 0 \\[2mm] 0 & \dfrac{v_r}{r} & 0 \\[2mm] 0 & 0 & 0 \end{bmatrix} = \frac{2(\text{const})}{r^2}\begin{bmatrix} -1 & 0 & 0 \\ 0 & 1 & 0 \\ 0 & 0 & 0 \end{bmatrix}$$

From Table 3.3,2, the second invariant of the rate of strain tensor for this flow field is

$$-II = 2\left[\left(\frac{dv_r}{dr}\right)^2 + \left(\frac{v_r}{r}\right)^2\right] = \frac{4(\text{const})^2}{r^4}$$

Now for a Power law fluid, the apparent viscosity was given in Chap. 2 as:

$$\eta(\dot{\gamma}) = \eta_o|\dot{\gamma}|^{n-1}$$

For this deformation, $\dot{\gamma}$ in the above equation must be replaced by $\sqrt{-II}$. Thus

$$\eta(\sqrt{-II}) = \eta_o|-II|^{(n-1)/2} = \eta_o\left[2\left[\left(\frac{dv_r}{dr}\right)^2 + \left(\frac{v_r}{r}\right)^2\right]\right]^{(n-1)/2}$$

or

$$\eta(\sqrt{-II}) = \eta_o\left[\frac{2(\text{const})}{r^2}\right]^{n-1}$$

The stress components are:

$$\tau_{ij} = \eta \, \Delta_{ij}$$

or

$$\tau_{rr} = 2\eta_o\left[2\left(\frac{dv_r}{dr}\right)^2 + 2\left(\frac{v_r}{r}\right)^2\right]^{(n-1)/2} \cdot \left(\frac{dv_r}{dr}\right) = -\eta_o\left[\frac{2(\text{const})}{r^2}\right]^n$$

$$\tau_{\theta\theta} = 2\eta_o\left[2\left(\frac{dv_r}{dr}\right)^2 + 2\left(\frac{v_r}{r}\right)^2\right]^{(n-1)/2} \cdot \left(\frac{v_r}{r}\right) = -\tau_{rr}$$

all others being identically zero.

The "constant" in these expressions may be related to the total volumetric flow rate through a cylinder of length L:

$$Q = 2\pi r L v_r$$

or

$$v_r = \frac{Q}{2\pi r L} = \frac{const}{r}$$

Therefore,

$$const = \frac{Q}{2\pi L}$$

--------------------------------- 0 ---------------------------------

3.4.3. Vorticity

Before concluding our discussion of kinematics, some additional comments concerning the vorticity tensor are in order. This will be especially pertinent to the discussion of finite and continuous measures of deformations in memory materials in Chap. 7.

In Sec. 1.10.2, it was shown that the velocity gradient tensor, when separated into symmetric and antisymmetric parts, contributes to both a deformation rate (Δ_{ij}) and a rotation rate (Ω_{ij}) [Eq. (1.10.16)]:

$$\frac{\partial v_i}{\partial x_j} = \frac{1}{2}\left(\frac{\partial v_i}{\partial x_j} + \frac{\partial v_j}{\partial x_i}\right) + \frac{1}{2}\left(\frac{\partial v_i}{\partial x_j} - \frac{\partial v_j}{\partial x_i}\right) \qquad (1.10.16)$$

$$= \frac{1}{2}(\Delta_{ij} + \Omega_{ji})$$

where Ω_{ji} is the antisymmetric (or skew symmetric) vorticity tensor. In terms of the more general covariant derivative, it is

$$\Omega_{ji} = (v_{i,j} - v_{j,i}) = -\Omega_{ij} \qquad (3.4\text{-}18)$$

That Ω_{ji} represents the rotation rate of a material element can be seen by considering the average positive (counterclockwise) rotation of the sides of an element undergoing deformation (Fig. 3.7):

$$\Delta\alpha = \tfrac{1}{2}\,(\alpha_2 - \alpha_1) \qquad\qquad (3.4\text{-}19)$$

Now in the limit as the dimensions of the element approach zero, the angles α_1 and α_2 are given by

$$\alpha_1 = \lim_{\Delta x_2 \to 0} \left(\frac{\Delta u_1}{\Delta x_2}\right) = \frac{\partial u_1}{\partial x_2} \qquad\qquad (3.4\text{-}20)$$

$$\alpha_2 = \lim_{\Delta x_1 \to 0} \left(\frac{\Delta u_2}{\Delta x_1}\right) = \frac{\partial u_2}{\partial x_1} \qquad\qquad (3.4\text{-}21)$$

and the net rate of counterclockwise rotation is:

$$\lim_{\Delta t \to 0} \left(\frac{\Delta\alpha}{\Delta t}\right) = \frac{1}{2}\frac{\partial}{\partial t}\left(\frac{\partial u_2}{\partial x_1} - \frac{\partial u_1}{\partial x_2}\right) \qquad\qquad (3.4\text{-}22)$$

$$= \frac{1}{2}\left(\frac{\partial v_2}{\partial x_1} - \frac{\partial v_1}{\partial x_2}\right) = \omega_3 = \frac{1}{2}\,\Omega_{12}$$

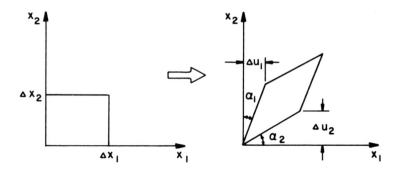

FIG. 3.7   Rotation of a deformed element.

where ω_3 represents the instantaneous rotation rate about the x_3 axis. By a similar procedure, the rotation rates about the other two axes are found to be

$$\omega_1 = \frac{1}{2}\left(\frac{\partial v_3}{\partial x_2} - \frac{\partial v_2}{\partial x_3}\right) = \frac{1}{2}\Omega_{23} \tag{3.4-23}$$

$$\omega_2 = \frac{1}{2}\left(\frac{\partial v_1}{\partial x_3} - \frac{\partial v_3}{\partial x_1}\right) = \frac{1}{2}\Omega_{31} \tag{3.4-24}$$

These three components define the angular velocity vector, which expressed in vector notation is

$$\vec{\omega} = \frac{1}{2}\vec{\nabla}\times\vec{v} \tag{3.4-25}$$

or in index notation is

$$\omega_i = \frac{1}{2}\sum_{k}^{3}\sum_{j}^{3} e_{ijk}v_{k,j} \tag{3.4-26}$$

where e_{ijk} represents the *permutation symbol*, defined as follows:

$$e_{ijk} = \begin{cases} 1 \text{ for an even permutation of } i, j, k \\ \quad \text{from the order } 1, 2, 3 \\ -1 \text{ for an odd permutation of } i, j, k \\ 0 \text{ if any two indices are equal} \end{cases} \tag{3.4-27}$$

The components of the vorticity tensor in Cartesian, cylindrical, and spherical coordinates are given in Table 3.4. Note that there are only three independent components of Ω_{ij}, and these are each proportional to one of the three components of the angular velocity vector. In fact, the components of the vorticity tensor and angular velocity vector are simply related by

$$\Omega_{ij} = 2\sum_{k}^{3} e_{ijk}\omega_k \tag{3.4-28}$$

TABLE 3.4

Components of the Vorticity Tensor

1.   Cartesian coordinates

$$
\Omega_{ij} =
\begin{bmatrix}
0 & \left(\dfrac{\partial v_y}{\partial x} - \dfrac{\partial v_x}{\partial y}\right) & \left(\dfrac{\partial v_z}{\partial x} - \dfrac{\partial v_x}{\partial z}\right) \\[3ex]
\left(\dfrac{\partial v_x}{\partial y} - \dfrac{\partial v_y}{\partial x}\right) & 0 & \left(\dfrac{\partial v_z}{\partial y} - \dfrac{\partial v_y}{\partial z}\right) \\[3ex]
\left(\dfrac{\partial v_x}{\partial z} - \dfrac{\partial v_z}{\partial x}\right) & \left(\dfrac{\partial v_y}{\partial z} - \dfrac{\partial v_z}{\partial y}\right) & 0
\end{bmatrix}
$$

2.   Cylindrical coordinates

$$
\Omega_{ij} =
\begin{bmatrix}
0 & \dfrac{1}{r}\left[\dfrac{\partial}{\partial r}(rv_\theta) - \dfrac{\partial v_r}{\partial \theta}\right] & \left(\dfrac{\partial v_z}{\partial r} - \dfrac{\partial v_r}{\partial z}\right) \\[3ex]
\dfrac{1}{r}\left[\dfrac{\partial v_r}{\partial \theta} - \dfrac{\partial}{\partial r}(rv_\theta)\right] & 0 & \left(\dfrac{1}{r}\dfrac{\partial v_z}{\partial \theta} - \dfrac{\partial v_\theta}{\partial z}\right) \\[3ex]
\left(\dfrac{\partial v_r}{\partial z} - \dfrac{\partial v_z}{\partial r}\right) & \left(\dfrac{\partial v_\theta}{\partial z} - \dfrac{1}{r}\dfrac{\partial v_z}{\partial \theta}\right) & 0
\end{bmatrix}
$$

3.   Spherical coordinates

$$
\Omega_{ij} =
\begin{bmatrix}
0 & \dfrac{1}{r\sin\theta}\left[\dfrac{\partial v_\theta}{\partial \phi} - \dfrac{\partial(v_\phi \sin\theta)}{\partial \theta}\right] & \left(\dfrac{1}{r\sin\theta}\dfrac{\partial v_r}{\partial \phi} - \dfrac{1}{r}\dfrac{\partial(rv_\phi)}{\partial r}\right) \\[3ex]
\dfrac{1}{r\sin\theta}\left[\dfrac{\partial(v_\phi \sin\theta)}{\partial \theta} - \dfrac{\partial v_\theta}{\partial \phi}\right] & 0 & \dfrac{1}{r}\left[\dfrac{\partial v_r}{\partial \theta} - \dfrac{\partial(rv_\theta)}{\partial r}\right] \\[3ex]
\left[\dfrac{1}{r}\dfrac{\partial}{\partial r}(rv_\phi) - \dfrac{1}{r\sin\theta}\dfrac{\partial v_r}{\partial \phi}\right] & \dfrac{1}{r}\left[\dfrac{\partial(rv_\theta)}{\partial r} - \dfrac{\partial v_r}{\partial \theta}\right] & 0
\end{bmatrix}
$$

Conversely, the inverse of this relation is

$$\omega_i = \frac{1}{4} \sum_j^3 \sum_k^3 e_{ijk} \Omega_{jk} \qquad (3.4\text{-}29)$$

──────────────────── 0 ────────────────────

Example 3.5 Determine the components of the vorticity tensor for
(a) the radial flow field of Fig. 3.6, and (b) the flow field surrounding a circular cylinder rotating slowly about its axis inside a
larger concentric cylinder.

In (a) above, the only nonzero velocity component is

$$v_r(r)$$

Consulting Eq. 2 of Table 3.4 reveals no term containing the derivative of v_r with respect to r, and all other derivatives are zero.
It follows that

$$\Omega_{ij} = 0$$

for this flow. Flows for which the vorticity tensor is zero are
known as *irrotational*.

For the flow in (b) above, it is readily seen that the velocity
components relative to cylindrical coordinates are

$$v_\theta(r) \qquad v_r = v_z = 0$$

provided the region of interest is far enough from the ends of the
cylinder, and the flow is slow enough. Under these conditions,
Eq. 2 of Table 3.4 reduces to

$$\Omega_{ij} = \begin{bmatrix} 0 & \dfrac{1}{r}\dfrac{d}{dr}(rv_\theta) & 0 \\[2ex] -\dfrac{1}{r}\dfrac{d}{dr}(rv_\theta) & 0 & 0 \\[2ex] 0 & 0 & 0 \end{bmatrix} = \begin{bmatrix} 0 & \left(\dfrac{dv_\theta}{dr} + \dfrac{v_\theta}{r}\right) & 0 \\[2ex] -\left(\dfrac{dv_\theta}{dr} + \dfrac{v_\theta}{r}\right) & 0 & 0 \\[2ex] 0 & 0 & 0 \end{bmatrix}$$

──────────────────── 0 ────────────────────

PROBLEMS

3-1. Consider a film of fluid of depth δ in steady laminar flow
      down a flat plane which is inclined at an angle β with the
      vertical (see figure). By application of Newton's second law
      [Eq.(3.2-6)], derive the velocity distribution in the film and
      the relation between the film depth, δ, and the total volumet-
      ric flow rate per unit width of the plane, Q, if the fluid is
      (a) Newtonian; (b) Power law; (c) Bingham plastic (note that
      for the Bingham plastic, the film depth must exceed a minimum
      depth (say, δ_o) before it will flow); and (d) derive an expres-
      sion relating this minimum depth to the material properties
      and the inclination angle β.

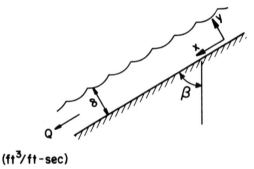

(ft³/ft-sec)

3-2. For an incompressible fluid, determine the second invariant of
      the rate of strain tensor for the flow field in Fig. 3.6 from
      (a) Table 3.3, (b) Eq. (3.4-9), (c) Eq. (3.4-10). Show that
      the results are equivalent.

3-3. Consider the steady laminar flow of two immiscible Newtonian
      fluids between two horizontal flat plates (i.e., a rectangular
      channel with large width/depth ratio) (see figure). By appli-
      cation of Eq. (3.2-6) to a shell of fluid in each phase, with
      appropriate boundary conditions at the interface, derive an
      expression for the relative depth of the two phases ($y = h'/h$)
      as a function of the relative flow rates ($F = Q'/Q$) and the
      relative viscosities ($M = \mu'/\mu$) of the two fluids.

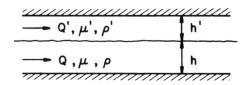

3-4.   Consider the laminar angular flow of a Newtonian fluid between
        two cylinders, the inner of which is stationary and the outer
        rotates with angular velocity Ω_o (see figure). Attempt a
        derivation of the equations for the stress distribution between
        the cylinders by a method analogous to that used in Example 3.1
        for the analysis of Poiseuille flow. Compare your result with
        the equations derived by reduction of the appropriate equations
        from Tables 3.1 and 3.2. If the two do not agree, can you
        explain the discrepancy?

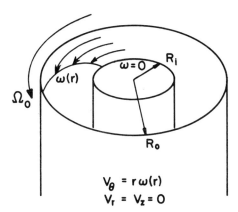

$$V_\theta = r\omega(r)$$
$$V_r = V_z = 0$$

3-5.   Prove that the stress tensor is symmetric, by considering the
        conservation of angular momentum applied to the differential
        element shown in the figure, and taking the limit as the dim-
        mensions of the element approach zero. The symmetry of all
        off-diagonal components may be demonstrated by following a
        similar procedure for orientation of the axis of rotation in
        each of the three coordinate directions.

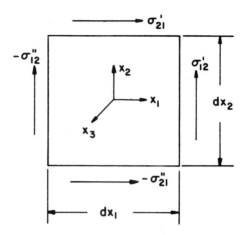

Two-dimensional stress components.

3-6.   Derive the continuity equation by a method analogous to that
        employed in Sec. 3.3.2, but with respect to cylindrical
        coordinates and an appropriate volume element relative to this
        coordinate system.

3-7.   Repeat Prob. 3-6 for spherical coordinates.

3-8.   Derive the expression in Table 3.3 from the expressions for
        the rate of strain tensor in Table 3.2 by application of
        (a) Eq. (3.4-9), (b) Eq. (3.4-10).

3-9.   Show that Eqs. (3.4-9) and (3.4-10) are equivalent.

3-10.   Derive the generalized tensor form of the following non-
        Newtonian (generalized Newtonian) fluid models, in terms of
        the total shear stress and shear rate tensors: (a) Eyring,
        (b) Reiner-Philippoff, (c) Ellis, (d) Meter, (e) Cross,
        (f) Williams.

3-11.   Write the specific form of each of the fluid models in Prob.
        3-10 which would apply to the flow field in (a) radial flow

between concentric cylinders (Fig. 3.6), (b) angular flow between concentric cylinders (Prob. 3-4).

3-12. Make use of the results of Example 3.1 to derive an equation relating volumetric flow rate and pressure drop for the following fluids in Poiseuille flow: (a) Power law, (b) Bingham plastic, (c) Reiner-Philippoff.

3-13. Show that

$$\sum_{i}^{3} e_{ijk} e_{ist} = \delta_{js} \delta_{kt} - \delta_{jr} \delta_{ks}$$

where the δs are Kronecker deltas.

3-14. Derive the general expression for the vorticity tensor, Eq. (3.4-18), from Eqs. (3.4-26) and (3.4-28).

3-15. Show that Eqs. (3.4-28) and (3.4-29) are consistent by (a) substituting (3.4-28) into (3.4-29), (b) substituting (3.4-29) into (3.4-28), and showing that the result is an identify in each case.

NOTES

1. The definition of "steady state" with respect to the Eulerian or Lagrangian frame of reference can now be expressed quantitatively in terms of the material derivative, $DA/Dt = \partial A/\partial t + \vec{v} \cdot \vec{\nabla}A$. Thus, "steady" in the Eulerian sense implies $\partial A/\partial t = 0$, while "steady" in the Lagrangian sense implies both $\partial A/\partial t = 0$ and $\vec{v} \cdot \vec{\nabla}A = 0$; i.e., $DA/Dt = 0$.

2. For this expression to be generally valid, the operation $\vec{v} \cdot (\vec{\nabla}\vec{v})$ must be carefully defined. See, e.g., Ref. 3.6.

3. That is, the density of a given fluid element remains constant. Different fluid elements may have different densities.

4. A more elegant derivation of the equations of change using vector notation is given in Appendix B, which involves application of the laws of conservation to a fluid element of arbitrary size and shape.

5.   Steady in both the Eulerian and Lagrangian sense.

6.   This criterion is based upon the *tensor* velocity components,
     defined as the time rate of change of the coordinates of a mate-
     rial point. These are not identical to the *physical* components
     having dimensions of length/time, except for coordinates with
     dimensions of length. The relation between tensor and physical
     components will be discussed in Chap. 6. This definition of
     viscometric flow is somewhat more restrictive than that of
     Coleman et al. [3-10].

Chapter 4

SOLUTION OF FLOW PROBLEMS

4.1. INTRODUCTION

In this chapter we will outline a general procedure for analyzing any laminar flow problem, utilizing the generalized equations developed in the previous chapter. The procedure will then be illustrated by setting up and solving a number of problems for non-Newtonian purely viscous fluids, and for linear viscoelastic fluids in small deformation unsteady flows. Some examples of the effect of normal stresses in steady tube flow will also be considered. A more complete consideration of the flow characteristics or more general nonlinear viscous and viscoelastic fluids will be left until Chap. 7, after a discussion of the transformation properties of tensors, which is necessary to a proper understanding of the more general behavior of these materials.

4.2. GENERAL PROCEDURE FOR ANALYZING FLOW PROBLEMS

As already noted, the determination of how a given fluid will behave in a given system involves the simultaneous solution of the appropriate equations of motion as they apply to the system together with the rheological equations of state for the fluid. From a consideration of Tables 3.1, 3.2, and 3.3, these equations may seem

quite formidable and complex. Indeed this is true in general, for
the result is a set of complex coupled nonlinear partial differential
equations, for which no general analytical solution is possible. However, many flow situations of interest are such that a number of the
terms in these equations are either identically zero or may be neglected, so that the resulting equations reduce to a form that can be
readily solved.

The process of determining which terms in these equations may be
discarded involves some a priori reasoning which constitutes restrictive assumptions about the flow field. Specifically it is necessary
to decide, on physical grounds, intuition, etc., which velocity components and velocity gradient components are to be considered for a
given flow system. All other terms in the equations of motion are
then discarded, to arrive at the specific form of the equations applicable to the problem. For example, the restrictive assumptions
associated with Poiseuille flow (described in Sec. 3.3) are equivalent to the only nonzero velocity component being the axial component (v_z), which in turn varies only in the radial direction, so
that dv_z/dr is the only nonzero component of the velocity gradient.
A similar reasoning process is inevitably required to reduce any flow
problem to a manageable form. Of course, the final solution of any
problem is no better than the assumptions or restrictions upon which
it is based. In fact, a listing of those terms which have been
dropped from the general equations of motion in order to simplify
them, together with the assumption employed to justify elimination of
each term, provides a ready-made list of the restrictive conditions
for which the resulting solution should be valid.

We are now in a position to outline a general procedure for
analyzing any laminar flow problem.

Step 1. Choose an appropriate coordinate system. This is normally one which coincides with the geometry of the boundaries of the
flow field. If these boundaries do not coincide with one of the
more common coordinate geometries, more complex procedures involving
mapping transformations or approximate methods are usually required.

Step 2. Determine, by physical reasoning intuition, or geometrical considerations, which velocity and velocity gradient components are significant and which are identically zero or may be neglected. This step constitutes the definition of the problem, and is
the most important part of the entire procedure. For example, velocity components parallel to confining boundaries are generally nonzero,
and these will normally vary in the direction normal to the boundary.
Also, variations of any quantity in an angular direction about an
axis of symmetry are usually zero. The result must also satisfy the
continuity equation, which should be considered at this stage of the
problem formulation.

Step 3. Determine the nonzero components of the rate of strain
tensor from Table 3.2, consistent with the results of step 2 above.

Step 4. Determine the corresponding nonzero components of the
shear stress tensor. For Newtonian and generalized Newtonian fluids,
these components correspond directly to the nonzero rate of strain
components. For other more complex fluids, the nonzero stress components must be determined from the appropriate material functions or
rheological equation of state for the fluid and the given deformation
(this will be illustrated in Chap. 7). As an example, for a class
of common flow systems called "viscometric flows" (which includes
Poiseuille flow), the velocity components are of the form

$$v_1 = v_1(x_2) \qquad v_2 = v_3 = 0 \tag{4.2-1}$$

so that there is only one nonzero velocity gradient component. The
rate of strain tensor for these flows thus takes on the general form

$$\Delta_{ij} = \dot{\gamma} \begin{bmatrix} 0 & 1 & 0 \\ 1 & 0 & 0 \\ 0 & 0 & 0 \end{bmatrix} \tag{4.2-2}$$

For Newtonian and generalized Newtonian fluids, the shear stress tensor is proportional to Δ_{ij} so that the nonzero components are

$$\tau_{ij} = \tau \begin{bmatrix} 0 & 1 & 0 \\ 1 & 0 & 0 \\ 0 & 0 & 0 \end{bmatrix} \qquad (4.2\text{-}3)$$

However, for more general fluids, including viscoelastic fluids, the normal (deviatoric) stress components may also be nonzero in such flows, so that the nonzero components of the stress tensor are at most:

$$\tau_{ij} = \begin{bmatrix} \tau_{11} & \tau_{12} & 0 \\ \tau_{12} & \tau_{22} & 0 \\ 0 & 0 & \tau_{33} \end{bmatrix} \qquad (4.2\text{-}4)$$

Step 5. Choose the appropriate set of equations from Table 3.1 for the coordinates employed, and discard all but the nonzero terms resulting from steps 2 and 4 above. The resulting momentum equations of motion apply to the flow system of interest, in terms of the non-zero stress components. These equations may often be integrated directly to give information concerning the stress distribution in the system, and how they relate to the external forces acting on the system, independent of the specific rheological nature of the fluid.

Step 6. To determine the flow behavior of a specific fluid in the given system, the equations from step 5 must be solved simulta-neously with those describing the stress–deformation properties of the fluid (i.e., the rheological equations of state). This involves substituting for the stress components in the momentum equations from the equation of state, in terms of the rate of strain (hence, velocity gradient) components. For incompressible Newtonian fluids the stresses are directly proportional to the rate of strain compo-nents. For generalized Newtonian fluids, an additional substitution in the apparent viscosity function is required. The apparent viscos-

ity is normally expressed as a function of a single component of
such equations may be used directly with the specific expression for
the shear rate evaluated from Table 3.2. For more complex flows,
involving more than one nonzero shear rate component, the shear rate
in the apparent viscosity function must be replaced by the second
invariant of the rate of strain tensor (Table 3.3), or the corresponding invariant of the shear stress tensor, as appropriate.

Step 7. The resulting equations for the nonzero velocity components as a function of position and time must then be solved subject
to appropriate boundary and initial conditions. This velocity distribution can then be used to evaluate shear rates and corresponding
stresses on solid boundaries, total flow rates, and other flow properties characteristic of the specific fluid in the specific system.

In all, there are a total of 10 partial differential equations
(continuity, 3 momentum equations of motion, and 6 independent rheological equations for the stress components as a function of the
rate of strain components) to solve for 10 variables as a function
of position and time (3 velocity components, 6 components of stress,
and pressure to within an arbitrary constant). As previously mentioned, a general solution of this entire set of equations is not
possible, but the simplified equations appropriate to many practical
systems are readily soluble. Of course, many systems of equations
which are too complex to solve analytically may nevertheless be
susceptible to analysis by numerical or approximate methods. However, in such cases, the nonlinear terms in the equations usually
give rise to considerable difficulty.

4.3. STEADY FLOW OF VISCOUS FLUIDS

We shall now illustrate the applicability of the procedure just
outlined to the steady laminar flow of viscous fluids.

4.3.1. Poiseuille Flow

The steady isothermal axial laminar flow of an incompressible fluid in a cylindrical tube is known as Poiseuille flow, and was first considered in Sec. 3.2. Cylindrical coordinates, which conform with the geometry of the tube, are used to describe the flow field. It is assumed that fluid properties are constant, and that the axial (z) velocity component is the only nonzero component. Because of symmetry, none of the variables should depend upon the angular (θ) coordinate. These conditions can only be satisfied if

$$v_r = v_\theta = 0 \qquad\qquad v_z \neq f(\theta) \tag{4.3-1}$$

The equation of continuity (Table 3.1) in cylindrical coordinates under these conditions reduces to

$$\frac{\partial v_z}{\partial z} = 0 \qquad \text{i.e.,} \quad v_z \neq f(z) \tag{4.3-2}$$

so that

$$v_z = v_z \text{ (r only)} \tag{4.3-3}$$

The rate of strain tensor from Table 3.2 therefore becomes

$$\Delta_{ij} = \begin{bmatrix} 0 & \dfrac{dv_z}{dr} & 0 \\ \dfrac{dv_z}{dr} & 0 & 0 \\ 0 & 0 & 0 \end{bmatrix} = \dot{\gamma} \begin{bmatrix} 0 & 1 & 0 \\ 1 & 0 & 0 \\ 0 & 0 & 0 \end{bmatrix} \tag{4.3-4}$$

This is a viscometric flow, so that the shear stress tensor has, at most, the following nonzero components

$$\tau_{ij} = \begin{bmatrix} \tau_{zz} & \tau_{rz} & 0 \\ \tau_{rz} & \tau_{rr} & 0 \\ 0 & 0 & \tau_{\theta\theta} \end{bmatrix} \tag{4.3-5}$$

Thus the three component momentum equations of motion from Table 3.1 (cylindrical coordinates) reduce to

z comp:

$$\frac{\partial P}{\partial z} - \rho g_z = \frac{1}{r} \frac{\partial}{\partial r} (r \tau_{rz}) \qquad (4.3\text{-}6)$$

r comp:

$$\frac{\partial P}{\partial r} - \rho g_r = \frac{1}{r} \frac{\partial}{\partial r} (r \tau_{rr}) - \frac{\tau_{\theta\theta}}{r} \qquad (4.3\text{-}7)$$

θ comp:

$$\frac{1}{r} \frac{\partial P}{\partial \theta} - \rho g_\theta = 0 \qquad (4.3\text{-}8)$$

where use has been made of the fact that, since the velocity varies only in the r direction, all internal stresses which depend upon the flow (deformation) must also be a function only of r. Using this result, differentiating Eq. (4.3-7) with respect to z leads to

$$\frac{\partial}{\partial z} \left(\frac{\partial P}{\partial r} \right) = 0 = \frac{\partial}{\partial r} \left(\frac{\partial P}{\partial z} \right) \qquad (4.3\text{-}9)$$

That is, the pressure gradient $(\partial P/\partial z)$ must be independent of r.

Considering Eq. (4.3-6), the left side is independent of r, whereas the right side is a function only of r. This can be true only if both are equal to a constant (say, Φ):

$$\frac{\partial P}{\partial z} - \rho g_z = \Phi = \frac{1}{r} \frac{d}{dr} (r \tau_{rz}) \qquad (4.3\text{-}10)$$

where $\Phi = \text{const} = \dfrac{\partial P}{\partial z} = \dfrac{\Delta P}{L}$ and $P = P + \rho g h$ (4.3-11)

Here h is the vertical distance above some reference plane and g is the acceleration of gravity (which acts vertically). The term P is simply the fluid pressure relative to that which exists in a closed system in a state of static equilibrium. Equation (4.3-10) is the final form of the z component equation of motion. It can be integrated to give:

$$\tau_{rz} = \frac{r\Phi}{2} + \frac{C_1}{r} \qquad (4.3\text{-}12)$$

The integration constant, C_1, must be zero, since otherwise an infinite stress would be predicted at the center ($r = 0$), which is impossible Thus Eq. (4.3-12) becomes:

$$\tau_{rz} = \frac{r\Phi}{2} = -\frac{r}{R} \tau_w \qquad (4.3\text{-}13)$$

where $\tau_w = -R\Phi/2 = -R\,\Delta P/2L$ is the stress exerted by the fluid on the wall.

We have now completed the first three steps of the procedure, and have yet to specify the rheological nature of the fluid. In fact, Eq. (4.3-13) is not only independent of the fluid properties, but also of the flow regime; i.e., it is valid for either laminar or turbulent flow. The result is identical to that derived by the momentum or force balance procedure in Example 3.1. We will now complete the solution for three specific fluids: Newtonian, Power law, and Bingham plastic.

A.   Newtonian

The general rheological equation of state for an incompressible Newtonian fluid, from Chap. 2 is

$$\tau_{ij} = \mu\,\Delta_{ij} \qquad (4.3\text{-}14)$$

Employing Eq. (4.3-4) for the rate of strain tensor, this becomes

$$\tau_{ij} = \tau_{rz}\begin{bmatrix} 0 & 1 & 0 \\ 1 & 0 & 0 \\ 0 & 0 & 0 \end{bmatrix} = \mu\,\frac{dv_z}{dr}\begin{bmatrix} 0 & 1 & 0 \\ 1 & 0 & 0 \\ 0 & 0 & 0 \end{bmatrix} \qquad (4.3\text{-}15)$$

Substituting for τ_{rz} from Eq. (4.3-13) results in a differential equation for the velocity distribution

$$\frac{r\tau_w}{\mu R} = -\frac{dv_z}{dr} \tag{4.3-16}$$

Integrating over $0 \leq r \leq R$ and making use of the boundary condition $v_z = 0$ at $r = R$ (see note 1), we obtain the velocity distribution

$$v_z = \frac{\tau_w R}{2\mu} \left[1 - \left(\frac{r}{R}\right)^2 \right] \tag{4.3-17}$$

The volumetric flow may be obtained by integrating Eq. (4.3-16) over the flow cross-sectional area:

$$Q = \int_A v_z \, dA = \int_0^R v_z 2\pi r \, dr = \frac{\pi R^3 \tau_w}{4\mu} \tag{4.3-18}$$

Solving Eq. (4.3-17) for τ_w:

$$\tau_w = \mu \left(\frac{4Q}{\pi R^3}\right) = \mu\Gamma \tag{4.3-19}$$

shows, by comparison with Eq. (4.3-16), that $\Gamma = (4Q/\pi r^3)$ is the negative of the shear rate evaluated at the wall of the tube (at $r = R$). The same result could be obtained by differentiating Eq. (4.3-17), evaluating the result at $r = R$, and substituting for τ_w from Eq. (4.3-18).

This example illustrates the stepwise procedure for solving flow problems outlined in Sec. 4.1. The result is identical to that obtained in Sec. 3.1 by the "shell momentum balance" method.

──────────────────────────────── 0 ──────────────────────

Example 4.1 Establish the restrictive conditions associated with Poiseuille flow by listing each term omitted from the general equations, together with the reason for discarding it.

Equation	Term omitted	Reason
Table 3.1A, 2	$\dfrac{\partial \rho}{\partial t}$	Incompressible
	$\dfrac{\partial}{\partial r} (\rho_r v_r)$	$v_r = 0$
	$\dfrac{1}{r} \dfrac{\partial}{\partial \theta} (\rho\, v_\theta)$	$v_\theta = 0$
	Result is that $v_z \neq fn(z)$	
Table 3.2, 3	$\dfrac{\partial v_r}{\partial r}$	$v_r = 0$
	$\dfrac{1}{r} \dfrac{\partial v_r}{\partial \theta}$	$v_r = 0$
	$r \dfrac{\partial}{\partial r} \dfrac{v_\theta}{r}$	$v_\theta = 0$
	$\dfrac{\partial v_r}{\partial z}$	$v_r = 0$
	$\dfrac{1}{r} \dfrac{\partial v_\theta}{\partial \theta}$	$v_\theta = 0$
	$\dfrac{v_r}{r}$	$v_r = 0$
	$\dfrac{\partial v_\theta}{\partial z}$	$v_\theta = 0$

$$\frac{1}{r}\frac{\partial v_z}{\partial \theta} \qquad\qquad v_z \neq f(\theta)$$

$$\frac{\partial v_z}{\partial z} \qquad\qquad v_z \neq f(z)$$

Since the only nonzero term in Δ_{ij} is $\Delta_{rz} = \Delta_{zr} = \dfrac{\partial v_z}{\partial r}$, which depends only upon r, it follows that the only nonzero terms of τ_{ij} will at most be τ_{rz}, τ_{zz}, τ_{rr}, $\tau_{\theta\theta}$, and these, too, will depend only upon the r coordinate. This conclusion enables us to discard certain terms from the equations of motion in Table 3.1:

Equation	Term dropped	Reason
7	$\dfrac{\partial v_r}{\partial t}$	$v_r = 0$ steady flow
	$v_r \dfrac{\partial v_r}{\partial r}$	$v_r = 0$
	$\dfrac{v_\theta}{r}\dfrac{\partial v_r}{\partial \theta}$	$v_\theta = v_r = 0$
	$\dfrac{v_\theta^2}{r}$	$v_\theta = 0$
	$v_z \dfrac{\partial v_r}{\partial z}$	$v_r = 0$
	$\dfrac{1}{r}\dfrac{\partial \tau_{r\theta}}{\partial \theta}$	$\tau_{r\theta} = 0$
	$\dfrac{\partial \tau_{rz}}{\partial z}$	$\tau_{rz} \neq f(z)$
8	$\dfrac{\partial v_\theta}{\partial t}$	$v_\theta = 0$ steady flow

8      $v_r \dfrac{\partial v_\theta}{\partial r}$ $v_r = v_\theta = 0$

        $\dfrac{v_\theta}{r} \dfrac{\partial v_\theta}{\partial \theta}$ $v_\theta = 0$

        $v_r \dfrac{v_\theta}{r}$ $v_r = v_\theta = 0$

        $v_z \dfrac{\partial v_\theta}{\partial z}$ $v_\theta = 0$

        $\dfrac{1}{r^2} \dfrac{\partial}{\partial r} (r^2 \tau_{r\theta})$ $\tau_{r\theta} = 0$

        $\dfrac{1}{r} \dfrac{\partial \tau_{\theta\theta}}{\partial \theta}$ $\tau_{\theta\theta} \neq f(\theta)$

        $\dfrac{\partial \tau_{\theta z}}{\partial z}$ $\tau_{\theta z} = 0$

9      $\dfrac{\partial v_z}{\partial t}$ Steady flow

        $v_r \dfrac{\partial v_z}{\partial r}$ $v_r = 0, \; v_z \neq f(r)$

        $\dfrac{v_\theta}{r} \dfrac{\partial v_z}{\partial \theta}$ $v_\theta = 0, \; v_z \neq f(\theta)$

        $v_z \dfrac{\partial v_z}{\partial z}$ $v_z \neq f(z)$

        $\dfrac{1}{r} \dfrac{\partial \tau_{\theta z}}{\partial \theta}$ $\tau_{\theta z} = 0$

        $\dfrac{\partial \tau_{zz}}{\partial z}$ $\tau_{zz} \neq f(z)$

The above "Reasons" constitute a set of restrictive conditions for the problem. For example, the solution would obviously not be valid near the entrance of the tube, where v_z would vary with z, and thus from continuity $v_r \neq 0$.

$$\text{———————————— 0 ————————————}$$

B. Power Law

The rheological equation of state for the power law fluid, Eq. (2.2-24), is

$$\tau = \eta_P \left| \frac{\dot{\gamma}}{\dot{\gamma}_P} \right|^{n-1} \dot{\gamma} \qquad (4.3-20)$$

For Poiseuille flow, this equation can be used directly since there is only one nonzero component of shear stress ($\tau = \tau_{rz}$) and of strain rate ($\dot{\gamma} = dv_z/dr$). However, for more complex flows which might involve more than one nonzero component, the generalized form of Eq. (4.3-20) would be required, namely,

$$\tau_{ij} = \eta_P \left| \frac{\sqrt{-II}}{\dot{\gamma}_P} \right|^{n-1} \Delta_{ij} \qquad (4.3-21)$$

where $\sqrt{-II} = \sqrt{1/2\ \Delta:\Delta}$ (for incompressible materials). (The "reference shear rate, $\dot{\gamma}_P$ may be taken to be 1 $\sec^{-1}$ with no loss of generality.) From Table 3.3 we see that

$$\frac{1}{2} \vec{\Delta}:\vec{\Delta} = \left(\frac{dv_z}{dr} \right)^2 \qquad (4.3-22)$$

so that Eq. (4.3-21) becomes

$$\tau_{ij} = \eta_P \left| \frac{dv_z}{dr} \right|^{n-1} \frac{dv_z}{dr} \begin{bmatrix} 0 & 1 & 0 \\ 1 & 0 & 0 \\ 0 & 0 & 0 \end{bmatrix} = \tau_{rz} \begin{bmatrix} 0 & 1 & 0 \\ 1 & 0 & 0 \\ 0 & 0 & 0 \end{bmatrix} \qquad (4.3-23)$$

or

$$\tau_{rz} = \eta_P \left| \frac{dv_z}{dr} \right|^{n-1} \frac{dv_z}{dr} \tag{4.3-24}$$

which corresponds directly to Eq. (4.3-20).

Equation (4.3-24) is somewhat awkward in its present form, but it can be rearranged by realizing that the absolute magnitude notation preserves the sign correspondence between τ and $\dot{\gamma}$ (i.e., τ_{rz} and dv_z/dr), both of which are negative for Poiseuille flow. These conditions can therefore be satisfied by writing Eq. (4.3-23) as

$$\tau_{rz} = -\eta_P \left(-\frac{dv_z}{dr} \right)^n \tag{4.3-25}$$

Equation (4.3-25) must be solved simultaneously with Eq. (4.3-13) to determine the velocity distribution for a Power law fluid in Poiseuille flow.

As before, eliminating τ_{rz} from Eqs. (4.3-13) and (4.3-25), and integrating with the condition that $v_z = 0$ at $r = R$, gives the velocity profile:

$$v_z = \left(\frac{n}{n+1} \right) \left(\frac{\tau_w}{\eta_P} \right)^{1/n} R \left[1 - \left(\frac{r}{R} \right)^{(1+n)/n} \right] \tag{4.3-26}$$

Integrating Eq. (4.3-26) over the flow cross section gives the volumetric flow rate:

$$Q = \int_0^R 2\pi r v_z \, dr = \left(\frac{n}{3n+1} \right) \left(\frac{\tau_w}{\eta_P} \right)^{1/n} R^3 \tag{4.3-27}$$

Solving Eq. (4.3-27) for τ_w:

$$\tau_w = \eta_P \left[\frac{Q}{\pi R^3} \left(\frac{3n+1}{n} \right) \right]^n \tag{4.3-28}$$

and comparing the result with Eq. (4.3-25) shows that the shear rate
at the tube wall is given by:

$$\dot{\gamma}_w = \left(\frac{dv_z}{dr}\right)_{r=R} = -\frac{Q}{\pi R^3}\left(\frac{3n+1}{n}\right) = -\Gamma\left(\frac{3n+1}{4n}\right) \qquad (4.3\text{-}29)$$

Whereas the wall shear rate for a Newtonian fluid (Γ) is determined
uniquely by the flow rate only, for a Power law fluid it is a function of the fluid property n as well. It is evident that all of the
above equations reduce to the corresponding expressions for Newtonian
fluid if n = 1.

———————————————————— 0 ————————————————————

Example 4.2 Determine expressions for the shear stress components
in a Power law fluid in steady laminar flow transverse to a circular
cylinder, as a function of the velocity and velocity gradient components.

From the flow field illustrated in the figure, it is evident
that the fluid velocity at any point will have components in both
the radial and angular directions. Furthermore, these components

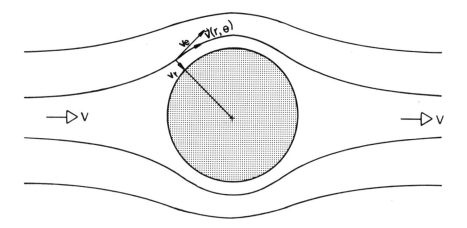

Flow transverse to a cylinder.

will vary in both the r and θ directions. It is reasonable to assume,
therefore, that the velocity components are of the form

$$v_r(r,\ \theta) \qquad v_\theta(r,\ \theta) \qquad v_z = 0$$

if we neglect the region near the ends of the cylinder.

Under these conditions, for a constant density fluid, the continuity equation from Table 3.1A reduces to

$$\frac{\partial}{\partial r}(rv_r) + \frac{\partial v_\theta}{\partial \theta} = 0$$

The components of the rate of strain tensor from Eq. 3 of Table 3.2
become

$$\Delta_{ij} = \begin{bmatrix} 2\dfrac{\partial v_r}{\partial r} & \left[\dfrac{1}{r}\dfrac{\partial v_r}{\partial \theta} + r\dfrac{\partial}{\partial r}\left(\dfrac{v_\theta}{r}\right)\right] & 0 \\[3ex] \left[\dfrac{1}{r}\dfrac{\partial v_r}{\partial \theta} + r\dfrac{\partial}{\partial r}\left(\dfrac{v_\theta}{r}\right)\right] & 2\left[\dfrac{1}{r}\dfrac{\partial v_\theta}{\partial \theta} + \dfrac{v_r}{r}\right] & 0 \\[3ex] 0 & 0 & \end{bmatrix}$$

and the second invariant from Eq. 2 of Table 3.3 is

$$-\mathrm{II} = 2\left[\left(\frac{\partial v_r}{\partial r}\right)^2 + \left(\frac{1}{r}\frac{\partial v_\theta}{\partial \theta} + \frac{v_r}{r}\right)^2\right] + \left[r\frac{\partial}{\partial r}\left(\frac{v_\theta}{r}\right) + \frac{1}{r}\frac{\partial v_r}{\partial \theta}\right]^2$$

Thus, from Eq. (4.3-20), the nonzero stress components for a Power
law fluid in this deformation are:

$$\tau_{rr} = 2\eta_p \left\{ 2\left[\left(\frac{\partial v_r}{\partial r}\right)^2 + \left(\frac{1}{r}\frac{\partial v_\theta}{\partial \theta} + \frac{v_r}{r}\right)^2\right] + \left[r\frac{\partial}{\partial r}\left(\frac{v_\theta}{r}\right) + \frac{1}{r}\frac{\partial v_r}{\partial \theta}\right]^2 \right\}^{(n-1)/2} \frac{\partial v_r}{\partial r}$$

$$\tau_{r\theta} = \tau_{\theta r} = \eta_p \{-II\}^{(n-1)/2} \left[\frac{1}{r} \frac{\partial v_r}{\partial \theta} + r \frac{\partial}{\partial r} \left(\frac{v_\theta}{r} \right) \right]$$

$$\tau_{\theta\theta} = 2\eta_p \{-II\}^{(n-1)/2} \left(\frac{1}{r} \frac{\partial v_\theta}{\partial \theta} + \frac{v_r}{r} \right)$$

(all others are zero)

where $\{-II\} = -II$ as given above.

It is evident that this flow field is considerably more complex
than that of Poiseuille flow. Indeed, if these expressions are substituted into the appropriate forms of the equations of motion, a
very complex set of equations would result, which are impossible to
solve analytically.

One very serious restriction inherent in the definition of
this problem, which is implied but not stated, is that the flow is
slow enough that separation and eddying do not occur on the downstream surface of the cylinder. This would seriously limit the
applicability of the solution, if it were obtained.

———————————————— 0 ————————————————

C. Bingham Plastic

If the material in the pipe is assumed to follow the Bingham
plastic rheological model, Eqs. (2.2-19) to (2.2-21) apply. A procedure similar to that leading from Eqs. (4.3-20) to (4.3-25) above,
leads to the following equations for the Bingham plastic in
Poiseuille flow:

$$\tau_{ij} = \eta \, \Delta_{ij}$$

where

$$\eta = \mu_o + \left| \frac{\tau_o}{\sqrt{\frac{1}{2}\vec{\Delta}:\vec{\Delta}}} \right| \quad \text{for} \quad \left| \sqrt{\frac{1}{2}\vec{\tau}:\vec{\tau}} \right| > \tau_o \tag{4.3-30}$$

$$\Delta_{ij} = 0 \quad \text{for} \quad \left| \sqrt{\frac{1}{2}\vec{\tau}:\vec{\tau}} \right| < \tau_o \tag{4.3-31}$$

In Poiseuille flow, for which the rate of strain tensor is given by Eq. (4.3-4) and both τ_{rz} and $\dot{\gamma}$ are negative, Eqs. (4.3-30) and (4.3-31) reduce to:

$$\tau_{rz} = -\tau_o + \mu_o \frac{dv_z}{dr} \quad \text{for} \quad \left| \tau_{rz} \right| > \tau_o \tag{4.3-32}$$

and

$$\frac{dv_z}{dr} = 0 \quad \text{for} \quad \left| \tau_{rz} \right| < \tau_o \tag{4.3-33}$$

Note that a Bingham plastic is not a pure fluid, inasmuch as it behaves as a rigid solid for stresses below the yield stress, τ_o, as indicated by Eq. (4.3-31). However, the stress distribution derived for Poiseuille flow, Eq. (4.3-13), applies as well as to a Bingham plastic. If $\left| \tau_w \right| > \tau_o$, the material will be a fluid at the wall, and will flow. However, since $\left| \tau_{rz} \right|$ decreases as r decreases (with a minimum value of zero at the center), there will be some finite value of r at which $\left| \tau_{rz} \right| = \tau_o$. At this point, the transition from fluid to solid occurs, and Eq. (4.3-33) applies. Thus there will be a solid "plug" of material moving in the center of the tube, surrounded by a continuously deforming (flowing) fluid. The transition occurs at the position where $\tau_{rz} = \tau_o$, which we shall designate r_o (see Fig. 4.1).

For the fluid region ($r \geq r_o$), Eq. (4.3-12) applies, so that at the edge of this region

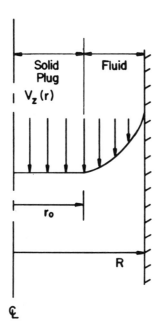

FIG. 4.1 Bingham plastic in a tube.

$$\tau_o = \frac{r_o}{R} \tau_w = - \frac{r_o \, \Delta P}{2L} \qquad\qquad (4.3\text{-}34)$$

which relates the transition point r_o to the Bingham yield stress, τ_o, and the wall stress, τ_w. (Note that both τ_o and τ_w are positive, and ΔP is negative.)

Thus, for $r_o < r < R$, Eqs. (4.3-13) and (4.3-32) combine to give

$$r \frac{\tau_w}{R} = \tau_o - \mu_o \frac{dv_z}{dr} \qquad\qquad (4.3\text{-}35)$$

This may be integrated, with the "no slip" boundary condition at the wall, to give the velocity distribution in the fluid region:

$$v_z = \frac{\tau_w R}{2\mu_o} \left[1 - \left(\frac{r}{R}\right)^2 \right] - \frac{\tau_o R}{\mu_o} \left(1 - \frac{r}{R} \right) \tag{4.3-36}$$

which applies only for $(r_o < r < R)$.

For $r \leq r_o$ ("plug" region), the velocity is uniform. Since it is also continuous over the tube, it must also be equal to the value given by Eq. (4.3-36) at $r = r_o$. Thus, the plug velocity is obtained by evaluating Eq. (4.3-36) at $r = r_o$:

$$v_{plug} = \frac{\tau_w R}{2\mu_o} \left[1 - \left(\frac{r_o}{R}\right)^2 \right] - \frac{\tau_o R}{\mu_o} \left(1 - \frac{r_o}{R} \right) \tag{4.3-37}$$

or

$$v_{plug} = \frac{\tau_w R}{2\mu_o} \left(1 - \frac{\tau_o}{\tau_w} \right)^2 \tag{4.3-38}$$

where Eq. (4.3-34) has been used to eliminate r_o from Eq. (4.3-37).

The total volumetric flow rate can now be calculated as the sum of that in the "plug" and the "fluid" regions:

$$Q = Q_{plug} + Q_{fluid} = \pi r_o^2 v_{plug} + 2\pi \int_{r_o}^{R} v_z r \, dr \tag{4.3-39}$$

Inserting Eq. (4.3-36) into the integral, integrating, and again using Eq. (4.3-34) to eliminate r_o gives

$$Q = \frac{\pi R^3 \tau_w}{4\mu_o} \left[1 - \frac{4}{3} \left(\frac{\tau_o}{\tau_w}\right) + \frac{1}{3} \left(\frac{\tau_o}{\tau_w}\right)^4 \right] \tag{4.3-40}$$

This is often referred to as the "Buckingham-Reiner" equation. Note that there is no simple expression for the shear rate at the tube wall in terms of Q, as in the two previous cases.

Note that all of these results have been obtained by use of the
z component momentum equation only [Eq. (4.3-6)]. The only stress
component in this equation is the shearing stress τ_{rz}, whereas the
r and θ component equations involve only the normal stress components
τ_{rr} and $\tau_{\theta\theta}$. We are therefore led to the important conclusion that
the velocity profile and pressure drop versus flow rate relations for
any fluid in Poiseuille flow are independent of whether or not the
fluid exhibits anisotropic normal stresses in viscometric flows.
(This conclusion does not apply for nonviscometric flows.) This
result is important in that it permits the use of Poiseuille flow
variables to determine the viscous properties (i.e., the apparent
viscosity function) of any fluid, regardless of whether the fluid
exhibits elastic or normal stress effects.

All of these results for Poiseuille flow could have been derived
from the results of the momentum balance approach in Chap. 3. We
will now consider a system which could not be readily analyzed by
that method.

———————————————————— 0 ————————————————————

Example 4.3 A certain mud suspension has been found to behave approximately as a Bingham plastic, with a yield stress of 65 dyn/cm^2
and a plastic viscosity of 800 cP. Calculate the maximum flow rate
in gallons per minute that can be achieved with this fluid in a 1 in.
pipe, 500 ft long, by a pump that develops 50 psi. Compare with the
flow rate that could be achieved with a Newtonian fluid with a viscosity of 800 cP under the same conditions

The solution to this problem for the Bingham plastic is given
by the Buckingham-Reiner equation (4.3-39). The value of τ_w in
this equation is given by

$$\tau_w = -\frac{\Delta PR}{2L} = \frac{(50\ \#f/in.^2)(144\ in.^2/ft^2)(0.5\ in.)}{2(500\ ft)(12\ in./ft)} = 0.30\ \frac{\#f}{ft^2}$$

or

$$\left(0.30 \ \frac{\#f}{in.^2}\right) \left(4.79 \times 10^2 \ \frac{dyn/cm^2}{\#f/ft^2}\right) = 143.7 \ \frac{dyn}{cm^2}$$

Thus

$$\frac{\tau_w}{\tau_o} = \frac{143.7}{65} = 2.21$$

The flow rate is, therefore,

$$Q = -\frac{\pi R^3 \tau_w}{4\mu_o} \left[1 - \frac{4}{3}\left(\frac{\tau_o}{\tau_w}\right) + \frac{1}{3}\left(\frac{\tau_o}{\tau_w}\right)^4\right]$$

$$= \frac{\pi\left(0.5 \ in.\right) \left(\frac{0.3 \ \#f}{ft^3}\right)\left(7.48 \ \frac{gal}{ft^3}\right)\left(60 \ \frac{sec}{min}\right)}{4\left(1728 \ \frac{in.^3}{ft^3}\right)\left(800 \ cP\right)\left(2.05 \times 10^{-5} \ \frac{\#f \ sec}{cP \ ft^2}\right)} \left[1 - \frac{4}{3(2.21)} + \frac{1}{3(2.21)^4}\right]$$

$$= 0.192 \ gpm$$

For a Newtonian fluid of 800 cP viscosity, the flow rate is given by
Eq. (4.3-17), which is just the coefficient of the bracketed term
above:

$$Q = \frac{\pi R^3 \tau_w}{4\mu} = 0.467 \ gpm$$

Note that the non-Newtonian character of a Bingham plastic is
evident from the Buckingham-Reiner equation, which illustrates the
nonlinear relation between flow rate and wall shear (i.e., pressure
drop) in a tube.

———————————————————————— 0 ————————————————————————

4.3.2. Couette Flow

The steady angular (rotational) laminar flow in an annulus between concentric cylinders, one or both of which is rotating, is
called Couette flow (Fig. 4.2). The system is conveniently described
in terms of cylindrical coordinates, centered on the axis of the cylinders.

For the situation depicted in Fig. 4.2, the inner cylinder
(radius R_i) is rotating at an angular velocity Ω_i, while the outer
cylinder (radius R_o) rotates with angular velocity Ω_o. The net
torque or moment applied to the system which produces the motion is
designated T. At steady state, this torque is the same at all points
within the fluid, as will be shown by application of a moment balance (or a conservation of angular momentum).

For these conditions, the flow field is assumed to be defined
by the velocity components:

$$v_r = v_z = 0 \qquad v_\theta(r) = r\omega(r) \qquad\qquad (4.3\text{-}41)$$

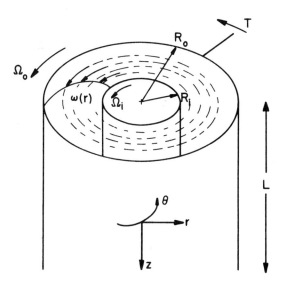

FIG. 4.2   Couette flow.

where $\omega(r)$ is the angular velocity $(d\theta/dt)$ about the cylinder axis at any radial position r $(R_i \le r \le R_o)$. There is obviously no axial flow, and the influence of the ends (top and bottom) on the flow field is neglected.

The nonzero components of the rate of strain tensor follow from Eq. (4.3-41) and Table 3.2:

$$\Delta_{ij} = \begin{bmatrix} 0 & r\dfrac{d\omega}{dr} & 0 \\ r\dfrac{d\omega}{dr} & 0 & 0 \\ 0 & 0 & 0 \end{bmatrix} = \dot{\gamma} \begin{bmatrix} 0 & 1 & 0 \\ 1 & 0 & 0 \\ 0 & 0 & 0 \end{bmatrix} \tag{4.3-42}$$

Thus the stress tensor has, at most, the following nonzero components:

$$\tau_{ij} = \begin{bmatrix} \tau_{rr} & \tau_{r\theta} & 0 \\ \tau_{\theta r} & \tau_{\theta\theta} & 0 \\ 0 & 0 & \tau_{zz} \end{bmatrix} = \tau_{ij}(r) \tag{4.3-43}$$

The component momentum equations of motion from Table 4.1B, after discarding terms which are zero as a consequence of Eqs. (4.3-41) and (4.3-42), reduce to:

r comp:

$$\frac{-\rho v_\theta^2}{r} = -\frac{\partial P}{\partial r} + \frac{1}{r}\frac{\partial}{\partial r}(r\tau_{rr}) - \frac{\tau_{\theta\theta}}{r} \tag{4.3-44}$$

θ comp:

$$0 = \frac{1}{r^2}\frac{\partial}{\partial r}\left(r^2\tau_{r\theta}\right) \tag{4.3-45}$$

z comp:

$$0 = -\frac{\partial P}{\partial z} + \rho g_z \tag{4.3-46}$$

Note that r is the only independent variable in these equations.

Equation (4.3-45) can be integrated directly to give:

$$\tau_{r\theta} = \frac{C_1}{r^2} \tag{4.3-47}$$

where C_1 is a constant of integration, and can be evluated by considering a balance of moments acting on any r surface in the fluid. Since the net applied torque (T) is the product of force times the lever arm at which it is measured, it must be balanced by the moment due to the shear force developed within the fluid:

$$T = \tau_{r\theta} \cdot (2\pi r L) \cdot r \tag{4.3-48}$$

This applies for all values of r for which $(R_i \leq r \leq R_o)$. Eliminating $\tau_{r\theta}$ from Eqs. (4.3-47) and (4.3-48) shows the constant C_1 to be $T/2\pi L$. Thus the shear stress at any point r in the fluid is given by:

$$\tau_{r\theta} = \frac{T}{2\pi L r^2} \tag{4.3-49}$$

Thus we see from Eq. (4.3-49) that, as for Poiseuille flow, the shearing stress distribution in Couette flow is determined only by the equations of motion (independent of the properties of the fluid in the annulus) and is directly related to the applied torque, T.

We will now determine how several specific fluids will behave in this system in response to the above stress distribution. As before, we will consider Newtonian, Power law, and Bingham plastic materials.

A. Newtonian Fluid

From Table 3.2, the Newtonian equation of state for the flow field defined by the rate of strain tensor of Eq. (4.3-42) is:

$$\tau_{ij} = \tau_{r\theta} \begin{bmatrix} 0 & 1 & 0 \\ 1 & 0 & 0 \\ 0 & 0 & 0 \end{bmatrix} = \mu \cdot r \frac{d\omega}{dr} \begin{bmatrix} 0 & 1 & 0 \\ 1 & 0 & 0 \\ 0 & 0 & 0 \end{bmatrix}$$

or

$$\tau_{r\theta} = \mu r \frac{d}{dr} \left(\frac{v_\theta}{r} \right) \qquad\qquad (4.3\text{-}50)$$

Eliminating $\tau_{r\theta}$ from Eqs. (4.3-49) and (4.3-50), and integrating the result with respect to r leads to:

$$v_\theta = rC_2 - \frac{T}{4\pi\mu Lr} \qquad\qquad (4.3\text{-}51)$$

Now we actually have two boundary conditions on v_θ:

$$v_\theta = \Omega_i R_i \qquad \text{at} \qquad r = R_i$$

and   (4.3-52)

$$v_\theta = \Omega_o R_o \qquad \text{at} \qquad r = R_o$$

Even though Eq. (4.3-51) contains only one constant of integration, C_2, there are actually two, the other being the C_1 of Eq. (4.3-47), which has been expressed in terms of the applied torque. Evaluating these constants from Eqs. (4.3-52), they become

$$C_1 = \frac{T}{2\pi L} = \frac{2\mu(\Omega_o - \Omega_i)R_o^{\,2}}{(\alpha^2 - 1)} \qquad\qquad (4.3\text{-}53)$$

$$C_2 = \Omega_o + \frac{(\Omega_o - \Omega_i)}{(\alpha^2 - 1)} \qquad\qquad (4.3\text{-}54)$$

where

$$\alpha = \frac{R_o}{R_i} \qquad\qquad (4.3\text{-}55)$$

It should be noted that Eq. (4.3-49) is general in that it applies
for any fluid, whereas the right side of Eqs. (4.3-53) and (4.3-54)
are specific for a Newtonian fluid. The velocity distribution between the cylinder follows from Eqs. (4.3-51), (4.3-53), and
(4.3-54):

$$v_\theta = \frac{R_o^{\,2}}{r(\alpha^2 - 1)} \left[\Omega_o \left(\frac{r^2}{R_i^{\,2}} - 1 \right) - \Omega_i \left(\frac{r^2}{R_o^{\,2}} - 1 \right) \right] \qquad (4.3\text{-}56)$$

Note that if $\Omega_o = \Omega_i = \Omega$, Eq. (4.3-55) reduces to

$$v_\theta = r\Omega \qquad (4.3\text{-}57)$$

i.e., the fluid and cylinders rotate as a rigid body, all at the
same velocity. If the outer cylinder is absent ($R_o = \infty$ and $\Omega_o = 0$;
i.e., a single cylinder in a "sea" of fluid), Eq. (4.3-56) reduces
to

$$v_\theta = \frac{\Omega_i R_i^{\,2}}{r} \qquad (4.3\text{-}58)$$

An alternate expression for the velocity distribution follows by
introducing the expression for T from Eq. (4.3-53):

$$v_\theta = \frac{T}{4r\pi\mu L(\Omega_o - \Omega_i)} \left[\Omega_o \left(\frac{r^2}{R_i^{\,2}} - 1 \right) - \Omega_i \left(\frac{r^2}{R_o^{\,2}} - 1 \right) \right] \qquad (4.3\text{-}59)$$

This result readily reduces to the special case in which either the
inner or outer cylinders are stationary, by setting Ω_i or Ω_o equal
to zero, respectively.

The dependence of the applied torque upon the fluid viscosity
can readily be determined in several ways. For example, by equating
the torque to the moment due to fluid drag at either cylinder surface, we have

Inner:

$$T = (2\pi R_i L)\tau_{r\theta}\Big|_{r=R_i} R_i \qquad (4.3\text{-}60)$$

Outer:

$$T = (2\pi R_o L)\tau_{r\theta}\Big|_{r=R_o} R_o \qquad (4.3\text{-}61)$$

where $\tau_{r\theta}$ can be evaluated from Eqs. (4.3-50) and (4.3-56). Both Eqs. (4.3-60) and (4.3-61) give the same result, as can easily be verified from Eq. (4.3-49). This procedure has essentially already been carried out in the evaluation of the constant C_1, i.e., Eq. (4.3-53):

$$T = \frac{4\pi\mu L(\Omega_o - \Omega_i)R_o^2}{(\alpha^2 - 1)} \qquad (4.3\text{-}62)$$

Note that if $\Omega_o = \Omega_i$, then $T = 0$, i.e., no net torque is required to rotate a rigid body at constant velocity (neglecting friction in the supports).

Substituting T from Eq. (4.3-62) into Eq. (4.3-49), and comparing the result with the Newtonian rheological equation:

$$\tau(r) = \mu\dot{\gamma}(r) \qquad (4.3\text{-}63)$$

leads directly to expressions for the distribution of both shear stress and shear rate.

$$\tau(r) = \frac{T}{2\pi r^2 L} \qquad (4.3\text{-}64)$$

$$\dot{\gamma}(r) = \frac{2R_o^2(\Omega_o - \Omega_i)}{r^2(\alpha^2 - 1)} \qquad (4.3\text{-}65)$$

It is emphasized that Eq. (4.3-64) is general in that it is valid regardless of the type of fluid in the system, while Eq. (4.3-65) is valid only for a Newtonian fluid.

B. Power Law Fluid

The rheological equation of state for the Power law fluid is given in general form by Eq. (4.3-21). Setting the reference shear rate $(\dot{\gamma}_p)$ equal to 1 sec^{-1}, and evaluating the second invariant of the rate of strain tensor for Couette flow [Eq. (4.3-42] from Table 3.3, the only nonzero stress component becomes:

$$\tau_{r\theta} = \eta_p \left(r \frac{d\omega}{dr} \right)^n = \eta_p \left[r \frac{d}{dr} \left(\frac{v_\theta}{r} \right) \right]^n \tag{4.3-66}$$

Note that if the outer cylinder is moving faster than the inner, the net torque and $\tau_{r\theta}$ are positive and the shear rate is everywhere positive. If, however, the inner cylinder is moving faster than the outer, the net torque and $\tau_{r\theta}$ are negative so that the shear rate ($r \, d\omega/dr$) will also be negative. In the latter case, the right side of Eq. (4.3-66) as well as the shear rate (in brackets) should be multiplied by -1, as was done for Poiseuille flow.

The velocity distribution for a Power law fluid in Couette flow is thus determined by eliminating $\tau_{r\theta}$ from Eq. (4.3-49) and Eq. (4.3-66), and integrating to solve for $v_\theta(r)$, subject to the boundary conditions Eq. (4.3-52). The result is:

$$\omega(r) = \frac{v_\theta(r)}{r} = \frac{R_o^{2/n}}{r^{2/n}(\alpha^{2/n} - 1)} \left\{ \left[\Omega_o \left(\frac{r}{R_i} \right)^{2/n} - 1 \right] - \Omega_i \left[\left(\frac{r}{R_o} \right)^{2/n} - 1 \right] \right\} \tag{4.3-67}$$

where $\alpha = R_o/R_i$.

The shear rate distribution can be determined as a function of position by differentiating Eq. (4.3-67):

$$\dot{\gamma} = r \frac{d\omega}{dr} = \frac{2(\Omega_o - \Omega_i)}{n(\alpha^{2/n} - 1)} \left(\frac{R_o}{r}\right)^{2/n} \qquad (4.3\text{-}68)$$

The total net torque on the system as a function of the fluid properties can now be evaluated from Eqs. (4.3-49), (4.3-66) and (4.3-68) as follows:

$$T = 2\pi r^2 L \tau_{r\theta} = 2\pi r^2 L \eta_p [\dot{\gamma}(r)]^n$$

or

$$T = 2\pi L R_o^2 \eta_p \left[\frac{2(\Omega_o - \Omega_i)}{n(\alpha^{2/n} - 1)}\right]^n \qquad (4.3\text{-}69)$$

which is, of course, independent of r as previously demonstrated.

——————————————————— 0 ———————————————————

Example 4.4 A fluid, which may be characterized as a Power law fluid, is contained in the annulus between two concentric cylinders of radii 1 cm and 3 cm, and length of 6 cm. The outer cylinder is rotated at a velocity of 10 rpm, and the inner cylinder is attached to a clutch which will slip when a torque of 6 dyn-cm is applied to it. If the fluid Power law parameters are n = 0.85 and η_o = 10 cP, what will be the angular velocity of the inner cylinder?

The solution to this problem is given by Eq. (4.3-69), rearranged to solve for Ω_i:

$$\Omega_i = \Omega_o - \left(\frac{T}{2\pi L R_o^2 \eta_o}\right)^{1/n} \frac{n(\alpha^{2/n} - 1)}{2}$$

$$= 10 - \left[\frac{6}{2\pi(6)(9)(0.1)}\right]^{1/0.85} \frac{(0.85)(3^{2/0.85} - 1)}{2} \frac{60}{2\pi} = 1.6 \text{ rpm}$$

Note that the nonintegral value of n does not result in an odd set of units in the answer as long as consistent units are used for each term. This is because η_p is the apparent viscosity at a reference shear rate of 1 sec^{-1}, and as such effectively has dimensions of $[(\text{viscosity})(\text{time})^{n-1}]$.

———————————————— o ————————————————

C. Bingham Plastic

The rheological description of the Bingham plastic [Eqs. (4.3-29) and (4.3-30)], together with the rate of strain tensor for Couette flow [Eq. (4.3-42)], reduce to

$$\tau_{r\theta} = \tau_o + \mu_o \left(r \frac{d\omega}{dr} \right) \qquad \text{for} \qquad |\tau_{r\theta}| > \tau_o \qquad (4.3\text{-}70)$$

and

$$\frac{d\omega}{dr} = 0 \qquad \text{for} \qquad |\tau_{r\theta}| < \tau_o \qquad (4.3\text{-}71)$$

The flow situation is similar to that of Poiseuille flow in that a region of solid "plug" flow will occur in any region where the magnitude of the shear stress is less than the yield stress, τ_o. Again making use of Eq. (3.4-49), which is applicable to the flow region:

$$\tau_{r\theta} = \frac{T}{2\pi r^2 L} \qquad (4.3\text{-}49)$$

we see that the minimum stress in the system is not zero, as in Poiseuille flow, but is finite and occurs at the outer cylinder wall (where r is maximum at R_o). Therefore, if the applied torque and the dimensions of the system are such that the shear stress at $r = R_o$ given by Eq. (4.3-49) is greater than the yield stress τ_o, there will be no "plug flow" region in the system and all of the material will flow as a fluid. Of course, if $\tau_{r\theta}$ evaluated at R_i is less than τ_o,

there will be no flow at all, since the applied torque will be
insufficient to overcome the yield stress at any point in the system.

For the most general case we shall assume that the transition
from solid to fluid occurs within the annular gap, i.e.,

$$\left| \tau_{r\theta} \right|_{R_i} > \tau_o > \left| \tau_{r\theta} \right|_{R_o} \tag{4.3-72}$$

as depicted in Fig. 4.3. The other situations discussed above become
special cases of this general case. The radial position r_o at which
the transition from solid to fluid occurs is, from Eq. (4.3-49):

$$r_o = \left(\frac{T}{2\pi L \tau_o} \right)^{1/2} \tag{4.3-73}$$

Thus Eq. (4.3-70) applies for $r < r_o$ and Eq. (413-71) for $r > r_o$.
For the flow region, eliminating $\tau_{r\theta}$ from Eqs. (4.3-70) and (4.3-49)
and solving for $\omega(r) = v_\theta/r$ subject to the boundary conditions

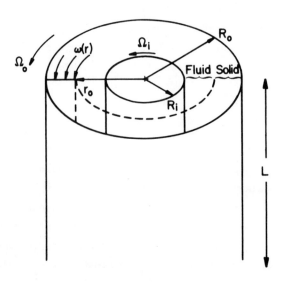

FIG. 4.3 Couette flow of a Bingham plastic.

$$\omega = \Omega_i \qquad \text{at} \qquad r = R_i$$

$$\omega = \Omega_o \qquad \text{at} \qquad r = r_o \qquad\qquad (4.3\text{-}74)$$

yields, for $R_i < r < r_o$:

$$\omega(r) = \Omega_o - \frac{\tau_o}{\mu_o} \ell n \frac{r}{r_o} - \left[\Omega_o - \Omega_i + \frac{\tau_o}{\mu_o} \ell n \, \alpha_o \right] \frac{(r_o^2 - r^2)}{r^2(1 - \alpha_o^2)} \qquad (4.3\text{-}75)$$

where $\alpha_o = r_o/R_i$. In the plug flow region $(r_o < r < R_o)$:

$$\omega(r) = \Omega_o \qquad\qquad (4.3\text{-}76)$$

Substituting Eq. (4.3-75) into Eq. (4.3-70) and eliminating $\tau_{r\theta}$ by use of Eq. (4.3-49) leads to:

$$T = 4\pi L \mu_o \left[\Omega_o - \Omega_i + \frac{\tau_o}{\mu_o} \ell n \, \alpha_o \right] \left[\frac{r_o^2}{\alpha_o^2 - 1} \right] \qquad (4.3\text{-}77)$$

This expression is implicit for the torque T as a function of the rotational velocities (Ω_o, Ω_i), since the definition of r_o [Eq. (4.3-73)] involves T. However, it can be solved for the relative velocity $(\Omega_o - \Omega_i)$ explicitly as a function of applied torque:

$$\Omega_o - \Omega_i = \frac{\tau_o}{\mu} \left[\frac{\alpha_o^2 - 1}{2} - \ell n \, \alpha_o \right] \qquad (4.3\text{-}78)$$

where

$$\alpha_o = \frac{r_o}{R_i} = \left(\frac{T}{2\pi L \tau_o R_i^2} \right)^{1/2} \qquad (4.3\text{-}79)$$

As with Poiseuille flow, Couette flow is a viscometric flow and the relation between torque and angular velocity in steady flow depends only upon the shearing (off-diagonal) stress component, which,

in turn, is determined only by the viscous properties (apparent viscosity) of the fluid. The presence of elastic properties in a fluid
gives rise to normal stress components in these flows, which do not
affect the pressure drop or torque but, as will be shown, do result
in such steady flow anomalies as the swell of a fluid jet issuing
from an open tube or the elevation of the free surface at the inner
cylinder in Couette flow if this cylinder rotates and the outer is
stationary (Weissenberg effect).

Some of these effects will be considered later. However, we
shall first consider some of the effects of elastic forces in unsteady
flows, in which they may be most pronounced.

4.4. VISCOELASTIC FLUIDS
IN SMALL DEFORMATION TIME-DEPENDENT FLOWS

So far, we have been concerned with steady (time-invariant)
flows, in which the only forces of interest are those determined by
the shearing (off-diagonal) components of the shear stress tensor.
These forces (e.g., pressure drop in tube flow, torque in rotational
flow, etc.) are thus determined by the material functions involving
only the off-diagonal stress components as a function of the (steady)
shear rate, i.e., the apparent viscosity function. An apparent vis-
costity function may be determined for any fluid, whether or not it
exhibits elastic properties. Thus the influence of elastic properties in steady flows is not immediately evident with regard to the
fluid stresses which give rise to such forces as pressure drop and
torque. Indeed, since only the apparent viscosity material function is involved, it may be said that these forces are a consequence
only of the viscous properties of the fluid. However, as will be
seen when nonlinear viscoelastic models are considered in Chap. 7,
various material properties or parameters which govern elastic behavior also influence nonlinear viscous behavior, so that these
characteristics are not necessarily separate and distinct.

Nevertheless, elastic properties are directly responsible for certain forces generated in steady flows, as illustrated in Fig. 2.20. These effects are a consequence of the "extra" normal stresses, or diagonal components of the shear stress tensor, which are present in elastic fluids in deformations for which the generalized Newtonian fluid model would predict the absence of such stresses. Indeed, we have retained these stress components in the equations of motion of the flows so far considered [e.g., Eqs. (4.3-7) and (4.3-43)], but have not yet considered the flow properties arising from solutions to specific equations. In Chap. 5, it will be shown how these equations can be solved for the various normal stress components in terms of measureable forces which they produce in different flow systems.

In Chap. 2, some of the striking consequences of elastic properties in unsteady deformations were illustrated. However, the situations considered at that time assumed a simple shear type of deformation; i.e., homogeneous stress and strain, and neglected the mass effects. The latter is equivalent to neglecting inertial forces relative to the forces required to deform the material, an assumption which is rarely valid for fluids undergoing unsteady deformations.

In this section we will illustrate the solution of the equations of motion (with nonnegligible mass or inertia), for time-dependent deformations of viscoelastic materials. We will restrict our consideration only to linear materials, since the equations describing nonlinear (i.e., non-Newtonian) materials in unsteady flows are generally nonlinear partial differential equations, and are not readily solved by elementary methods. However, the results may nevertheless be valid for real materials under conditions of small magnitude deformations, since even a nonlinear material may be approximated quite accurately by a "linearized" model if the deformation is sufficiently small. Additional principles are required in order to properly define the large amplitude or continuous deformation of a time-dependent (viscoelastic) material, and these principles will be developed in Chap. 7.

4.4.1. Wave Propagation

Consider a flat plate which is oscillating in its own plane
with an angular frequency ω and amplitude X, in contact with a large
volume of a viscoelastic fluid (of semi-infinite extent) (Fig. 4.4).
The oscillation will produce a shear wave which propagates into the
fluid, and we desire to determine the characteristics of the wave
and the force on the plate in terms of the fluid properties.

The position of the oscillating plate as a function of time may
be expressed as

$$x_o(t) = X\ e^{j\omega t} = x_o(\omega t) \tag{4.4-1}$$

and its instantaneous velocity as

$$v_o(t) = \frac{dx_o}{dt} = j\omega X\ e^{j\omega t} = V_o\ e^{j\omega t} \tag{4.4-2}$$

where V_o is the magnitude of the plate velocity. In expressions
such as this, it is to be understood that physical quantities correspond to the real part of the complex quantities. It is evident
that the velocity V_o leads the displacement X by 90°.

As there is no net motion perpendicular to the plate (in the y
direction), the velocity field in the fluid is (in Cartesian coordinates):

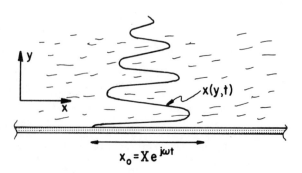

FIG. 4.4 Oscillating plate.

$$v_x = v_x(y, t) \qquad v_y = v_z = 0 \qquad (4.4\text{-}3)$$

Thus the components of the rate of strain tensor are

$$\Delta_{ij} = \dot{\gamma} \begin{bmatrix} 0 & 1 & 0 \\ 1 & 0 & 0 \\ 0 & 0 & 0 \end{bmatrix} \qquad (4.4\text{-}4)$$

where

$$\dot{\gamma} = \dot{\gamma}_{yx}(y, t) = \frac{\partial v_x(y, t)}{\partial y} \qquad (4.4\text{-}5)$$

From Eq. (4.4-3) and Table 3.1, the x component of the equation of motion reduces to

$$\rho \frac{\partial v_x}{\partial t} = \frac{\partial \tau_{yx}}{\partial y} \qquad (4.4\text{-}6)$$

This is a partial differential equation, and cannot be solved until $\tau_{yx}(y, t)$ is specified, i.e., the fluid rheological properties which relate the stress to the deformation must be specified. The appropriate boundary conditions in v_x are

$$v_x(y, t) = v_0(t) \qquad \text{at} \qquad y = 0$$
$$\qquad (4.4\text{-}7)$$
$$v_x(y, t) = 0 \qquad \text{as} \qquad y \to \infty$$

Since only the shear stress and shear rate components τ_{yx} and $\dot{\gamma}_{yx}$ in oscillatory deformation are involved, the appropriate rheological properties for any linear viscoelastic material are suitably specified by the complex viscosity of the material:

$$\eta^*(j\omega) = \frac{\tau(\omega t)}{\dot{\gamma}(\omega t)} \qquad (4.4\text{-}8)$$

This material function may be defined empirically from suitable oscillatory response measurements on the material (Chap. 5) or in

terms of an appropriate derivative or integral model (Chap. 2).
For example, the complex viscosity of a Maxwell fluid is [Eqs.
(2.4-65) and (2.4-70)]:

$$\eta^*(j\omega) = \frac{G\lambda}{1 + j\omega\lambda} = \frac{\mu}{1 + j\omega\lambda} \qquad (4.4-9)$$

Since [from Eqs. (2.4-132) and (2.4-134) the complex viscosity
is given by the ratio of the Laplace transforms of stress to strain
rate, with the Laplace variable s replaced by $j\omega$, Eqs. (4.4-6) and
(4.4-8) are best solved by transforming (4.4-6) with respect to the
time variable:

$$\rho s \bar{v}(s, y) = \frac{d\bar{\tau}(s, y)}{dy} \qquad (4.4-10)$$

where the overbars represent the transform of the variables, and
initial conditions have been taken to be zero (subscripts have been
dropped for simplicity). Replacing s by $j\omega$ in Eq. (4.4-10) gives
an equation relating the point oscillatory stress and velocity components:

$$j\omega\rho v(\omega t, y) = \frac{d\tau(\omega t, y)}{dy} \qquad (4.4-11)$$

Eliminating τ from Eqs. (4.4-8) and 4.4-11) and evaluating $\dot{\gamma}$ from
the transform of Eq. (4.4-5) results in an equation for the distribution of the oscillatory velocity component:

$$\frac{j\omega\rho}{\eta^*(j\omega)} v(\omega t, y) = \frac{d^2 v(\omega t, y)}{dy^2} \qquad (4.4-12)$$

which is subject to the boundary conditions:

$$v(\omega t, y) = v_0(j\omega) = V_0 e^{j\omega t} \qquad \text{at} \qquad y = 0$$

$$\qquad (4.4-13)$$

$$v(\omega t, y) \to 0 \qquad \qquad \text{as} \qquad y \to \infty$$

The solution of Eqs. (4.4-12) and (4.4-13) may be written:

$$v(\omega t, y) = V_o \, e^{j\omega t} \, e^{-\alpha^*(j\omega)y} \qquad (4.4\text{-}14)$$

where

$$\alpha^*(j\omega) = \left[\frac{j\omega\rho}{\eta^*(j\omega)} \right]^{1/2} \qquad (4.4\text{-}15)$$

Combining the real and imaginary parts of the exponents in Eq. (4.4-14) results in an alternate expression for the velocity field:

$$v(\omega t, y) = V_o \, e^{j(\omega t - \alpha_i y)} \, e^{-\alpha_r y} \qquad (4.4\text{-}16)$$

or

$$v(\omega t, y) = V_o \, e^{-\alpha_r y} [\cos(\omega t - \alpha_i y) + \sin(\omega t - \alpha_i y)] \qquad (4.4\text{-}17)$$

where α_r and α_i are the real and imaginary parts of α^*:

$$\alpha_r = \left\{ \frac{\omega\rho}{2(\eta'^2 + \eta''^2)} \left[(\eta'^2 + \eta''^2)^{1/2} - \eta'' \right] \right\}^{1/2} \qquad (4.4\text{-}18)$$

$$\alpha_i = \left\{ \frac{\omega\rho}{2(\eta'^2 + \eta''^2)} \left[(\eta'^2 + \eta''^2)^{1/2} + \eta'' \right] \right\}^{1/2} \qquad (4.4\text{-}19)$$

Equation (4.4-16) may be compared with the general wave equation for a propagating oscillatory wave

$$\phi = \phi_o \, e^{j(\omega t - \kappa y)} \qquad (4.4\text{-}20)$$

in which

$$\phi_o = \text{amplitude} = V_o \, e^{-ay}$$
$$\omega = \text{frequency (radians/sec)}$$
$$\kappa = \text{wave number} = 2\pi/\ell$$

ℓ = wavelength, $1/a$ = damping factor

c = ω/κ = $\omega\ell/2\pi$ = wave propagation velocity

It is evident that the amplitude of the wave in the viscoelastic medium decays exponentially, with a damping factor of $1/\alpha_r$, the wavelength of the propagating wave is $2\pi/\alpha_i$ and the velocity of propagation is ω/α_i.

The stress distribution in the fluid may be determined from Eqs. (4.4-6) and (4.4-16). The result is

$$\tau(y, \omega t) = \int_o^y \rho \frac{\partial v_x}{\partial t} \, dy = - \frac{j\omega\rho V_o}{\alpha^*(j\omega)} e^{j(\omega t - \alpha_i y)} e^{-\alpha_r y} \qquad (4.4-21)$$

or

$$\tau(y, \omega t) = -V_o\sqrt{j\omega\rho\eta^*} \, e^{j(\omega t - \alpha_i y)} e^{-\alpha_r y} \qquad (4.4-22)$$

which, when evaluated at the plate (y = 0) becomes

$$\tau_o(\omega t) = -V_o\sqrt{j\omega\rho\eta^*} \, e^{j\omega t} \qquad (4.4-23)$$

The stress exerted by the plate on the fluid is, of course, the negative of Eq. (4.4-23).

The ratio of the oscillatory stress at the plate to its oscillatory velocity is sometimes termed the *mechanical impedance*, $Z^*(j\omega)$. From Eqs. (4.4-23) and (4.4-2) this becomes:

$$Z^*(j\omega) = - \frac{\tau_o(\omega t)}{v_o(\omega t)} = \sqrt{j\omega\rho\eta^*} \qquad (4.4-24)$$

Separating the impedance into real and imaginary components determines the mechanical *resistance*, $R(\omega)$, and *reactance*, $X(\omega)$:

$$Z^*(j\omega) = R(\omega) + jX(\omega) \qquad (4.4-25)$$

where [from Eq. (4.4-24)]:

$$R(\omega) = \left(\frac{\omega\rho}{2}\right)^{1/2} \left(\sqrt{\eta'^2 + \eta''^2} + \eta''\right)^{1/2} \qquad (4.4-26)$$

and

$$X(\omega) + \left(\frac{\omega\rho}{2}\right)^{1/2} \left(\sqrt{\eta'^2 + \eta''^2} - \eta''\right)^{1/2} \qquad (4.4-27)$$

The mechanical impedance represents the amplitude ratio and phase between the force exerted by the plate (stress) and its velocity. Note that for the special case of a Newtonian fluid ($\eta'' = 0$) the mechanical resistance and reactance are equal, so that the force and velocity would be 45° out of phase. Compare this to the result for simple shear, neglecting inertia, for which the phase angle would be 90°. (This analysis neglects the mass or inertia of the plate itself, which would have to be considered in interpreting actual data. This will be considered further in Chap. 5.)

———————————————— 0 ————————————————

Example 4.5 Determine the time varying stress on a flat plate in contact with a semi-infinite Jeffreys (three-parameter) viscoelastic fluid, when the plate is subjected to a step change in velocity from zero to V_o at time zero [4.8].

Since the transient response rather than the oscillatory response is desired, it is appropriate to work in terms of Laplace transforms. The governing rransformed equation is Eq. (4.4-10):

$$\rho s \bar{v} = \frac{d\bar{\tau}}{dy}$$

where $\bar{\tau}$ is determined by the transform of the rheological function for any linear viscoelastic material:

$$\bar{\tau} = \eta(s)\dot{\bar{\gamma}} = \eta(s) \frac{d\bar{v}}{dy}$$

The transformed governing equation and boundary conditions are therefore:

$$\frac{d^2 \bar{v}}{dy^2} - \frac{\rho s}{\eta(s)}\, \bar{v} = 0$$

$v = 0$ for $t < 0$

$v = V_o U(t)$ or $\bar{v} = \dfrac{V_o}{s}$ for $y = 0$ $t \geq 0$

v and $\bar{v} \to 0$ for $y \to \infty$ $t \geq 0$

the solution of which is

$$\bar{v}(s,\, y) = \frac{V_o}{s} \exp\left[-y\sqrt{\frac{\rho s}{\eta(s)}}\,\right]$$

The transform of the stress distribution may be obtained from the integral (or derivative) of this expression, by either of the first two equations:

$$\bar{\tau}(s,\, y) = \rho s \int \bar{v}(s,\, y)\, dy = \eta(s)\, \frac{d\bar{v}(s,\, y)}{dy}$$

$$= V_o \sqrt{\frac{\rho \eta(s)}{s}} \, \exp\left[-y\sqrt{\frac{\rho s}{\eta(s)}}\,\right]$$

These relations apply to any linear viscoelastic material, in terms of the appropriate $\eta(s)$. For a three-constant Jeffreys fluid:

$$\tau + \lambda_1 \dot{\tau} = \mu(\dot{\gamma} + \lambda_2 \ddot{\gamma})$$

The corresponding $\eta(s)$ is obtained from the transform of this rheological equation:

$$\eta(s) = \frac{\bar{\tau}}{\dot{\bar{\gamma}}} = \frac{\mu(1 + \lambda_2 s)}{1 + \lambda_1 s}$$

The transform of the stress at the plate ($y = 0$) is therefore

$$\bar{\tau}_o(s) = V_o \sqrt{\frac{\rho\mu(1 + \lambda_2 s)}{s(1 + \lambda_1 s)}}$$

The inverse transform of this function has been given by Hansen [4.8] as:

$$\tau_o(t) = V_o \sqrt{\frac{\rho\mu}{2\pi\lambda_1 k}} \left\{ \sqrt{\frac{1}{T}} + (k - 1) \int_o^T \frac{\exp\,[-z(1 + k)]}{(T - z)^{1/2}} \left[I_o(z[k - 1]) + I_1(z[k - 1]) \right] dz \right\}$$

where

$$T = \frac{t}{2\lambda_1}$$

$$k = \frac{\lambda_1}{\lambda_2}$$

and I_o and I_1 are modified Bessel functions of order 0 and 1.

This expression has been evaluated numerically by Hansen, and the results are shown in the accompanying plot for various values of k. The limiting cases of k = 1 and k = ∞ correspond go Newtonian and Maxwell fluids, respectively. Also shown is the calculated average wall stress:

$$\bar{\tau}_o = \frac{1}{T_1} \int_o^{T_1} \tau_o\, dt$$

which is evidently lower than that for a purely Newtonian (inelastic) fluid for all values of k > 1.

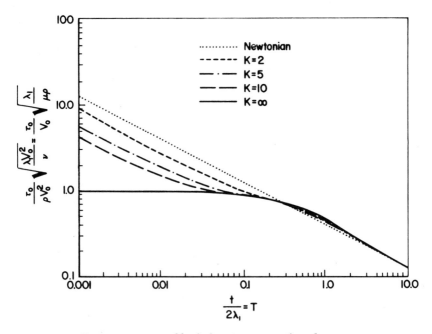

Instantaneous wall shear stress on the plate.
Reprinted from Ref. 4.8, p. 21, by courtesy
of the American Institute of Chemical Engineers.

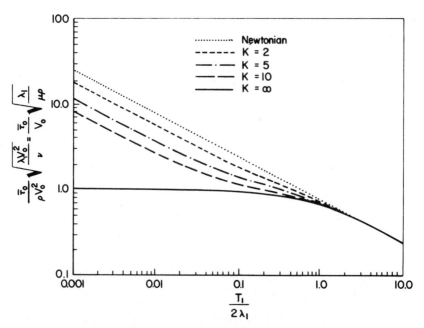

Time-average wall shear stress on the plate.
Reprinted from Ref. 4.8, p. 21, by courtesy
of the American Institute of Chemical Engineers.

4.4.2. Unsteady Response in Simple Shear

In Chap. 2, we considered the unsteady response of linear viscoelastic materials in simple shear, under the assumption that inertial
effects are negligible. In order to evaluate the conditions under
which this assumption is valid, we shall consider a more exact analysis of unsteady flow of a general linear viscoelastic fluid in simple shear. The situation is as depicted in Fig. 4.5, in which the
velocity of the moving plate, $V_x(t)$, is a function of time (and may
be transient or oscillatory). The equation of motion for this flow
is the same as Eq. (4.4-6):

$$\rho \frac{\partial v_x}{\partial t} = \frac{\partial \tau_{yx}}{\partial y} \tag{4.4-6}$$

The stress is determined by the rheological properties which, for any
linear viscoelastic fluid may be described by the relaxation function:

$$\tau_{yx} = \int_0^t \psi(t - t') \frac{\partial v_x(t')}{\partial y} \, dt \tag{4.4-28}$$

Since these equations are linear, they may be transformed to give:

$$\rho s \bar{v}(s) = \frac{d\bar{\tau}(s)}{dy} \tag{4.4-29}$$

and

$$\bar{\tau}(s) = \bar{\psi}(s) \cdot \frac{d\bar{v}(s)}{dy} \tag{4.4-30}$$

in which all initial conditions are assumed to be zero. Elimination
of $\bar{\tau}$ from these equations gives the differential equation

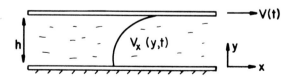

FIG. 4.5 Unsteady simple shear.

$$\frac{d^2\bar{v}(s)}{dy^2} - \frac{\rho s \bar{v}(s)}{\bar{\psi}(s)} = 0 \qquad (4.4\text{-}31)$$

which must be solved together with the boundary conditions (B.C.):

(1) $v_x = 0$ at $y = 0$

(2) $v_x = V(t)$ at $y = h$
$$(4.4\text{-}32)$$

or the equivalent in terms of the transformed variables:

(1) $\bar{v}(s) = 0$ at $y = 0$

(2) $\bar{v}(s) = \bar{V}(s)$ at $y = h$
$$(4.4\text{-}33)$$

If the plate is in steady osccilatory state, then
$\bar{V}(s) = V(\omega t) = V_o e^{j\omega t}$ and $\bar{\psi}(s) = \psi(\omega t) = \eta^*(j\omega)$, as illustrated in
the previous section. The solution of Eqs. (4.4-31) and (4.4-33) is

$$\bar{v}(s) = \bar{V}\left[\frac{e^{\bar{\alpha}y} - e^{-\bar{\alpha}y}}{e^{\bar{\alpha}h} - e^{-\bar{\alpha}h}}\right] = \bar{V}(s)\frac{\sinh\,(\bar{\alpha}y)}{\sinh\,(\bar{\alpha}h)} \qquad (4.4\text{-}34)$$

where

$$\bar{\alpha} = \alpha(s) = \sqrt{\frac{\rho s}{\bar{\psi}(s)}} \qquad (4.4\text{-}35)$$

For oscillatory flow, $\bar{\alpha}$ is identical to Eq. (4.4-15) since

$$[\bar{\psi}(s)]_{s=j\omega} = \eta^*(j\omega) \qquad (4.4\text{-}36)$$

Now for values of $\bar{\alpha}h$ less than about 0.3, the ratio of hyperbolic sines in Eq. (4.4-34) is equal to the ratio of the arguments (to within 2%). Thus, if

$$|\bar{\alpha}|h \leq 0.3 \qquad (4.4\text{-}37)$$

then, Eq. (4.4-34) reduces to

$$\bar{v}(s) = \bar{V}(s)\frac{y}{h} \qquad (4.4\text{-}38)$$

This is identical to the steady-state velocity distribution for simple shear. We are therefore led to the conclusion that inertial effects are indeed negligible if the condition of Eq. (4.4-37) holds.

For oscillatory motion, it follows from Eqs. (4.4-18) and (4.4-19) that

$$|\bar{\alpha}| = \sqrt{\alpha_r^2 + \alpha_i^2} = \left(\frac{\omega\rho}{\sqrt{\eta'^2 + \eta''^2}} \right)^{\frac{1}{2}} \tag{4.4-39}$$

We have also shown that the wavelength of the propagated shear wave is

$$\ell = \frac{2\pi}{\alpha_i} \geq \frac{2\pi}{|\bar{\alpha}|} \tag{4.4-40}$$

where the inequality follows from the fact that

$$\frac{\alpha_i}{|\bar{\alpha}|} \leq 1 \tag{4.4-41}$$

Therefore, the criterion of Eq. (4.4-37) may also be written

$$h \leq \frac{0.3}{|\bar{\alpha}|} \leq \frac{0.3\ell}{2\pi} \tag{4.4-42}$$

or

$$h \leq 0.05\ell \tag{4.4-43}$$

The conclusion is that the fluid inertia will have a negligible influence (i.e., less than 2% error) on unsteady response in simple shear if the plate spacing is less than about 5% of the wavelength of the propagated wave in the fluid. In terms of components of the complex viscosity, this is equivalent to

$$h \leq 0.3 \left[\frac{\sqrt{\eta'^2 + \eta''^2}}{\omega\rho} \right]^{\frac{1}{2}} \tag{4.4-44}$$

———————————————————— 0 ————————————————————

Example 4.6 Consider a Newtonian fluid contained between parallel plates in which the upper plate is subjected to a step force of magnitude F_o at time zero, so that the stress at this surface is

$$\tau\Big|_{y=h} = \frac{F_o U(t)}{A}$$

Derive an expression for the velocity in the fluid as a function of position and time, and thus determine a criterion analogous to Eq. (4.4-43) for the conditions under which simple shear (i.e., a linear profile) may be assumed to prevail.

In principle this problem could be solved by inverting the transforms in Eq. (4.4-34), with $\bar{\psi}(s) = \mu$ (Newtonian viscosity). However, the solution is simpler if we employ an alternative approach utilizing separation of variables, following McKelvey [4-9].

We begin with the reduced form of the equation of motion, Eq. (4.4-6):

$$\rho \frac{\partial v_x}{\partial t} = \frac{\partial \tau_{yx}}{\partial y}$$

For a Newtonian fluid, the shear stress tensor in this deformation is given by:

$$\tau_{yx} = \mu \frac{\partial v_x}{\partial y}$$

Eliminating τ_{yx} from these two equations results in the equation for the velocity distribution:

$$\frac{\partial v_x}{\partial t} = \frac{\mu}{\rho} \frac{\partial^2 v_x}{\partial y^2} = \nu \frac{\partial^2 v_x}{\partial y^2}$$

which must be solved with the boundary conditions:

(1) $v_x = 0$ at $y = 0$ all t

(2) $v_x = 0$ at $t = 0$ all y

(3) $\tau_{yx} = \frac{F_o}{A}$ at $y = h$ all $t \geq 0$

The last boundary condition, for a Newtonian fluid, is equivalent to

$$(3)' \quad \frac{\partial v_x}{\partial y} = \frac{F_o}{\mu A} \qquad at \qquad y = h \qquad all \ t \geq 0$$

Since the solution must approach the steady-state linear distribution for suffuciently long time, the final solution can be expressed as the sum (or difference) of the steady state and transient parts:

$$v_x(y, \ t) = v_x(y, \ \infty) - v_x'(y, \ t)$$

where

$$v_x(y, \ \infty) = \frac{F_o y}{\mu A}$$

is the limiting steady-state solution, which may be obtained from the general differential equation by setting $\partial v_x / \partial t = 0$.

Substitution of this expression for $v_x(y, \ t)$ into the differential equation results in an equation for the transient component, v_x':

$$\frac{\partial v_x'}{\partial t} = \nu \frac{\partial^2 v_x'}{\partial y^2}$$

The solution for v_x' may be obtained by the method of separation of variables, whereby the solution is assumed to be a product of two functions, one a function only of y, Y(y), and other a function only of t, T(t):

$$\frac{1}{\nu T} \frac{dT}{dt} = \frac{1}{Y} \frac{d^2 Y}{dy^2} = -K^2$$

where $-K^2$ is an arbitrary constant, independent of both y and t. We have now two ordinary differential equations

$$\frac{dT}{dt} = -K^2 \nu$$

and

$$\frac{d^2Y}{dy^2} = -K^2 y$$

The solution of the first equation is:

$$T = C_1 e^{-K^2 \nu t}$$

and that of the second equation is

$$Y = C_2 \sin Ky + C_3 \cos Ky$$

where C_3 must be zero because of B.C. (1). B.C. (3)' now reduces to

$$\frac{F_o}{\mu A} = \frac{F_o}{\mu A} - KC_1 C_2 e^{-K^2 \nu t} \cos Kh$$

or

$$\cos Kh = 0$$

which can only be satisfied if

$$Kh = \left(\frac{2n + 1}{2}\right)\pi$$

where n is any integer. If we rewrite the constant $KC_1 C_2$ as C_n, the solution to this point is

$$v_x = \frac{F_o y}{A\mu} - \sum_{n=0}^{\infty} C_n \exp\left[\frac{-\nu(2n + 1)^2 \pi^2 t}{4h^2}\right] \sin\left[\frac{(2n + 1)\pi y}{2h}\right]$$

The infinite series of constants C_n may be evaluated using B.C. (2) and the orthogonal properties of the sine function over the interval $0 \le y \le h$. By applying B.C. (2), multiplying the result by

$$\sin\left[\frac{(2m + 1)\pi y}{2h}\right]$$

and then integrating over this range, the expression for C_n results:

$$C_n = \frac{F_o h}{A\mu} \frac{8}{(2n + 1)^2 \pi^2} \sin\left[\frac{(2n + 1)\pi}{2}\right] = \frac{8F_o h(-1)^n}{A\mu(2n + 1)^2 \pi^2}$$

The final solution for the velocity distribution is therefore

$$v_x = \frac{F_o h}{\mu}\left\{\frac{y}{h} - \frac{8}{\pi^2}\sum_{n=0}^{\infty}\frac{(-1)^n}{(2n + 1)^2}\exp\left[\frac{-\nu(2n + 1)^2\pi^2 t}{4h^2}\right]\sin\left[\frac{(2n + 1)\pi y}{2h}\right]\right\}$$

The displacement at any point is given by

$$x = \int_o^t v_x \, dt$$

and the displacement gradient (shear strain) is:

$$\gamma = \frac{\partial x}{\partial y} = \frac{\partial}{\partial y}\int_o^t v_x \, dt = \int_o^t \frac{\partial v_x}{\partial y} \, dt$$

Evaluation of this expression gives

$$\gamma = \frac{F_o t}{\mu A}\left\{1 + \frac{4}{\pi\Phi}\sum_{n=0}^{\infty}\frac{(-1)^n}{(2n + 1)^3}\exp[-(2n+1)^2\Phi]\cos\left[\frac{(2n + 1)\pi y}{2h}\right]\right\}$$

where

$$\Phi = \frac{\pi^2 \nu t}{2h^2}$$

At y = h, as well as for sufficiently large t, this reduces to

$$\gamma = \frac{F_o t}{\mu A}$$

This also follows from the rheological equation evaluated in the upper plate:

$$(\tau)\Big|_{y=h} = \mu(\dot{\gamma})_{y=h} = \frac{F_o}{A}$$

or

$$(\gamma)\Big|_{y=h} = \left(\left|\int_o^t \frac{F_o\,dt}{\mu A}\right|\right)\Bigg|_{y=h} = \frac{F_o t}{\mu A}$$

Thus the shear strain, strain rate, and shear stress evaluated at the upper (moving) plate are the same as in simple shear.

The entire flow field approaches that of simple shear (i.e., homogeneous displacement gradient) as the strain becomes independent of y. This happens (to within about 2%) when $\Phi \geq 3$; i.e., if

$$h \leq 0.9\sqrt{\nu t}$$

Conversely, the entire flow field is essentially that of simple shear for all time greater than

$$t \geq h^2/0.8\nu$$

This would be expected to apply approximately to a viscoelastic fluid as well, if the viscosity is replaced by

$$\mu = \sqrt{\eta_o'^2 + \eta_o''^2}$$

where η_o' and η_o'' are the limiting values at zero frequency.

──────────────────────── 0 ────────────────────────

4.3.3 Oscillatory Flow in a Tube [4.4]

Consider a linear viscoelastic fluid in a cylindrical tube, subjected to a small amplitude oscillatory pressure gradient, represented by

$$\Phi(\omega t) = \frac{\partial P}{\partial z} = \Phi_o e^{j\omega t} \qquad\qquad (4.4\text{-}45)$$

The velocity components and rate of stain tensor for this flow situation are of the form:

$$v_z = v_z(r, t) \qquad v_\theta = v_r = 0 \qquad (4.4\text{-}46)$$

and the rate of strain tensor is

$$\Delta_{ij} = \dot{\gamma} \begin{bmatrix} 0 & 1 & 0 \\ 1 & 0 & 0 \\ 0 & 0 & 0 \end{bmatrix} \qquad (4.4\text{-}47)$$

where $\dot{\gamma} = \dot{\gamma}(r, t) = \dfrac{\partial v_z}{\partial r}$ (4.4-48)

The z equation of motion for this flow from Table 3.1 reduces to

$$\rho \frac{\partial v_z}{\partial t} = -\frac{\partial P}{\partial z} + \frac{1}{r}\frac{\partial}{\partial r}(r\tau_{rz}) \qquad (4.4\text{-}49)$$

As before, the shear properties of any linear viscoelastic fluid in oscillatory deformation are characterized by its complex viscosity:

$$\tau(\omega t, y) = \eta^*(j\omega)\dot{\gamma}(\omega t, y) \qquad (4.4\text{-}50)$$

Simultaneous solution of Eqs. (4.4-45), (4.4-49), and (4.4-50), subject to the boundary conditions:

(1) $v_z = 0$ at $r = R$

                                                                    (4.4-51)

(2) v_z is finite at $r = 0$

determines the velocity distribution in the tube as a function of position and frequency, for steady oscillatory conditions. As before, this is most easily accomplished by transforming the equations to replace the time-dependent variables by their transforms, and then replacing the transform variable by $j\omega$. The result is the following second-order ordinary differential equation for $v_z(r, j\omega)$:

$$j\omega\rho v_z = \Phi + \frac{1}{r}\frac{d}{dr}\left(r\frac{dv_z}{dr}\right)\left[\eta^*(j\omega)\right] \qquad (4.4\text{-}52)$$

The solution of Eq. (4.4-52), subject to the boundary conditions (4.4-51), can be written in terms of Bessel functions [10]:

$$v_z(r, \omega t) = \frac{\Phi_o\, e^{j\omega t}}{j\omega\rho}\left[1 - \frac{J_o(\kappa^* r)}{J_o(\kappa^* R)}\right] \qquad (4.4\text{-}53)$$

where

$$\kappa^* = \left[\frac{-j\omega\rho}{\eta^*(j\omega)}\right]^{1/2} = j\alpha^*(j\omega) \qquad (4.4\text{-}54)$$

and J_o is the Bessel function of the first kind and zero order. Equation (4.4-53) can be integrated over the cross section of the tube to give the volumetric flow rate:

$$Q = 2\pi \int_o^R v_z(r, j\omega)\, dr$$

$$= \frac{\pi R^2\Phi_o}{j\omega\rho}\left[1 - \frac{2J_1(\kappa^* R)}{\kappa^* R\, J_o(\kappa^* R)}\right]e^{j\omega t} = Q_o e^{j\omega t} \qquad (4.4\text{-}55)$$

This result is valid for any linear viscoelastic material. The quantity in brackets in Eq. (4.4-55) is a complex number, since the argument of the Bessel functions involves κ^*, which is complex. This result shows that the flow rate will oscillate with the same frequency as the applied pressure gradient, but will be out of phase with it. The phase difference will depend upon the value of $\kappa^* R$, which, in turn, depends upon the fluid properties ρ and η^*, as well as frequency.

For small enough frequencies (i.e., for $|\kappa^* R| \ll 1$), the Bessel functions can be expanded in a series. Under these conditions, Eq. (4.4-55) takes the form [4.4]:

$$Q = \frac{j\kappa^{*2} \pi \Phi_o R^4}{8\rho\omega} \left[1 + \frac{1}{6} \kappa^{*2} R^2 + \cdots \right] e^{j\omega t} \tag{4.4-56}$$

The fluid impedance for this system may be defined as the ratio of the oscillatory pressure gradient to the oscillatory flow rate. If the second and higher order terms in the series are negligible; (i.e., $|\kappa^* R|^2 \ll 1$), this becomes

$$z^*(j\omega) = \frac{\Phi(\omega t)}{Q(\omega t)} = \frac{8\rho\omega}{j\kappa^{*2} \pi R^4} \tag{4.4-57}$$

Separating this into real and imaginary components gives the fluid resistance and reactance:

$$z^*(j\omega) = R(\omega) + jX(\omega) \tag{4.4-58}$$

where

$$R(\omega) = \frac{8\eta'}{\pi R^4} \tag{4.4-59}$$

and

$$X(\omega) + \frac{8\eta''}{\pi R^4} \tag{4.4-60}$$

The fluid impedance thus determines the amplitude ratio and phase angle between oscillatory pressure drop and flow rate. Note that for a Newtonian fluid the reactance is zero, and Eq. (4.4-56) reduces to the Hagen—Poiseuille equation for steady flow. This result is valid only for conditions in which the inertia of the fluid is negligible compared to the fluid stresses; i.e., for ($|\kappa^* R| \ll 1$). If such is not the case, additional terms of the series in Eq. (4.4-56) would have to be considered, which would lead to more complex expressions for $R(\omega)$ and $X(\omega)$ above.

4.5. NORMAL STRESS EFFECTS IN TUBE FLOW

As previously indicated, incompressible fluids with elastic properties develop "extra" internal stresses in various flows or deformations, which are not exhibited by purely viscous (Newtonian or generalized Newtonian) fluids. These stresses result in various flow phenomena which are peculiar to elastic fluids, such as the Weissenberg (rod-climbing) and jet-swell effects. The specific stress components responsible for these phenomena are the normal stresses, characterized by the first and second normal stress differences:

$$N_1 = (\tau_{11} - \tau_{22}) = (\sigma_{11} - \sigma_{22}) \tag{4.5-1}$$

$$N_2 = (\tau_{22} - \tau_{33}) = (\sigma_{22} - \sigma_{33}) \tag{4.5-2}$$

These normal stress differences must be even functions of the shear rate (or stress), since their sign is independent of the flow direction (for a viscometric flow). These two functions are sufficient to completely define the normal stress properties of a given fluid, inasmuch as the definition of pressure provides an independent relation between the three components:

$$\tau_{11} + \tau_{22} + \tau_{33} = 0 \tag{4.5-3}$$

Methods for measuring these normal stress functions will be discussed in Chap. 5.

In this section we will consider some of the consequences of normal stresses in Poiseuille flow. The equations of motion for Poiseuille flow have been given in Eqs. (4.3-6) to (4.3-8). These equations, in terms of the components of the total stress tensor are as follows:

z comp:

$$0 = \frac{\partial \sigma_{zz}}{\partial z} + \frac{1}{r} \frac{\partial}{\partial r} (r \sigma_{rz})$$

(4.5-4)

r comp:

$$0 = \frac{\partial \sigma_{rr}}{\partial r} + \frac{\sigma_{rr} - \sigma_{\theta\theta}}{r}$$

(4.5-5)

θ comp:

$$0 = \frac{\partial \sigma_{\theta\theta}}{\partial \theta}$$

(4.5-6)

Since the deformation in Poiseuille flow (i.e., dv_z/dr) varies only in the r direction, all fluid stress (τ_{rz}, τ_{rr}, τ_{zz}, and $\tau_{\theta\theta}$, at most) which depend upon the deformation also vary in only the r direction and thus must be independent of z and θ. Consequently, the above equations reduce to

z comp:

$$0 = -\frac{\partial P}{\partial z} + \frac{1}{r} \frac{d}{dr} (r \tau_{rz})$$

(4.5-7)

r comp:

$$0 = -\frac{\partial P}{\partial r} + \frac{d\tau_{rr}}{dr} + \frac{\tau_{rr} - \tau_{\theta\theta}}{r}$$

(4.5-8)

θ comp:

$$0 = -\frac{\partial P}{\partial \theta}$$

(4.5-9)

Inasmuch as the z component equation contains only the τ_{rz} stress component and no normal stresses, and the other equations contain only normal stress components, the solution of Eq. (4.5-7) is independent of the existence of the normal stresses. That is, such characteristics as the velocity distribution and flow rate versus pressure gradient in fully developed flow which depend only on the solution of Eq. (4.5-7) are determined only by the viscous (i.e., apparent viscosity) properties, which relate τ_{rz} to the deformation or shear rate. However, for fluids exhibiting normal stresses in Poiseuille flow (i.e., viscoelastic fluids), Eqs. (4.5-8) and (4.5-9) must also be considered, and the resulting effects on the forces developed in the tube accounted for.

4.5.1. Axial Thrust and Extra Pressure

We shall now consider the effects of fluid normal stress on the resistance to the flow of a viscoelastic fluid through a tube. As pointed out above, the fluid stress component τ_{rz} produces the wall stress or drag τ_{w}, which must be resisted by the pressure gradient. In addition, the axial stress σ_{zz} which may be developed in the flow must also be resisted by an additional force or "pressure" in order to force the fluid through the tube. This may be manifested by an axial "thrust," which, at any axial position z, is given by

$$T_z = 2\pi \int_o^R r\sigma_{zz} \, dr \qquad\qquad (4.5\text{-}10)$$

In reality, when any fluid enters a tube from a reservoir or other source, an axial force or thrust is developed as a reaction to the increase in fluid momentum. Thus, T_z is actually the reduction in this thrust due to the elasticity of the fluid, which is responsible for the existence of the stress component τ_{zz}. Equation (4.5-10) may also be written:

$$T_z = -2\pi \int_o^R rP(r, z) \, dr + 2\pi \int_o^R r\tau_{zz}(r) \, dr \qquad (4.5\text{-}11)$$

Note that, by previous arguments, we have concluded that the fluid stresses (τ_{rz}, τ_{zz}, τ_{rr}, $\tau_{\theta\theta}$) must vary only in the radial direction. It follows, therefore, from Eq. (4.5-8), that the pressure P must also vary in the radial direction if the normal stresses are nonzero. For a Newtonian or generalized Newtonian (inelastic) fluid, however, these normal stresses are identically zero, and it thus follows that the pressure for such fluids must be independent of r. The shear stress component τ_{zz} depends only upon the shear deformation (i.e., shear rate), so that it exists only in the tube as a function of shear rate. It therefore varies with r from the centerline to the wall, but is independent of z in fully developed flow. If the fluid enters the tube from a reservoir in which the shear rate is negligibly small, the stress component τ_{zz} will likewise be small in the reservoir. This stress is developed in the entrance region of the tube, and may be considered to be associated with elastic straining in this region, inasmuch as it exists only for elastic fluids. Thus an additional force or pressure must exist in the reservoir to balance this extra elastic stress, and force the fluid through the tube.

That this "extra stress" is equivalent to an additional "pressure" superimposed upon the fluid in the tube may be readily shown as follows [4.11]. Integrating Eq. (4.5-10) by parts gives:

$$\frac{T_z}{\pi} = [\sigma_{zz} r^2]_0^R - \int_0^R r^2 \frac{\partial \sigma_{zz}}{\partial r} \, dr \qquad (4.5\text{-}12)$$

The derivative in the integrand can be evaluated with the aid of Eq. (4.5-5) to give

$$\frac{\partial \sigma_{zz}}{\partial r} = \frac{\partial \sigma_{rr}}{\partial r} + \frac{\partial (\sigma_{zz} - \sigma_{rr})}{\partial r} = \frac{\partial (\sigma_{zz} - \sigma_{rr})}{\partial r} + \frac{\sigma_{\theta\theta} - \sigma_{rr}}{r} \qquad (4.5\text{-}13)$$

so that Eq. (4.5-12) becomes:

$$\frac{T_z}{\pi} = R^2\sigma_{zz}(R, z) - \int_o^R (\sigma_{\theta\theta} - \sigma_{rr})r \, dr - \int_o^R r^2 d(\sigma_{zz} - \sigma_{rr}) \quad (4.5\text{-}14)$$

Again evaluating the last integral by parts:

$$\int_o^R r^2 \, d(\sigma_{zz} - \sigma_{rr}) = [r^2(\sigma_{zz} - \sigma_{rr}]_o^R - \int_o^R (\sigma_{zz} - \sigma_{rr})2r \, dr \quad (4.5\text{-}15)$$

and substituting the result into Eq. (4.5-14) gives, upon cancelling the $\sigma_{zz}(R)$ terms:

$$T_z = \pi R^2 \sigma_{rr}(R, z) + \pi \int_o^R (2\sigma_{zz} - \sigma_{rr} - \sigma_{\theta\theta})r \, dr \quad (4.5\text{-}16)$$

where $(2\sigma_{zz} - \sigma_{rr} - \sigma_{\theta\theta})$ in the integrand is identical to $2N_1 + N_2$. Rearranging Eq. (4.5-16), and noting from Eq. (4.5-10) that T_z cancels with the first term in the integral, there results

$$-\sigma_{rr}(R, z) = \frac{1}{R^2} \int_o^R - (\sigma_{rr} + \sigma_{\theta\theta})r \, dr$$

$$= \frac{2}{R^2} \int_o^R rP(r, z) \, dr + \frac{1}{R^2} \int_o^R \tau_{zz}r \, dr \quad (4.5\text{-}17)$$

where the second form follows from Eq. (4.5-3). Evaluating the first integral by parts, this may be written

$$-\sigma_{rr}(R, z) = P(R, z) - \frac{1}{R^2} \int_o^R r^2 \frac{\partial P(r, z)}{\partial r} \, dr + \frac{1}{R^2} \int_o^R \tau_{zz}r \, dr$$

$$(4.5\text{-}18)$$

Eliminating the pressure gradient by means of Eq. (4.5-8), this becomes

$$-\sigma_{rr}(R, z) = P(R, z) - \frac{1}{R^2} \int_0^R [r^2 \frac{d\tau_{rr}}{dr} + r(\tau_{rr} - \tau_{\theta\theta} + \tau_{zz})] \, dr$$

$$(4.5-19)$$

which may also be written in terms of the normal stress differences

$$\sigma_{rr}(R, z) = -P(R, z) + \frac{1}{3R^2} \int_0^R [r^2 \frac{d(N_2 - N_1)}{dr} + 2r(N_1 + 2N_2)] \, dr$$

$$(4.5-20)$$

where the following relations from rearrangement of Eqs. (4.5-1) to
(4.5-3) have been used:

$$\tau_{zz} = \frac{1}{3}(N_2 + 2N_1) \qquad\qquad (4.5-21)$$

$$\tau_{rr} = \frac{1}{3}(N_2 - N_1) \qquad\qquad (4.5-22)$$

$$\tau_{\theta\theta} = -\frac{1}{3}(2N_2 + N_1) \qquad\qquad (4.5-23)$$

Now $-\sigma_{rr}(R)$ is simply the total stress exerted by the fluid on
the inside of the tube wall, which is that which is measured when the
"wall pressure" is sensed. It is evident from above that this is
identical to the true pressure for an inelastic fluid in fully developed flow for which all normal stresses and normal stress differences
are zero.

Since the normal stresses are independent of z, they contribute
uniformly to an increase in wall stress along the tube right up to
the exit. When the fluid exits the tube, all shear stresses relax
and the pressure is equal to the ambient pressure. However, the normal stress effects persist right up to the exit plane (assuming un-
disturbed fully developed flow exists at this point), resulting in
an "exit pressure" at the open end of the tube which is greater than
the ambient pressure. This may be detected by measuring the "pressure"

(i.e., total wall stress) at various points along the tube, and
extrapolating to the end. This "exit pressure" should be identical
to the increased pressure accompanying the elastic entrance effect
mentioned earlier.

This increased "pressure" or wall stress due to the elastic normal stresses may be evaluated quantitatively from Eq. (4.5-20) if
the normal stress differences as a function of shear rate are known
or can be determined (e.g., by methods to be described in Chap. 5).
Relatively few data exist for N_2, although what there are indicate
that it is negative and smaller in magnitude than N_1. Assuming such
data are available, the following illustrates a possible method of
utilizing them to evaluate expressions such as Eq. (4.5-20).

If first and second normal stress difference data are available,
it may be assumed that they may be represented adequately by a
straight line on a log-log plot over the range of shear rates of interest (often a very reasonable assumption). Likewise we may assume
that the viscous character of the fluid may also be represented by
the Power law model. Thus the assumed stress-shear rate relations
are:

$$\tau_{rz} = -m \left(-\frac{dv_z}{dr} \right)^n = -\tau_w \frac{r}{R} \tag{4.5-24}$$

$$N_1 = A \left(-\frac{dv_z}{dr} \right)^a = A \left(\frac{\tau_w r}{Rm} \right)^{a/n} \tag{4.5-25}$$

$$N_2 = -B \left(-\frac{dv_z}{dr} \right)^b = -B \left(\frac{\tau_w r}{Rm} \right)^{b/n} \tag{4.5-26}$$

Recall that the wall stress, τ_w, is not affected by the normal stresses,
since it is determined by the pressure gradient. Substituting Eqs.
(4.5-25) and (4.5-26) into Eq. (4.5-20), and performing the integration, results in:

$$\sigma_{rr}(R, z) = -P(R, z) - \frac{B_1}{3} \left(\frac{b+4n}{b+2n} \right) R^{b/n} - \frac{A_1}{3} \left(\frac{a-2n}{a+2n} \right) R^{a/n} \tag{4.5-27}$$

where $A_1 = A\tau_w/Rm$, $B_1 = B\tau_w/Rm$. A similar process could be used to evaluate the axial thrust component from Eq. (4.5-16) in terms of normal stress parameters.

PROBLEMS

4-1. What pressure drop would be required to pump a fluid at a rate of 3 gal/h through a 50-ft length of 1/4 in. pipe, if the fluid is:

(a) Newtonian, with a viscosity of 5 cP

(b) Power law, with a flow index of 1.5 and an apparent viscosity of 5 cP at a shear rate of 100 sec^{-1}

(c) Bingham plastic, with a plastic viscosity of 2 cP and an apparent viscosity of 5 cP at a shear rate of 100 sec^{-1}

4-2. Derive an expression relating the pressure drop and volumetric flow rate for the following fluids in Poiseuille flow:

(a) Reiner-Philippoff

(b) Casson (see Prob. 2-2)

(c) Meter

(d) Ellis

4-3. Derive the "Buckingham-Reiner" equation, (4.3-40), starting with Eq. (4.3-36).

4-4. For a Reiner-Philippoff fluid flowing around a cylinder, as in Example 4.2, determine expressions for the nonzero stress components in terms of the nonzero velocity gradient components.

4-5. A torque of 10^6 dyn-cm is applied to the outer cylinder of a Couette apparatus, for which the radius of the inner cylinder is 3 cm and that of the outer is 5 cm. If the inner cylinder is stationary, calculate the velocity of the outer cylinder for each of the fluids in Prob. 4-1. The length is 10 cm.

4-6. The Bingham plastic mud of Example 4.3 ($\tau_o = 65$ dyn/cm^2, $\mu = 800$ cP) is contained in a cylindrical bucket of 6 in. I.D. and

8 in. long. A cylindrical rod 1 in. in diameter is inserted
into the center of the bucket, and a torque applied to it.
What is the minimum torque required to start the rod moving?
If the torque is twice this minimum value, how much of the mud
will be moving?

4-7. Derive an expression relating pressure drop and volumetric flow
rate per unit width for each of the following fluids in a narrow
rectangular slit (e.g., between two stationary parallel planes
a distance of h apart) with a very small depth/width ratio
(see figure):
(a) Newtonian
(b) Power law
(c) Bingham plastic

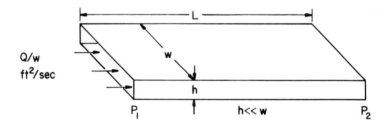

4-8. Derive an expression for the radial pressure distribution between the cylinders in a Couette flow of a Power law fluid.

4-9. Derive the equations for the velocity distribution and the relation between applied torque and angular velocity of the moving cylinder for a Meter fluid in Couette flow.

4-10. Set up the equations which must be solved to determine the flow
field in a Power law fluid in steady laminar flow around a
stationary sphere.

4-11. Set up the equations which must be solved to determine the
       flow field in a Bingham plastic in steady laminar flow in a
       uniformly diverging duct of square cross section.

4-12. Set up the equations which must be solved to determine the
       flow field in a Cross fluid in steady radial flow between two
       flat parallel discs (see figure). Assume that the hole is
       much smaller than the plates so that its influence on the
       velocity distribution is negligible, that is, the traverse
       velocity component, v_z, may be neglected.

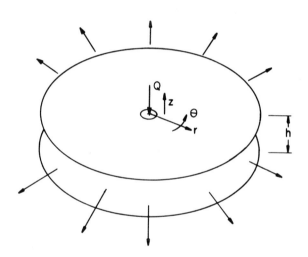

4-13. Set up the equations which must be solved to determine the
       flow field in the radial flow between concentric porous cyl-
       inders, shown in Fig. 3.7, for a Power law fluid.

4-14. Derive the specific equations which must be solved to deter-
       mine the flow field (velocity distribution) for an Ellis
       fluid in steady laminar flow in a conical conduit (see figure).
       Don't forget to include the appropriate boundary conditions

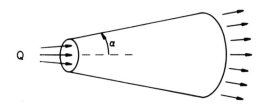

which must be used to determine the solution. Pay particular
attention to the choice of a coordinate system which results
in the simplest equations and boundary conditions.

4-15.   The flow of drilling mud during the process of drilling an
oil well can be described as helical flow in the annulus between the fixed casing and the rotating drilling shaft (see
figure). The shaft rotates with an angular velocity Ω and at
the same time translates in the axial (z) direction with a
velocity V. At steady state, there is a pressure drop
$(P_1 - P_2)$ per length L in the annulus.

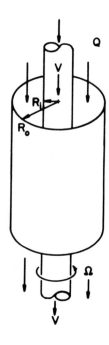

(a) Define the flow situation in the annulus, by specifying the nonzero velocity components, velocity gradient components, and the nonzero components of the rate of strain tensor Δ_{ij}. What stress components in the fluid would be nonzero if the fluid is assumed to be purely viscous?

(b) What is the second invariant of the rate of strain tensor in terms of the nonzero velocity components if the fluid is incompressible?

(c) If the fluid is assumed to be a Bingham plastic, write the appropriate expressions for the nonzero stress components.

(d) Write the specific equations of motion for this system which must be solved with the equations from (c) to determine the velocity distribution in the system.

(e) If the fluid is assumed to be Newtonian, repeat (c) and (d) above, and solve the resulting equations for the distribution of the nonzero components. State explicitly the boundary conditions you use to determine the solution.

(f) Derive an expression for the total volumetric flow of the (Newtonian) fluid as a function of the shaft velocity and pressure gradient in the annulus, and an expression for the torque on the shaft required to overcome fluid drag in the annulus.

4-16. Derive expressions for the real and imaginary components of the complex viscosity of an unknown linear viscoelastic fluid in terms of measured values of the wavelength and damping factor of a wave propagated into the fluid from an oscillating plate.

4-17. For an oscillating plate in contact with a large volume of a viscoelastic material, derive expressions for the real and imaginary components of the complex modulus of the material from measurements of the "in-phase" and "out-of-phase" components of the force exerted by the plate on the fluid and its displacement.

4-18. Verify Eqs. (4.4-18) and (4.4-19) for the real and imaginary
       components of the complex parameter $\alpha^*(j\omega)$.

4-19. Consider a Maxwell fluid with a density of 1.0 g/cm^3, viscos-
       ity of 1.2 P, and relaxation time at 0.5 sec, contained be-
       tween parallel plates. Estimate: (a) the maximum separation
       between the plates for which the fluid inertia may be neglected
       if one plate is subjected to a constant applied force for a
       duration of 0.1 sec; and (b) the maximum mass/area of the
       moving plate for which recoil would be expected, if the plate
       separation is equal to the value calculated in part (a).

4-20. Consider a viscoelastic fluid described by the Jeffreys model:

$$\tau + \lambda_1 \dot{\tau} = \mu(\dot{\gamma} + \lambda_2 \ddot{\gamma})$$

       contained between parallel flat plates, one of which is sub-
       jected to a pulse stress of magnitude τ_w and duration t_1.
       Derive a criterion for "recoil" of the plate, accounting for
       its inertia (assume inertia of the fluid to be negligible).

4-21. Derive an expression for the fluid impedance of a viscoelastic
       fluid with complex viscosity $\eta^*(j\omega)$ in a cylindrical tube,
       taking into account the first two terms in the series in Eq.
       (4.5-56). Determine a criterion for the limits of validity
       of the result.

4-22. The results of Sec. 4.5 illustrated the influence of both the
       first and second normal stress differences upon total "pres-
       sure" in tube flow. Determine criteria for which (a) the
       influence of the second normal stress difference is negligi-
       ble, and (b) the influence of all normal stress components
       is negligible.

4-23. Consider the swell of a jet of viscoelastic fluid issuing
       from the end of an open tube. Derive an equation for R_j/R
       for a Maxwell fluid, from a consideration of the recoil or

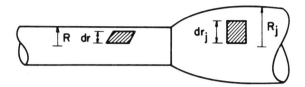

"recoverable shear" experienced by the fluid due to sudden release of the stress when the fluid leaves the tube. With respect to the figure, determine the value of the ratio dr/dr_j for a fluid element in terms of the strain recoil (recoverable shear), and integrate the result over the tube radius to obtain

$$\frac{R_j}{R} = \frac{1}{2}\left[\sqrt{1 + \gamma_{Rw}^2} + \frac{1}{\gamma_{Rw}} \ln\left(\gamma_{Rw} + \sqrt{1 + \gamma_{Rw}^2}\right)\right]$$

where

γ_{Rw} = wall value of "recoverable shear"

$$= \frac{\lambda\tau_w}{\mu} = \frac{\tau_w}{G}$$

NOTE

1. That is, there is "no slip" between a fluid and a solid boundary in contact with it. This condition has been generally confirmed experimentally.

Chapter 5

VISCOMETRY AND RHEOGONIOMETRY

5.1. INTRODUCTION

In this chapter some of the experimental methods which may be used to determine various material functions are considered. Specifically, we will consider methods for determining the apparent viscosity and normal stress material functions in steady flows, and certain (linear) viscoelastic functions in unsteady flows. An analysis of the equations of motion for the various flow systems will be presented, with the objective of determining relations between measurable system variables (such as pressure and flow rate, or force and displacement or velocity) and the values of the fundamental dynamic and kinematic variables (stress and strain or rate of strain components) at a common material point in the system. The latter serve to define the empirical material functions, and hence the rheological properties, of the material under test.

5.2. MEASURED VERSUS FUNDAMENTAL VARIABLES

Chapter 4 illustrated the role of the fluid mechanic, which is the determination of the forces or stresses arising when a given material (fluid) with known rheological properties is caused to deform or flow in a given manner. The result is a relation between certain

measurable forces and displacements in the system (such as pressure
drop as a function of flow rate, or torque as a function of angular
velocity), which are a unique function of the rheological properties
of the deforming material. It should thus be possible to "work back-
ward" from measurements of these forces and displacements and a knowledge of the system equations which relate them to stress and strain
components in order to determine the unknown rheological properties
of a material. This is the objective of the rheologist.

Since rheological properties are defined by relations between
certain specific components of stress and strain, for an isotropic
material they are characteristic only of the material, and are independent of the system in which the material is deformed. However,
the directly measurable variables, e.g., forces and displacements, are
characteristic of the system as well as the material and are inde-
not always simply and directly related to the components of stress
and strain which are necessary to define the desired rheological properties. Only in the ideal case of simple shear are the external
forces and displacements simply and directly related to components
of shear stress and strain at a given point in the material. This
is because simple shear is "homogeneous"; i.e., all stress and strain
components have the same values at all points within the material as
well as at the boundaries. A true simple shear configuration, however, presents certain experimental difficulties which make it impractical to use with many materials. In most practical testing systems, the stress and strain components are not homogeneous, and
hence vary from point to point within the deforming material. As a
consequence, measured values of external forces and displacements
are not simply related to appropriate components of stress and strain
at a point in the material. The problem is not only to determine
the relation between measurable variables and corresponding stress
and strain components, but to evaluate these components at the same
point in the material. It should be evident that, where stress and
strain components are inhomogeneous, evaluation of each of these at
the same material point (i.e., same element of material) is necessary
if relations between them are to be used to define material properties.

In this chapter we will describe methods for determining the
steady viscous (apparent viscosity) and normal stress material functions from measurements of system forces and displacements in various
test systems. The term *viscometry* refers to the former (determination of shear stress–shear rate relations), while the term *rheogoniometry* implies the determination of other (normal) stress functions
as well. We will also consider some methods which may be used to
determine certain of the linear (small deformation) time-dependent
material functions for viscoelastic fluids.

A distinction should be made between the terms "viscometer" and
"viscosimeter." As used herein, viscometer will refer to an instrument which can be used to measure absolute values of shear stress
and shear rate (and hence explicitly define the apparent viscosity of
any fluid material). The term viscosimeter, on the other hand, implies an instrument for measuring some quantity which is an unspeci-
fied function of the viscous properties of the fluid (such as the
flow time for a given volume through an orifice), but which does not
provide a direct measure of shear stress or shear rate. Viscosim-
eters can often be calibrated with Newtonian fluids to provide an
accurate relative measure of Newtonian viscosity, but are generally
useless for non-Newtonian fluids. We shall, therefore, be concerned
only with viscometers. Details of some of the commercially available
instruments for making viscometric and rheogoniometric measurements
are given in Ref. 5.7. However much of the equipment being used in
research laboratories for such measurements is of special design and
construction.

There is no guarantee that a knowledge of all of the material
functions discussed herein provides a complete rheological description of a given viscoelastic fluid. Indeed, other material functions
may be defined, such as the oscillatory response of normal stresses,
transient stress or strain response, superimposed oscillatory and
steady deformations, etc. There is no way to determine exactly how
many material functions are sufficient to completely define the rheological behavior of a given material, since this depends largely on
the complexity of the material. A typical approach is to postulate

a general constitutive model relating stress and strain tensors which may be used, in principle, to predict any material function for a specified deformation. Measurements of the most common functions would serve to guide formulation of the model and the evaluation of the constants or parameters contained therein. The validity of the model would then be its ability to correctly predict other response characteristics or material functions in other deformations. The principles necessary for the formulation of such general models will be discussed in Chaps. 6 and 7.

5.3. VISCOMETRIC FLOWS

Simple shear is one of a class of flows in which only one velocity component (see note 1) is nonzero, and this component varies in only one direction which is normal to the direction of flow. Consequently there is one component of the rate of strain tensor, which is designated the shear rate. These deformations are known as *viscometric flows*, so named because these flow systems are those commonly employed for determining viscous properties. Some of the most common viscometric flows are illustrated in Fig. 5.1. For all such systems it is convenient to label the coordinate axes so that the "z^1" direction coincides with the direction of the nonzero velocity component, the "z^2" direction is the direction in which this velocity varies, and "z^3" is the "neutral" direction. Thus in each case, the shear rate involves only the gradient of the "1" velocity component (v_1) in the "2" direction, and hence $\dot{\gamma}_{12} = \dot{\gamma}$ is the nonzero strain rate component. The state of stress in a material subjected to such a deformation is completely defined by the stress components τ_{12}, τ_{11}, τ_{22}, and τ_{33}. Note that this convention results in the same general form for the stress and strain rate tensors for all viscometric flows:

I. <u>Simple Shear</u> (Drag Flow)

Measure: F, V

Require: $\tau_{12} = \dfrac{F}{A}$, $\dot{\gamma}_{12} = \dfrac{V}{h}$

II. <u>Pressure Flow in Channel</u> (Plane Poiseuille)

Measure: Q, $\dfrac{\Delta P}{L}$

Require: $\tau_{12} = \tau_{xy}$, $\dot{\gamma}_{12} = \dot{\gamma}_{xy}$

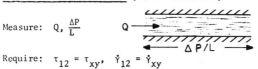

III. <u>Pressure Flow in Tube</u> (Poiseuille)

Measure: Q, $\dfrac{\Delta P}{L}$

Require: $\tau_{12} = \tau_{zr}$, $\dot{\gamma}_{12} = \dot{\gamma}_{zr}$

IV. <u>Rotational Flow Between Concentric Cylinders</u> (Couette)

Measure: T, Ω

Require: $\tau_{12} = \tau_{\theta r}$, $\dot{\gamma}_{12} = \dot{\gamma}_{\theta r}$

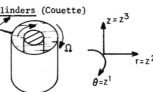

V. <u>Rotational Flow Between Cone and Plate</u>

Measure: T, Ω

Require: $\tau_{12} = \tau_{\phi\theta}$, $\dot{\gamma}_{12} = \dot{\gamma}_{\phi\theta}$

VI. <u>Rotational Flow Between Disc and Plate</u>

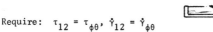
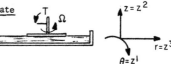

FIG. 5.1 Viscometric flows.

$$
\sigma_{ij} = \begin{bmatrix} -P + \tau_{11} & \tau_{12} & 0 \\ \tau_{21} & -P + \tau_{22} & 0 \\ 0 & 0 & -P + \tau_{33} \end{bmatrix}
$$

$$
= -P \begin{bmatrix} 1 & 0 & 0 \\ 0 & 1 & 0 \\ 0 & 0 & 1 \end{bmatrix} + \begin{bmatrix} \tau_{11} & 0 & 0 \\ 0 & \tau_{22} & 0 \\ 0 & 0 & \tau_{33} \end{bmatrix} + \tau \begin{bmatrix} 0 & 1 & 0 \\ 1 & 0 & 0 \\ 0 & 0 & 0 \end{bmatrix} \qquad (5.3\text{-}1)
$$

$$
\Delta_{ij} = \begin{bmatrix} 0 & \dot{\gamma}_{12} & 0 \\ \dot{\gamma}_{21} & 0 & 0 \\ 0 & 0 & 0 \end{bmatrix} = \dot{\gamma} \begin{bmatrix} 0 & 1 & 0 \\ 1 & 0 & 0 \\ 0 & 0 & 0 \end{bmatrix} \qquad (5.3\text{-}2)
$$

For Newtonian and generalized Newtonian viscous incompressible fluids, the 1:1 correspondence between τ_{ij} and Δ_{ij} would preclude the existence of the nonzero normal (deviatoric) stress components in Eq. (5.3-1). However, as will be illustrated later, a more general nonlinear relation between τ_{ij} and Δ_{ij} would predict one or more nonzero normal stress components in viscometric flows. These stress components may also arise in fluids as a consequence of elastic properties. The effects of these normal stresses may be exhibited in flow systems in many ways, some of which have been illustrated in Fig. 2.20.

Note that a given coordinate system may have different "numbers" associated with a given coordinate direction, depending upon the flow direction. For example, both Poiseuille and Couette flows are described in terms of cylindrical coordinates, although the θ direction is the "3" coordinate in the former, and the "1" direction in the latter.

For each viscometric flow in Fig. 5.1, the measured dynamic (force or pressure) and kinematic (flow or velocity) variables are indicated, together with the corresponding shear stress and strain rate components to which they are related. It is the object of the following section on viscometry to derive the relations between these measured variables and appropriate shear stress and shear rate components at a given point in the material. Since these components are, in general, a function of position within the system, it is necessary that they both be evaluated at the same point, and are hence relative to the same material element if they are to be meaningful in the definition of material properties.

5.4. VISCOMETRY

In this section we shall present all component equations of motion for various steady viscometric flows including all possible non-zero terms consistent with the stress tensor of Eq. (5.3-1). However, solutions will be obtained here only for those equations which are needed to define the shear stress and shear rate components in terms of measured variables, which in turn serve to define the apparent viscosity function, $\eta(\dot{\gamma}) = \tau_{12}/\dot{\gamma}$. The remaining equations, which involve the normal stress components, will be utilized in the section on Rheogoniometry to determine relationships between these normal stress components and other measurable forces or displacements on the system [i.e., the normal stress material functions $\theta_1(\dot{\gamma})$ and $\theta_2(\dot{\gamma})$].

5.4.1. Poiseuille Flow

As described initially in Sec. 3.2, Poiseuille flow involves the steady axial laminar flow of an incompressible fluid in a circular tube, under conditions in which end effects can be ignored. With reference to cylindrical coordinates which coincide with the tube geometry, the velocity components are:

$$v^1 = \frac{dz}{dt} = v_z(r) \qquad v^2 = v^3 = 0 \qquad\qquad (5.4\text{-}1)$$

The physical and tensor velocity components $v^1 = v_z(r)$ are identical for this system. Hence the rate of strain tensor components from Table 3.2 become:

$$\Delta_{ij} = \begin{bmatrix} 0 & \Delta_{rz} & 0 \\ \Delta_{rz} & 0 & 0 \\ 0 & 0 & 0 \end{bmatrix}$$

where

$$\Delta_{rz} = \dot{\gamma} = \frac{dv_z(r)}{dr} \tag{5.4-2}$$

and the stress tensor components are, at most

$$\sigma_{ij} = \begin{bmatrix} -P + \tau_{zz} & \tau_{zr} & 0 \\ \tau_{rz} & -P + \tau_{rr} & 0 \\ 0 & 0 & -P + \tau_{\theta\theta} \end{bmatrix} \tag{5.4-3}$$

where $\tau_{zr} = \tau_{rz} = \tau(r)$. Since the deviatoric stress components are unique functions of the rate of strain, which varies only in the radial direction, they must therefore depend only upon the r coordinate. The component equations of motion from Table 3.1 (cylindrical coordinates) reduce to:

$z = z^1$:

$$\frac{\partial P}{\partial z} = \frac{1}{r} \frac{\partial}{\partial r} (r\tau_{rz}) \tag{5.4-4}$$

$r = z^2$:

$$\frac{\partial P}{\partial r} = \frac{1}{r} \frac{\partial}{\partial r} (r\tau_{rr}) - \frac{\tau_{\theta\theta}}{r} \tag{5.4-5}$$

$\theta = z^3$:

$$\frac{1}{r} \frac{\partial P}{\partial \theta} = 0 \tag{5.4-6}$$

where

$$P = P + \rho gh \tag{5.4-7}$$

and h is the vertical elevation above a reference level.

As shown in Sec. 4.3.1, Eq. (5.4-4) can readily be solved for the radial distribution of the stress component τ_{rz}:

$$\tau_{rz} = -r \frac{\tau_w}{R} = \frac{\Delta Pr}{2L} \tag{5.4-8}$$

where

$$\tau_w = -(\tau_{rz})_{r=R} = -\frac{\Delta PR}{2L} \tag{5.4-9}*$$

is the shear stress exerted by the fluid on the wall (see note 2).

A. Apparent Viscosity (Viscosity Function)

From Eq. (5.4-8) it is evident that measurement of the pressure gradient ($\Delta P/L$) provides a direct determination of the shear stress at any point in tube. The definition of the apparent viscosity of the fluid also requires the determination of the shear rate at some point in the tube. An expression for the shear rate can be derived by considering the following expression for the volumetric flow rate, Q:

$$Q = \int_{o}^{R} 2\pi r v_z(r) \ dr \tag{5.4-10}$$

Integrating Eq. (5.4-10) by parts, with the condition that $v_z = 0$ at r = R, leads to

$$Q = -\pi \int_{o}^{R} r^2 \ dv_z = -\pi \int_{o}^{R} r^2 \left(\frac{dv_z}{dr}\right) dr \tag{5.4-11}$$

Equation (5.4-8) can now be used to change variables from r to τ (for a given τ_w and R) to give

$$Q = \frac{\pi R^3}{\tau_w^3} \int_0^{\tau_w} \tau^2 \dot{\gamma} \, d\tau \tag{5.4-12}$$

or

$$\Gamma \tau_w^3 = 4 \int_0^{\tau_w} \tau^2 \dot{\gamma} \, d\tau \tag{5.4-13}$$

where

$$\Gamma = \frac{4Q}{\pi R^3} \tag{5.4-14}*$$

As shown in Chap. 4, Γ is identical to the shear rate evaluated at the tube wall for a Newtonian fluid. However, it does not have the same significance for any general (non-Newtonian) fluid, as seen below. If $\dot{\gamma}_w$ represents the true shear rate at the wall, the derivative of Eq. (5.4-13) with respect to τ_w [by use of Leibnitz' rule (see note 3) for differentiating an integral] can be written:

$$\frac{d(\Gamma \tau_w^3)}{d\tau_w} = 4\tau_w^2 \dot{\gamma}_w \tag{5.4-15}$$

Solving for $\dot{\gamma}_w$ and rearranging:

$$\dot{\gamma}_w = \frac{1}{4\tau_w^2} \frac{d(\Gamma \tau_w^3)}{d\tau_w} = \frac{\tau_w}{4} \left[\frac{d\Gamma}{d\tau_w} + 3 \frac{\Gamma}{\tau_w} \right] \tag{5.4-16}$$

It is evident that, although the wall shear stress is determined explicitly from pressure measurements, both pressure drop (τ_w) and corresponding flow rate (Γ) measurements are required to determine the wall shear rate.

Equation (5.4-16) can also be written:

$$\dot{\gamma}_w = \left(\frac{3n' + 1}{4n'}\right)\Gamma \qquad\qquad (5.4\text{-}17)^*$$

where

$$n' = \frac{d \ln \tau_w}{d \ln \Gamma} \qquad\qquad (5.4\text{-}18)^*$$

is the point slope of the τ_w versus Γ plot on log-log coordinates, at a specific value of τ_w. Note that if the fluid obeys the Power law model, the plot will be a straight line of slope n, the Power law index. Thus, for a true Power law fluid, n' is identical to the flow index [compare Eqs. (4.3-29) and (5.4-17)]. Of course for a Newtonian fluid n = n' = 1, and $\dot{\gamma}_w = \Gamma$ as previously shown.

Equation (5.4-12) is known as the *Rabinowitsch equation*, and the above development is attributed variously to Rabinowitsch, Mooney, and Weisenberg [5.1, 5.2]. Note that Eq. (5.4-12) can be used to calculate (numerically) the volumetric flow rate in a tube from independent data for shear stress versus shear rate, obtained from any source.

The quantities τ_w and Γ are sometimes referred to as consistency variables, as these are the directly measurable variables which determine the material consistency. The latter is defined by the viscous material function, or apparent viscosity:

$$\eta(\dot{\gamma}) = \frac{\tau_w}{\dot{\gamma}_w} = \frac{\tau_w}{\Gamma}\left(\frac{4n'}{3n' + 1}\right) \qquad\qquad (5.4\text{-}19)$$

This should not be confused with the quantity:

$$\mu_e \equiv \frac{\tau_w}{\Gamma} \qquad\qquad (5.4\text{-}20)$$

which is the viscosity the fluid would have if it were Newtonian, and may be called the *effective viscosity*. As seen from Eq. (5.4-19), the difference between μ_e and η depends upon the value of the parameter n', and may often be neglected in approximate work (e.g., for n' = 2, μ_e and η differ by about 13%).

——————————————————————————— 0 ———————————————————————————

Example 5.1   The following data on pressure drop and flow rate of a polymer solution were obtained on a tube of 0.1 cm radius and 10 cm long:

$-\Delta P$ (mm H$_2$O)	Q (cm^3/sec)
16.3	0.0157
40.8	0.0393
69.4	0.0785
108	0.157
173	0.393
240	0.785
306	1.57
398	3.93
490	7.85

a.   Convert these data to corresponding values of τ_w and Γ.

b.   From an appropriate plot of these data, determine corresponding values of $\dot{\gamma}_w$, and hence $\eta(\dot{\gamma})$.

c.   What can you conclude with regard to the viscous character of this fluid in steady shear?

Solution:

a.   Conversion factors for determining τ_w and Γ are:

$$\tau_w = \frac{\Delta P R}{2L} = \Delta P \left(\frac{0.1}{20}\right) \left(\frac{1}{0.0102} \frac{dyn/cm^2}{mm \ H_2O}\right) = 0.49 \ \Delta P \ (dyn/cm^2)$$

$$\Gamma = \frac{4Q}{\pi R^3} = Q \frac{4}{\pi(10^{-3})} = 1.27 \times 10^3 Q \ (sec^{-1})$$

The converted data are shown plotted in the figure.

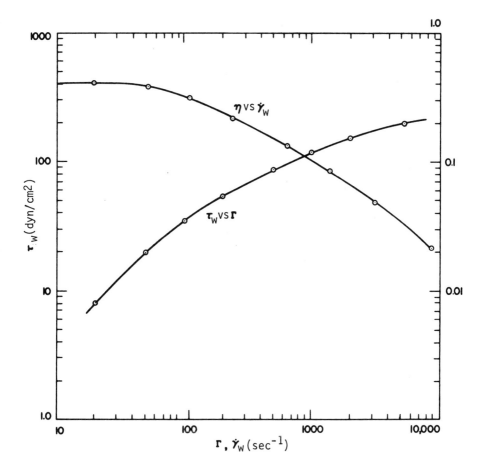

b. Values of $\dot{\gamma}_w$ are obtained by use of Eq. (5.4-17):

$$\dot{\gamma}_w = \Gamma\left(\frac{3n' + 1}{4n'}\right)$$

where n' is the point slope of the above curve. Values of these slopes obtained manually from tangents drawn to the curve are given below, together with calculated values of $\dot{\gamma}_w$ and corresponding values of τ_w from the curve:

$\Gamma(\sec^{-1})$	$\tau_w(\text{dyn/cm}^2)$	n'	$\dfrac{3n'+1}{4n'}$	$\dot\gamma_w(\sec^{-1})$	$\eta = \tau_w/\dot\gamma_w$
20	08	1.04	0.99	19.8	0.404
50	20	0.867	1.04	52.0	0.385
100	34	0.693	1.11	111	0.306
200	53	0.550	1.20	240	0.220
500	85	0.466	1.29	644	0.132
1,000	118	0.400	1.38	1,380	0.0855
2,000	150	0.310	1.56	3,120	0.0481
5,000	195	0.245	1.77	8,850	0.0220
10,000	220	0.161	2.30	23,000	0.00955

The values of η are shown plotted on the graph versus $\dot\gamma_w$.

    c. It is quite evident that the fluid is not Newtonian, nor can
it be represented by the Power law model over this range of data.
Comparison of the viscosity curve with the empirical models in Chap. 2
indicates that it might be fit adequately by the Ellis model, or one
of the models which predict a limiting low shear viscosity. Just
because these data do not indicate a limiting viscosity at higher
shear does not mean that there might not be one if sufficient data
were available over the proper range.

    Note also that a qualitative evaluation of the fluid shear char-
acter can be obtained directly from a log-log plot of $-\Delta P$ versus Q.
Since these are directly proportional to τ_w and Γ, respectively, the
curve would merely be shifted vertically and horizontally from the
τ_w versus Γ curve. For a Newtonian fluid, this plot would be linear
with a slope of 1.0. For a Power law fluid, the plot would also be
linear, but with a slope other than 1.0. A nonlinear plot thus indicates more complex properties.

————————————————————— 0 —————————————————————

B. End Effects and Corrections

    The major error which may arise in tube flow measurements is
due to "end effects." Near the entrance and exit regions of the
tube, the velocity profile is not constant along the tube but is in
a state of transition between the flow configurations outside and

inside the tube, and the pressure gradient is not constant over these regions. Also, if the flow is from a large reservoir in which the velocity is low, the fluid must be accelerated in the tube entrance region to the final tube velocity. This results in an increased pressure gradient over this region due to the change in momentum and energy loss in eddies. For viscoelastic fluids, there is an additional entrance pressure drop due to elastic or normal stress effects, as discussed in Chap. 4. For Newtonian fluids, the extent of the developing inlet region is a function only of the Reynolds number, and is approximately [5.3]:

$$\frac{L_e}{D} \doteq 0.06 \; N_{Re} \qquad\qquad (5.4\text{-}21)$$

However, for non-Newtonian, and particularly viscoelastic fluids, it may be much longer than this, and is a more complex function of the viscous and elastic fluid properties.

One way of minimizing this error is to use tubes which are so long that the pressure drop due to the end effect is a negligible fraction of the total pressure drop. An exact criterion for this length has not been established, but it is commonly assumed that tubes for which $L/D \geq 100$ satisfy this condition.

Entrance effects can be corrected for experimentally in various ways. One method is to determine an equivalent "extra length" (L_e) of tube which would have to be added to the actual length if the total measured ΔP were that for an entirely fully developed region [5.4]. This can be done as follows. Consider the total pressure gradient due to friction in fully developed flow in the tube (length L), plus the "extra" pressure drop due to entrance effects which would be equivalent to friction in fully developed flow in an additional length L_e:

$$\Phi = \frac{\Delta P}{L + L_e} - \rho g = \frac{2\tau_w}{R} \qquad\qquad (5.4\text{-}22)$$

If the tube is horizontal ($g = 0$), and noting that τ_w is a unique function of Γ, Eq. (5.4-22) can be rearranged to give:

$$\Delta P = 2\tau_w \left(\frac{L}{R} + \frac{L_e}{R} \right) = f(\Gamma) \left(\frac{L}{R} + \frac{L_e}{R} \right) \qquad (5.4\text{-}23)$$

Hence, if several tubes of different L/R ratios are used, and ΔP is plotted versus L/R for the same value of Γ in each tube, the plot should be linear if the flow becomes fully developed within each tube, and the intercept at $\Delta P = 0$ determines L_e (Fig. 5.2). The intercept on the ΔP axis at $L/R = 0$ is the pressure drop due to the combined end effects (ΔP_e). Since a different value of L_e would be obtained for each value of Γ, L_e/R can be correlated with Γ.

An alternate procedure involves the use of two tubes of the same diameter, operating at the same flow rate (Q or Γ) [5.5]. Using the subscript S for the shorter tube and L for the longer, the various lengths and pressure components are defined in Fig. 5.3. For tubes of the same diameter with the same flow rate, the "extra length" (L_e) due to end effects should be the same in both tubes, if the flow becomes fully developed within the shorter tube:

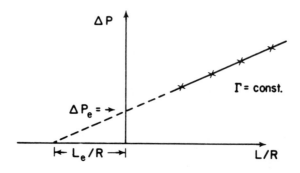

FIG. 5.2 Equivalent "extra length" due to end effects.

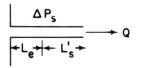

Short Tube, Radius R

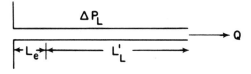

Long Tube, Radius R

FIG. 5.3 Length and pressure components in two tubes.

Long tube:

$$L_L = L_e + L_L' \qquad \Delta P_L = \Delta P_e + \Delta P_L' \qquad (5.4-24)$$

Short tube:

$$L_S = L_e + L_S' \qquad \Delta P_S = \Delta P_e + \Delta P_S' \qquad (5.4-25)$$

The true pressure gradient in the fully developed section is:

$$\Phi = \frac{\Delta P_L'}{L_L'} - \rho g = \frac{\Delta P_S'}{L_S'} - \rho g \qquad (5.4-26)$$

Using this to eliminate L_S' and L_L' from Eqs. (5.4-24) and (5.4-25):

$$L_L = L_e + \frac{\Delta P_L'}{\Phi + \rho g} = L_e + \frac{\Delta P_L - \Delta P_e}{\Phi + \rho g} \qquad (5.4-27)$$

$$L_S = L_e + \frac{\Delta P_S'}{\Phi + g} = L_e + \frac{\Delta P_S - \Delta P_e}{\Phi + \rho g} \qquad (5.4-28)$$

Subtracting (5.4-28) from (5.4-27):

$$L_L - L_S = \frac{\Delta P_L - \Delta P_S}{\Phi} \tag{5.4-29}$$

or

$$\Phi = \frac{\Delta P_L - \Delta P_S}{L_L - L_S} \tag{5.4-30}$$

Thus the appropriate pressure gradient for use in determining the wall stress τ_w corresponding to the flow rate Q (or equivalent Γ) is determined from the difference in pressure drop divided by the difference in tube lengths. Of course, care must be taken in choosing the tube lengths so that errors in pressure measurements are not unduly compounded by taking differences of large numbers.

C. Slip [5.6]

Another error which may arise, particularly with dispersions or suspensions, is due to preferred orientation or migration of the suspended material in the shear field. This can result in a region near the wall which is relatively free of the dispersed material, and results in a much lower effective viscosity in the immediate vicinity of the wall, giving the effect of an apparent slip between the fluid and the solid wall. The effect is actually due to the general inhomogeneity of the fluid near the wall and possible anisotropic properties in this region. However, the extent of the region affected is often very small, so that the effect may be accounted for by assuming an effective slip velocity (u_s) superimposed upon the fluid in in the tube. This slip velocity can be incorporated into the Rabinowitsch equation, and the final result written in terms of an effective slip coefficient, β[5.6]:

$$Q = \pi u_s R^2 + \frac{\pi R^3}{\tau_w^3} \int_o^{\tau_w} \tau^2 \dot{\gamma} \, d\tau \tag{5.4-31}$$

or

$$\frac{\Gamma}{4\tau_w} = \frac{\beta}{R} + \frac{1}{\tau_w^4} \int_0^{\tau_w} \tau^2 \dot{\gamma} \ dt \qquad (5.4\text{-}32)$$

where $\beta = u_s/\tau_w$ = "slip coefficient." The slip coefficient, β, can be evaluated as follows:

1. Using various tubes of the same length but different radii, plot $(\Gamma/4\tau_w)$ vs. τ_w for each tube. If $\beta = 0$, these curves should coincide. If not, the curves will be distinct, in which case proceed as follows.

2. At constant τ_w, plot $(\Gamma/4\tau_w)$ vs. 1/R from the above curves. This plot should be linear with slope = β.

3. Repeat 2 for various values of τ_w, and then plot β vs. τ_w.

The appropriate value of Γ to use in evaluating $\dot{\gamma}_w$ is then a "corrected" value corresponding to no slip:

$$\Gamma_{\text{no slip}} = (\Gamma_{\text{slip}})_{\text{measured}} - \frac{4\beta\tau_w}{R} \qquad (5.4\text{-}33)$$

where τ_w is the measured value.

Other errors may arise from viscous heating effects, particularly at high shear rates. However, these are difficult to correct for, and may be partially alleviated by jacketing with close temperature control. This problem is not so great in tube flow systems which have relatively short residence times, as it is with rotational systems in which the residence time is equal to the run time for making the measurements. For an extensive discussion of viscous heating, see Refs. 4.5 and 5.45

───────────────────────────── 0 ─────────────────────────────

Example 5.2 Suppose the measurements of Example 5.1 were repeated with the same fluid in a tube of the same diameter, but twice the length (20 cm), and the following data were obtained:

$-\Delta P$	Q
(mm H_2O)	(cm^3/sec)
80	0.0393
126	0.0785
212	0.157
340	0.393
470	0.785
600	1.57
780	3.93
960	7.85

What can you conclude with respect to possible errors in one or both sets of data?

It is evident that the pressure drop is less than twice the previous values at the same flow rate, even though the tube is twice as long. This indicates the presence of entrance effects, which would affect both sets of data. The appropriate procedure in this case would be to use the procedure illustrated in Fig. 5.3, whereby the difference in pressure drops is used with the difference in tube lengths as the appropriate pressure gradient for calculating τ_w. This should give accurate results provided the flow has reached a fully developed state in the shorter tube. In order to confirm this, it would be necessary to repeat the data again, using a still longer tube.

────────────────────────────── 0 ──────────────────────────────

5.4.2. Couette Flow [5.7-5.10]

This flow system involves the angular (rotational) laminar flow in the annulus between concentric cylinders, and was described initially in Sec. 4.3.2. The general configuration is illustrated in Fig. 5.4. Figure 5.4 indicates a stationary inner cylinder (bob) and moving outer cylinder (cup), although the opposite situation provides no complication. The torque, T, may also be measured at either cylinder. The most generally satisfactory arrangement involves rotating the outer cylinder or cup and measuring the torque at the

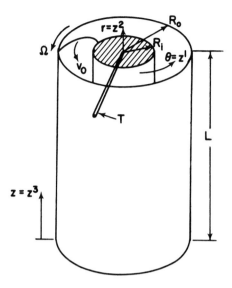

FIG. 5.4 Couette flow.

stationary inner cylinder, or bob. This is because centrifugal force
acts in the outward direction, proportional to $\omega^2 r$. Thus if the bob
rotates, this force is largest at the inner cylinder and tends to
force the fluid from the inner wall to the outer, thus setting up
radial circulation cells and instabilities. However with the cup
rotating, the centrifugal force is greatest at the outer wall, which
restrains the fluid from radial motion, thus resulting in a relatively
more stable situation.

The flow field, as described in Sec. 4.3.2, is defined by the
velocity components:

Tensor:

$$v^1 = \frac{d\theta}{dt} = \omega(r) \qquad v^2 = v^3 = 0 \qquad\qquad (5.4\text{--}34)$$

Physical:

$$v_\theta(r) = r\,\omega(r) \qquad v_r = v_z = 0 \qquad\qquad (5.4\text{--}35)$$

and the rate of strain components are, therefore,

$$\Delta_{ij} = \dot{\gamma} \begin{bmatrix} 0 & 1 & 0 \\ 1 & 0 & 0 \\ 0 & 0 & 0 \end{bmatrix} \tag{5.4-36}$$

where $\dot{\gamma} = r \, d\omega/dr$. The appropriate component equations of motion from Table 3.1 reduce to:

$\theta = z^1$ comp:

$$0 = \frac{\partial}{\partial r} (r^2 \tau_{r\theta}) \tag{5.4-37}$$

$r = z^2$ comp:

$$-\frac{\rho \, v_\theta^2}{r} = -\frac{\partial P}{\partial r} + \frac{1}{r} \frac{\partial}{\partial r} (r\tau_{rr}) - \frac{\tau_{\theta\theta}}{r} \tag{5.4-38}$$

$r = z^3$ comp:

$$0 = \frac{\partial P}{\partial z} \tag{5.4-39}$$

As illustrated in Sec. 4.3.2, integration of Eq. (5.4-37), and evaluating the integration constant by use of a balance of moments, gives the stress distribution:

$$\tau_{r\theta} = \tau(r) = \frac{T}{2\pi L r^2} \tag{5.4-40}*$$

Hence the shear stress at any radial position in the flow field can be determined directly from measurement of the torque.

In order to determine an expression for shear rate in terms of measurable quantities, we consider the following expression for the angular velocity, recalling that $\omega = 0$ at $r = R_i$:

$$\Omega = \int_0^\Omega d\omega = \int_{R_i}^{R_o} \frac{\dot{\gamma}}{r} \, dr \tag{5.4-41}$$

Now changing variables from r to τ by use of Eq. (5.4-40):

$$r = \sqrt{\frac{T}{2\pi L \tau}} \qquad \frac{dr}{d\tau} = -\frac{r}{2\tau}$$

or

$$\frac{dr}{r} = -\frac{d\tau}{2\tau} \tag{5.4-42}$$

Thus Eq. (5.4-41) becomes:

$$\Omega = -\int_{T/2\pi LR_i^2}^{T/2\pi LR_o^2} \frac{\dot{\gamma} \, d\tau}{2\tau} = -\int_{\tau_i}^{\tau_i/\alpha^2} \frac{\dot{\gamma} \, d\tau}{2\tau} \tag{5.4-43}$$

where

$$\alpha = \frac{R_o}{R_i} \tag{5.4-44}$$

and

$$\tau_i = (\tau)_{r=R_i} = \frac{T}{2\pi LR_i^2} \tag{5.4-45}$$

Following a procedure analogous to that in Sec. 5.4.3, Eq. (5.4-43) can be differentiated with respect to τ_i using Leibnitz' rule, to yield

$$\frac{d\Omega}{d\tau_i} = -\frac{1}{2\tau_i}\left[\dot{\gamma}\left(\frac{\tau_i}{\alpha^2}\right) - \dot{\gamma}(\tau_i)\right] \tag{5.4-46}$$

or

$$2\frac{d\Omega}{d \ln \tau_i} = \dot{\gamma}(\tau_i) - \dot{\gamma}\left(\frac{\tau_i}{\alpha^2}\right) \tag{5.4-47}$$

where $\dot{\gamma}(\tau_i/\alpha^2)$ is the shear rate at the point where the shear stress is τ_i/α^2, etc. Now Eq. (5.4-47) is a difference equation involving two separate values of shear rate, instead of one value at a specific position, as desired. It can be solved for a specific value of shear rate, however, as follows.

A. Iterative Solution--Single Bob [5.8]

A solution of the difference of Eq. (5.4-47) is possible, by the following procedure. Let $S(\tau_i)$ represent the function defined by the left side of Eq. (5.4-47), i.e.,

$$S(\tau_i) = 2 \frac{d\Omega}{d \ln \tau_i} \qquad (5.4\text{-}48)$$

so that Eq. (5.4-47) becomes:

$$S(\tau_i) = \dot{\gamma}(\tau_i) - \dot{\gamma}\left(\frac{\tau_i}{\alpha^2}\right) \qquad (5.4\text{-}49)$$

Likewise we may write

$$S\left(\frac{\tau_i}{\alpha^2}\right) = \dot{\gamma}\left(\frac{\tau_i}{\alpha^2}\right) - \dot{\gamma}\left(\frac{\tau_i}{\alpha^4}\right) \qquad (5.4\text{-}50)$$

$$S\left(\frac{\tau_i}{\alpha^4}\right) = \dot{\gamma}\left(\frac{\tau_i}{\alpha^4}\right) - \dot{\gamma}\left(\frac{\tau_i}{\alpha^6}\right) \qquad (5.4\text{-}51)$$

etc. Continuing the above procedure indefinitely, summing the result, and noting that $\alpha > 1$ and $\dot{\gamma}(0) = 0$, we have

$$\sum_{k=0}^{\infty} S\left(\frac{\tau_i}{\alpha^{2k}}\right) = \dot{\gamma}(\tau_i) \qquad (5.4\text{-}52)$$

This is the desired relation, giving the value of the shear rate corresponding to the shear stress at the wall of the bob. The function S in the summation may also be expressed as

$$S\left(\frac{\tau_i}{\alpha^{2k}}\right) = 2\left(\frac{d\Omega}{d \ln \tau_i}\right)_{\tau_i\alpha^{-2k}} = 2\left(\Omega \frac{d \ln \Omega}{d \ln \tau_i}\right)_{\tau_i\alpha^{-2k}} \qquad (5.4\text{-}53)$$

so that Eq. (5.4-52) becomes:

$$\dot{\gamma}_i = \sum_{k=0}^{\infty} 2\left(\Omega \frac{d \ln \Omega}{d \ln T}\right)_{\tau_i\alpha^{-2k}} \qquad (5.4\text{-}54)$$

where, from Eq. (5.4-45):

$$\tau_i\alpha^{-2k} = \frac{\tau_i}{\alpha^{2k}} = \frac{T}{2\pi LR_i^2\alpha^{2k}} \qquad (5.4\text{-}55)$$

The shear rate $\dot{\gamma}(\tau_i)$ is that which corresponds to the bob stress τ_i, i.e., $\dot{\gamma}(\tau_i) = \dot{\gamma}_i$. In order to evaluate $\dot{\gamma}_i$ from Eq. (5.5-54) corresponding to a specific value of Ω_i, an extensive range of Ω vs. T data would be required which cover, in principle, all corresponding values of τ from zero to τ_i. The initial term in the series (k = 0) would be evaluated from the slope of a log-log plot of the data and the value of Ω at a value of T corresponding to τ_i. The second term (k - 1) would be determined likewise from the plot at T/α^2, the third (k = 2) from the plot at T/α^4, etc. These terms, for all integral values of k, would then be summed to determine the value of $\dot{\gamma}_i$. The process would then be repeated starting with a different initial value of τ_i (and corresponding T) to determine the corresponding value of $\dot{\gamma}_i$, etc., until a range of τ vs. $\dot{\gamma}$ (i.e., τ_i vs. $\dot{\gamma}_i$) values for the fluid are generated.

For values of α near unity, the series in Eq. (5.4-55) converges slowly, thus requiring a large number of terms in the series and a corresponding wide range of data for accuracy. However, in this case, the series may be expanded by the Euler-McLaurin formula as shown by Krieger [5.9], and rearranged in the form:

$$\dot{\gamma}_{R_i} = \frac{2\Omega\alpha^{2/m}}{m(\alpha^{2/m} - 1)} \left\{ 1 + m^2 m' \ f\left(\frac{2 \ \ell n \ \alpha}{m}\right) \right\} \tag{5.4-56}*$$

where

$$m = \frac{d \ \ell n \ \tau_{R_i}}{d \ \ell n \ \Omega} = \frac{d \ \ell n \ T}{d \ \ell n \ \Omega} \tag{5.4-57}$$

$$m' = \frac{d(1/m)}{d \ \ell n \ \tau_{R_i}} = - \frac{1}{m^2} \frac{dm}{d \ \ell n \ T} = - \frac{1}{m} \frac{d \ \ell n \ m}{d \ \ell n \ T} \tag{5.4-58}$$

and

$$f(x) = \frac{x[e^x(x - 2) + x + 2]}{2(e^x - 1)^2} = \frac{x^2}{12} \left[1 - \frac{x}{2} + \frac{x^2}{15} \cdots \right] \tag{5.4-59}$$

The function $f(x)$ is shown in Fig. 5.5.

Comparison of Eq. (5.4-56) with the expression for the shear rate at the inner cylinder for a Power law fluid [Eq. (4.3-68)] shows that the coefficient of the bracketed term is identical to the Power law expression, if $m = n$ (the Power law flow index). Indeed for a Power law fluid, m and n are both constants and are identical, being given by Eq. (5.4-57).

The term in brackets in Eq. (5.4-56) is generally very nearly 1, since the maximum value of $f(x)$ is less than 0.1 (as seen in Fig. 5.5), and hence represents a small correction. Thus the use of the Power law expression for the shear rate, with the flow index n replaced by the point slope of the (ℓn T) vs. (ℓn Ω) curve, provides a very good approximation for any fluid.

B. Exact Solution--Multiple Bob [5.10]

The above procedure involves only data for angular velocity (Ω) versus torque (T) from a single instrument; that is, for fixed values of R_o and R_i (hence fixed α).

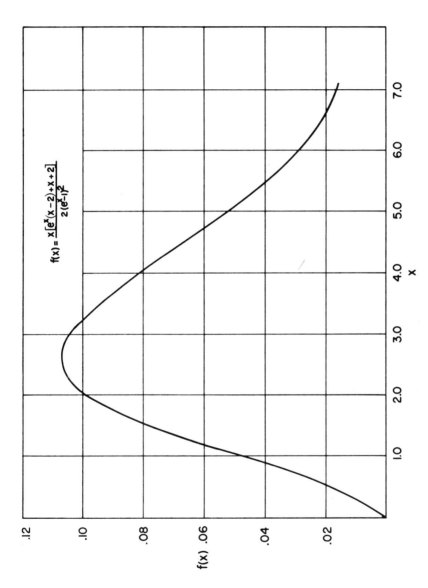

$$f(x) = \frac{x[e^x(x-2)+x+2]}{2(e^x-1)^2}$$

FIG. 5.5   Function of $f(x)$.   (Reprinted from Ref. 5.9, p. 10, by courtesy of John Wiley & Sons.)

An alternate method which requires combined data using various sized cylinders can be developed as follows. Rewriting Eq. (5.4-43) in terms of α and R_o instead of R_i and R_o, it becomes

$$\Omega = - \int_{\alpha^2 T/2\pi LR_o^2}^{T/2\pi LR_o^2} \frac{\dot{\gamma}}{2\tau} \, d\tau \qquad (5.4-60)$$

Now differentiating with respect to α by Leibnitz' rule, for constant T and R_o, leads to:

$$\left(\frac{d\Omega}{d\alpha}\right)_{R_o,T} = \frac{\dot{\gamma}_i}{\alpha} \qquad (5.4-61)$$

Thus the shear rate at the inner cylinder is:

$$\dot{\gamma}_i = \alpha \left(\frac{d\Omega}{d\alpha}\right)_{R_o,T} = \left(\frac{d\Omega}{d \ln \alpha}\right)_{R_o,T} \qquad (5.4-62)$$

In order to evaluate the derivative in Eq. (5.4-62), it is necessary to vary α while holding R_o constant; that is, by varying R_i. This requires several sets of data for Ω versus T, each for a different sized inner cylinder. The derivative can thus be evaluated from a cross plot of these data, as indicated in Fig. 5.6. The shear stress (τ_i) corresponding to the above shear rate is calculated from Eq. (5.4-40) using the values of T and R_i corresponding to the point at which the slope is measured. The procedure can be repeated using the different T curves (i.e., varying torque) at a given value of α (hence the same R_o and R_i), and by taking various values of α (using the appropriate value of R_i to calculate τ_i), to generate a τ_i versus $\dot{\gamma}_i$ (or $\eta = \tau_i/\dot{\gamma}_i$ vs. $\dot{\gamma}_i$) material function for the fluid. However, the extensive amount of data manipulation required by this method generally renders it impractical for normal usage.

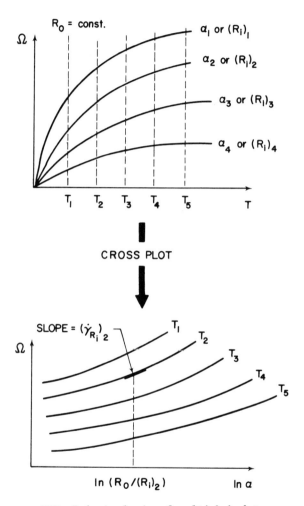

FIG. 5.6 Analysis of multi-bob data.

C.   Single Bob in Large Vessel

If $R_o \gg R_i$ (i.e., a single cylinder in a much larger container), it follows from Eq. (5.4-40) that $\tau_{R_o} \ll \tau_{R_i}$ (or $\tau_{\alpha R_i} \ll \tau_{R_i}$). Because of the unique relation between τ and $\dot{\gamma}$, it also follows that $\dot{\gamma}_{R_i} \ll \dot{\gamma}_{R_i}$, so that Eq. (5.4-45) becomes:

$$\dot{\gamma}_{R_i} \doteq 2\tau_{R_i} \left(\frac{d\Omega}{d\tau} \right)_{R_i} \tag{5.4-63}$$

which can also be written:

$$\dot{\gamma}_{R_i} = 2 \left(\frac{d\Omega}{d \ln T} \right) = 2\Omega \left(\frac{d \ln \Omega}{d \ln T} \right) \tag{5.4-64}$$

This relation is exactly valid, of course, only if $R_o/R_i \sim \infty$. In practice, it would be accurate to within 1% for $R_o = 10(R_i)$ if the material is Newtonian. For shear thinning materials, the accuracy is considerably less (depending upon the flow index). The volume of fluid required for accurate results is normally quite large, so that this situation is of limited usefulness.

D.   Approximate Relations

Although the expressions derived in Secs. 5.4.2A and B are exact, they both require considerable manipulation of data to determine appropriate values of shear rate at a given point within the system from measured values of torque and angular velocity. There are many situations in which approximated relations, involving explicit relations between shear rate and measured quantities, are sufficiently accurate. Some of these are presented below.

1.   Two Bobs

If only two inner cylinders are used, with radii R_a and R_b, respectively, so that:

$$\alpha_a = \frac{R_o}{R_a} \qquad \alpha_b = \frac{R_o}{R_b} \qquad\qquad\qquad (5.4\text{-}65)$$

Equation (5.4-62) can be approximated by:

$$\dot{\gamma}_i = \alpha \left(\frac{d\Omega}{d\alpha}\right)_{R_o,T} \cong \alpha_m \left(\frac{\Omega_b - \Omega_a}{\alpha_b - \alpha_a}\right) \qquad\qquad (5.4\text{-}66)$$

where

$$\alpha_m = \frac{1}{2}\,(\alpha_a + \alpha_b)$$

An estimate of the error involved in this approximation is given by [5.7]:

$$E = \frac{(2 - n)(1 - n)}{12n^2} \left(\frac{\alpha_b}{\alpha_a} - 1\right)^2 \qquad\qquad (5.4\text{-}67)$$

where n is the power law exponent (flow index) characteristic of the non-Newtonian behavior of the fluid.

2. *Power Law Approximation*

The exact expression for the shear rate for a Power law fluid was derived in Sec. 4.3 2, and is given by Eq. (4.3-68). This can be written:

$$\dot{\gamma}(r) = \frac{2\alpha^{2/n}\Omega}{n(\alpha^{2/n} - 1)} \left(\frac{R_i}{r}\right)^{2/n} \qquad\qquad (5.4\text{-}68)$$

or

$$\dot{\gamma}_i = \frac{2\alpha^{2/n}\Omega}{n(\alpha^{2/n} - 1)} \qquad\qquad\qquad (5.4\text{-}69)$$

The Power law index, n, can be determined from the slope of the log
T versus log Ω curve, which is a straight line for a Power law fluid.
For other fluids for which this plot is not linear, the point slope
will still provide a good estimate of the appropriate value of n,
but of course it will vary with T (or Ω).

3. Newtonian Approximation

As derived in Sec. 4.3.2, the exact expression for the shear
rate for a Newtonian fluid is given by Eq. (4.3-65);

$$\dot{\gamma}(r) = \frac{2\alpha^2 \Omega}{(\alpha^2 - 1)} \left(\frac{R_i}{r}\right)^2 \tag{5.4-70}$$

or

$$\dot{\gamma}_i = \frac{2\alpha^2 \Omega}{(\alpha^2 - 1)} \tag{5.4-71}$$

This is exact only for a Newtonian fluid but is often used as an
approximation for other materials. If the material is non-Newtonian,
the "correction factor" which converts Eq. (5.4-71) to Eq. (5.4-69)
is:

$$\frac{\alpha^{2[(1-n)/n]}(\alpha^2 - 1)}{n(\alpha^{2/n} - 1)} \tag{5.4-72}$$

where, again, n is the Power law index and can be taken as the point
slope of the (log T) versus (log Ω) curve at the value of T corresponding to τ_i.

4. Simple Shear Approximation

If the annulus between the cylinders is small enough that
$(R_o - R_i) \ll R_i$ [or $(\alpha - 1) \ll 1$] (see note 4), then the curvature
of the walls may be assumed negligible, and the system then approxi-
mates that of simple shear. Under these conditions the shear stress

and shear rate are approximately uniform across the gap, and the shear rate is given by:

$$
\dot{\gamma} = \frac{\Omega R_o}{R_o - R_i} = \frac{\Omega \alpha}{\alpha - 1}
\tag{5.4-73}
$$

If we take this value as the average shear rate across the annulus, the corresponding average shear stress is given by:

$$
\bar{\tau} = \tfrac{1}{2}(\tau_o + \tau_i) = \frac{T(\alpha^2 + 1)}{4\pi L R_o^2}
\tag{5.4-74}
$$

This value is greater than τ_o by approximately the factor α, which is essentially unity if the initial restrictions are satisfied.

Most Couette viscometers are constructed with a sufficiently narrow annulus which satisfies the assumption inherent in this approximation, so that these expressions are used frequently.

E. Correction Factors

A major source of error in the Couette viscometer can arise from end effects. The stress developed within the fluid between the bottom of the inner cylinder (bob) and the outer (cup) contributes to the total torque and must be corrected for. Although an approximate correction factor may be calculated theoretically, it is usually more satisfactory to determine it experimentally. This may be done by determining an additional effective length of the inner cylinder (L_e) which must be added to the actual length to account for extra stress due to the end effects. This also includes any correction required at the upper end resulting from an uneven or uncertain surface level resulting from centrifugal forces, the Weissenberg effect, etc.

This correction may be determined in several ways. One method is simply to make two runs at the same angular velocity (i.e., same shear rate) but with the annulus filled to a different level for

each run. Assuming the end effects to be same for the two runs, the
difference in the two torques is used along with the difference in
fluid levels to calculate the appropriate shear stress, the end
effects cancelling out.

   Another method employs a series of measurements of Ω and T at
various fluid levels, L. A plot of T/Ω vs. L should give a straight
line for sufficiently large L, with a nonzero intercept (Fig. 5.7).
The additional equivalent length, L_e, is then added to the total immersed length L to get the total effective length for use in the
equations.

   A special design of the inner cylinder (bob) is often employed
which effectively eliminates the end effect. This is sometimes
called a Mooney-Couette configuration, and employs a shallow conical
bottom surface on the inner cylinder, the apex of which almost
touches the bottom. The shear rate in the conical gap is essentially
uniform, and can be made equal to the mean shear rate in the annulus
by choosing the appropriate cone angle so that the end effect is
eliminated. This configuration is shown in Fig. 5.8. The shear
stress on the fluid in the annulus is obtained from the measured
torque after subtracting the contribution due to the stress in the
conical gap. This stress component is determined from the relations
for the cone and plate viscometer, described in the following section.

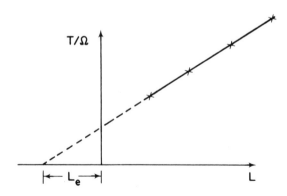

FIG. 5.7 Couette end correction.

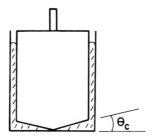

FIG. 5.8 Mooney-Couette configuration.

─────────────────────────────── 0 ───────────────────────────────

Example 5.3 Assume the following data were obtained in a Couette viscometer with a bob radius of 2 cm, a cup radius of 4 cm and a fluid depth of 10 cm:

T (dyn-cm)	(rpm)
281	10
753	30
1200	60
1630	100
2710	300
3520	600

Determine the apparent viscosity versus shear rate from these data by means of Eqs. (5.4-56), (5.4-69), (5.4-71) and (5.4-73) for the shear rate. Comment on the degree of validity of each of these expressions.

To convert the torque to shear stress at the bob, Eq. (5.4-45) applies

$$\tau_{R_i} = \frac{T}{2\pi L R_i^2} = \frac{T}{2\pi(10)(4)} = 3.98 \times 10^{-3} T \ (\text{dyn/cm}^2)$$

For each of the expressions for shear rate, the appropriate conversion formula is:

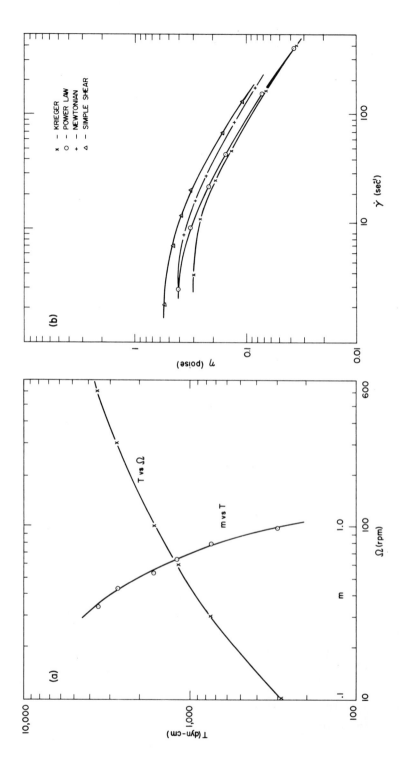

Krieger (see note 5):

$$\dot{\gamma}_{R_i} = \Omega\left(\frac{2\pi}{60}\right) \frac{2 \cdot (2)^{2/m}}{m(2^{2/m} - 1)} \left\{1 + m^2 m' \left(\frac{1.39}{m}\right)\right\}$$

Power law:

$$\dot{\gamma}_{R_i} = \Omega\left(\frac{2\pi}{60}\right) \frac{2 \cdot 2^{2/n}}{n(2^{2/n} - 1)}$$

Newtonian:

$$\dot{\gamma}_{R_i} = \Omega\left(\frac{2\pi}{60}\right)\left(\frac{2 \cdot 2^2}{3}\right) = 0.279\Omega$$

Simple shear:

$$\dot{\gamma}_{R_i} = \Omega\left(\frac{2\pi}{60}\right)\left(\frac{2}{1}\right) = 0.209\Omega$$

Note that only the "Newtonian" and "simple shear" values can be com-
puted without further manipulation. For both the Krieger and Power
law formulas, we shall take m = n as the point slope of the (log T)
vs. (log Ω) curve. Evaluating these from the plot (a), and using the
above formulas, the calculated values are tabulated in the accompanying table. The calculated values of the apparent viscosities from
each method are plotted versus shear rate for comparison in plot (b).

The results using the Krieger formula are essentially exact.
Note that the fluid approaches Newtonian behavior at low shear rates,
and Power law behavior at high shear rates. The Power law formula
is consequently considerably in error at low shear rates, but becomes more exact at high shear rates. The Newtonian formula agrees
with the Power law result at low shear rates, but is everywhere in
considerable error as the fluid is far from Newtonian. The simple
shear formula is off appreciably in magnitude but the general shape
of the curve is surprisingly true. The error in magnitude would
have been reduced if the average shear stress over the gap were
used in place of τ_{R_i}.

τ_{R_i} (dyne/cm^2)	$m = \dfrac{d \ln T}{d \ln \Omega}$	$\dfrac{d \ln m}{d \ln T}$	m'	$f(x)$	Krieger		Power law		Newtonian		Simple Shear	
					$\dot\gamma_{R_i}$	η	$\dot\gamma_{R_i}$	η	$\dot\gamma_{R_i}$	η	$\dot\gamma_{R_i}$	η
1.12	0.99	-5.1	5.15	0.075	3.86	0.290	2.80	0.400	2.79	0.401	2.09	0.536
3.00	0.79	-3.2	4.05	0.090	11.8	0.254	9.62	0.311	8.37	0.358	6.72	0.446
4.78	0.64	-2.2	3.44	0.103	25.3	0.189	22.1	0.216	16.7	0.286	12.5	0.382
6.49	0.53	-1.9	3.58	0.107	47.1	0.138	42.5	0.153	27.9	0.233	20.9	0.310
10.8	0.44	-1.7	3.86	0.102	160	0.068	149	0.072	83.7	0.129	67.2	0.161
14.00	0.34	-1.5	4.41	0.079	390	0.036	375	0.037	16.7	0.084	125	0.112

Note that the accuracy of the simple shear formula depends primarily upon the dimensions of the apparatus (i.e., annulus width), whereas the validity of the other formulas depend primarily upon the degree of fluid nonlinearity. A reduction in the width of the annulus would increase the accuracy of the simple shear method considerably, but would also improve the accuracy of the other methods somewhat.

--- 0 ---

5.4.3. Cone and Plate

One of the most useful configurations for the determination of material functions is a shallow cone ($\theta_c \leq 4°$), the apex of which is essentially in contact with a flat plate. Either the cone or the plate may be rotated, and the fluid in the gap undergoes rotational flow. The shear stress is determined from the measured torque, and the shear rate from the angular velocity. Describing the flow field in terms of the spherical coordinates (ϕ, θ, r) shown in Fig. 5.9, the tensor velocity components are:

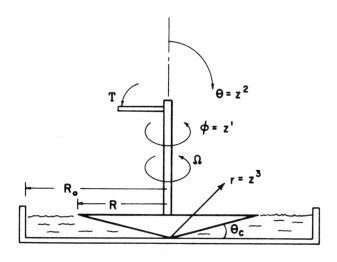

FIG. 5.9 Cone and plate geometry.

$$v^1 = \frac{d\phi}{dt} = \omega(\theta) \qquad\qquad v^2 = v^3 = 0 \qquad\qquad (5.4\text{-}75)$$

and the corresponding physical velocity components are:

$$v_\phi = r \sin \theta \cdot \omega(\theta) \qquad\qquad v_\theta = v_r = 0 \qquad\qquad (5.4\text{-}76)$$

The assumed absence of a radial velocity component restricts the rotational velocity to values below that at which centrifugal force causes the fluid to be expelled radially from the gap. For sufficiently small angles, for which the total mass of fluid in the gap is quite small, angular velocities approaching 100 rpm may be attained for some materials before this occurs (see note 6).

In light of Eq. (5.4-75) the rate of strain tensor for this flow field becomes:

$$\Delta_{ij} = \dot{\gamma} \begin{bmatrix} 0 & 1 & 0 \\ 1 & 0 & 0 \\ 0 & 0 & 0 \end{bmatrix}$$

where

$$\dot{\gamma} = \Delta_{\phi\theta} = \sin \theta \, \frac{d\omega}{d\theta} = \dot{\gamma}(\theta) \qquad\qquad (5.4\text{-}77)$$

and the equations of motion from Table 3.1 reduce to:

$z^1 = \phi$ comp:

$$0 = \frac{\partial \tau_{\theta\phi}}{\partial \theta} + 2\tau_{\theta\phi} \cot \theta \qquad\qquad (5.4\text{-}78)$$

$z^2 = \theta$ comp:

$$-\frac{\rho v_\phi^2 \cot \theta}{r} = -\frac{1}{r} \frac{\partial P}{\partial \theta} + \frac{1}{r \sin \theta} \frac{\partial}{\partial \theta} (\tau_{\theta\theta} \sin \theta) - \frac{\cot \theta}{r} \tau_{\phi\phi}$$

$$(5.4\text{-}79)$$

z^3 = r comp:

$$-\frac{\rho v_\phi^2}{r} = -\frac{\partial P}{\partial r} - \frac{\tau_{\theta\theta} + \tau_{\phi\phi} - 2\tau_{rr}}{r} \qquad (5.4\text{-}80)$$

The $\tau_{r\phi}$ stress component which appears in the ϕ equation has been
set equal to zero as a consequence of neglecting the fluid stress
acting on the r surface at the edge of the gap. This will be a very
good assumption if the dimensions of the apparatus are such that, with
reference to Fig. 5.10, $(R_o - R) \gg (R\theta_c)$. This is easily satisfied
in most equipment. Many fluids of interest are sufficiently thick
that they will not flow from the small gap, so that no external
barrier is required. For such cases, the fluid surface is exposed
to the atmosphere at the cone edge (perpendicular to r). Assuming
this surface to be spherical, the only stress at this surface is a
σ_{rr} component due to surface tension, which is generally negligible.
    Equation (5.4-78) can be integrated to give:

$$\tau_{\theta\phi} = \frac{c_1}{\sin^2 \theta} \qquad (5.4\text{-}81)$$

where c_1 is the constant of integration. The relative variation of
shear stress over the gap $[(\pi/2) - \theta_c] < \theta < \pi/2$, from Eq. (5.4-81),
is:

$$\frac{\tau_{\theta\phi}\Big|_{(\frac{\pi}{2} - \theta_c)} - \tau_{\theta\phi}\Big|_{\pi/2}}{\tau_{\theta\phi}\Big|_{\pi/2}} = \tan^2 \theta_c \qquad (5.4\text{-}82)$$

This ratio, expressed as a percentage, is shown in the following
table (from Ref. [5.5, p. 208]):

θ_c (°)	Variation in $\tau_{\theta\phi}$ between cone and plate (%)
0.5	0.0076
1.0	0.0306
2.0	0.1218
4.0	0.4886

From this table, it is obvious that for cone angles less than about 4° the shear stress may be assumed uniform over the gap with negligible error. Thus the cone and plate geometry, with sufficiently small cone angle, may be considered the rotational equivalent of simple shear, since shear stress and strain are essentially homogeneous. In this case, the expression for the shear rate becomes:

$$\dot{\gamma} \doteq \frac{d\omega}{d\theta} = \text{const} = c_2 \qquad (5.4\text{-}83)$$

Integrating this:

$$\omega = c_2\theta + c_3 \qquad (5.4\text{-}84)$$

and using the following conditions to evaluate C_2 and C_3:

$$(1) \quad \omega = 0 \text{ at } \theta = \frac{\pi}{2}$$

$$(2) \quad \omega = \Omega \text{ at } \theta = \frac{\pi}{2} - \theta_c \qquad (5.4\text{-}85)$$

gives an expression for the variation of angular velocity over the gap:

$$\omega = \Omega \left(\frac{\frac{\pi}{2} - \theta}{\theta_c} \right) \qquad (5.4\text{-}86)$$

The shear rate, therefore, follows from Eqs. (5.4-83) and (5.4-86):

$$\dot{\gamma} = - \frac{\Omega}{\theta_c} \qquad\qquad\qquad (5.4\text{-}87)*$$

The shear stress can be determined from the expression for the total torque on the cone surface due to the fluid stress:

$$T = \int_o^R (r \cos \theta_c)(\tau_{\theta\phi})_c (2\pi r \cos \theta_c)\ dr \qquad\qquad (5.4\text{-}88)$$

or

$$T = \frac{2\pi R^3 \cos^2 \theta_c}{3} (\tau_{\theta\phi})_c \qquad\qquad (5.4\text{-}89)$$

So that

$$\tau_{\theta\phi} = \frac{3T}{2\pi R^3 \cos^2 \theta_c} = \frac{3T}{2\pi R^3} \qquad\qquad (5.4\text{-}90)*$$

It is evident from Eqs. (5.4-87) and (5.4-90) that both the shear stress and shear rate are uniquely determined by the measurable torque and angular velocity, respectively, with no complex manipulations of the data necessary. The only limitations are on the dimensions of the apparatus, so that the simple shear approximations are valid, and on the maximum rotation rate, so that radial velocities resulting from centrifugal forces are absent. It is because of this simplicity of the final relations that the cone and plate is a popular configuration for viscometric measurements. (See note 7.)

———————————————————————— 0 ————————————————————————

Example 5.4 A Mooney-Couette viscometer (Fig. 5.8) is to be designed so that the average shear rate in the annular gap and that in the conical gap are equal. If the diameter of the outer cylinder is 10 cm and that of the inner cylinder is 9.8 cm, what should be the cone angle on the bob?

For the annulus, we have

$$\alpha = \frac{R_o}{R_i} = \frac{10}{9.8} = 1.024$$

Since this satisfies the criterion

$$(\alpha - 1) = 0.0204 << 1$$

we may employ the simple shear approximation [Eq. (5.4-73)]:

$$\dot{\gamma} = \frac{\Omega \alpha}{\alpha - 1}$$

The criterion that the shear rate in the annulus and conical gap be equal requires that

$$\dot{\gamma} = \frac{\Omega \alpha}{\alpha - 1} = \frac{\Omega}{\theta_c}$$

from which we have

$$\theta_c = \frac{\alpha - 1}{\alpha} = \frac{0.0204}{1.0204} = 0.02 \text{ radians} = 1.15°$$

------------------------------------- 0 -------------------------------------

5.4.4. Disc and Plate

This geometry is similar to that of the cone and plate, except that the cone is replaced by a flat disc (Fig. 5.10). The measured quantities are angular velocity (Ω) as a function of torque (T). Again, it is immaterial whether the plate or disc is the rotating member.

The flow field is described in terms of the cylindrical coordinates shown in Fig. 5.10, for which the tensor velocity components are:

$$v^1 = \frac{d\theta}{dt} = \omega(z) \qquad v^2 = v^3 = 0 \qquad (5.4-91)$$

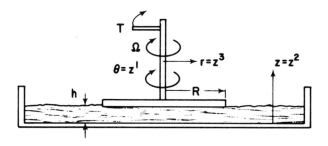

FIG. 5.10 Disc and plate geometry.

and the corresponding physical components are:

$$v_\theta = r\omega(z) \qquad\qquad v_z = v_r = 0 \qquad\qquad (5.4\text{-}92)$$

The rate of strain tensor thus takes the form:

$$\Delta_{ij} = \dot\gamma \begin{bmatrix} 0 & 1 & 0 \\ 1 & 0 & 0 \\ 0 & 0 & 0 \end{bmatrix} \qquad\qquad (5.4\text{-}93)$$

where $\dot\gamma = \Delta_{z\theta} = r\, d\omega/dz$. The equations of motion from Table 3.1, consistent with Eq. (5.4-91), reduce to

$z^1 = \theta$ comp:

$$0 = \frac{\partial\tau_{\theta z}}{\partial z} \qquad\qquad (5.4\text{-}94)$$

$z^2 = z$ comp:

$$0 = -\frac{\partial P}{\partial z} + \frac{\partial\tau_{zz}}{\partial z} \qquad\qquad (5.4\text{-}95)$$

$z^3 = r$ comp:

$$-\frac{\rho v_\theta^2}{r} = -\frac{\partial P}{\partial r} + \frac{\partial\tau_{rr}}{\partial r} + \frac{\tau_{rr} - \tau_{\theta\theta}}{r} \qquad\qquad (5.4\text{-}96)$$

Equation (5.4-94) states that $\tau_{\theta z}$ must be independent of z. Now $\tau_{\theta z}$ must also be independent of the θ direction because of symmetry, so that it must be at most a function only of r. Because there must be a unique relation between $\tau_{\theta z}$ and $\dot{\gamma} = \Delta_{\theta z}$, the latter must also be at most a function of r, and hence independent of z. With this in mind, integration of Eq. (5.4-93) with respect to z gives:

$$\omega = \frac{\dot{\gamma}z}{r} + \cancel{C_1}^{\,0} \qquad\qquad (5.4\text{-}97)$$

The constant of integration, C_1, must be zero since $\omega = 0$ at $z = 0$, so that the shear rate is given by:

$$\dot{\gamma} = \dot{\gamma}(r) = \frac{\omega r}{z} \qquad \text{or} \qquad \dot{\gamma}(r) = \frac{\Omega r}{h} \qquad\qquad (5.4\text{-}98)$$

where we have used the condition that $\omega = \Omega$ at $z = h$. Thus, the shear rate at any point within the system may be determined directly from the angular velocity of the disc and the dimensions of the apparatus.

The shear stress may be determined from the expression for the total torque on the disc:

$$T = \int_0^R r\tau_{\theta z}\, 2\pi r \, dr = 2\pi \int_0^R r^2 \tau \, dr \qquad\qquad (5.4\text{-}99)$$

Using Eq. (5.4-98) to change variables from r to $\dot{\gamma}$, Eq. (5.4-99) becomes

$$T = 2\pi \left(\frac{h}{\Omega}\right)^3 \int_0^{\Omega R/h} \tau \dot{\gamma}^2 \, d\dot{\gamma} \qquad\qquad (5.4\text{-}100)$$

which can also be written:

$$T = \frac{4}{\dot{\gamma}_R^3} \int_o^{\dot{\gamma}_R} \tau \dot{\gamma}^2 \, d\dot{\gamma} \tag{5.4-101}$$

where

$$T = \frac{2T}{\pi R^3} \tag{5.4-102}*$$

and

$$\dot{\gamma}_R = \dot{\gamma}\Big|_{r=R} = \frac{\Omega R}{h} \tag{5.4-103}*$$

is the shear rate evaluated at $r = R$. Comparison of Eq. (5.4-101) with the Rabinowitsch equation [Eq. (5.4-12)] for Poiseuille flow reveals that the two equations become identical if the following interchange of variables is made:

Poiseuille Flow Variable		Disc and Plate Variable
$\Gamma = \dfrac{4Q}{\pi R^3}$	$\longrightarrow$	$T = \dfrac{2T}{\pi R^3}$
$\tau_w = \dfrac{\Delta PR}{2L}$	$\longrightarrow$	$\dot{\gamma}_R = \dfrac{\Omega R}{h}$
$\dot{\gamma}_w$	$\longrightarrow$	τ_R
τ	$\longrightarrow$	$\dot{\gamma}$
$\dot{\gamma}$	$\longrightarrow$	τ

Thus differentiation of Eq. (5.4-101) with respect to $\dot{\gamma}_R$ and solving for τ_R results in an expression identical to that for $\dot{\gamma}_w$ derived from Eq. (5.4-12), if the above substitutions are made. The resulting equation for τ_R is analogous to Eq. (5.4-16) or (5.4-16) for $\dot{\gamma}_w$:

$$\tau_R = \frac{1}{4\dot{\gamma}_R^2} \frac{d(T\dot{\gamma}_R^3)}{d\dot{\gamma}_R} = \frac{1}{4}\left[\dot{\gamma}_R \frac{dT}{d\dot{\gamma}_R} + 3T\right]$$

or

$$\tau_R = T\left[\frac{3n' + 1}{4n'}\right] \hspace{3cm} (5.4\text{-}104)^*$$

where

$$n' = \frac{d \ln \dot{\gamma}_R}{d \ln T} \hspace{3cm} (5.4\text{-}105)^*$$

It is evident that shear stress (τ_R) and shear rate ($\dot{\gamma}_R$) at a common point in the fluid are determined from measurements of torque and angular velocity by a procedure identical to that used for analyzing pressure drop-flow rate data from Poiseuille flow.

The major limitations on this method are the same as for the cone and plate, namely, that rotational rates must be sufficiently small that no radial flow due to centrifugal force develops. This is somewhat more restrictive for this system than for the cone and plate, since there is generally a greater mass of fluid in the gap and hence centrifugal forces are greater at a given rotational velocity. No general criterion for suitable dimensions of this apparatus can be given other than h $\ll$ R, since the specific conditions depend upon the nature of the material under test. The upper limit for the velocity is that at which the fluid tends to be expelled. However, as for the cone and plate, the existence of nonzero normal stresses can result in secondary flows at speeds below which expulsion occurs.

───────────────────────────── 0 ─────────────────────────────

Example 5.5 Show that for a Newtonian fluid in a disc and plate geometry, the shear stress at the edge of the disc is given by

$$\tau_R = \frac{2T}{\pi R^3} = T$$

where T is the torque on the disc.

For a Newtonian fluid:

$$\tau_{ij} = \mu \, \Delta_{ij}$$

or

$$\tau_{\theta z} = \mu \, \Delta_{\theta z} = \mu \, \frac{dv_\theta}{dz}$$

where

$$v_\theta = r\omega$$

From Eq. (5.4-94):

$$0 = \frac{\partial \tau_{\theta z}}{\partial z} = \mu \, \frac{d^2 v_\theta}{dz^2}$$

Integrating this equation:

$$v_\theta = a + bz$$

and applying the boundary conditions:

(1) $v_\theta = 0$ at $z = 0$

(2) $v_\theta = r\Omega$ at $z = h$

gives the velocity distribution:

$$v_\theta = \frac{r\Omega z}{h}$$

The shear stress is therefore:

$$\tau_{\theta z} = \mu \frac{dv_\theta}{dz} = \mu \frac{r\Omega}{h} = \tau(r)$$

Now the torque on the disc is given by Eq. (5.4-99):

$$T = 2\pi \int_0^R r^2 \tau \, dr = \frac{2\pi\mu\Omega}{h} \int_0^R r^3 \, dr = \frac{\pi\mu\Omega R^4}{2h}$$

so that

$$\tau_R = \frac{\mu\Omega R}{h} = \frac{2T}{\pi R^3} = T$$

by comparison with the preceding equation.

———————————————— 0 ————————————————

5.5. RHEOGONIOMETRY

The methods described so far in this chapter are suitable for
determining shear stress–shear rate relations for fluids, which
serve to define the apparent viscosity material function. A complete
description of the state of stress in a fluid in steady flow requires
a knowledge of all stress components as a function of the state of
deformation. For the viscometric flows described so far, this requires a determination of the normal or deviatoric stress components
(or stress differences) as well as the shear stress component as a
function of shear rate. These relations serve to define the normal
stress material functions, θ_1 and θ_2:

$$N_1 = \tau_{11} - \tau_{22} = \theta_1(\dot{\gamma})\dot{\gamma}^2 \tag{5.5-1}$$

$$N_2 = \tau_{22} - \tau_{33} = \theta_2(\dot{\gamma})\dot{\gamma}^2 \tag{5.5-2}$$

Furthermore, as discussed in Chap. 1, the definition of isotropic
stress requires that

$$\tau_{11} + \tau_{22} + \tau_{33} = 0 \qquad\qquad (5.5\text{-}3)$$

Thus a knowledge of the two normal stress material functions is sufficient to define all three normal stress components as a function of shear rate. The experimental determination of these material functions is the objective of rheogoniometry. Strictly speaking, the term rheogoniometry implies determination properties in all possible directions, and as such would include viscometry as a special case.

The same viscometric flow systems used for the determination of viscous material functions can also be used for the determination of one or more of the normal stress material functions, as a function of shear rate. The shear rate is determined from the measured variables (forces and displacements or velocities) as previously decribed. However, the determination of normal stress components requires the measurement of additional forces, which are related to the fluid normal stress components by those components of the equations of motion which were not considered previously. We will now reconsider these flow systems, and derive relations between certain measurable forces and one or more of the normal stress differences. The reader is also referred to the monograph by Middleman [5.45] and the book by Lodge [5.14] for a review of rheogoniometric methods.

5.5.1. Cone and Plate

This geometry, illustrated in Fig. 5.9, can be used to determine certain normal stress components from measurement of the total thrust developed normal to the surface of shear, and/or the radial distribution of this normal force, as a function of shear rate.

The flow field, rate of strain tensor, and equations of motion are given by Eqs. (5.4-75) to (5.4-80). The latter are repeated here for convenience.

$z^1 = \phi$:

$$0 = \frac{\partial \tau_{\theta\phi}}{\partial \theta} + 2\tau_{\theta\phi} \cot \theta \qquad\qquad (5.5\text{-}4)$$

$z^2 = \theta$:

$$-\frac{\rho v_\phi^2 \cot \theta}{r} = -\frac{1}{r}\frac{\partial P}{\partial \theta} + \frac{1}{r \sin \theta}\frac{\partial}{\partial \theta}(\tau_{\theta\theta} \sin \theta) - \frac{\cot \theta}{r}\tau_{\phi\phi}$$

$$(5.5\text{-}5)$$

$z^3 = r$:

$$-\frac{\rho v_\phi^2}{r} = -\frac{\partial P}{\partial r} - \frac{\tau_{\theta\theta} + \tau_{\phi\phi} - 2\tau_{rr}}{r}$$

$$(5.5\text{-}6)$$

The components of the shear stress tensor are, at most,

$$\tau_{ij} = \begin{bmatrix} \tau_{11} & \tau_{12} & 0 \\ \tau_{12} & \tau_{22} & 0 \\ 0 & 0 & \tau_{33} \end{bmatrix} \begin{bmatrix} \tau_{\phi\phi} & \tau_{\theta\phi} & 0 \\ \tau_{\theta\phi} & \tau_{\theta\theta} & 0 \\ 0 & 0 & \tau_{rr} \end{bmatrix}$$

$$(5.5\text{-}7)$$

Now the total stress component normal to the plane of shear (the surface of the cone or plate) is:

$$\sigma_{22} = \sigma_{\theta\theta} = -P + \tau_{\theta\theta}$$

$$(5.5\text{-}8)$$

By substituting for P from Eq. (5.5-8) into (5.5-6), and noting that $\tau_{\theta\theta}$ is independent of r (i.e., τ_{ij} is a unique function of $\dot{\gamma}$, which in turn is independent of r), the latter can be written

$$-\rho v_\phi^2 = \frac{d\sigma_{\theta\theta}}{d \ln r} - N$$

$$(5.5\text{-}9)$$

where

$$N = \tau_{\theta\theta} + \tau_{\phi\phi} - 2\tau_{rr} = (\tau_{\phi\phi} - \tau_{\theta\theta}) + 2(\tau_{\theta\theta} - \tau_{rr}) = N_1 + 2N_2$$

$$(5.5\text{-}10)$$

Combination of Eqs. (5.5-3) and (5.5-10) provides an alternate expression for N:

$$N = -3\tau_{rr} = -3\tau_{33} \tag{5.5-11}$$

The left-hand side of Eq. (5.5-9) represents the stress resulting from centrifugal force. For sufficiently low velocities and/or highly viscous fluids, this term is negligible. Furthermore, it is impossible to obtain a solution to the equations of motion if this term is retained, so it is customary to neglect it and write Eq. (5.5-9) as:

$$r \frac{d\sigma_{\theta\theta}}{dr} = \frac{d\sigma_{\theta\theta}}{d \ln r} = N \tag{5.5-12}$$

When centrifugal force effects are not small, however, they may be accounted for by an empirical correction factor, which will be discussed presently.

A. Total Thrust

The total thrust or force exerted normal to the cone (or plate) is related to the normal stress components as follows:

$$F = - \int_{o}^{R} 2\pi r\sigma_{\theta\theta} \, dr = -\pi \int_{o}^{R} \sigma_{\theta\theta} \, d(r^2) \tag{5.5-13}$$

Integrating by parts, this becomes

$$F = -\pi \left\{ R^2\sigma_{\theta\theta} \Big|_{R} - \int_{o}^{R} r^2 \frac{\partial\sigma_{\theta\theta}}{\partial r} \, dr \right\} \tag{5.5-14}$$

Introducing Eq. (5.5-12) into the integral term, and noting that N is independent of r, this becomes

$$F = -\pi R^2 \left(\sigma_{\theta\theta} - \frac{N}{2} \right)_{r=R} \tag{5.5-15}$$

Upon substitution of Eq. (5.5-10) for N, this becomes

$$F = -\pi R^2 [-P + \tau_{\theta\theta} - \frac{1}{2} (\tau_{\theta\theta} + \tau_{\phi\phi} - 2\tau_{rr})]_{r=R} \tag{5.5-16}$$

Now if the edge of the gap is open to the atmosphere, then

$$\sigma_{rr_R} = -P \Big|_R + \tau_{rr} \Big|_R = -P_0 \tag{5.5-17}$$

where P_0 is the atmosphere (ambient) pressure (see note 8). (This, of course, assumes that any stress due to surface tension is negligible, which is normally a very good assumption [5.16].) Combining Eqs. (5.5-16) and (5.5-17) to eliminate P:

$$\frac{2F'}{\pi R^2} = (\tau_{\phi\phi} - \tau_{\theta\theta}) = N_1 \tag{5.5-18}*$$

where $F' = (F - \pi R^2 P_0)$ is the net measured thrust on the cone (or plate), in excess of that due to ambient pressure. Thus a measurement of the total net normal thrust, F', provides a direct measurement of the first normal stress difference.

B. Stress Distribution

Equation (5.5-12), which is valid if inertial (centrifugal force) effects are negligible, indicates that the total stress normal to the plate (or cone), $\sigma_{\theta\theta}$, should be a linear function of the logarithm of the radial position, r, since the normal stress parameter N is independent of r. Now if pressure taps or transducers are located at various radial positions along the stationary surface, the quantity measured is $\bar{P}(r) = -\sigma_{\theta\theta}(r)$ (plus or minus an arbitrary constant). Hence the plot of $\bar{P}(r)$ vs. $\ln r$ should be linear with a slope of $-N$. By Eq. (5.5-10), this is identical to $(N_1 + 2N_2) = N$.

If the first normal stress difference from total thrust measurements is subtracted from N, determined from stress distribution data
at the same value of shear rate (i.e., same angular velocity), the
result is the second normal stress difference:

$$N - N_1 = 2N_2 \qquad (5.5\text{-}19)$$

This, then, provides a means for determining the second normal stress
difference.

C. Rim Pressure

A force balance on the fluid at the edge of the gap shows that
the total stress component $\sigma_{rr} = \sigma_{33}$ must equal the ambient (static)
pressure at this point (neglecting surface tension and centrifugal
force effects):

$$\left. \sigma_{rr} \right|_R = -P_o \qquad (5.5\text{-}20)$$

It follows, therefore, that

$$\left. \tau_{rr} \right|_R = \left. \tau_{33} \right|_R = \left. \sigma_{rr} \right|_R + P_o = 0 \qquad (5.5\text{-}21)$$

The second normal stress difference at the rim is therefore given by

$$\left. N_2 \right|_R = \left. (\tau_{\theta\theta} - \tau_{rr}) \right|_R = \left. (\tau_{\theta\theta}) \right|_R = \left. \sigma_{\theta\theta} \right|_R + P_o \qquad (5.5\text{-}22)$$

The quantity on the right, however, is simply the stress relative to
the ambient pressure which would be measured by a sensor on the
plate (or cone) surface at the rim; i.e., the *gauge pressure*. Thus
extrapolation of the stress (pressure) distribution, referred to in
B above, to the edge of the cone ($r = R$) provides an independent
measure of the second normal stress difference.

D. Errors and Correction Factors [5.17]

The primary error that arises in all of the above measurements results from neglecting the effect of centrifugal forces; i.e., the left side of Eq. (5.5-9) (see note 9). The influence of this factor can be evaluated for a Newtonian fluid (for which N = 0, and $\sigma_{\theta\theta}$ = -P), by introducing the velocity distribution Eq. (5.4-86) into Eq. (5.5-6):

$$\frac{\partial P}{\partial r} = \frac{\rho v_\phi^2}{r} = r\Omega^2\rho \cdot \left(\frac{\psi}{\theta_c}\right)^2 \tag{5.5-23}$$

where

$$\psi = \frac{\pi}{2} - \theta \tag{5.5-24}$$

Also, from Eq. (5.5-5),

$$\frac{\partial P}{\partial \psi} = -\frac{\partial P}{\partial \theta} = -\rho v_\phi^2 \cot \theta = -\frac{\rho r^2\Omega^2\psi^2 \tan \psi}{\theta_o^2} \tag{5.5-25}$$

The pressure distribution is therefore determined by

$$P(r, \psi) - P(0) = \int_0^r \frac{\partial P}{\partial r} dr + \int_0^\psi \frac{\partial P}{\partial \psi} d\psi = \frac{\rho\Omega^2 r^2\psi^2}{2\theta_o^2}\left[1 - \frac{\psi^2}{2}\right] \tag{5.5-26}$$

where P(0) is the pressure at r = 0, i.e., at the cone apex.

Although Eq. (5.5-26) indicates that the pressure at the stationary surface (ψ = 0) is independent of the radial position, this is contrary to observations. This apparent discrepancy can be explained if it is assumed that the measured pressure (force) is not that corresponding to the boundary surface, but is instead a value proportional to the average normal stress over the gap:

$$\bar{P}(r) = \frac{1}{\theta_c}\int_0^{\theta_c} P(r, \psi) \, d\psi = \frac{1}{2}\rho\Omega^2 r^2\left[\frac{1}{3} - \frac{\theta_c^2}{10}\right] + \bar{c} \tag{5.5-27}$$

For an ideal spherical air-liquid interface at the rim, evaluation of
Eq. (5.5-27) at r = R shows the integration constant $\bar{c}$ to be
$(P_o - \rho\Omega^2 R^2[1/6 - \theta_c^2/20])$. For a fluid reservoir beyond the rim, an
analysis by Williams [5.18] leads to a value of $(P_o - \rho\Omega^2 R^2/10)$.
However, perturbations from the ideal flow field near the rim may
result in secondary flows which could alter these values [5.12, 5.15].
Because of these uncertainties, it is generally more satisfactory to
determine the centrifugal force correction empirically. This can be
done by measuring the pressure distribution or total thrust for a
Newtonian fluid of comparable viscosity, as a function of rotational
speed. This method inherently assumes there is no coupling between
fluid stress and centrifugal force effects.

1. Total Thrust Correction

The contribution to total thrust from centrifugal forces is,
from Eq. (5.5-27):

$$F_c = -2\pi \int_o^R r \bar{P}(r) \, dr = -\frac{\pi\rho\Omega^2 R^2}{4}\left[\frac{1}{3} - \frac{\theta_c^2}{10}\right] \qquad (5.5-28)$$

which is relative to that due to the static pressure. Uncertainties
due to the above-mentioned edge effects still remain, howevever.
Nevertheless, plots of $F_c/\rho R^4$ vs. Ω^2 determined from measurements on
Newtonian fluids (with no normal stress effects) are found to be
linear, and can be used to correct total thrust data for non-
Newtonian fluids empirically for centrifugal force effects. Note
that F_c is a negative number, the magnitude of which must be added
to the measured total thrust to correct for the effect of fluid
inertia.

2. Stress Distribution Correction [5.13]

A similar procedure can be used to determine a correction to
stress distribution measurements. As discussed in B above, the measured quantity is the gradient $(-d\bar{P}(r)/d \ln r)$. For a Newtonian
(inelastic) fluid with significant inertia, this is given by the

negative of Eq. (5.5-23), multiplied by r. The average of this quantity over the gap $(0 < \psi < \theta_c)$ then constitutes a correction factor, $(d\bar{P}_c/d \ln r)$, which must be added to the measured gradient to account for the (negative) contribution of the centrifugal (inertial) force:

$$\frac{d\bar{P}_c}{d \ln r} = \frac{1}{\theta_c} \int_0^{\theta_c} \frac{d\bar{P}(\psi)}{d \ln r} \, d\psi = - \frac{r^2\Omega^2\rho}{\theta_c^3} \int_0^{\theta_c} \psi^2 \, d\psi = - \frac{\rho\Omega^2 r^2}{3} \qquad (5.5\text{-}29)$$

An alternate derivation of this correction factor has been given by Walters and Waters [5.11], with the result:

$$\frac{d\bar{P}_c}{d \ln r} = - \frac{3\rho\Omega^2 r^2}{10} \qquad (5.5\text{-}30)$$

Again, because of uncertainties associated with the assumptions in these theories (especially with regard to boundary conditions), as well as slight variations in the experimental set up, it is usually best to determine the correction empirically from direct measurements on Newtonian (inelastic) fluids. These data should correlate as a linear dependence of $(d\bar{P}_c/d \ln r)$ upon $(\rho\Omega^2 r^2)$.

A critical evaluation of these equations and variations on them, as applied to data on various polymer solutions, has been made by Olabisi and Williams [5.12] and also by Miller and Christiansen [5.19]. Care must be taken in experimental determination of stress distribution because of errors which can arise from the use of pressure taps with viscoelastic fluids. This "hole error" is independent of the size of the pressure tap and can be quite significant, as discussed by Olabisi and Williams [5.12], and Tanner and Pipkin [5.47, 5.48]. For this reason, measurements of point values of wall stress or "pressure" should be made with flush-mounted transducers instead of pressure taps wherever possible. This applies to succeeding sections as well, where measurements of point values of pressure or wall stress are indicated.

5.5.2. Disc and Plate

Measurements of total thrust and normal stress distribution can be made on the disc and plate system, illustrated in Fig. 5.10, in a manner similar to those just described for the cone and plate system. These may be used to derive normal stress information as follows [5.17, 5.20-5.22].

As discussed in Sec. 5.4.4, the flow field is described relative to cylindrical coordinates, with physical velocity components:

$$v_\theta = r\omega(z) \qquad v_r = v_z = 0 \qquad (5.5-31)$$

The corresponding component equations of motion are repeated below:

$z^1 = \theta$:

$$0 = \frac{\partial \tau_{\theta z}}{\partial z} \qquad (5.5-32)$$

$z^2 = z$:

$$0 = -\frac{\partial P}{\partial z} + \frac{\partial \tau_{zz}}{\partial z} \qquad (5.5-33)$$

$z^3 = r$:

$$-\frac{\rho v_\theta^2}{r} = -\frac{\partial P}{\partial r} + \frac{\partial \tau_{rr}}{\partial r} + \frac{(\tau_{rr} - \tau_{\theta\theta})}{r} \qquad (5.5-34)$$

The velocity and shear rate distribution, assuming no radial flow component, were previously determined to be:

$$v_\theta = r\omega = \frac{r\Omega z}{h} \qquad (5.5-35)$$

and

$$\dot{\gamma}(r) = \frac{r\Omega}{h} \qquad (5.5-35)$$

where h is the width of the gap between the plate and the disc.
Note that, since $\dot{\gamma}$ is independent of z and θ, the shear stress components must also be independent of these coordinate directions.

By introducing $-P = \sigma_{zz} - \tau_{zz}$ into Eq. (5.5-34), it becomes:

$$\frac{\partial \sigma_{zz}}{\partial r} = \frac{d(\tau_{zz} - \tau_{rr})}{dr} + \frac{\tau_{\theta\theta} - \tau_{rr}}{r} - \frac{\rho v_\theta^2}{r} \qquad (5.5-37)$$

Integrating this from r to R and neglecting the centrifugal force
term, we find

$$\sigma_{zz}(R) - \sigma_{zz}(r) = (\tau_{zz} - \tau_{rr})_R - (\tau_{zz} - \tau_{rr})_r + \int_r^R \frac{\tau_{\theta\theta} - \tau_{rr}}{r} dr \qquad (5.5-38)$$

If the fluid at the edge of the disc is exposed to ambient pressure
P_o, and surface tension effects are negligible, the stresses at the
edge are:

$$\sigma_{zz}(R) = -P(R) + \tau_{zz}(R) \qquad (5.5-39)$$

$$\sigma_{rr}(R) = -P(R) + \tau_{rr}(R) = -P_o \qquad (5.5-40)$$

i.e.,

$$\tau_{rr}(R) = P(R) - P_o \qquad (5.5-41)$$

Combining Eqs. (5.5-38), (5.5-39), and (5.5-41) to eliminate $\sigma_{zz}(R)$,
τ_{zz} (R), and τ_{rr} (R), the result is:

$$-\sigma_{zz}(r) = P_o - (\tau_{zz} - \tau_{rr})_r + \int_r^R \frac{\tau_{\theta\theta} - \tau_{rr}}{r} dr \qquad (5.5-42)$$

A. Total Thrust

Equation (5.5-42) is an expression for the total stress exerted by the fluid normal to the plate. Now the total force or thrust on the plate is given by:

$$F = -2\pi \int_o^R r \, \sigma_{zz}(r) \, dr \qquad (5.5\text{-}43)$$

which, upon introducing Eq. (5.5-42), becomes

$$F' = F - \pi R^2 P_o$$

$$= 2\pi \int_o^R r \left[\int_r^R \left(\frac{\tau_{\theta\theta} - \tau_{rr}}{r} \right) dr' - \tau_{zz}(r) + \tau_{rr}(r) \right] dr \quad (5.5\text{-}44)$$

where F' is the net force in excess of that due to ambient pressure. Changing the order of integration of the double integral term (integrating by parts) leads to:

$$F' = 2\pi \left[\int_o^R \left(\frac{\tau_{\theta\theta} - \tau_{rr}}{r} \right) \int_o^r r' \, dr' \, dr - \int_o^R r(\tau_{zz} - \tau_{rr}) \, dr \right]$$

$$(5.5\text{-}45)$$

or

$$F' = \pi \int_o^R [r(\tau_{\theta\theta} - \tau_{rr}) - 2r(\tau_{zz} - \tau_{rr})] \, dr \qquad (5.5\text{-}46)$$

$$F' = \pi \int_o^R r(\tau_{\theta\theta} - \tau_{zz} + \tau_{rr} - \tau_{zz}) \, dr = \pi \int_o^R (N_1 - N_2) \, dr$$

$$(5.5\text{-}47)$$

Using Eq. (5.5-36) to change variables from r to $\dot{\gamma}$, this may be written:

$$F' = \pi \left(\frac{h}{\Omega}\right)^2 \int_0^{\dot{\gamma}_R} (N_1 - N_2)\dot{\gamma} \, d\dot{\gamma} = \pi \left(\frac{R}{\dot{\gamma}_R}\right)^2 \int_0^{\dot{\gamma}_R} (N_1 - N_2)\dot{\gamma} \, d\dot{\gamma} \quad (5.5\text{-}48)$$

Now differentiating this with respect to $\dot{\gamma}_R$ by Leibnitz' rule gives

$$\frac{d(F'\dot{\gamma}_R^2)}{d\dot{\gamma}_R} = \pi R^2 (N_1 - N_2)_R \dot{\gamma}_R \quad (5.5\text{-}49)$$

or

$$(N_1 - N_2)_R = \frac{2F'}{\pi R^2} \left[\frac{1}{R}\frac{d \ln F'}{d \ln \dot{\gamma}_R} + 1\right] \quad (5.5\text{-}50)^*$$

Thus measurement of the total net thrust, F', as a function of shear rate (e.g., angular velocity) provides a means of determining the difference between the first and second normal stress differences.

B. Pressure Measurements

The value of the pressure at the center of the plate [P(0)] is given by Eq. (5.5-42) with $\tau_{zz}(0) = \tau_{rr}(0) = 0$:

$$P(0) = -\sigma_{zz}(0) = P_0 + \int_0^R \frac{\tau_{\theta\theta} - \tau_{rr}}{r} \, dr \quad (5.5\text{-}51)$$

Again changing variables from r to $\dot{\gamma}$ by Eq. (5.5-36), this becomes:

$$P(0) - P_0 = \int_0^{\dot{\gamma}_R} \frac{\tau_{\theta\theta} - \tau_{rr}}{\dot{\gamma}} \, d\dot{\gamma} \quad (5.5\text{-}52)$$

Differentiating this with respect to $\dot{\gamma}_R$ gives:

$$\frac{d(P_{(0)} - P_o)}{d \ln \dot{\gamma}_R} = (\tau_{\theta\theta} - \tau_{rr})_R = (N_1 + N_2)_R \qquad (5.5-53)^*$$

Note that the sum of Eqs. (5.5-50) and (5.5-53) is twice the first normal stress difference, and their difference is twice the second normal stress difference. Hence complete normal stress data may be obtained in principle from a combination of total thrust and pressure at the center of the plate, as a function of shear rate.

C. Errors and Correction Factors

As for cone and plate measurements, the primary source of error arises from the neglect of centrifugal force effects. Again, these may be evaluated for a Newtonian fluid, for which the deviatoric normal stresses are zero, with the assumption that centrifugal force and elastic normal stress effects are superimposed. Introducing Eq. (5.5-35) into Eq. (5.5-34) for a Newtonian (inelastic) fluid:

$$\frac{\partial P}{\partial r} = \frac{\rho \Omega^2}{h^2} rz^2 \qquad (5.5-54)$$

and integrating from $r = 0$ to r, gives the pressure distribution due to centrifugal force:

$$P(r, z) - P(0, z) = \frac{\rho}{2} \left(\frac{\Omega rz}{h}\right)^2 \qquad (5.5-55)$$

Averaging this pressure over the gap, it becomes:

$$\bar{P}(r) = \frac{1}{h} \int_o^h P(r, z) \, dz = \bar{P}(0) + \frac{1}{6} \rho \Omega^2 r^2 \qquad (5.5-56)$$

1. Total Thrust Correction

The contribution of centrifugal force to the total thrust is given by:

$$F_c = -2\pi \int_0^R r\bar{P}(r)\ dr = -\frac{\pi\rho\Omega^2 R^4}{12} \tag{5.5-57}$$

where F_c is the net normal thrust in excess of the static value at $\Omega = 0$. This is seen to be identical to the corresponding result for the cone and plate geometry. Thus a plot of $F_c/\rho R^4$ vs. Ω^2 as determined for a Newtonian fluid may be used to estimate the appropriate centrifugal force correction factor, for non-Newtonian fluids (see note 10).

2. *Pressure Correction*

The influence of centrifugal forces upon the pressure distribution is given by Eq. (5.5-56). However, the only pressure measurement proposed is $\bar{P}(0)$ (at $r = 0$), and Eq. (5.5-56) indicates that this value should be independent of angular velocity. Therefore, no correction is indicated for this pressure.

D. Combined Measurements

As total thrust data are easier to obtain than point pressure measurements (and subject to fewer errors and ambiguities in interpretation), it is informative to determine what information can be obtained from a combination of total normal thrust data from the cone and plate and disc and plate geometries.

As shown by Eq. (5.5-18), total thrust data from the cone and plate as a function of rotation rate provide information on the first normal stress difference at a given shear rate. For the disc and plate, Eq. (5.5-50) relates normal thrust and rotation rate measurements to the difference between the first and second normal stress difference at a given shear rate. For the disc and plate, Eq. (5.5-50) relates normal thrust and rotation rate measurements to the difference between the first and second normal stress differences at a given shear rate. Thus for the same value of shear rate, these data may be combined to give the second normal stress difference:

$$(N_1)_{\text{cone plate}} - (N_1 - N_2)_{\text{disc plate}} = N_2 \qquad\qquad (5.5\text{-}58)^*$$

Thus all steady normal stress properties may be obtained by combining total normal thrust data from the cone and plate and disc and plate geometries. It should be emphasized that data from the two systems can only be combined when both correspond to the same value of shear rate.

5.5.3. Concentric Cylinders

As previously mentioned, the Weissenberg effect, which refers to the phenomenon of the fluid climbing up the shaft of a rotating cylinder or rod, is a consequence of normal stresses. A quantitative measure of the corresponding normal stress difference obtained from the wall stress difference across the annular gap in a concentric cylinder system with the inner cylinder rotating can consequently be used to evaluate normal stress components (Fig. 5.11) [5.23].

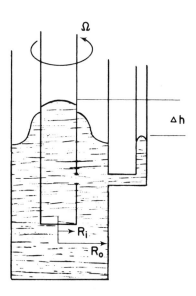

FIG. 5.11 Normal stress measurement in concentric cylinders.

For this system, the physical velocity components are identical to those of Couette flow:

$$v_\theta(r) = r\omega(r) \qquad v_r = v_z = 0$$

the rate of strain tensor is:

$$\Delta_{ij} = \dot{\gamma} \begin{bmatrix} 0 & 1 & 0 \\ 1 & 0 & 0 \\ 0 & 0 & 0 \end{bmatrix} \qquad \dot{\gamma} = r\frac{d\omega}{dr} = \Delta_{r\theta} \qquad (5.5\text{-}59)$$

and the equations of motion are:

$z^1 = \theta$ comp:

$$0 = \frac{\partial(r^2\tau_{r\theta})}{\partial r} \qquad\qquad (5.5\text{-}60)$$

$z^2 = r$ comp:

$$-\frac{\rho v_\theta^2}{r} = -\frac{\partial P}{\partial r} + \frac{\partial\tau_{rr}}{\partial r} + \frac{\tau_{rr} - \tau_{\theta\theta}}{r} \qquad (5.5\text{-}61)$$

$z^3 = z$ comp:

$$\rho g = -\frac{\partial P}{\partial z} \qquad\qquad (5.5\text{-}62)$$

If intertia is neglected, Eq. (5.5-61) can be integrated with respect to r to give:

$$\Delta\sigma_{rr} = \left(-P + \tau_{rr}\right)_{R_i}^{R_o} = -\rho g\,\Delta h = -\int_{R_i}^{R_o} \frac{\tau_{rr} - \tau_{\theta\theta}}{r}\,dr \qquad (5.5\text{-}63)$$

Now the variable of integration can be changed from r to $\tau_{r\theta}$ by use of Eq. (5.5-40), i.e.:

$$r = \left(\frac{T}{2\pi L\tau_{r\theta}}\right)^{\frac{1}{2}}$$ (5.5-64)

Making the change of variable and differentiating the result with respect to the shear rate at the inner surface $(\dot{\gamma}_i)$ leads to:

$$\frac{d \, \Delta\sigma_{rr}}{d\dot{\gamma}_i} = \frac{1}{2}\frac{d}{d\dot{\gamma}_i} \int_{\tau_i}^{\tau_o} \frac{\tau_{rr} - \tau_{\theta\theta}}{\tau_{r\theta}} \, d\tau_{r\theta}$$ (5.5-65)

Evaluating the integral form by application of Leibnitz' rule, this becomes:

$$\frac{d \, \Delta\sigma_{rr}}{d\dot{\gamma}_i} = \frac{1}{2} \left[\frac{\tau_{rr} - \tau_{\theta\theta}}{\tau_o}\right]_{R_o} \frac{d\tau_o}{d\dot{\gamma}_i} - \left[\frac{\tau_{rr} - \tau_{\theta\theta}}{\tau_i}\right]_{R_i} \frac{d\tau_i}{d\dot{\gamma}_i}$$ (5.5-66)

Now from Eq. (5.5-64) we see that $\tau_i = \alpha^2\tau_o$ where $\alpha = R_o/R_i$, so that

$$\frac{d \, \ell n \, \tau_o}{d \, \ell n \, \dot{\gamma}_i} = \frac{d \, \ell n \, \tau_i}{d \, \ell n \, \dot{\gamma}_i} = m = \frac{d \, \ell n \, T}{d \, \ell n \, \Omega}$$ (5.5-67)

where use has been made of the fact that $\dot{\gamma}_i$ is proportional to Ω. Here m is the point slope of the $(\ell n \, T$ vs. $\ell n \, \Omega)$ plot at a point corresponding to a specific shear rate $(\dot{\gamma}_i)$. Hence Eq. (5.5-66) can be written:

$$2\frac{d \, \Delta\sigma_{rr}}{d \, \ell n \, \tau} = \frac{2}{m}\frac{d \, \Delta\sigma_{rr}}{d \, \ell n \, \dot{\gamma}_i} = (\tau_{rr} - \tau_{\theta\theta})_{R_o} - (\tau_{rr} - \tau_{\theta\theta})_{R_i}$$ (5.5-68)

It is desired, of course, to determine a specific value of the normal stress difference as a function of shear rate, whereas Eq. (5.5-68) involves two different values of the first normal stress difference. However, experience indicates that the normal stress difference varies approximately in proportion to the square of the shear rate which, in turn, varies inversely with the square of the radius.

Hence for $\alpha = R_o/R_i = 2$, the value of $(\tau_{rr} - \tau_{\theta\theta})_{R_o}$ would be expected to be roughly 1/16 of $(\tau_{rr} - \tau_{\theta\theta})_{R_i}$. Therefore, if $R_o \geq 2R_i$, Eq. (5.5-68) can be approximated by

$$(\tau_{rr} - \tau_{\theta\theta})_{R_i} = -N_1 = -\frac{2}{m}\frac{d\,\Delta\sigma_{rr}}{d\,\ln\dot\gamma_i} = \frac{2\rho g}{m}\frac{d\,\Delta h}{d\,\ln\dot\gamma_i} \qquad (5.5\text{-}69)*$$

which gives the first normal stress difference, evaluated at the conditions at the inner cylinder wall, in terms of measurable quantities.

Equation (5.5-68) is a difference equation for the first normal stress difference similar to Eq. (5.4-47) for the shear rate from the analysis of the Couette viscometer, and can be solved by a similar series method. The result is [5.24]:

$$(\tau_{11} - \tau_{22})_{R_i} = 2\sum_{k=0}^{\infty}\left(\tau\frac{d\,\Delta\sigma_{rr}}{d\tau}\right)_{\tau_i\alpha^{-2k}} = 2\sum_{k=0}^{\infty}\left(\Delta\sigma_{rr}\frac{d\,\ln\sigma_{rr}}{d\,\ln\tau}\right)_{\tau_i\alpha^{-2k}}$$

$$(5.5\text{-}70)$$

This equation can be used to determine the first normal stress difference from a plot of $\Delta\sigma_{rr} = -\rho g\,\Delta h$ as a function of τ_i. The series may be expanded and rearranged in a manner analogous to that leading to Eq. (5.4-56). In fact, the latter may be applied directly to the determination of the first normal stress difference by appropriate change of notation as seen by comparison of Eqs. (5.5-70) and (5.4-54).

Errors and Corrections. Just as with the other rotational geometries, the primary error results from the neglect of the influence of inertial or centrifugal forces on normal stress or pressure measurements. As seen from Eqs. (5.5-61) and (5.5-63), the effect of inertia can be corrected for by adding the quantity

$$P_c = \int_{R_i}^{R_o}\frac{\rho v^2}{r}\,dr \qquad (5.5\text{-}71)$$

to the measured values of $\Delta\sigma_{rr}$, again assuming the effect of centrifugal force to be superimposed upon the fluid normal stresses. However, the above integral cannot be evaluated unless the velocity distribution is known. If the fluid viscosity is assumed to follow the Power law model, Eq. (5.5-71) can be evaluated to give [5.25]:

$$P_c = \frac{\rho R_o^2 n^3}{8\alpha^{4/n}} \left[\frac{1 - \alpha^{[2(2-n)]/n}}{n - 2} + \frac{2(1 - \alpha^{[2(1-n)]/n})}{n - 1} + \frac{1 - \alpha^2}{n\alpha^2} \right] \dot\gamma_{in}^2$$

(5.5-72)

where $\dot\gamma_{in}$ is the shear rate at the inner wall calculated for a Power law fluid, and n is the Power law flow index.

Experimental inertia correction factors may be determined from data on Newtonian fluids, as in Secs. 5.4.3 and 5.4.4. However, due to the probability that the velocity profile in the test fluid will deviate significantly from the Newtonian profile, these results can be seriously in error (see note 11).

As previously discussed, the use of pressure taps for measuring pressure may also give rise to considerable error, especially for highly elastic fluids. It is therefore desirable to avoid recessed taps by using flush mounted transducers or some other method where possible.

If the correction factor is determined properly, the resulting corrected values of $(\tau_{11} - \tau_{22})$ vs. $\dot\gamma$ should all fall on a common curve, independent of R_o or α. This can provide a check on the method used to determine the correction factor if data are taken in more than one system with different dimensions.

5.4.4. Slits and Capillaries [5.26]

Measurements of "exit pressure" (i.e., the total wall stress extrapolated to the end) and the net axial thrust developed when a viscoelastic fluid exits from fully developed laminar flow in a capillary tube or a slit may be employed to determine both first and second normal stress differences as a function of shear rate.

Various interpretations of such measurements appearing in the literature have led to different and sometimes conflicting results, however, primarily due to the assumptions involved in the interpretation
of the influence of the isotropic pressure term in the equations.
These effects have been carefully considered by Davies et al. [5-26],
who expanded upon an initial analysis by Lodge [5.14]. The following
analysis therefore closely follows that of this reference.

A. Capillary Tube Flow

Considering first the flow emerging from a capillary tube,
assuming a fully developed profile exists up to the end of the tube,
the relevant equations in cylindrical coordinates are as follows.
The velocity components are

$$v_z(r) = v^1(z^2) \qquad\qquad v_r = v_\theta = 0 \tag{5.5-73}$$

so that the corresponding rate of strain components are

$$\Delta_{ij} = \dot{\gamma}\begin{bmatrix} 0 & 1 & 0 \\ 1 & 0 & 0 \\ 0 & 0 & 0 \end{bmatrix} \qquad\qquad \dot{\gamma} = \Delta_{rz} = \frac{dv_z}{dr} \tag{5.5-74}$$

The corresponding equations of motion in terms of total stress components thus reduce to:

z^1 = z comp:

$$\frac{\partial \sigma_{zz}}{\partial z} + \frac{1}{r}\frac{\partial}{\partial r}(r\sigma_{rz}) = 0 \tag{5.5-75}$$

z^2 = r comp:

$$\frac{\partial \sigma_{rr}}{\partial r} + \frac{\sigma_{rr} - \sigma_{\theta\theta}}{r} = 0 \tag{5.5-76}$$

$z^3 = \theta$ comp:

$$\frac{\partial \sigma_{\theta\theta}}{\partial \theta} = 0 \qquad\qquad\qquad (5.5\text{-}77)$$

Equation (5.5-75) determines the shear stress at any radial position
in terms of the pressure gradient [i.e., Eq. (5.4-9)], and the wall
shear rate is determined from pressure gradient and flow rate data
as before [Eq. (5.4-17)]. It should be noted that the fluid shear
stresses (i.e., τ_{rz}, τ_{zz}, τ_{rr}, and $\tau_{\theta\theta}$) depend only upon the deformation (i.e., shear rate), which, in turn, varies only in the radial,
but is independent of the axial, direction. Therefore these stresses
are all independent of z, so that the axial gradient of the total
wall stress is identical to the (negative) isotropic pressure gradient
regardless of whether or not the fluid develops anisotropic normal
stresses.

Now when the fluid exits the tube, an axial thrust is exerted
on the tube by the change in momentum transported by the fluid.
When an axial normal stress is developed within the fluid, the integral of this stress over the cross section of the fluid exerts an
additional axial thrust which is in the opposite direction to that
due to the change in momentum transport. Assuming the fluid enters
the tube normal to its axis so that no axial momentum is carried in,
a momentum balance on the fluid gives the net thrust on the tube:

$$F = \int_o^R 2\pi r \rho v_z^2 \, dr - \int_o^R 2\pi r \sigma_{zz}(L) \, dr \qquad\qquad (5.5\text{-}78)$$

It is assumed here that gravity and surface tension forces are negligible. The second term is thus the reduction in total thrust due
to the fluid stress, and will be designated T_L. Integrating this
term by parts gives

$$T_L = 2\pi \int_0^R r\sigma_{zz}(L)\, dr = \pi R^2 \sigma_{zz}(R,\ L) - \pi \int_0^R r^2 \frac{\partial \sigma_{zz}(L)}{\partial r}\, dr$$

$$(5.5\text{-}79)$$

By substituting $\sigma_{zz} = \sigma_{rr} + (\sigma_{zz} - \sigma_{rr})$, this may be written

$$T_L = \pi R^2 \sigma_{zz}(R,\ L) - \pi \int_0^R r^2 \frac{\partial \sigma_{rr}(L)}{\partial r}\, dr - \pi \int_0^R r^2 \frac{\partial (\sigma_{zz} - \sigma_{rr})}{\partial r}\, dr$$

$$(5.5\text{-}80)$$

Substituting Eq. (5.5-76) into the first integrand, and integrating the second by parts, this becomes

$$T_L = \pi R^2 \sigma_{rr}(R,\ L) + \pi \int_0^R (2\sigma_{zz} - \sigma_{rr} - \sigma_{\theta\theta})r\, dr \qquad (5.5\text{-}81)$$

Note that $\sigma_{rr}(R,\ L)$ is the radial wall stress at the tube exit, i.e., the negative of the "pressure" that would be measured at the tube wall extrapolated to the end, or "exit pressure," P_{RL}. Also, the integrand in the last term is a combination of the first and second normal stress difference, i.e.,

$$2\sigma_{zz} - \sigma_{rr} - \sigma_{\theta\theta} = 2(\tau_{zz} - \tau_{rr}) + (\tau_{rr} - \tau_{\theta\theta}) = 2N_1 + N_2$$

$$(5.5\text{-}82)$$

Changing variables in Eq. (5.5-81) from r to τ (using $\tau = -\tau_w r/R$), multiplying by τ_w^2, and differentiating the result with respect to τ_w gives the following:

$$(2N_1 + N_2)_R = \frac{1}{\pi R^2 \tau_w} \frac{\partial}{\partial \tau_w} [\tau_w^2 + \pi R^2 P_{RL})] \qquad (5.5\text{-}83)^*$$

The right side of Eq. (5.5-83) may be evaluated from measurements of jet thrust and "exit pressure" as a function of wall stress (i.e., at various flow rates), giving the normal stress combination $(2N_1 + N_2)$ as a function of wall stress or the corresponding wall shear rate.

A separate expression for the second normal stress difference may be determined as follows. Integration of Eq. (5.5-76) from 0 to R gives

$$\sigma_{rr}(R, z) = \sigma_{rr}(0, z) - \int_0^R \frac{\sigma_{rr} - \sigma_{\theta\theta}}{r} \, dr \qquad (5.5-84)$$

Since the shear rate at $r = 0$ is zero, it follows that $\sigma_{rr}(0, z) = -P(0, z)$ and Eq. (5.5-84) evaluated at $z = L$ becomes

$$P_{RL} - P(0, L) = \int_0^R \frac{N_2}{r} \, dr \qquad (5.5-85)$$

where P_{RL} has been written for $-\sigma_{rr}(R, L)$, i.e., the total wall normal stress. Again changing variables from r to τ and differentiating the result with respect to τ_w as before leads to

$$(N_2)_R = \tau_w \frac{\partial}{\partial \tau_w} [P_{RL} - P(0, L)] \qquad (5.5-86)$$

Thus, in order to measure the second normal stress difference, both the "exit pressure" and the pressure at the center line in the exit plane would have to be measured. Some workers have assumed the latter is zero (i.e., atmospheric), although this assumption leads to various inconsistencies as pointed out by Davies et al. [5.26]. Nevertheless, the pressure P(0, L) cannot be measured directly.

B. Slit (Narrow Channel) Flows

Now measurements of wall stress in a slit geometry (i.e., a channel of rectangular cross section with aspect ratio of 10 or more) can also be used to deduce values of the first normal stress

difference. The flow field is described in terms of cartesian
coordinates with the z axis in the longitudinal (flow) direction, the
y axis parallel to the short side of the slit, and the walls of the
channel at $y = \pm b$ and $x = \pm a$ with $a/b \geq 10$. The velocity field is
therefore

$$v_z(y) = v^1(z^2) \qquad\qquad v_x = v_y = 0 \qquad\qquad (5.5\text{-}87)$$

and the rate of strain components are

$$\Delta_{ij} = \dot{\gamma}\begin{bmatrix} 0 & 1 & 0 \\ 1 & 0 & 0 \\ 0 & 0 & 0 \end{bmatrix} \qquad\qquad \dot{\gamma} = \frac{dv_z}{dy} \qquad\qquad (5.5\text{-}88)$$

The component equations of motion are:

z comp:

$$\frac{\partial\sigma_{zz}}{\partial z} + \frac{\partial\sigma_{yz}}{\partial y} = 0 \qquad\qquad (5.5\text{-}89)$$

y comp:

$$\frac{\partial\sigma_{yy}}{\partial y} = 0 \qquad\qquad (5.5\text{-}90)$$

x comp:

$$\frac{\partial\sigma_{xx}}{\partial x} = 0 \qquad\qquad (5.5\text{-}91)$$

Since τ_{zz} is independent of z and τ_{yz} varies only with y, Eq. (5.5-89)
becomes

$$\frac{\partial P}{\partial z} = \frac{d\tau_{yz}}{dy} \qquad\qquad (5.5\text{-}92)$$

which, since $\partial P/\partial z$ is independent of y, integrates to

$$\tau_{yz} = y \frac{\partial P}{\partial z} = \tau_w \frac{y}{b} \tag{5.5-93}$$

As with the capillary tube flow, the reduction in axial thrust due to the normal stress component σ_{zz} is

$$T_L = 4a \int_0^b \sigma_{zz}(y, L) \, dy \tag{5.5-94}$$

which can be integrated by parts to give

$$T_L = 4a \left[b\sigma_{zz}(b, L) - \int_0^b y \frac{\partial \sigma_{zz}}{\partial y} \, dy \right] \tag{5.5-95}$$

Using Eq. (5.5-90), we may write

$$\frac{\partial \sigma_{zz}}{\partial y} = \frac{\partial}{\partial y} (\sigma_{zz} - \sigma_{yy}) = \frac{\partial N_1}{\partial y} \tag{5.5-96}$$

Substituting this into Eq. (5.5-95) and integrating again by parts leads to

$$T_L = 4a \left[b\sigma_{yy}(b, L) + \int_0^b N_1 \, dy \right] \tag{5.5-97}$$

or

$$\int_0^b N_1 \, dy = \frac{T_L}{4a} + bP_{bL} \tag{5.5-98}$$

where P_{bL} has been written for $-\sigma_{yy}(b, L)$, the total wall stress extrapolated to the end of the slit. Using Eq. (5.5-93) to change variables from y to τ_{yz}, this may be written

$$\int_{0}^{\tau_w} N_1 \, d\tau_{yz} = \frac{\tau_w}{4ab} (T_L + 4abP_{bL}) \qquad (5.5\text{-}99)$$

Differentiating this with respect to τ_w using Leibnitz' rule and rearranging gives

$$(N_1)_b = P_{bL} + \tau_w \frac{\partial P_{bL}}{\partial \tau_w} + \frac{1}{4ab} \frac{\partial}{\partial \tau_w} (\tau_w T_L) \qquad (5.5\text{-}100)^*$$

From the sparse data existing on slit flow measurements (e.g., Ref. 5.27), it would appear that the axial thrust term in the above equation is small compared with the other terms, at least for polymer melts. Assuming this to hold in capillary tube flow as well, Eqs. (5.5-83) and (5.5-86) may be combined to yield the following expression for the first normal stress difference in tube flow:

$$(N_1)_R = P_{RL} + \frac{\tau_w}{2} \frac{\partial}{\partial \tau_w} P(0, L) \qquad (5.5\text{-}101)$$

Now data obtained by Han [5.27] for polymer melts indicate that the "exit pressures" in slits and tubes (P_{bL}, P_{RL}) are approximately the same although the two sets of data were taken over different ranges of shear rate. Since the first normal stress differences must be independent of geometry this implies, from Eq. (5.5-100) and (5.5-101), that

$$P(0, L) \cong 2P_{bL} \cong 2P_{RL} \qquad (5.5\text{-}102)$$

i.e., the pressure at the center line in the exit plane of a tube is twice that at the wall at the end of the tube. Using this approximation, the expressions for the first and second normal stress differences in terms of total wall stress measurements for capillary tube flow become

$$N_1 \cong P_{RL} + \tau_w \frac{\partial}{\partial \tau_w} (P_{RL}) \qquad (5.5\text{-}103)^*$$

$$N_2 \cong -\tau_w \frac{\partial}{\partial \tau_w} (P_{RL})$$

(5.5-104)*

Since experience shows that P_{RL} is a monotonically increasing function of τ_w, these results indicate that N_2 is negative and smaller in magnitude than N_1. This is qualitatively consistent with most normal stress observations in the literature to date. However, such observations are generally limited to a relatively narrow range of shear rates, as a consequence of the nature of the measurements.

A considerable volume of literature has been built up concerning the evaluation of normal stress components from measurements of the swell of the fluid as it exits the tube or a die. The data are usually interpreted in terms of a momentum balance analysis, following that of Metzner et al. [5.28]. Although results obtained by this method appear to agree with other methods for some fluids (i.e., solutions), they are often in disagreement by orders of magnitude in the case of some polymer melts [5.29-5.31]. The discrepancy may be due to certain assumptions in the analysis relative to center line and exit pressures, as pointed out by Davies et al. [5.26]. An alternate analysis of the die swell phenomena based upon the concept of elastic strain recovery upon relaxation of the stress as the fluid exits the tube or die appears to be more generally consistent with data for polymer melts [5.32, 5.33].

A note of caution: measurements of normal wall stress obtained from "pressure taps" at the wall should be made with flush mounted transducers whenever possible, to avoid possible "hole errors" resulting from normal stress effects [5.46, 5.47].

5.6. TIME-DEPENDENT MATERIAL FUNCTIONS

The methods discussed so far are suitable for determining the steady flow viscous and normal stress material functions. Although normal stress effects are generally considered to be a consequence of the elastic properties of a fluid, they do not provide a specific measure of the time-dependent characteristics which are more directly indicative of viscoelasticity. In this section we will present

analyses of some of the testing methods which may be used to determine the linear time-dependent material functions which were defined
and discussed in Chap. 2. As in Chap. 2, the assumption is made
that the materials behave in a linear fashion, which in effect restricts the testing conditions to deformation magnitudes which are
sufficiently small to validate this assumption. Whenever possible,
it is advisable to carry out the tests at more than one amplitude
in order to check the linearity assumption. As with previous sections, the material in this section is not exhaustive, but is representative of the most commonly employed techniques. For the most
part, the material in this section is taken from the various publi-
cations of Walters [5.35-5.39]. For additional methods and details
the reader is referred to the book by Ferry [5.34] and references
therein.

5.6.1. Forced Oscillatory Testing--
Negligible Sample Inertia [5.13, 5.35]

The most common time varying test involves the imposition of an
oscillating shear strain on the sample and measurement of the relative
amplitude and phase shift of the resulting shear stress, as a function
of frequency. For fluid samples, the tests are typically conducted
in a rotational viscometer configuration, such as the Couette or cone
and plate geometry. If the gap width in the instrument is small
enough [i.e., if Eq. (4.4-44) is satisfied], the influence of the
sample mass or inertia will be negligible compared to the material
stresses. The criterion for this condition to be satisfied is essentially that the instrument gap (h) be small relative to the wavelength of a shear wave propagating in the fluid [See Eq. (4.4-44).]
Under these conditions, the shear field is homogeneous for all practical purposes and hence may be approximated by the simple shear
equivalent.

We have demonstrated that the simple shear approximation for
shear rate in the Couette and cone and plate geometries is valid if

the gap is sufficiently small. The shear rate for these geometries is given by Eqs. (5.4-73) and (5.4-87), respectively:

Couette:

$$\dot{\gamma} = \frac{\Omega\alpha}{\alpha - 1} \qquad \alpha = \frac{R_o}{R_i} \qquad\qquad (5.6\text{-}1)$$

Cone plate:

$$\dot{\gamma} = \frac{\Omega}{\theta_c} \qquad\qquad (5.6\text{-}2)$$

The corresponding expressions for shear stress are given by Eqs. (5.4-74) and (5.4-90).

Couette:

$$\tau = \frac{T(\alpha^2 + 1)}{4\pi L R_o^2} \qquad\qquad (5.6\text{-}3)$$

Cone plate:

$$\tau = \frac{3T}{2\pi R^3} \qquad\qquad (5.6\text{-}4)$$

With reference to these equations, the following analysis may be considered applicable to either geometry if we write:

$$\dot{\gamma} = A\Omega \qquad\qquad (5.6\text{-}5)$$

and

$$\tau = BT \qquad\qquad (5.6\text{-}6)$$

where the constants A and B are simply geometrical factors which are characteristic of the specific instrument:

Couette:

$$A = \frac{\alpha}{\alpha - 1} \qquad\qquad B = \frac{\alpha^2 + 1}{4\pi LR_o^2} \qquad\qquad (5.6\text{-}7)$$

Cone plate:

$$A = \frac{1}{\theta_c} \qquad\qquad B = \frac{3}{2\pi R^3} \qquad\qquad (5.6\text{-}8)$$

It is noted that the corresponding expressions for the shear stress and shear rate for the disc and plate geometry [Eqs. (5.4-102) and (5.4-103)] also appear to be of the form of Eqs. (5.6-7) and (5.6-8), i.e.,

Disc plate:

$$\dot{\gamma} = \frac{\Omega R}{h} \qquad\qquad\qquad (5.6\text{-}9)$$

$$\tau = \frac{2T}{\pi R^3} \qquad\qquad\qquad (5.6\text{-}10)$$

However for this geometry the shear field is not homogeneous but varies with the radial coordinate regardless of the dimensions of the gap, as seen by Eq. (5.4-98). Thus a sample in this geometry will be subjected to a continuous range of shear rate magnitudes, from zero at the center to some maximum value at the rim. Therefore, this geometry would be suitable for evaluation of material properties only for materials which are essentially linear (i.e., independent of the magnitude of the deformation) over this range of shear rates.

A. Oscillatory Response--Amplitude Ratio and Phase Angle

A typical arrangement involves imposition of a known oscillatory motion on one member of the instrument (the input) and measurement of the force or torque transmitted to the other member (the output) by the deflection of a torsion bar by which it is suspended. Since both

members move, the shear rate is proportional to the relative velocity between them. If ϕ_i is the deflection of the driving or input
member and ϕ_o the deflection of the driven or output member, this is

$$\dot{\gamma} = A(\dot{\phi}_i - \dot{\phi}_o) \qquad (5.6\text{-}11)$$

Measurements are made of the amplitude ratio $r = |\Phi_o/\Phi_i|$ and phase
angle ε between the output and input deflections as a function of
frequency, and these are related to the viscous and elastic properties of the material.

The fluid stress transmitted to the surface of the output member
must overcome its inertia (I) and any friction in the mountings (coefficient U) as well as the restoring force of the torsion bar
(spring constant K). The system equation therefore follows from a
force or moment balance:

$$I\ddot{\phi}_o + U\dot{\phi}_o + K\phi_o = T = \frac{\tau}{B} \qquad (5.6\text{-}12)$$

It would seem that the ideal situation would involve a very
sensitive detector and a very stiff torsion bar, so that the deflection of the torsion sensing output member would be kept to a minimum.
This could be achieved by keeping the driving frequency well below
the natural frequency of the sensing element, which from Eq. (5.6-12)
is seen to be $\sqrt{K/I} = \omega_o$. However the general characteristics of
the amplitude ratio r and phase angle ε as a function of frequency
are illustrated in Fig. 5.12 for the case of a Maxwell fluid [5.35].
As illustrated, r goes through unity and ε through zero at a frequency
near ω_o for both viscous and elastic fluids and, furthermore, r
approaches zero and ε approaches $-\pi/2$ for all materials in all geometries. Consequently, the curves at frequencies below ω_o are not
very sensitive to the relative viscous and elastic properties of the
fluid, whereas for frequencies above ω_o these properties have a very
marked influence on the curves. For example, a very marked peak can
occur in the r curve at a frequency just above ω_o for highly elastic
fluids, whereas the maximum for a purely viscous fluid corresponds

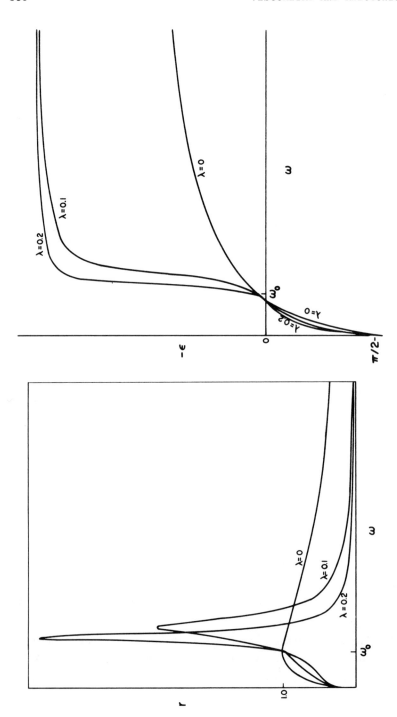

FIG. 5.12 Frequency dependence of amplitude ratio and phase angle (Ref. 5.35). (Reprinted from Ref. 5.35, p. 10, by courtesy of Sangamo Controls Limited.)

to r = 1. It is therefore advisable to operate at imposed frequencies greater than the natural frequency of the system whenever possible.

If the material is lienarly viscoelastic, then Eq. (5.6-12) is a linear differential equation and a sinusoidal input will produce a sinusoidal output, which is out of phase with the input. The input and output deflections can thus be represented by:

$$\phi_i(j\omega) = \phi_i e^{j\omega t} \tag{5.6-13}$$

$$\phi_o(j\omega) = \phi_o e^{j(\omega t + \varepsilon)} \tag{5.6-14}$$

If the fluid is characterized by its complex modulus, $G^*(j\omega)$, the oscillatory stress and strain will be related by:

$$\tau(\omega t) = G^*(j\omega)\gamma(\omega t) = G^*(j\omega)A(\Phi_i - \Phi_o e^{j\varepsilon})e^{j\omega t} \tag{5.6-15}$$

where

$$\Phi_o e^{j\varepsilon} = \Phi_o \cos \varepsilon + j\Phi_o \sin \varepsilon = \Phi_o' + j\Phi_o'' \tag{5.6-16}$$

Substituting Eqs. (5.6-14) to (5.6-16) into Eq. (5.6-12) and solving for $G^*(j\omega)$ gives:

$$G^*(j\omega) = \frac{B}{A}\left[\frac{(\Phi_o' + j\Phi_o'')(K - \omega^2 I + j\omega U)}{\Phi_i - \Phi_o' - j\Phi_o''}\right]$$

$$= \frac{rB}{A}\left[\frac{(\cos \varepsilon + j \sin \varepsilon)(K - \omega^2 I + j\omega U)}{1 - r \cos \varepsilon - jr \sin \varepsilon}\right] \tag{5.6-17}$$

Separating Eq. (5.6-17) into real and imaginary parts provides expressions for the material functions $G'(\omega)$ and $G''(\omega)$ as follows:

$$G'(\omega) = \frac{rB}{A}\left[\frac{(K - \omega^2 I)(\cos \varepsilon - r) - \omega U \sin \varepsilon}{1 - 2r \cos \varepsilon + r^2}\right] \tag{5.6-18}*$$

$$G''(\omega) = \frac{rB}{A}\left[\frac{(K - \omega^2 I)\ \sin\ \varepsilon + \omega U(\cos\ \varepsilon - r)}{1 - 2r\ \cos\ \varepsilon + r^2}\right] \qquad (5.6\text{-}19)^*$$

Thus $G'(\omega)$ and $G''(\omega)$ may be determined from measurements of the amplitude ratio (r) and phase angle (ε) between the output (driven) member and the input (driving) member. The components of the complex viscosity function, $\eta^*(j\omega) = \eta' - j\eta''$, are likewise determined, since $\eta' = G''/\omega$ and $\eta'' = G'/\omega$.

B. Instrument Inertia and Drag Parameters

In order to use the preceding formulas, the instrument parameters K, I, and U must be known. The torsion bar constant, K, may be determined by direct calibration. However, the inertia, I, and viscous drag coefficient, U, are dynamic parameters and can best be determined indirectly from measurements of the natural frequency and damping factor of resonance oscillations with no sample present.

If the driven (output) member is subjected to an impulsive or transient deflection of amplitude Φ_o with no material sample in the gap (e.g., in air), the motion will be described by Eq. (5.6-12) with τ replaced by the impulse function:

$$\ddot{\phi}_o + \frac{U}{I}\ \dot{\phi}_o + \frac{K}{I}\ \phi_o = \Phi_o\ \delta(t) \qquad (5.6\text{-}20)$$

The solution of this equation will describe a damped oscillatory motion provided $(U^2/4IK) < 1$, which is practically always true, since U is normally very small in a properly designed instrument. Under these conditions the solution is:

$$\phi_o = \frac{\Phi_o}{\omega_o\sqrt{1 - \zeta^2}}\ e^{-\omega_o\zeta_d t}\ \sin\left[\omega_o\sqrt{1 - \zeta_d^2}\ t\right] \qquad (5.6\text{-}21)$$

where

$$\omega_o = \sqrt{\frac{K}{I}} = \text{natural frequency} \qquad (5.6\text{-}22)$$

$$\zeta_d = \frac{U}{2\sqrt{IK}} = \text{damping factor} \qquad (5.6\text{-}23)$$

The result is illustrated in Fig. 5.13. Thus if the torsion spring constant (K) is known, the instrument inertia (I) and viscous coefficient (U) may be determined from measurements of the wave frequency and damping factor, as follows.

Note from Eq. (5.6-21) that the actual frequency of the oscillatory wave is not the natural frequency, ω_o, but is instead

Actual frequency:

$$\omega = \omega_o \sqrt{1 - \zeta_d^2} \qquad (5.6\text{-}24)$$

Thus measurement of the wave period, T, gives the actual frequency. If the total period of n successive waves is T_n, we have

$$\omega = \frac{2\pi n}{T_n} \qquad (5.6\text{-}25)$$

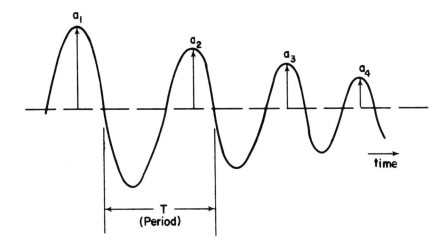

FIG. 5.13 Damped oscillatory response.

In order to calculate the damping factor ζ_d, consider the ratio of the amplitudes of two waves, a_1 and a_n, separated by period T_n (i.e., $T_n = 2\pi n/\omega$). From Eq. (5.6-21) this is

$$\frac{\phi_o(t + T_n)}{\phi_o(t)} = \frac{a_n}{a_1} = \exp\left[\frac{-2\pi n\zeta_d}{\sqrt{1 - \zeta_d^2}}\right] \tag{5.6-26}$$

If the ratio a_1/a_n is denoted by r_n:

$$r_n = \frac{a_1}{a_n} \tag{5.6-27}$$

Eq. (5.6-26) can be written

$$\ln r_n = \frac{2\pi n\zeta_d}{\sqrt{1 - \zeta_d^2}} = 2\pi n\ell_r \tag{5.6-28}$$

where

$$\ell_r = \frac{\ln r_n}{2\pi n} \tag{5.6-29}$$

The damping factor may thus be determined from the measurement of any two amplitudes, a_1 and a_n:

$$\zeta_d = \frac{\ell_r}{\sqrt{1 + \ell_r^2}} \tag{5.6-30}$$

However, to average out possible variations due to experimental error and measurement precision, it is often more desirable to measure a number of amplitude ratios (r_n) for various values of n. The slope of a plot of $\log r_n$ vs. n is $(2\pi\ell_r/2.3)$. Knowing ℓ_r, the damping factor is thus determined by Eq. (5.6-30), which in turn is used with the measured value of ω and Eq. (5.6-24) to determine the natural frequency, ω_o.

Having thus determined ω and ζ_d from the damped oscillatory wave, the instrument parameters I and U follow from Eqs. (5.6-22) and (5.6-23).

$$I = \frac{K}{\omega_o^2} \tag{5.6-31}$$

$$U = \frac{2\zeta_d K}{\omega_o} \tag{5.6-32}$$

C. Mechanical Impedance

If it is possible to measure force and displacement (or velocity) simultaneously on the moving member of the instrument while holding the other fixed, these measurements may be converted to stress and strain (or strain rate) at the surface of that member. The ratio of the oscillatory driving force to the resulting oscillatory velocity is analogous to electrical impedance, and is defined as the *mechanical impedance*:

$$Z^*(j\omega) = \frac{\text{Force }(\omega t)}{\text{Velocity }(\omega t)} = |Z|e^{j\varepsilon}$$

$$= R(\omega) + jX(\omega) = |Z|(\cos \varepsilon + j \sin \varepsilon) \tag{5.6-33}$$

For rotating geometries, the force and velocity would be replaced by torque and angular velocity. Determination of the mechanical impedance from measurements of the ratio of the amplitudes of the force and velocity, $|Z|$, and the phase angle between them, ε, [i.e., the "in-phase: and "out-of-phase" components of force and velocity, $R(\omega)$ and $X(\omega)$] enables evaluation of the viscous and elastic properties of linear materials as follows.

A torque (or force) balance on the moving member, analogous to Eq. (5.6-12), may be written:

$$I\ddot{\phi} + U\dot{\phi} + K\phi + \frac{\tau}{B} = T \tag{5.6-34}$$

Here, T represents the total torque (or force) applied to the instrument member to produce the motion, I is its inertia, U and K are the
viscous and elastic coefficients of the bearings or mountings of the
moving member, and τ is the stress exerted by the material in contact
with the surface of the member. In most cases, K would be negligible,
although it will be retained here for completeness.

     For an oscillatory applied torque of magnitude T_o and frequency
ω of the form

$$T = T(\omega t) = T_o e^{j(\omega t+\varepsilon)} \tag{5.6-35}$$

the moving member will oscillate at frequency ω with amplitude Φ and
phase angle ε relative to the applied torque, if the material is
linear. Thus the motion will be described by:

$$\phi = \phi(\omega t) = \Phi e^{j\omega t} \tag{5.6-36}$$

If the material stress is characterized by the complex modulus, as
before, it may be expressed as:

$$\tau = \tau(\omega t) = G^*(j\omega)\gamma(\omega t) = AG^*(j\omega)\phi(\omega t) \tag{5.6-37}$$

Substituting Eqs. (5.6-35) to (5.6-37) into Eq. (5.6-34) and solving
for $T_o/\Phi \, e^{j\varepsilon}$, there results:

$$\frac{T_o}{\Phi} e^{j\varepsilon} = K + \frac{AG^*(j\omega)}{B} - I\omega^2 + j\omega U \tag{5.6-38}$$

Separating this into real and imaginary parts, it becomes

$$\frac{T_o}{\Phi} e^{j\varepsilon} = \left[K - I\omega^2 + \frac{G'A}{B} \right] + j\left[\omega U + \frac{G''A}{B} \right]$$

$$= \frac{T_o}{\Phi} (\cos\varepsilon + j\sin\varepsilon) \tag{5.6-39}^*$$

where the real and imaginary parts of Eq. (5.6-39) represent the
"in-phase" and "out-of-phase" components of torque (force) and

displacement, respectively. This can also be expressed in terms of
velocity instead of displacement, since

$$\Omega(\omega t) = \dot{\phi}(\omega t) = j\omega\phi(\omega t) = \Omega_o e^{j\omega t} = \omega\Phi e^{j[\omega t+(\pi/2)]} \tag{5.6-40}$$

The mechanical impedance is thus defined by:

$$Z^*(j\omega) = \frac{T(\omega t)}{\Omega(\omega t)} = \frac{T_o}{j\omega\Phi} e^{j\varepsilon} = R(\omega) + jX(\omega) \tag{5.6-41}$$

which, from Eq. (5.6-39) is related to the system and material parameters by:

$$Z^*(j\omega) = \left[U + \frac{G''A}{\omega B}\right] - j\left[\frac{K}{\omega} - I\omega + \frac{G'A}{\omega B}\right] \tag{5.6-42}^*$$

Note that $R(\omega)$ is the "in-phase" and $X(\omega)$ the "out-of-phase" component of the ratio of applied torque (force) to resulting velocity
(of magnitude Ω_o). Solving Eqs. (5.6-41) and (5.6-42) for the loss
and storage modulus in terms of $R(\omega)$ and $X(\omega)$, we find:

$$G'(\omega) = \frac{\omega B}{A}\left[I\omega - \frac{K}{\omega} - X(\omega)\right] = \left[\frac{B}{A}\right]\left[\left[\frac{T_o}{\Phi}\right] \cos\varepsilon + I\omega^2 - K\right] \tag{5.6-43}^*$$

$$G''(\omega) = \frac{\omega B}{A}\left[R(\omega) - U\right] = \left[\frac{B}{A}\right]\left[\left[\frac{T_o}{\Phi}\right] \sin\varepsilon - \omega U\right] \tag{5.6-44}^*$$

The result can also be expressed in terms of the real and imaginary
components of the complex viscosity, since

$$\eta'(\omega) = \frac{G''(\omega)}{\omega} \qquad \eta''(\omega) = \frac{G'(\omega)}{\omega} \tag{5.6-45}$$

The instrument parameters I and U can be obtained from free oscillation or resonance vibrations of the moving member, as outlined
previously in Sec. B. If there is no elasticity in the instrument
mounting itself (i.e., K = 0), a known spring or torsion bar may
sometimes be inserted to produce resonance oscillations for the purpose of evaluating I and U. An alternate method is to "calibrate"

the instrument with a material of known properties, solving Eqs. (5.6-43) and (5.6-44) for I and U in terms of the measured values $X(\omega)$ and $R(\omega)$ and known values of G' and G''.

An experimental device for determining the mechanical impedance of a viscoelastic fluid by means of the axial oscillation of a cylindrical shaft in a concentric cylinder geometry with the fluid in the annular gap is the "Birnboim apparatus" [5.34, 5.40]. In this system, the driving force is supplied by an a-c electrical signal through a coil coupled to the shaft. The driving force is proportional to the current through the coil and the displacement is proportional to the back emf, so that the mechanical impedance of the system is directly related to its electrical impedance.

5.6.2. Forced Oscillatory Testing-- Sample Inertia Considered

Each of the analyses presented so far depends upon the assumption that the shear in the material sample is uniform or homogeneous. The validity of this assumption depends not only upon the geometry and dimensions of the instrument gap, but also upon the fluid viscous, elastic, and density properties relative to the oscillatory frequency. A criterion for this was established in Sec. 4.4.2. If this condition is not satisfied, the equations previously derived will be in error and interpretation of experimental data in terms of these equations may lead to serious errors in the derived material properties. In order to alleviate this difficulty, it is necessary to account for local variations in the flow field due to the finite mass or inertia of the sample by solving the momentum equations of motion for the system.

A. Wave Propagation

An example of the influence of finite fluid mass or inertia is the situation involving a flat plate oscillating parallel to itself in contact with a relatively large volume of viscoelastic material.

This is the problem considered in Sec. 4.4.1. The viscoelastic properties of the material can be determined either from measured characteristics of the propagating wave (i.e., wave velocity and wavelength), or from the amplitude and phase relations between the force on the plate and its velocity (i.e., mechanical impedance). By "large volume of material" is meant a sample with dimensions which are large compared with the exponential decay distance or damping factor $1/\alpha_r$ of the propagating wave, as given by Eq. (4.4-17). Although the analysis of this problem was presented in Sec. 4.4.1, the pertinent equations will be repeated here for the sake of convenience.

The equation of motion for the system is:

$$\rho \frac{\partial v_x}{\partial t} = \frac{\partial \tau_{yx}}{\partial y} \tag{5.6-46}$$

For oscillatory motion, the viscoelastic material properties may be characterized by the complex viscosity providing an expression for the shear stress in terms of the velocity gradient. The resulting solution for the velocity distribution is Eq. (4.4-16):

$$v_x(y, \omega) = V_o e^{j(\omega t - \alpha_i y)} e^{-\alpha_r y} \tag{5.6-47}$$

where V_o = magnitude of the oscillating plate velocity, and

$$\alpha_r = \left\{ \frac{\omega \rho}{2(\eta'^2 + \eta''^2)} \left[(\eta'^2 + \eta''^2)^{\frac{1}{2}} - \eta'' \right] \right\}^{\frac{1}{2}} \tag{5.6-48}$$

$$\alpha_i = \left\{ \frac{\omega \rho}{2(\eta'^2 + \eta''^2)} \left[(\eta'^2 + \eta''^2)^{\frac{1}{2}} + \eta'' \right] \right\}^{\frac{1}{2}} \tag{5.6-49}$$

Thus the wave length, ℓ, is given by:

$$\ell = \frac{2\pi}{\alpha_i} \tag{5.6-50}$$

and the wave amplitude is damped exponentially with a damping factor
of

$$\frac{1}{\alpha_r} \tag{5.6-51}$$

this being the distance over which the amplitude falls by a factor
of 1/e or to 37% of the original value. Hence measurements of the
propagating wave amplitude and damping factor may be made (e.g., by
optical methods) and used to determine α_i and α_r. These in turn may
be used to determine η' and η'' by rearrangement of Eqs. (5.6-48)
and (5.6-49):

$$\eta' = \frac{2\omega\rho\alpha_r\alpha_i}{(\alpha_r^2 + \alpha_i^2)^2} \tag{5.6-52}*$$

$$\eta'' = \frac{\omega\rho(\alpha_i^2 - \alpha_r^2)}{(\alpha_r^2 + \alpha_i^2)^2} \tag{5.6-53}*$$

These viscoelastic properties can also be determined from measurements of the mechanical impedance, derived from the amplitude
ratio and phase relations between the stress acting on the plate and
its velocity. The results have also been presented in Sec. 4.4 as
Eqs. (4.4-24) to (4.4-27), repeated here for convenience:

$$z^*(j\omega) = -\frac{\tau_o(j\omega)}{v_o(j\omega)} = R(\omega) + jX(\omega) = (j\omega\rho\eta^*)^{\frac{1}{2}} \tag{5.6-54}$$

where

$$R(\omega) = \left(\frac{\omega\rho}{2}\right)^{\frac{1}{2}} [(\eta'^2 + \eta''^2)^{\frac{1}{2}} + \eta'']^{\frac{1}{2}} \tag{5.6-55}$$

$$X(\omega) = \left(\frac{\omega\rho}{2}\right)^{\frac{1}{2}} [(\eta'^2 + \eta''^2)^{\frac{1}{2}} - \eta'']^{\frac{1}{2}} \tag{5.6-56}$$

These equations may be solved for η' and η'' in terms of R and X:

$$\eta' = \frac{2X(\omega)\ R(\omega)}{\omega\rho} \tag{5.6-57}^*$$

$$\eta'' = \frac{R^2(\omega)\ -\ X^2(\omega)}{\omega\rho} \tag{5.6-58}^*$$

Now the mechanical impedance as defined above involves the stress exerted by the plate on the fluid, and not the stress that must be exerted on the plate to make it oscillate. These differ by the influence of the inertia (mass) of the plate and the viscous and elastic properties of its support. Thus if τ_i is the stress exerted on the plate which has mass M and viscous and elastic support coefficients U and K (all per unit plate area), a force balance on the plate yields:

$$M\ddot{X} + U\dot{X} + KX + \tau_o = \tau_i \tag{5.6-59}$$

in the absence of a sample, $\tau_o = 0$, and the resulting ratio of oscillatory stress, $\tau_i(j\omega)$ to oscillatory velocity, $v_o(j\omega)$ is the impedance of the plate and support, Z_o^*. From Eq. (5.6-59) with $\tau_o = 0$, this becomes:

$$Z_o^* = \frac{\tau_i(j\omega)}{v_o(j\omega)} = R_o + jX_o \tag{5.6-60}$$

where

$$R_o = U \qquad X_o = (-\frac{K}{\omega} + \omega M) \tag{5.6-61}$$

This is analogous to Eq. (5.6-42) with no sample. Therefore, the total measured impedance, Z_T^*, is the sum of that due to the fluid (Z^*) plus that due to the plate (Z_o^*):

$$Z_T^* = Z_o^* + Z^* = R_T + jX_T \tag{5.6-62}$$

or

$$R = R_T - R_o \qquad\qquad X = X_T - X_o \qquad\qquad\qquad (5.6\text{-}63)$$

That is, the measured resistance and reactance (i.e., the in-phase and out-of-phase components of applied stress and the velocity) must be corrected for the impedance of the plate by Eq. (5.6-63) before being used in Eqs. (5.6-57) and (5.6-58) to compute the viscoelastic material properties.

B. Mechanical Impedance--Parallel Plates

If the sample dimension perpendicular to the plate is not large relative to the propagated wavelength but is constrained by a stationary parallel plate located a distance h from the oscillating plate, the situation becomes identical to that considered in Sec. 4.4.2. The solution for the oscillatory velocity distribution is given by Eq. (4.4-34), with the transform variable s replaced by $j\omega$:

$$v(y,\ \omega) = \bar{V}(\omega)\ \frac{\sinh \alpha^* y}{\sinh \alpha^* h} \qquad\qquad\qquad (5.6\text{-}64)$$

where

$$\alpha^{*2} = \frac{j\omega\rho}{\bar{\psi}(j\omega)} = \frac{j\omega\rho}{\eta^*} \qquad\qquad\qquad (5.6\text{-}65)$$

as before, and $\bar{V}(\omega) = v_o(\omega t) = V_o e^{j\omega t}$ is the velocity of the oscillatory plate. The stationary plate is located at $y = 0$ and the oscillatory plate at $y = h$. The stress exerted by the moving plate on the fluid is given by

$$\tau_o(j\omega) = \eta^* \left(\frac{\partial v}{\partial y}\right)_{y=h} = \eta^* \alpha^* V_o e^{j\omega t}\ \coth \alpha^* h \qquad\qquad (5.6\text{-}66)$$

so that the mechanical impedance is:

$$z^*(j\omega) = \frac{\tau_o(j\omega)}{v_o(j\omega)} = \eta^* \alpha^*\ \coth \alpha^* h \qquad\qquad\qquad (5.6\text{-}67)$$

The measured impedance may be corrected for the impedance of the plate (i.e., its mass and support restraints) with no sample (Z_o^*) as before Eqs. (5.6-60) and (5.6-61).

Equation (5.6-67) cannot be solved explicitly for the components of the complex viscosity as its stands. However, for sufficiently small or large values of the argument, the following approximations are good to within 2%:

$$\text{For} \quad \chi \leq 0.3: \quad \coth \chi \doteq \frac{1}{\chi} \left.\begin{array}{l}\\[2ex]\end{array}\right\} \tag{5.6-68}$$
$$\chi \geq 3 \quad : \quad \coth \chi \doteq 1$$

With this, Eq. (5.6-67) becomes:

$$\left|\alpha^* h\right| \leq 0.3: \qquad z^*(j\omega) = \frac{\eta^*}{h} \tag{5.6-69}$$

or

$$R(\omega) = \frac{\eta'}{h} \qquad X(\omega) = -\frac{\eta''}{h} \tag{5.6-70}$$

and

$$\left|\alpha^* h\right| \geq 3: \qquad z^*(j\omega) = \eta^* \alpha^* = (j\omega\rho\eta^*)^{\frac{1}{2}} \tag{5.6-71}$$

with $R(\omega)$ and $X(\omega)$ given by Eqs. (5.6-55) and (5.6-56).

Note that Eq. (5.6-69) is identical to the result which would be obtained by assuming simple shear between the plates (i.e., neglecting fluid inertia), while Eq. (5.6-71) is identical to Eq. (5.6-54) for the wave propagating in a semi-infinite medium. This therefore confirms the validity of these two as special cases, and furthermore Eq. (5.6-68) defines the conditions under which each is valid. It is clear that $\alpha^* h$ is a dimensionless parameter which characterizes the ratio of inertial to rheological (deformation) forces in the material.

C. Oscillatory Response--Couette Flow [5.36, 5.37, 5.42]

If the sample is contained in a Couette instrument with a narrow
gap and the cup is oscillated at a known frequency, the amplitude
ratio and phase angle between the cup and bob (suspended by a torsion
bar) provide information on the viscoelastic properties of the sample.
This arrangement is identical to that described in Sec. 5.61A, except
that the assumption of a uniform shear (i.e., negligible inertia) in
the annulus is not made in the analysis. It is necessary, therefore,
to solve the equations of motion for the flow in the annulus to determine the stress distribution resulting from the imposed oscillation,
and thereby relate observable quantities to material functions.

For this deformation, the equation of motion for the angular
(θ) component of velocity is:

$$\rho \frac{\partial v_\theta}{\partial t} = \frac{1}{r^2} \frac{\partial}{\partial r} (r^2 \tau_{r\theta}) \tag{5.6-72}$$

where

$$v_\theta = r \frac{\partial \theta}{\partial t} = r\Omega(r) \tag{5.6-73}$$

For steady oscillatory motion, the angular deflection, velocity, and
shear stress may be expressed as

$$\theta(\omega) = \Theta(r)e^{j(\omega t+\delta)} \qquad\qquad \Omega(\omega) = j\omega\Theta(r)e^{j(\omega t+\delta)} \tag{5.6-74}$$

and

$$\tau_{r\theta}(\omega) = \eta^* r \frac{d\Omega}{dr} = j\omega r \eta^* e^{j(\omega t+\delta)} \frac{d\Theta}{dr} \tag{5.6-75}$$

where δ is the phase angle between the local deflection and that of
the driven cylinder. These quantities vary with the radial position
in the sample as indicated, their distribution being determined by
the solution of Eq. (5.6-72). Substituting Eqs. (5.6-74) and (5.6-75)
into Eq. (5.6-72), there results

$$-\omega^2 \rho r \Theta = \frac{j\omega \overset{*}{\eta}}{r^2} \frac{d}{dr} \left(r^3 \frac{d\Theta}{dr} \right) \tag{5.6-76}$$

where it has been assumed that $\overset{*}{\eta}$ is independent of r; i.e., the fluid is linear over the range of shear rates existing in the annulus. This will be a good assumption, if the annulus is sufficiently narrow and the amplitude of oscillation sufficiently small, even for nonliner fluids.

Equation (5.6-76) can be rearranged to:

$$\frac{d^2\Theta}{dr^2} + \frac{3}{r} \frac{d\Theta}{dr} + \kappa^{*2}\Theta = 0 \tag{5.6-77}$$

where

$$\kappa^{*2} = \frac{-j\omega\rho}{\overset{*}{\eta}} = -\alpha^{*2} \tag{5.6-78}$$

is the same parameter encountered in previous problems. Equation (5.6-77) is a form of Bessel's equation, for which the general solution is:

$$\Theta(r) = \frac{1}{r}[C_1 J_1(\kappa^* r) + C_2 Y_1(\kappa^* r)] \tag{5.6-79}$$

where J_1 and Y_1 are first order Bessel functions of the first and second kind. The constants C_1 and C_2 must be determined from the boundary conditions:

$$
\begin{aligned}
&(1) \quad \Theta = \Theta_o \quad \text{at } r = R_o \\
&(2) \quad \Theta = \Theta_i \quad \text{at } r = R_i
\end{aligned} \tag{5.6-80}
$$

Now if the outer cylinder is driven in a specified sinusoidal oscillation, and the inner cylinder is suspended by a torsion wire with spring constant K, the outer cylinder deflection is:

$$\Theta_o = \Theta_o(\omega t) = |\Theta_o| e^{j\omega t} \tag{5.6-81}$$

while the deflection of the inner cylinder, Θ_i, is determined by a
force (moments) balance as follows:

$$I\ddot{\Theta}_i + K\Theta_i = T_i \tag{5.6-82}$$

where

$$\Theta_i = |\Theta_i|e^{j(\omega t - \varepsilon)} \tag{5.6-83}$$

and

$$T_i = 2\pi R_i^2 L(\tau_{r\Theta})\Big|_{r=R_i} \tag{5.6-84}$$

Here ε is the phase angle between the outer and inner cylinders
[Eq. (5.6-82) has neglected possible friction in the support of the
inner cylinder].

Now we are interested in determining an expression for the amplitude ratio and phase angle between the inner and outer cylinders
(measurable quantities). This may be done by evaluating C_1 and C_2 in
Eq. (5.6-75) to determine $(\tau_{r\Theta})_{R_i}$, and hence T_i from Eq. (5.6-84).

When this result is substituted into Eq. (5.6-82) the result is a
complex algebraic equation relating Θ_o and Θ_i which can be solved
for the amplitude ratio and phase. The result is [5.37] (where
$\kappa^* = j\alpha^*$):

$$\left|\frac{\Theta_o}{\Theta_i}\right|e^{j\varepsilon} = \frac{\pi R_i^2 \kappa^*}{2R_o}\left\{\left[J_2(\kappa^* R_i)Y_1(\kappa^* R_o) - Y_2(\kappa^* R_i)J_1(\kappa^* R_o)\right]\right.$$

$$\left. + \frac{\kappa^*}{2\pi\rho R_i^3 L}\left[\frac{K}{\omega^2} - I\right]\left[J_1(\kappa^* R_i)Y_1(\kappa^* R_o) - Y_1(\kappa^* R_i)J_1(\kappa^* R_o)\right]\right\}$$

$$\tag{5.6-85}$$

Since κ^* is a complex quantity, it is virtually impossible to separate Eq. (5.6-85) into real and imaginary components and solve explicitly for η' and η''. However, for sufficiently small (see note 12) values of $\alpha^*(R_o - R_i)$, Walters [5.37] has shown that this equation can be expanded in series and written in the form:

$$\left|\frac{\Theta_o}{\Theta_i}\right| e^{j\varepsilon} = 1 + \frac{j\omega\rho}{\eta^*}\left[\left[\frac{I - K/\omega^2}{4\pi L\rho R_i^3 R_o}\right]\left(2R_i(R_o - R_i) - (R_o - R_i)^2\right)\right.$$

$$\left. + \frac{R_i(R_o - R_i)^2}{2R_o}\right] \tag{5.6-86}$$

This can be readily solved for the real and imaginary components of the complex viscosity to give

$$\eta'(\omega) = \frac{Mr \sin \varepsilon}{r^2 - 2r \cos \varepsilon + 1} \tag{5.6-87}^*$$

$$\eta''(\omega) = \frac{M(1 - r \cos \varepsilon)}{r^2 - 2r \cos \varepsilon + 1} \tag{5.6-88}^*$$

where

$$M = \omega\rho\left[\frac{I - K/\omega^2}{4\ L\pi R_o R_i^2}\left(2R_i(R_o - R_i) - (R_o - R_i)^2\right) + \frac{R_i(R_o - R_i)^2}{2R_o}\right] \tag{5.6-89}$$

and

$$\left|\frac{\Theta_o}{\Theta_i}\right| e^{j\varepsilon} = r^* = re^{j\varepsilon} = r' + jr'' = r \cos \varepsilon + jr \sin \varepsilon$$

as before.

An asymptotic formula valid for large values of $\alpha^*(R_o - R_i)$ is also given by Oldroyd [5.42] and Walters [5.35, 5.37], which is implicit in η^*.

For values of $\kappa^* R$ such that terms of the order $(\kappa^* R)^6$ and higher are negligible, the following approximate formula has been given by Walters [5.13]:

$$\left|\frac{\Theta_o}{\Theta_i}\right| e^{j\varepsilon} = 1 + \kappa^{*2} \left[\frac{(K - \omega^2 I)(R_o^2 - R_i^2)}{4\pi\omega^2 \rho R_i^2 R_o^2 L} - \frac{(R_o^2 - R_i^2)^2}{8R_o^2} \right]$$

$$+ \kappa^{*4} \left\{ -\frac{K - \omega^2 I}{32\pi\omega^2 \rho L} \left[4 \ln \frac{R_i}{R_o} + \frac{R_o^2}{R_i^2} - \frac{R_i^2}{R_o^2} \right] \right.$$

$$+ \frac{1}{192R_o^2} \left[(R_o^2 - R_i^2)^2 (R_o^4 - 5R_o^2 R_i^2 - 2R_i^4) \right.$$

$$\left. \left. + 12R_o^2 R_i^4 \ln \frac{R_o}{R_i} \right] \right\} \tag{5.6-90}$$

This is a quadratic equation for κ^{*2}, which may thus be solved for this quantity in terms of the amplitude ratio and phase components of the output to input deflections, and the system parameters. The result may be separated into real and imaginary parts to give expressions for η' and η'' in terms of these measurable functions and parameters. This manipulation is left as an exercise for the student.

D. Oscillatory Response--Cone and Plate [5.35, 5.38]

This test situation is identical to that just described, except that the sample is contained between a cone and flat plate instead of between concentric cylinders (see note 13). It is assumed that the plate is subject to a sinusoidal oscillation, and the cone is suspended by a torsion bar (it is immaterial whether the cone or plate is the driven member). Amplitude ratio and phase angle between the cone and plate are measured, and are used to determine the linear viscoelastic properties.

Again, we do not neglect the inertia of the sample, so that the equations of motion for the system must be solved. An analysis of this system has been given by Walters and Kemp [5.38]. The flow field is assumed to be:

$$v_\phi(r, \theta, t) = v_\phi(r, \theta)e^{j(\omega t)} \qquad (5.6\text{-}91)$$

$$v_\theta = v_r = 0$$

so that, from Table 3.2, the components of the rate of strain tensor are

$$\Delta_{ij} = \begin{bmatrix} 0 & \dfrac{\sin\theta}{r}\dfrac{\partial}{\partial\theta}\left(\dfrac{v_\phi}{\sin\theta}\right) & r\dfrac{\partial}{\partial r}\left(\dfrac{v_\phi}{r}\right) \\[4mm] \dfrac{\sin\theta}{r}\dfrac{\partial}{\partial\theta}\left(\dfrac{v_\phi}{\sin\theta}\right) & 0 & 0 \\[4mm] r\dfrac{\partial}{\partial r}\left(\dfrac{v_\phi}{r}\right) & 0 & 0 \end{bmatrix} \qquad (5.6\text{-}92)$$

where $\phi = z^1$, $\theta = z^2$, $r = z^3$. It is assumed that the fluid stresses in oscillatory motion are:

$$\tau_{ij}(\omega t) = \begin{bmatrix} 0 & \tau_{\phi\theta} & \tau_{\phi r} \\[2mm] \tau_{\theta\phi} & 0 & 0 \\[2mm] \tau_{r\phi} & 0 & 0 \end{bmatrix} = \eta^*(\omega)\,\Delta_{ij}(\omega,\theta,r) \qquad (5.6\text{-}93)$$

so that the ϕ equation of motion, from Table 3.1, becomes:

$$\rho\frac{\partial v_\phi}{\partial t} = \frac{1}{r^2}\frac{\partial}{\partial r}(r^2\tau_{r\phi}) + \frac{1}{r}\frac{\partial\tau_{\theta\phi}}{\partial\theta} + \frac{\tau_{r\phi}}{r} + \frac{2\cot\theta}{r}\tau_{\theta\phi} \qquad (5.6\text{-}94)$$

By substituting Eqs. (5.6-91) to (5.6-93) into Eq. (5.6-94), and assuming that η^* is constant throughout the flow region, the latter equation reduces to:

$$\frac{1}{r^2} \frac{\partial}{\partial r} \left[r^2 \frac{\partial v_\phi}{\partial r} \right] + \frac{1}{r^2 \sin \theta} \left[\sin \theta \frac{\partial v_\phi}{\partial \theta} \right] - \frac{v_\phi}{r^2 \sin \theta} - \alpha^{*2} v_\phi = 0$$

$$(5.6\text{-}95)$$

where

$$\alpha^{*2} = \frac{j\omega\rho}{\eta^*}$$

$$(5.6\text{-}96)$$

as before. This is a partial differential equation, rather than an ordinary differential equation such as has resulted from analyses of the other geometries. It must be solved together with the boundary conditions:

$$(1) \quad \phi = \phi_1 = r \sin \left[\frac{\pi}{2} - \theta_c \right] \Phi_1 e^{j\omega t} \quad \text{at} \quad \theta = \left(\frac{\pi}{2} - \theta_c \right) \quad (5.6\text{-}97)$$

$$= r\Phi_1 e^{j\omega t} \cos \theta_c$$

$$(2) \quad \phi = \phi_2 = r\Phi_2 e^{j(\omega t + \varepsilon)} \qquad \text{at} \quad \theta = \frac{\pi}{2} \qquad (5.6\text{-}98)$$

where

θ_c = cone angle

ε = phase lag of cone behind plate

Φ_1 = amplitude of cone (or restrained member) oscillation

Φ_2 = amplitude of plate (or driven member) oscillation

In terms of the angular velocity, the boundary conditions become:

$$(1) \quad v_\phi = j\omega r \cos \theta_c \Phi_1 e^{j\omega t} \quad \text{at} \quad \theta = \left(\frac{\pi}{2} - \theta_c \right)$$

$$(5.6\text{-}99)$$

$$(2) \quad v_\phi = j\omega r \Phi_2 e^{j(\omega t + \varepsilon)} \qquad \text{at} \quad \theta = \frac{\pi}{2}$$

If the cone is suspended from a torsion wire with spring constant K, its motion must satisfy the equation:

$$I\ddot{\phi}_1 + K\phi_1 = T_i \qquad (5.6\text{-}100)$$

where

$$T_i = 2\pi \cos \theta_c \int_0^R r^2 (\tau_{\theta\phi}) \Big|_{\frac{\pi}{2} - \theta_c} dr \qquad (5.6\text{-}101)$$

is the torque resulting from the fluid drag on the cone surface. The stress $\tau_{\theta\phi}$ must be evaluated from Eq. (5.6-93) and the solution to Eq. (5.6-95). This solution has been obtained by Walters and Kemp [5.38] in a series form which is valid when values of $\alpha^{*8} r^9$ and higher order are negligible. For values of the cone angle θ_c small enough that θ_c^4 and higher powers are negligible, their final solution for the amplitude ratio and phase angle between cone and plate reduces to:

$$\left| \frac{\Phi_2}{\Phi_1} \right| e^{j\varepsilon} = r^* = r' + jr'' = |r|(\cos \varepsilon + j \sin \varepsilon)$$

$$= 1 - \alpha^{*2} R^2 \left[S\theta_c \left(1 + \frac{\theta_c^2}{2} \right) - \frac{3\theta_c^2}{10} \right] - \alpha^{*4} R^4 \left(\frac{S\theta_c^3}{10} \right) \qquad (5.6\text{-}102)$$

where

$$S = \frac{3(K - \omega^2 I)}{2\pi\omega^2 R^5 \rho} \qquad (5.6\text{-}103)$$

and R is the cone radius. Equation (5.6-102) can be solved explicitly for α^{*2} to give:

$$\alpha^{*2} = \frac{j\omega\rho}{\eta^*} = -E \left[1 - \sqrt{1 - F(r' + jr'' - 1)} \right] = -\kappa^{*2} \qquad (5.6\text{-}104)$$

where

$$E = \frac{S}{R^2} \left[\frac{1}{\theta_c^2} + \frac{1}{2} - \frac{3}{10S\theta_c} \right] \qquad (5.6\text{-}105)$$

$$F = \frac{10}{R^4 S\theta^3 E_c^2} \qquad\qquad (5.6\text{-}106)$$

If Eq. (5.6-104) is separated into real and imaginary components:

$$\alpha^{*2} = (\alpha^2)_r + j(\alpha^2)_i \qquad\qquad (5.6\text{-}107)$$

the real and imaginary components of the complex viscosity may be expressed in terms of these components as follows:

$$\eta'(\omega) = \frac{\omega\rho(\alpha^2)_i}{(\alpha^2)_i^2 + (\alpha^2)_r^2} \qquad\qquad (5.6\text{-}108)$$

$$\eta''(\omega) = -\frac{\omega\rho(\alpha^2)_r}{(\alpha^2)_i^2 + (\alpha^2)_r^2} \qquad\qquad (5.6\text{-}109)$$

The exercise of separating Eq. (5.6-104) into its real and imaginary components, and hence expressiong $(\alpha^2)_r$ and $(\alpha^2)_i$ in terms of the measurable quantities E, F, r', and r'' is left as an exercise for the student.

E. Fluid Impedance--Tube Flow [5.43]

The application of an oscillatory pressure gradient to a fluid in a cylindrical tube and measurement of the amplitude ratio and phase angle between the pressure gradient and resulting flow rate provides data which are a unique characteristic of the fluid viscous and elastic properties. The ratio of oscillatory pressure gradient to oscillatory flow rate is known as the *fluid impedance*:

$$z^*(j\omega) = \frac{\frac{\partial P}{\partial z}(\omega t)}{Q(\omega t)} = \frac{\left|\frac{\Delta P}{L}\right| e^{j\epsilon}}{|Q|} = R(\omega) + jX(\omega) \qquad (5.6\text{-}110)$$

where

$$\frac{\partial P}{\partial z}(\omega t) = \left|\frac{\Delta P}{L}\right| e^{j\omega t} \qquad (5.6\text{-}111)$$

$$Q(\omega t) = Q\, e^{j(\omega t - \varepsilon)} \qquad (5.6\text{-}112)$$

The solution of the equation of motion for tube flow subject to a pressure gradient of the form of Eq. (5.6-110) for any linear visco-elastic fluid was obtained in Sec. 4.4.3. The result for the volumetric flow rate is given by Eq. (4.4-55), repeated here:

$$Q^*(\omega t) = \frac{\pi R^2 \left|\frac{\Delta P}{L}\right|}{j\omega\rho} \left[1 - \frac{2 J_1(\kappa^* R)}{\kappa^* R J_1(\kappa^* R)} \right] e^{j\omega t} \qquad (5.6\text{-}113)$$

where

$$\kappa^{*2} = -\frac{j\omega\rho}{\eta^*} = -\alpha^{*2} \qquad (5.6\text{-}114)$$

and J_1 and J_0 are Bessel functions of the first kind, order 0 and 1 (with complex argument).

It is not generally possible to solve Eq. (5.6-113) explicitly for η' and η'', and hence obtain expressions for these properties in terms of measurable variables. However for values of $|\kappa^*| \ll 1$, the Bessel functions may be expanded in series as indicated by Eq. (4.4-56), in which higher order terms are assumed negligible:

$$Q(\omega t) = \frac{j\kappa^{*2}\pi\left|\frac{\Delta P}{L}\right| R^4}{8\rho\omega} \left(1 + \frac{1}{6}\kappa^{*2}R^2 + \ldots\right) e^{j\omega t}$$

$$= \frac{\pi\left|\frac{\Delta P}{L}\right| R^4}{8\eta^*} \left(1 - j\frac{\rho\omega R^2}{6\eta^*} + \ldots\right) e^{j\omega t} \qquad (5.6\text{-}115)$$

Substitution of Eq. (5.6-115) into Eq. (5.6-110) gives the fluid impedance:

$$Z^*(j\omega) = \frac{\left|\frac{\Delta P}{L}\right| e^{j\omega t}}{Q(\omega t)} = \frac{8\rho\omega}{j\kappa^{*2}\pi R^4} \qquad (5.6\text{-}116)$$

or

$$R(\omega) = \frac{8\eta'}{\pi R^4} \qquad (5.6\text{-}117)$$

$$X(\omega) = \frac{8\eta''}{\pi R^4} \qquad (5.6\text{-}118)$$

For an inelastic Newtonian fluid ($\eta' = \mu$, $\eta'' = 0$), this result is identical to that which would be determined from the Hagen-Poiseuille equation for steady, laminar fully developed flow. This is valid, of course, only at sufficiently low frequencies and/or high viscosities that $(\kappa^* R)^2/6 \ll 1$ (see note 14), which is, therefore, the criterion for negligible fluid inertia. If this condition is not satisifed, it is necessary to use iterative or other methods for evaluating the arguments of the Bessel functions. However, if a specific linear viscoelastic model is postulated, its response can be calculated exactly from Eq. (5.6-113) and the values of the model parameters could then be determined by comparison of the calculated and measured fluid impedance.

F. Oscillatory Response--Disc and Plate [5.35, 5.39]

This system is identical to the cone and plate and concentric cylinder situations, except that the sample is contained in the cylindrical gap between a circular disc and a parallel flat plate, as illustrated in Fig. 5.10. One member (i.e., the plate at $z = 0$) is driven in oscillatory motion

$$\theta_i(\omega t) = \Theta_i e^{j\omega t} \qquad (5.6\text{-}119)$$

while the other member (i.e., the disc at z = h), which is suspended from a torsion bar, responds by oscillating at the same frequency with a different amplitude and phase:

$$\theta_o(\omega t) = \Theta_o e^{j(\omega t+\epsilon)} \tag{5.6-120}$$

Measurements of the amplitude ratio or $r = \Theta_o/\Theta_i$ and the phase angle ϵ are related to the material properties as follows.

The physical velocity components relative to cylindrical coordinates are

$$v_r = v_z = 0 \qquad v_\theta(r, z) = r\Omega(z)e^{j\omega t} \tag{5.6-121}$$

where

$$\Omega = \frac{d\theta}{dt}$$

and the θ component of the equation of motion is

$$\rho \frac{\partial v_\theta}{\partial t} = \frac{\partial \tau_{\theta z}}{\partial z} \tag{5.6-122}$$

As before, the oscillatory stress is characterized by the complex viscosity

$$\tau_{r\theta} = \eta^*(j\omega) \Delta_{r\theta} = \eta^*(j\omega) \frac{\partial v_\theta}{\partial z} \tag{5.6-123}$$

Introducing Eqs. (5.6-121) and (5.6-123) into Eq. (5.6-122), the latter becomes

$$\frac{d^2\Omega}{dz^2} + \kappa^{*2}\Omega = 0 \tag{5.6-124}$$

where, as before

$$\kappa^{*2} = -\frac{j\omega\rho}{\eta^*(j\omega)} = -\alpha^{*2} \tag{5.6-125}$$

The appropriate solution of Eq. (5.6-124), subject to the boundary
conditions:

(1) $\Omega(0) = j\omega\Theta_i e^{j\omega t}$

$$(5.6-126)$$

(2) $\Omega(h) = j\omega\Theta_o e^{j(\omega t+\varepsilon)}$

is

$$\Omega = A \sin (\kappa^* z) + B \cos (\kappa^* z) \qquad (5.6-127)$$

where

$$A = j\omega[\Theta_o e^{j\varepsilon} \, \mathrm{cosec} \, (\kappa^* h) = \Theta_i \cot (\kappa^* h)] \qquad (5.6-128)$$

$$B = j\omega\Theta_i \qquad (5.6-129)$$

Again, the motion of the constrained member (disc) is determined
by the moment's balance:

$$I\ddot\Theta_o + K\Theta_o = T = 2\pi \int_0^R \tau_{\theta z} r^2 \, dr \qquad (5.6-130)$$

The shear stress in the integral term may be evaluated from Eq.
(5.6-123), using Eq. (5.6-127) to determine the velocity gradient.
The result is

$$T = \frac{\pi\omega^2 R^4 \rho}{2\kappa^*} \left[\Theta_i \, \mathrm{cosec} \, (\kappa^* h) - \Theta_o e^{j\varepsilon} \cot (\kappa^* h)\right] e^{j\omega t} \qquad (5.6-131)$$

From Eqs. (5.6-120) and (5.6-130), the left side of Eq. (5.6-131)
reduces to

$$\Theta_o e^{j(\omega t+\varepsilon)} [K - \omega^2 I] = T \qquad (5.6-132)$$

Equating Eqs. (5.6-131) and (5.6-132) and rearranging gives the expression for the ratio of output to input and the phase difference:

$$\frac{\Theta_i}{\Theta_o} e^{-j\varepsilon} = re^{-j\varepsilon} = \frac{2\kappa^*}{\pi\rho R^4} \left(\frac{K}{\omega^2} - I\right) \sin(\kappa^* h) + \cos(\kappa^* h) \quad (5.6\text{-}133)$$

For small values of $\kappa^* h$, this may be written:

$$re^{-j\varepsilon} = 1 + \kappa^{*2}h^2\left(W - \frac{1}{2}\right) + \kappa^{*4}h^4\left(\frac{1}{24} - \frac{W}{6}\right) \quad (5.6\text{-}134)$$

where

$$W = \frac{2(K - \omega^2 I)}{\pi\rho R^4 \omega^2 h} \quad (5.6\text{-}135)$$

which is valid if term of the order $\kappa^{*6}h^6$ and higher are negligible. The solution of Eq. (5.6-134) for κ^{*2} is

$$\kappa^{*2} = G\left[1 + \sqrt{1 + H(1 - r' + jr'')}\right] = -\frac{j\omega\rho}{\eta^*} \quad (5.6\text{-}136)$$

where

$$G = \frac{3\left(W - \frac{1}{2}\right)}{h^2\left(W - \frac{1}{4}\right)} \qquad H = \frac{2\left(W - \frac{1}{4}\right)}{3\left(W - \frac{1}{2}\right)^2} \quad (5.6\text{-}137)$$

and

$$r'' = r \sin \varepsilon \qquad r' = r \cos \varepsilon$$

As before, separation of Eq. (5.6-136) into real and imaginary parts, along with Eq. (5.6-108), enables the determination of $\eta'(\omega)$ and $\eta''(\omega)$ in terms of the system parameters and the amplitude and phase of the input and output oscillations.

For the conditions under which fluid inertia is negligible, the equations for each of the systems considered here all reduce to the equivalent of Eqs. (5.5-18) and (5.5-19), with A and B replaced by the equivalent system parameters. Thus by comparison of these equations, it is a simple matter to include the appropriate term which accounts for viscous drag in the torsion bar or supports of the restrained member (i.e., the drag coefficient U). This term has not been included in these equations since it is generally negligible in a well-designed apparatus.

PROBLEMS

5-1.   Is the radial flow field between porous cylinders, illustrated in Fig. 3.7, a viscometric flow? Why?

5-2.   Is the flow field between parallel discs, illustrated in Prob. 4-12, a viscometric flow? Why?

5-3.   Is the flow in a conical section (Prob. 4-14) a viscometric flow? Why?

5-4.   With reference to the figure, does the manometer reading (H) provide a direct measure of ΔP or ΛP? Explain.

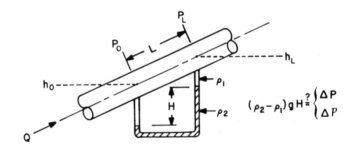

5-5.   Derive Eq. (5.4-17) for the true shear rate at the wall for Poiseuille flow, from Eq. (5.4-16).

5-6.   The consistency variable Γ is often equated to the wall shear rate when analyzing tube flow data. Determine the error in the apparent viscosity arising from this approximation for a fluid which can be described by the Power law, with $\eta_o = 0.1$ P and $n' = 0.5$.

5-7.   Explain how you would determine the extent of the entrance
        region (where the flow is not fully developed) for a given
        fluid in a given diameter tube, from measurements using dif-
        ferent tube lengths.

5-8.   If measurements of apparent viscosity derived from tube flow
        data on a given fluid in various diameter tubes of the same
        length did not agree, what would this indicate to you about
        the nature of the fluid? Explain in detail how you would
        proceed to characterize this fluid.

5-9.   The following data were taken in a Couette viscometer with the
        following dimensions: Cup = 5 cm i.d., Bob = 4 cm o.d.,
        Bob length = 10 cm (corrected for end effects).

T (dyn-cm)	Ω(rpm)	T (dyn-cm)	Ω(rpm)
2700	1000	230	40
2150	800	180	20
1600	600	145	10
1060	400	135	8
530	200	120	6
330	100	100	4
300	80	53	2
265	60	27	1

(1) Calculate and tabulate corresponding values of shear
    stress (dyn/cm^2) and shear rate (sec^{-1}) for each of these
    data points, using each of the following methods for de-
    termining shear rate:
    (a) Newtonian fluid approximation
    (b) Simple shear approximation
    (c) Krieger formula
    (d) Power law approximation
    Explain fully how you obtain any parameters you use in
    the above expressions.
(2) What conclusions can you draw with respect to the rheolog-
    ical nature of the fluid, in terms of well known models.
    Explain what basis you use for these conclusions.

(3) Plot η(cP) vs. $\dot{\gamma}$(sec^{-1}) on log-log coordinates for each of the four sets of data from (1) above.

(4) What conclusions can you draw with respect to the accuracy of the expressions for $\dot{\gamma}$ in (1) above, for this system? To what degree would you expect these conclusions to be generally valid for other fluids and/or Couette viscometers with different dimensions? Explain.

5-10. Calculate and plot the volumetric flow rate of the fluid in Example 5.3 in a circular tube 1 m long and 1 cm i.d. as a function of the total pressure drop through the tube over a range of $0.1 \leq \Delta P \leq 10$ lb/ft^2. Use the Couette data given in the problem, but do not make any assumption with regard to a model for the fluid properties.

5-11. Determine an expression for the shear rate at the outer wall of a Couette instrument, which corresponds to Eq. (5.4-56) for the shear rate at the inner wall.

5-12. Derive an expression relating the shear stress in the fluid to the total torque on the Mooney-Couette instrument, shown in Fig. 5.8, if $\theta_c < 4°$ and $(1 - R_i/R_o) \ll 1$.

5-13. Derive the equivalent of Eqs. (5.4-54), (5.4-56), (5.4-62), and (5.4-71) for the shear rate at the bob in Couette flow, for the case in which the cup is stationary and the bob rotates.

5-14. Derive Eqs. (5.4-81) and (5.4-82) for the stress distribution and the relative variation of shear stress throughout the gap in the cone and plate viscometer.

5-15. Assume that the data tabulated in Prob. 5-9 for torque versus angular velocity were obtained in a disc and plate viscometer with dimensions:

$R = 5$ cm $h = 0.1$ cm

(a) Calculate and plot the pressure drop versus volumetric flow rate of this fluid in a tube 1 m long and 1 cm i.d.

(b) Estimate the magnitude of the angular velocity at which you think centrifugal forces would have a significant influence on the flow field in this disc and plate viscometer. State the criterion you use for this estimate.

5-16. The accompanying plots represent actual data for: (1) the first normal stress difference for three concentrations (100, 250, and 500 ppm) of aqueous solutions of a high molecular weight polymer (see note 15); (2) the total (negative) normal thrust due to centrifugal force in a reservoir type cone and plate rheogoniometer with a cone angle of 0.0155 radians and a diameter of 10 cm, as determined from direct measurements on Newtonian (inelastic) fluids.

(a) Assuming the density of the polymer solutions is the same as that of water, calculate and plot the total normal thrust versus angular velocity which would be measured for these solutions in the instrument.

(b) Determine an equation which represents the given centrifugal force data, and compare with Eq. (5.5-25).

5-17. Derive Eq. (5.5-45) for the net normal thrust in the disc and plate from Eq. (5.5-44), by integration by parts.

5-18. Assume the fluids whose first normal stress difference properties are given in Prob. 5-16, and shear stress (apparent viscosity) properties are given in Prob. 2-3, are contained between concentric cylinders with $R_i = 0.5$ cm and $R_o = 5$ cm.

(a) Calculate the approximate height to which the fluid would climb up the center cylinder as a function of its angular velocity, if centrifugal forces are neglected.

(b) Estimate the error in this height due to centrifugal force as a function of angular velocity over a range of velocities corresponding to a range of shear rates at the inner

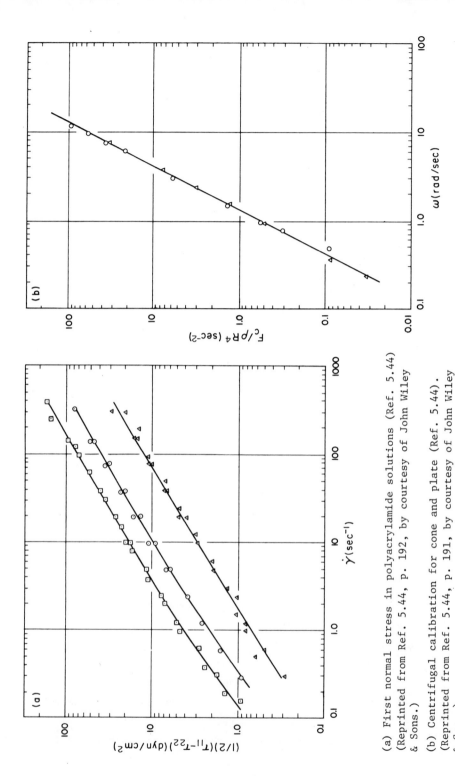

(a) First normal stress in polyacrylamide solutions (Ref. 5.44)
(Reprinted from Ref. 5.44, p. 192, by courtesy of John Wiley
& Sons.)

(b) Centrifugal calibration for cone and plate (Ref. 5.44).
(Reprinted from Ref. 5.44, p. 191, by courtesy of John Wiley
& Sons.)

cylinder of $0.5 < \dot{\gamma} < 100 \ \text{sec}^{-1}$. Clearly state any assumptions or approximations you use in these calculations.

5-19. From the results of Sec. 5.5.3 on normal stresses in Couette flow, derive an expression for the first normal stress difference in terms of the total radial stress in a function of shear stress which is analogous to Eq. (5.4-56) for the shear rate in Couette flow.

5-20. Derive the expressions for G' and G'' given by Eqs. (5.5-18) and (5.5-19) for oscillatory response testing with negligible sample inertia.

5-21. Show that the oscillatory transient response of any linear second order system to an impulsive disturbance, which is governed by an equation of the form:

$$\frac{d^2 y}{dt^2} + a \frac{dy}{dt} + by = \delta(t)$$

may be represented in the form of Eq. (5.6-21), i.e.,

$$y(t) = y_o e^{-\zeta \omega_o t} \sin \omega t$$

where

$$a = 2\zeta\omega_o, \ b = \omega_o^2$$

ω_o = natural frequency of the system

$\omega = \omega_o(1 - \zeta^2)^{\frac{1}{2}}$ = actual damped frequency

ζ = damping factor = $\dfrac{a}{2\sqrt{b}}$, $y_o = \dfrac{1}{\omega}$

5-22. What is the ratio of the amplitudes of successive waves propagating into a Newtonian fluid from an oscillating plate?

5-23. Discuss the effect of increasing the mass of the plate upon
       the determination of viscoelastic properties from the mechan-
       ical impedance of the oscillating plate with a large test
       sample.

5-24. Consider the situation in which a sample is contained between
       parallel plates and one plate is driven in forced oscillation
       (Sec. 5.6.3.B), the sample inertia not being negligible.
       If the stress is sensed on the driven plate (instead of the
       driving plate) by deflection of a force transducer, derive an
       expression for the oscillatory response (amplitude ratio and
       phase angle between the two plates) in terms of the linear
       viscoelastic material functions $\eta'(\omega)$ and $\eta''(\omega)$ of the material
       between the plates.

5-25. Derive an expression for the mechanical impedance of a Couette
       (concentric cylinder) geometry, which includes the effect of
       sample inertia.

5-26. For the oscillatory response of the cone and plate system
       including sample inertia (Sec. 5.6.3.D), express the relations
       for $\eta'(\omega)$ and $\eta''(\omega)$ [Eqs. (5.6-108) and (5.6-109)] explicitly
       in terms of the in-phase and out-of-phase components of the
       ratio of the plate to cone deflection (r' and r''), and the
       system parameters E and F.

5-27. Solve Eq. (5.6-90) explicitly for $\eta'(\omega)$ and $\eta''(\omega)$ in terms
       of the in-phase and out-of-phase components of the inner and
       outer cylinder response in the oscillatory Couette test (r'
       and r'') and the system parameters.

5-28. Solve Eq. (5.6-136) $\eta'(\omega)$ and $\eta''(\omega)$ explicitly in terms of r',
       r'', and the system parameters G and H for the oscillatory disc
       and plate system.

5-29. In the expression for the oscillatory flow rate in Poiseuille
       flow in response to an oscillatory pressure gradient, Eq.

(5.6-115), include the next term in the series and solve the
resulting expression explicitly for $\eta'(\omega)$ and $\eta''(\omega)$ in terms
of the fluid resistance $R(\omega)$ and reactance $X(\omega)$. Establish
a criterion for the validity of the result.

NOTES

1. The term "velocity component" as used herein is the tensor veloc-
    ity, defined as the time rate of change of a spatial coordinate
    component associated with a given fluid element. This velocity
    may have various dimensions, depending upon the dimensions of
    the particular coordinate, and thus differs from the "physical"
    velocity component which has dimensions of (length/time). This
    distinction will be discussed in greater detail in Chap. 6.

2. Those equations recommended for direct use in the reduction of
    data from various systems will be designated in this chapter by
    an asterisk following the equation number.

3. Leibnitz' rule:

$$\frac{\partial}{\partial x} \int_{A(x)}^{B(x)} I(x,\ y)\ dy = \int_{A(x)}^{B(x)} \frac{\partial I}{\partial x}\ dy + I(x,\ B)\ \frac{\partial B}{\partial x} - I(x,\ A)\ \frac{\partial A}{\partial x}$$

4. The accuracy of this approximation depends not only upon the
    value of α, but also upon the degree of nonlinearity of the
    fluid. For example, if $\alpha = 1.1$, Eq. (5.4-73) yields $\dot\gamma = 11\Omega$,
    while the Newtonian formula (5.4-71) gives $\dot\gamma = 12.6\Omega$, and the
    Power law formula (5.4-69) gives $\dot\gamma = 12.6\Omega$ if $n = 0.5$, and
    $\dot\gamma = 11\Omega$ if $n = 2$.

5. Note that Fig. 5.6 must be used to evaluate the function $f(x)$
    in the Krieger formula.

6. Misalignment of platens may also result in the fluid being ex-
    pelled from the gap. In addition, if the fluid is elastic, sec-
    ondary flows may also be set up which are contrary to those
    produced by centrifugal forces and which may be important at
    speeds below which centrifugal force effects are evident. These
    effects are discussed in Refs. 5.11-5.13, among others.

7. It should be noted that, even in the absence of inertial effects
    (centrifugal force), radial or secondary flows are possible in
    elastic fluids if $(\tau_{\theta\theta} + \tau_{\phi\phi} - 2\tau_{rr}) \neq 0$, since this will give
    rise to a nonzero radial pressure gradient by Eq. (5.4-80).
    See Refs. 5.11 and 5.12 and references included therein for a
    further discussion.

8. The effect of perturbations on this boundary condition due,
    e.g., to a liquid reservoir extending beyond the rim has been
    analyzed by Tanner [5.15], and discussed by Olabisi and
    Williams [5.12].

9. See, however, note 7 regarding secondary flows and normal
    stresses.

10. The same general comments concerning radial and secondary flows
    in elastic fluids and boundary (edge) perturbations apply here
    as for the cone and plate system.

11. Note 7 regarding secondary flows in viscoelastic fluids applies
    here as well.

12. "Small" here means that terms of the order $\alpha^*(R_o - R_i)^3$ are
    negligible.

13. The initial formulation of the problem is not limted to small
    cone angles, so that the velocity and shear field will, in
    general, vary in both the r and θ directions.

14. For an inelastic Newtonian fluid, this criterion reduces to

    $$\frac{\rho\omega R^2}{6\mu} \ll 1$$

15. The apparent viscosity data for these same fluids are given
    in Prob. 2-3.

Chapter 6

GENERALIZATION PRINCIPLES

6.1. INTRODUCTION

In preceding chapters, we have been largely concerned with the
definition, application, and determination of various material functions in terms of specific components of stress and strain. The
complete rheological or mechanical properties of a given material
should be definable by a single general expression (constitutive
equation) relating the complete stress and strain tensors. For any
given deformation, the component forms of this equation would define
relations between specific components of stress and strain, and thus
the material functions for the material in that deformation. The
proper formulation and manipulation of such equations requires an
understanding of the properties of general tensors and the principles
governing their manipulation. The objective of this chapter is to
establish these properties and principles.

6.2. PRINCIPLE OF MATERIAL INDIFFERENCE

A rheological equation of state, or constitutive equation, provides a complete description of the mechanical properties of the material it represents, which are independent of the system in which
the material is deformed including, of course, the reference frame

or system of coordinates employed to describe its deformation. This indifference of material properties to geometry or reference coordinates requires that the constitutive equation be formulated in terms of general quantities expressible in a form which is independent of any specific geometry or reference frame. This can be done if all such quantities are expressed in general tensor notation, defined in such a way that all such quantities are invariant with respect to a transformation of the coordinate frame which is used to describe their components. A corollary of this is that, by virtue of the transformation properties of tensor components, any tensor relation which is valid for one coordinate system is valid for all coordinate systems when expressed in suitably general notation.

Now a complete satisfaction of the principle of material indifference for time-dependent (viscoelastic) materials requires also that the deformation be described in a manner such that it always refers to the same element or point imbedded in the material as its position varies with time. This requirement will be considered in the following chapter, in which appropriate definitions of strain which satisfy this criterion will be presented.

In preceding chapters, reference to tensor components has generally been relative to Cartesian (linear orthogonal) coordinates. Generalized results applicable to other coordinate systems have been given for some relations without proof or derivation. Tensors and their components have been described by use of the index notation, with the indices indicated as subscripts. In this chapter we will derive relations which are valid for any generalized three dimensional (linear or curvilinear) coordinate system as well as for Cartesian coordinates. Although Cartesian tensor relations can be completely described by use of subscripted indices only, relations involving general tensor require the use of an additional indexing system involving superscripts. The relations between the subscripted and superscripted components will be derived.

6.3. VECTORS

A vector quantity can be specified by a magnitude and a direction, and can be represented by:

$$\vec{A} = A\vec{a} \tag{6.3-1}$$

where A is the magnitude and $\vec{a}$ is a unit vector indicating the appropriate direction. With reference to rectangular Cartesian coordinates (Fig. 6.1) any vector can be represented as the sum of three vector components, each lying in the direction of one of the reference axes:

$$\vec{A} = A_1\vec{i}_1 + A_2\vec{i}_2 + A_3\vec{i}_3 \tag{6.3-2}$$

The A_1, A_2 and A_3 are the scalar magnitudes of the components, and the $\vec{i}$s are unit vectors indicating the directions of the coordinate axes. The magnitudes of the vector components are related to the

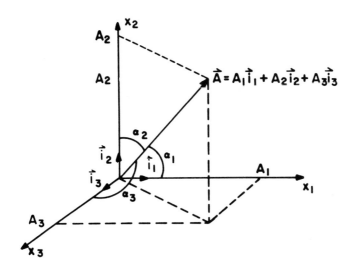

FIG. 6.1 Cartesian coordinates--unit vectors and direction cosines.

magnitude of the vector by the cosines of the angles between the
vector and the coordinate axes (unit vectors):

$$A_1 = |\vec{A}| \cos \alpha_1 = A \cos \alpha_1$$

$$A_2 = |\vec{A}| \cos \alpha_2 = A \cos \alpha_2$$

$$A_3 = |\vec{A}| \cos \alpha_3 = A \cos \alpha_3$$

where

$$|\vec{A}| = \sqrt{A_1^2 + A_2^2 + A_3^2}$$

Thus

$$\vec{A} = |\vec{A}| (\vec{i}_1 \cos \alpha_1 + \vec{i}_2 \cos \alpha_2 + \vec{i}_3 \cos \alpha_3) \qquad (6.3-3)$$

Hence, a vector may be completely determined by specifying the
magnitudes of each of its components relative to a given reference
frame, or its magnitude plus a set of direction cosines relative to
the reference frame. The vector itself (magnitude and direction) is
independent of the specific reference frame or coordinate system,
but its components (direction and magnitude) are not. This is an
important point which should be kept in mind.

Note that the vector expression [Eq. (6.3-2)] can be written
more concisely as:

$$\vec{A} = \sum_{j=1}^{3} A_j \vec{i}_j \qquad (6.3-4)$$

Since a maximum of three scalar components are required to define any vector in three-dimensional space, regardless of the specific coordinate system chosen for reference, the vector may also be
represented simply by specifying these three components in matrix
form:

$$\vec{A} = (A_1, A_2, A_3) = A_i \qquad (i = 1, 2, 3) \qquad (6.3\text{-}5)$$

where the actual magnitudes of the components depend on the specific coordinate system to which they are referred. Note that the single index term, A_i, implies the existence of three components since the range of the index is from one to three (for three-dimensional space).

All three of the notation forms in Eq. (6.3-5) are perfectly general in that they each imply three vector components, but do not specify any particular reference frame. However, the magnitudes of these components cannot be determined explicitly until a specific coordinate system is designated. The notation of Eqs. (6.3-2) to (6.3-4) is not general, however, since a specific (Cartesian) coordinate system is indicated by the designation of the unit vectors $(\vec{i}s)$.

6.3.1. Summation Convention

A useful convention commonly employed with index notation involves omitting the summation sign in expressions such as Eq. (6.3-4), with the understanding that whenever an index is repeated in a given term it is assumed to be summed over the range of that index. Since the index normally refers to a spatial component relative to three-dimensional space, the range of the implied summation will generally be from one to three. Thus Eq. (6.3-4) would be written:

$$\vec{A} = A_j \vec{i}_j \qquad (6.3\text{-}6)$$

which is identical to:

$$\vec{A} = A_1 \vec{i}_1 + A_2 \vec{i}_2 + A_3 \vec{i}_3 \qquad (6.3\text{-}7)$$

If a single term contains multiple pairs of repeated indices, the total number of terms in the implied summation will be $(3)^r$, where r is the number of repeated or *dummy* index pairs.

Number of terms in sum = (range of index)^r = (3)^r

where r is the number of repeated index pairs in the given term.

An index which is not repeated in a given term is called a *free index*. The number of free indices determines the net tensor character of that term, i.e., the tensorial order of the quantity. It follows, therefore, that the number of tensor components associated with a given term is related to the number of free indices (f) by:

Number of components = (index range)^f = (3)^f

This relation between the number of free indices and tensorial order of a term does not apply to indices on unit vectors, however, but only to the indices associated with tensor components. This is evident from Eq. (6.3-6), since a vector is obviously a first order tensor, identifiable by a single free index. The general index expression for a vector is given by (6.3-5).

As an example, a quantity designated by $B_{jkl}^{\cdots ijk}$ has two free indices (i, 1), and therefore represents a second-order tensor with a total of (3)^2 = 9 components. Furthermore, it has two repeated indices (j, k), so that each of the (9) components is composed of a sum of (3)^2 = 9 terms

6.3.2 Scalar and Vector Products

The scalar (or dot) product of two vectors is defined as:

$$\vec{A} \cdot \vec{B} = |\vec{A}||\vec{B}| \cos (\vec{A}, \vec{B}) \tag{6.3-8}$$

where $\cos (\vec{A}, \vec{B})$ is the cosine of the angle between $\vec{A}$ and $\vec{B}$.

If the vectors are Cartesian unit vectors, this angle is 90° for noncoincident vectors, so that:

$$\vec{i}_j \cdot \vec{i}_k = \delta_{jk} = \begin{cases} 1 \text{ if } j = k \\ 0 \text{ if } j \neq k \end{cases} \tag{6.3-9}$$

where δ_{jk} is the Kronecker delta. Thus, using index notation, the scalar product is:

$$\vec{A} \cdot \vec{B} = (A_i \vec{i}_i) \cdot (B_j \vec{i}_j) = A_i B_j (\vec{i}_i \cdot \vec{i}_j) = A_i B_j \delta_{ij} = A_i B_i$$

$$(6.3\text{-}10)$$

Since the final index is repeated, the summation convention applies so that Eq. (6.3-10) becomes

$$A_i B_i = A_1 B_1 + A_2 B_2 + A_3 B_3 \qquad (6.3\text{-}11)$$

The resulting sum has only a magnitude and no direction properties, and is hence a scalar (i.e., a zero-order tensor). Thus a repeated index is a "dummy" index, and does not contribute to the net tensor character of the term in which it appears. [This applies only to tensor components, and not to indexed unit vectors which may be included in expressions such as Eq. (6.3-10).]

The vector (or cross) product of two vectors is defined as:

$$\vec{A} \times \vec{B} = \vec{i} |\vec{A}| |\vec{B}| \sin(\vec{A}, \vec{B}) \qquad (6.3\text{-}12)$$

where $\vec{i}$ is a unit vector normal to both $\vec{A}$ and $\vec{B}$, in the direction that a right-hand screw would travel when rotated in the direction from $\vec{A}$ to $\vec{B}$. Of course if $\vec{A}$ is parallel to $\vec{B}$, then $(\vec{A} \times \vec{B}) = 0$.

Now if we consider the cross products of all possible combinations of the Cartesian unit vectors, we see that:

$$\vec{i}_i \times \vec{i}_j = e_{ijk} \vec{i}_k \qquad (6.3\text{-}13)$$

where

$$e_{ijk} = \begin{cases} 1 & \text{if } i,j,k \text{ are in cyclic order (even} \\ & \text{permutation of the order } 1,2,3) \\ -1 & \text{if } i,j,k \text{ are not in cyclic order (odd} \\ & \text{permutation of the order } 1,2,3) \\ 0 & \text{if any two indices are equal} \end{cases} \qquad (6.3\text{-}14)$$

The symbol e_{ijk} is known as the "permutation symbol."

Hence, from Eqs. (6.3-12) and (6.3-13), the vector product becomes:

$$\vec{A} \times \vec{B} = (A_i \vec{i}_i) \times (B_j \vec{i}_j) = A_i B_j (\vec{i}_i \times \vec{i}_j) = A_i B_j e_{ijk} \vec{i}_k \qquad (6.3\text{-}15)$$

Since the final form of Eq. (6.3-15) has three pairs of repeated indices, it represents a sum of $(3)^3 = 27$ terms. However, because of the permutation symbol only six of these are nonzero:

$$\vec{A} \times \vec{B} = (A_2 B_3 - A_3 B_2)\vec{i}_1 + (A_3 B_1 - A_1 B_3)\vec{i}_2 + (A_1 B_2 - A_2 B_1)\vec{i}_3$$

$$= \begin{vmatrix} \vec{i}_1 & \vec{i}_2 & \vec{i}_3 \\ A_1 & A_2 & A_3 \\ B_1 & B_2 & B_3 \end{vmatrix} \quad \text{(determinant)} \qquad (6.3\text{-}16)$$

Equation (6.3-15) implies Cartesian components (specified by the $\vec{i}_k$ unit vectors), and has a net vector or first-order tensor character. Note that the inclusion of the unit vector is not necessary, the vector character being implied by the free index k, which represents the third coordinate direction, normal to both i and j directions. Thus, the vector product of two Cartesian vectors is completely specified in index notation by:

$$\vec{A} \times \vec{B} = A_i B_j e_{kji} = C_k \qquad (6.3\text{-}17)$$

The single free index indicates the vector character of the result; i.e., three components. The two repeated indices represent the sum of nine (at most) terms in each component. Note that the indices also indicate the relative orientation of the respective vector components, i.e., C_k is normal to both A_i and B_j.

––––––––––––––––––––––––––––––––– 0 –––––––––––––––––––––––––––––––––

Example 6.1 Determine the vector product $\vec{C}$, of the vectors:

$$\vec{A} = 6\vec{i}_1 - 3\vec{i}_2 + 7\vec{i}_3$$

$$\vec{C} = \vec{A} \times \vec{B}$$

$$\vec{B} = 4\vec{i}_1 + 2\vec{i}_2 + \vec{i}_3$$

Solution. The vector product is given by Eq. (6.3-17):

$$\vec{C} = \vec{A} \times \vec{B} \qquad C_k = A_i B_j e_{kij}$$

where

$$A_i = (6, -3, 7) \qquad B_j = (4, 2, +1)$$

Thus

$$C_1 = \sum_i \sum_j A_i B_j e_{1ij}$$

$$= A_1 B_1 e_{111} + A_2 B_1 e_{121} + A_3 B_1 e_{131} + A_1 B_2 e_{112}$$

$$+ A_2 B_2 E_{122} + \underline{A_3 B_2 e_{132}} + A_1 B_3 e_{113} + \underline{A_2 B_3 e_{123}}$$

$$+ A_3 B_3 e_{133} = A_2 B_3 - A_3 B_2 = (-3)(1) - (7)(2) = \underline{-17}$$

$$C_2 = A_1 B_1 e_{211} + A_2 B_1 e_{221} + \underline{A_3 B_1 e_{231}} + A_1 B_2 e_{212}$$

$$+ A_2 B_3 e_{223} + A_3 B_2 e_{232} + \underline{A_1 B_3 e_{213}} + A_2 B_3 e_{223}$$

$$+ A_3 B_3 e_{233} = A_3 B_1 - A_1 B_3 = (7)(4) - (6)(+1) = \underline{22}$$

$$C_3 = A_1 B_1 e_{311} + \underline{A_2 B_1 e_{321}} + A_3 B_1 e_{331} + \underline{A_1 B_2 e_{312}}$$

$$+ A_2 B_2 e_{322} + A_3 B_2 e_{332} + A_1 B_3 e_{313} + A_2 B_3 e_{323}$$

$$+ A_3 B_3 e_{333} = A_1 B_2 - A_2 B_1 = (6)(2) - (-3)(4) = \underline{24}$$

$$\therefore \ \vec{C} = -17\vec{i}_1 + 22\vec{i}_2 + 24\vec{i}_3$$

6.3.3. Base Vectors

Any three-dimensional space can be described with reference to three *coordinate surfaces* (S_1, S_2, S_3), whose point of mutual intersection serves as the origin for the coordinate system (Fig. 6.2). The lines formed by the intersection of surfaces define the coordinate axes (which may be curves). These axes may also be defined by a set of *base vectors* ($\vec{e}_1$, $\vec{e}_2$, $\vec{e}_3$) which are tangent to the coordinate axes at the origin, and may or may not be unit vectors (for Cartesian coordinates, the base vectors $\vec{i}_1$, $\vec{i}_2$, $\vec{i}_3$, are always unit vectors). Note also that the base vectors, $\vec{e}$s, are not necessarily orthogonal. (Note that all surfaces parallel to S_1 are surfaces of constant "1" coordinate. That is, all points on any S_1 surface have

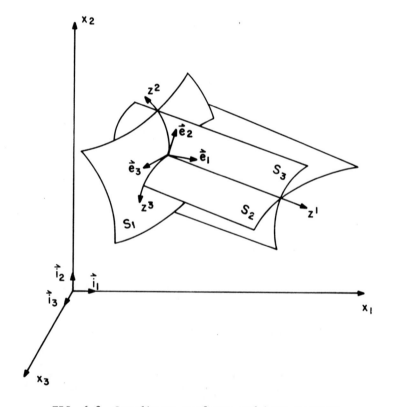

FIG. 6.2 Coordinate surfaces and base vectors.

the same value of the "1" coordinate.) Various orthogonal coordinate
systems and their defining surfaces are described in Appendix C.

As we shall see, the components of a vector (or tensor) relative
to any non-Cartesian coordinate reference frame may be defined in two
different ways, giving rise to two separate sets of components of a
given vector relative to a reference frame. These two sets of components (called *covariant* and *contravariant*) are not independent,
however, and we shall show how they are related and how one set can
be transformed into the other. To distinguish between these two
sets of components, different sets of indices are employed in the
form of subscripts and superscripts. For the general case, we require that all dummy repeated indices in a given term appear once as
a subscript and once as a superscript; i.e., they may be considered
to "cancel out" with respect to their contribution to the tensorial
order of the term. As will be shown, corresponding superscripted
and subscripted (contravariant and covariant) components of any
tensor quantity referred to Cartesian coordinates are identical,
so the distinction is superfluous for this reference frame.

The components of a vector with reference to a linear nonorthogonal coordinate system are indicated in Fig. 6.3. The vector $\vec{A}$ can

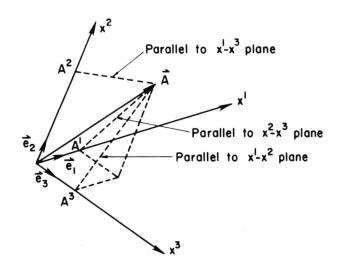

FIG. 6.3 Nonorthogonal linear coordinates.

be expressed in terms of its components as follows:

$$\vec{A} = A^1\vec{e}_1 + A^2\vec{e}_2 + A^3\vec{e}_3 \qquad (6.3\text{-}18)$$

However the base vectors $\vec{e}_i$ are not in general unit vectors, except with reference to Cartesian systems. The component A^1 is determined by the intersection on the X^1 axis of a surface parallel to the $X^2 - X^3$ surface through the end of the vector, and similarly for the other two components

6.3.4.   Reciprocal Base Vectors

Two sets of base vectors $(\vec{e}_1, \vec{e}_2, \vec{e}_3,$ and $\vec{e}^1, \vec{e}^2, \vec{e}^3)$ relative to a given coordinate frame may be defined as reciprocal sets if:

$$\vec{e}^1 \perp (\vec{e}_2, \vec{e}_3) \qquad\qquad \vec{e}_1 \perp (\vec{e}^2, \vec{e}^3)$$

$$\vec{e}^2 \perp (\vec{e}_3, \vec{e}_1) \qquad\qquad \vec{e}_2 \perp (\vec{e}^3, \vec{e}^1) \qquad (6.3\text{-}19)$$

$$\vec{e}^3 \perp (\vec{e}_1, \vec{e}_2) \qquad\qquad \vec{e}_3 \perp (\vec{e}^1, \vec{e}^2)$$

and

$$\vec{e}^1 \cdot \vec{e}_1 = \vec{e}^2 \cdot \vec{e}_2 = \vec{e}^3 \cdot \vec{e}_3 = 1 \qquad (6.3\text{-}20)$$

It is emphasized that neither set of base vectors need be orthogonal or of unit magnitude. All of the above relations may be represented by the single expression:

$$\vec{e}^i \cdot \vec{e}_j = \delta^i_j \qquad (6.3\text{-}21)$$

where δ^i_j is the Kronecker delta.

Note that a given set of Cartesian base vectors is identical to its reciprocal set. This is evident from Eqs. (6.3-19) and (6.3-20),

or by comparison of Eq. (6.3-21) with (6.3-9). Hence only one set
of indices (i.e., subscripts) are needed for Cartesian systems, and
the need for superscripts does not arise.

A set of two-dimensional nonorthogonal coordinates and their
reciprocal set of base vectors are illustrated in Fig. 6.4. From
Fig. 6.4, it is evident that:

$$\vec{e}_1 \cdot \vec{e}^1 = |\vec{e}_1||\vec{e}^1| \cos\left(\frac{\pi}{2} - \theta\right) = |\vec{e}_1||\vec{e}^1| \sin\theta \qquad (6.3\text{-}22)$$

Now from the geometry of the diagram:

$$|\vec{e}_1| = |\vec{e}^1| \sin\theta \qquad (6.3\text{-}23)$$

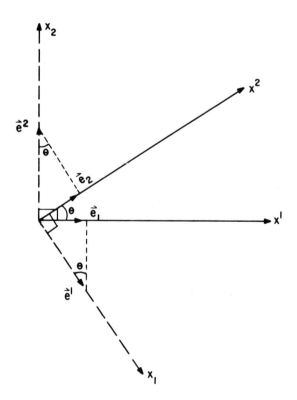

FIG. 6.4 Reciprocal coordinate sets in two dimensions.

so that Eq. (6.3-22) becomes:

$$\vec{e}_1 \cdot \vec{e}^1 = |\vec{e}_1| \frac{|\vec{e}_1|}{\sin \theta} \sin \theta = |\vec{e}_1|^2 = 1 \quad \text{if} \quad |\vec{e}_1| = 1 \quad (6.3\text{-}24)$$

Hence if the $\vec{e}_j$ are unit vectors, Eq. (6.3-23) shows that the $\vec{e}^j$ cannot be unit vectors, unless the coordinates are orthogonal. The same conclusions applies in the general three-dimensional case.

Now both $\vec{e}^1$ and $(\vec{e}_2 \times \vec{e}_3)$ are perpendicular to $\vec{e}_2$ and $\vec{e}_3$, by definition, so that we may write:

$$\vec{e}_2 \times \vec{e}_3 = V\vec{e}^1 \qquad\qquad\qquad\qquad (6.3\text{-}25)$$

where V is a proportionality constant. Taking the scalar product of $\vec{e}_1$ with Eq. (6.3-25), we find:

$$\vec{e}_1 \cdot (\vec{e}_2 \times \vec{e}_3) = V\vec{e}_1 \cdot \vec{e}^1 = V \qquad\qquad (6.3\text{-}26)$$

The left side of Eq. (6.3-26) is the volume of the parallelepiped defined by the vectors $\vec{e}_1$, $\vec{e}_2$, $\vec{e}_3$, hence the physical significance of the constant V. Considering a similar combination of other unit vectors, a general relation corresponding to Eq. (6.3-25) can be written:

$$\vec{e}_i \times \vec{e}_j = V e_{ijk} \vec{e}^k \qquad\qquad\qquad (6.3\text{-}27)$$

where e_{ijk} is the permutation symbol.

By a similar procedure, and making use of Eq. (6.3-19), it follows that

$$\vec{e}^i \times \vec{e}^j = \frac{e^{ijk} \vec{e}_k}{V} \qquad\qquad\qquad (6.3\text{-}28)$$

The permutation symbol e^{ijk} is identical to e_{ijk}. Equations (6.3-27) and (6.3-28) thus relate a given set of base vectors to its reciprocal set of base vectors.

Example 6.2 Consider the set of nonorthogonal coordinates in Fig. 6.4, in which $\theta = 60°$, $|\vec{e}_1| = 2$, $|\vec{e}_2| = 1$, and $|\vec{e}_3| = 0.5$, where $\vec{e}_3$ points upward perpendicular to the plane of the figure. Determine the reciprocal set of base vectors, $\vec{e}^j$.

For this we use Eq. (6.3-27):

$$V e_{ijk} \vec{e}^k = \vec{e}_i \times \vec{e}_j$$

where V is given by Eq. (6.3-28):

$$V = \vec{e}_1 \cdot (\vec{e}_2 \times \vec{e}_3)$$

$$= (|\vec{e}_1| \cos 30°)(|\vec{e}_2||\vec{e}_3| \sin 90°)$$

$$= (2)(0.866)(1)(0.5)(1) = 0.866$$

Thus

$$0.866 \ \vec{e}^3 = \vec{e}_1 \times \vec{e}_2 = (2)(1) \sin 60° = 1.732$$

$$0.866 \ \vec{e}^2 = \vec{e}_3 \times \vec{e}_1 = (0.5)(2) \sin 90° = 1.0$$

$$0.866 \ \vec{e}^1 = \vec{e}_2 \times \vec{e}_3 = (1)(0.5) \sin 90° = 0.5$$

hence

$$|\vec{e}^1| = 0.5/0.866 = 0.577, \text{ parallel to } \vec{e}_2 \times \vec{e}_3$$

$$|\vec{e}^2| = 1.0/0.866 = 1.15, \text{ parallel to } \vec{e}_3 \times \vec{e}_1$$

$$|\vec{e}^3| = 1.732/0.866 = 2.0, \text{ parallel to } \vec{e}_1 \times \vec{e}_2$$

-- 0 --

6.3.5. Covariant and Contravariant Vector Components

A given vector $(\vec{A})$ can be described in terms of its components relative to either the $\vec{e}_j$ or the $\vec{e}^j$ base vectors (i.e., either set of reciprocal axes), for a given coordinate system. Those scalar components relative to the $\vec{e}_j$ set are referred to as the *contravariant components* (A^1, A^2, A^3) and are designated by superscripts:

$$\vec{A} = A^1\vec{e}_1 + A^2\vec{e}_2 + A^3\vec{e}_3 = A^i\vec{e}_i \qquad (6.3\text{-}29)$$

while those referred to the coordinates defined by the reciprocal base vectors $\vec{e}^j$ are referred to as *covariant components* (A_1, A_2, A_3) and are designated by subscripts:

$$\vec{A} = A_1\vec{e}^1 + A_2\vec{e}^2 + A_3\vec{e}^3 = A_i\vec{e}^i \qquad (6.3\text{-}30)$$

By taking the scalar product of Eqs. (6.3-29) and (6.3-30) with $\vec{e}^j$ and $\vec{e}_j$, respectively, and using Eq. (6.3-21), we see that the scalar components of the vector $\vec{A}$ are:

Contravariant components:

$$A^j = \vec{A} \cdot \vec{e}^j \qquad (6.3\text{-}31)$$

Covariant components:

$$A_j = \vec{A} \cdot \vec{e}_j \qquad (6.3\text{-}32)$$

6.3.6. Metric and Conjugate Tensors

The scalar (dot) products of all combinations of the base vectors $\vec{e}_i$ define nine quantities, which are the components of the Euclidean metric tensor, g_{ij}:

$$g_{ij} = \vec{e}_i \cdot \vec{e}_j = \begin{bmatrix} \vec{e}_1 \cdot \vec{e}_1 & \vec{e}_1 \cdot \vec{e}_2 & \vec{e}_1 \cdot \vec{e}_3 \\ \vec{e}_2 \cdot \vec{e}_1 & \vec{e}_2 \cdot \vec{e}_2 & \vec{e}_2 \cdot \vec{e}_3 \\ \vec{e}_3 \cdot \vec{e}_1 & \vec{e}_3 \cdot \vec{e}_2 & \vec{e}_3 \cdot \vec{e}_3 \end{bmatrix} = \begin{bmatrix} g_{11} & g_{12} & g_{13} \\ g_{21} & g_{22} & g_{23} \\ g_{31} & g_{32} & g_{33} \end{bmatrix}$$

(6.3-33)

Similarly, the dot products of the reciprocal base vectors determine the components of the *conjugate tensor*, g^{ij}:

$$g^{ij} = \vec{e}^i \cdot \vec{e}^j = \begin{bmatrix} \vec{e}^1 \cdot \vec{e}^1 & \vec{e}^1 \cdot \vec{e}^2 & \vec{e}^1 \cdot \vec{e}^3 \\ \vec{e}^2 \cdot \vec{e}^1 & \vec{e}^2 \cdot \vec{e}^2 & \vec{e}^2 \cdot \vec{e}^3 \\ \vec{e}^3 \cdot \vec{e}^1 & \vec{e}^3 \cdot \vec{e}^2 & \vec{e}^3 \cdot \vec{e}^3 \end{bmatrix} = \begin{bmatrix} g^{11} & g^{12} & g^{13} \\ g^{21} & g^{22} & g^{23} \\ g^{31} & g^{32} & g^{33} \end{bmatrix}$$

(6.34)

A *mixed tensor* can similarly be defined, involving both the base and reciprocal base vectors, but this becomes identical to Eq. (6.3-21):

$$\vec{e}^i \cdot \vec{e}_j = \delta^i_{\ j} = \begin{bmatrix} 1 & 0 & 0 \\ 0 & 1 & 0 \\ 0 & 0 & 1 \end{bmatrix}$$

(6.3-35)

Since the scalar product is commutative (i.e., $\vec{e}_i \cdot \vec{e}_j = \vec{e}_j \cdot \vec{e}_i$), the tensors g_{ij} and g_{ji} must be symmetric, that is,

$$g_{ij} = g_{ji} \qquad g^{ij} = g^{ji}$$

(6.3-36)

It should be evident that for Cartesian coordinates, Eqs. (6.3-33) to (6.3-35) are all identical.

It is important to note that the components of the metric and conjugate tensors are uniquely determined once the base vectors are specified. That is, the metric and conjugate tensors are a unique

property of the coordinate system, and thus every coordinate system
may be characterized by its metric tensor.

Consider now the scalar product of two vectors $\vec{A}$ and $\vec{B}$:

Contravariant and covariant:

$$\vec{A} \cdot \vec{B} = (A^i \vec{e}_i) \cdot (B_j \vec{e}^j) = A^i B_j (\vec{e}_i \cdot \vec{e}^j) = A^i B_j \delta_i^j = A^i B_i \quad (6.3-37)$$

Both contravariant:

$$\vec{A} \cdot \vec{B} = (A^i \vec{e}_i) \cdot (B^j \vec{e}_j) = A^i B^j (\vec{e}_i \cdot \vec{e}_j) = A^i B^j g_{ij} \quad (6.3-38)$$

Both covariant:

$$\vec{A} \cdot \vec{B} = (A_i \vec{e}^i) \cdot (B_j \vec{e}^j) = A_i B_j (\vec{e}^i \cdot \vec{e}^j) = A_i B_j g^{ij} \quad (6.3-39)$$

Each of these results contains no independent free (nonrepeated) indices. Hence they are tensor quantities of net zero order, i.e.,
scalars. The first result, Eq. (613-37), involves the sum of three
terms, while the other two each comprise a sum of nine terms (many of
which may be zero, depending upon the components of g_{ij} and g^{ij})
Note also that each repeated index always appears once as a superscript and once as a subscript.

The dot product of a vector with the base vectors of a given
coordinate system may be used to establish a relation between the
covariant and contravariant components of a vector:

$$A_j = \vec{A} \cdot \vec{e}_j = A^k \vec{e}_k \cdot \vec{e}_j = A^k g_{kj} \quad (6.3-40)$$

$$A^j = \vec{A} \cdot \vec{e}^j = A_k \vec{e}^k \cdot \vec{e}^j = A_k g^{kj} \quad (6.3-41)$$

Note that the index k is repeated, and each term contains a single
net index j as either a subscript, as in Eq. (6.3-40), or a superscript as in Eq. (6.3-41). Thus covariant and contravariant components may be interconverted with the aid of the metric and conjugate
tensors. This operation is known as the *inner product*.

If the vector components of $\vec{A}$ in Eqs. (6.3-40) and (6.3-41) are replaced by base vectors, these equations become:

$$\vec{e}_i = \vec{e}^k g_{ki} \qquad \vec{e}^j = \vec{e}_k g^{kj} \qquad (6.3\text{-}42)$$

If we take the scalar product of $\vec{e}_i$ with $\vec{e}^j$, and employ Eq. (6.3-21), we have:

$$\vec{e}_i \cdot \vec{e}^j = g_{ki} g^{kj} = \delta_i{}^j = \begin{bmatrix} 1 & 0 & 0 \\ 0 & 1 & 0 \\ 0 & 0 & 1 \end{bmatrix} = g_{ik} g^{kj} \qquad (6.3\text{-}43)$$

which shows that the matrix of the components of g^{ij} is the inverse of the matrix of the components of g_{ij}, and vice versa.

Now consider the cross product of two vectors:

$$\vec{A} \times \vec{B} = (A_i \vec{e}^i) \times (B_j \vec{e}^j) = A_i B_j (\vec{e}^i \times \vec{e}^j) = A_i B_j \vec{e}_k \frac{e^{ijk}}{V} \qquad (6.3\text{-}44)$$

where Eq. (6.3-28) has been used for $(\vec{e}^i \times \vec{e}^j)$. If we replace $\vec{A}$ by $\vec{e}_1$ and $\vec{B}$ by $\vec{e}_2$, we have from Eq. (6.3-40):

$$A_i = \vec{A} \cdot \vec{e}_i \to \vec{e}_1 \cdot \vec{e}_i = g_{1i} = g_{i1}$$
$$B_j = \vec{B} \cdot \vec{e}_j \to \vec{e}_2 \cdot \vec{e}_j = g_{2j} = g_{j2} \qquad (6.3\text{-}45)$$

where the last relation follows from Eq. (6.3-33). With this substitution, Eq. (6.3-44) becomes

$$\vec{e}_1 \times \vec{e}_2 = \frac{e^{ijk}}{V} g_{i1} g_{j2} \vec{e}_k \qquad (6.3\text{-}46)$$

Taking the scalar product of Eq. (6.3-46) with $\vec{e}_3$, and noting from Eq. (6.3-26) that:

$$\vec{e}_1 \cdot (\vec{e}_2 \times \vec{e}_3) = V = (\vec{e}_1 \times \vec{e}_2) \cdot \vec{e}_3 \qquad (6.3\text{-}47)$$

there results:

$$(\vec{e}_1 \times \vec{e}_2) \cdot \vec{e}_3 = V = \frac{e^{ijk}}{V} g_{i1}g_{j2}(\vec{e}_k \cdot \vec{e}_3) \qquad (6.3\text{-}48)$$

or

$$V^2 = e^{ijk}g_{i1}g_{j2}g_{k3} \qquad (6.3\text{-}49)$$

The right side of Eq. (6.3-49) represents the determinant formed from the elements of g_{ij}:

$$\left| g_{ij} \right| \equiv g = \begin{vmatrix} g_{11} & g_{12} & g_{13} \\ g_{21} & g_{22} & g_{23} \\ g_{31} & g_{32} & g_{33} \end{vmatrix} = e^{ijk}g_{i1}g_{j2}g_{k3} = V^2 \qquad (6.3\text{-}50)$$

That is, the value of the determinant of the components of the metric tensor for a given coordinate system is equal to the square of the volume of the parallelepiped whose sides are the base vectors defining the system. In a like fashion it can be shown that:

$$\frac{1}{g} \equiv \left| g^{ij} \right| = \vec{e}^i \cdot \vec{e}^j = \frac{1}{V^2} \qquad (6.3\text{-}51)$$

Hence using these results, Eqs. (6.3-27) and (6.3-28) may be expressed in the alternate form:

$$\vec{e}^i \times \vec{e}^j = \frac{e^{ijk}}{\sqrt{g}} \vec{e}_k \qquad (6.3\text{-}52)$$

$$\vec{e}_i \times \vec{e}_j = \sqrt{g}\, e_{ijk}\vec{e}^k \qquad (6.3\text{-}53)$$

Two additional permutation symbols, defined as follows, are useful:

$$\varepsilon_{ijk} \equiv V e_{ijk} = \sqrt{g}\, e_{ijk} \qquad (6.3\text{-}54)$$

$$\varepsilon^{ijk} \equiv \frac{e^{ijk}}{V} = \frac{e^{ijk}}{\sqrt{g}} \tag{6.3-55}$$

Note that, for Cartesian coordinates, the quantities e_{ijk}, ε_{ijk}, e^{ijk}, and ε^{ijk} are all identical, since V has a value of unity. Using these symbols, Eq. (6.3-44) can be rewritten:

$$\vec{A} \times \vec{B} = \frac{e^{ijk}}{\sqrt{g}} A_i B_j \vec{e}_k = \varepsilon^{ijk} A_i B_j \vec{e}_k \tag{6.3-56}$$

or

$$\vec{A} \times \vec{B} = \varepsilon^{ijk} A_i B_j = C^k \qquad \vec{A} \times \vec{B} = \varepsilon_{ijk} A^i B^j = C_k \tag{6.3-57}$$

Inclusion of the base vector in expressions such as Eq. (6.3-56) is not necessary, it being implied by the single free index k.

———————————————————— 0 ————————————————————

Example 6.3   Consider a vector which has contravariant components

$$A^j = (7, 3, 9)$$

with respect to the coordinates of Example 6.2 (Fig. 6.4).

 a. Determine the metric and conjugate tensor components for this coordinate system.

 b. Use these results to determine V by Eqs. (6.3-50) and (6.3-51), and compare with the value determined in Example 6.2.

 c. Determine the covariant components of $\vec{A}$ with respect to these coordinates.

Solution.

 a. The metric tensor is given by Eq. (6.3-33):

$$g_{ij} = \vec{e}_i \cdot \vec{e}_j$$

  so that

$$g_{11} = (2)(2)(\cos\ 0) = 4$$

$$g_{12} = (2)(1)(\cos\ 60°) = 1 = g_{21}$$

$$g_{13} = (2)(0.5)(\cos\ 90°) = 0 = g_{31}$$

$$g_{22} = (1)(1)(\cos\ 0) = 1$$

$$g_{23} = (1)(0.5)(\cos\ 90°) = 0 = g_{32}$$

$$g_{33} = (0.5)(0.5)(\cos\ 0) = 0.25$$

Thus

$$g_{ij} = \begin{bmatrix} 4 & 1 & 0 \\ 1 & 1 & 0 \\ 0 & 0 & 0.25 \end{bmatrix}$$

The conjugate tensor can be obtained from either Eq. (6.3-34) or (6.3-43). By either method, we obtain:

$$g^{ij} = \begin{bmatrix} \dfrac{1}{3} & -\dfrac{1}{3} & 0 \\ -\dfrac{1}{3} & \dfrac{4}{3} & 0 \\ 0 & 0 & 4 \end{bmatrix}$$

b.   By Eq. (6.3-50), the value of V is:

$$V = \sqrt{g} = (|g_{ij}|)^{\frac{1}{2}} = \sqrt{0.75} = 0.866$$

and by Eq. (6.3-51) it is

$$V = \frac{1}{(|g^{ij}|)^{\frac{1}{2}}} = \frac{1}{\sqrt{4/3}} = 0.866$$

which agrees with Example 6.2.

c.   The covariant components of $\vec{A}$ are given by Eq. (6.3-40):

$$A_1 = A^1 g_{11} + A^2 g_{21} + A^3 g_{31}$$

$$= (7)(4) + (3)(1) + (9)(0) = 31$$

$$A_2 = A^1 g_{12} + A^2 g_{22} + A^3 g_{32}$$

$$= (7)(1) + (3)(1) + (9)(0) = 10$$

$$A_3 = A^1 g_{13} + A^2 g_{23} + A^3 g_{33}$$

$$= (7)(0) + (3)(0) + (9)(0.25) = \frac{9}{4} = 2.25$$

Thus

$$A_i = (31, 10, 2.25)$$

──────────────────────────────── 0 ────────────────────────────────

6.4. COORDINATE TRANSFORMATIONS

The basic characteristic of general tensor notation is that it is independent of the specific frame of reference (i.e., coordinate system) chosen to describe the system. Of course the evaluation of specific tensor components can only be done with reference to a given set of coordinates. Thus, because of the invariant nature of tensors, the transformation of tensor components from one coordinate reference frame to another must follow very specific rules. Such transformation rules must, of course, be intimately involved with the fundamental properties of coordinate systems. Consequently, an understanding of coordinate systems and their transformation relations is basic to an understanding of tensor properties.

All coordinate systems can be interrelated in terms of their representation of a specific invariant quantity; namely, the square

of a differential length of a line segment in space. Expressions for
the components of this element with reference to various coordinate
systems then serve to define the transformation relations between
the systems.

6.4.1. Transformation Relations

Let us consider first a Cartesian (rectangular orthogonal) coordinate system, illustrated in Fig. 6.5. The square of the differential line segment, in terms of its Cartesian components, is:

$$(ds)^2 = (dx)^2 + (dy)^2 + (dz)^2 \qquad\qquad (6.4\text{-}1)$$

The same differential segment can be described with reference
to its components referred to a cylindrical coordinate system, shown
in Fig. 6.6, as follows. Any given point in space can be located
(relative to a reference origin) in terms of either Cartesian or
cylindrical coordinates, so that there must be a unique relation

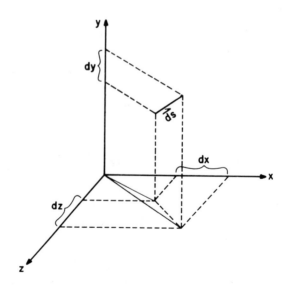

FIG. 6.5 A differential line segment in Cartesian coordinates.

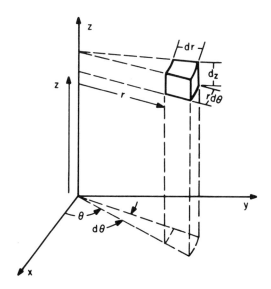

FIG. 6.6 Cylindrical coordinates.

between the two. These relations may be readily determined from the geometry of the coordinates, and are:

$$x = r \cos \theta = x(r, \theta, z) \qquad r = (x^2 + y^2)^{\frac{1}{2}} = r(x, y, z)$$

$$y = r \sin \theta = y(r, \theta, z) \qquad \theta = \arctan \frac{y}{x} = \theta(x, y, z) \qquad (6.4\text{-}2)$$

$$z = z \qquad = z(r, \theta, z) \qquad z = z \qquad = z(x, y, z)$$

Thus the Cartesian and cylindrical components of the differential line segment $\vec{ds}$ may be related by application of the chain rule and the above transformations:

$$dx = \frac{\partial x}{\partial r} dr + \frac{\partial x}{\partial \theta} d\theta + \frac{\partial x}{\partial z} dz = \cos \theta \, dr - r \sin \theta \, d\theta$$

$$dy = \frac{\partial y}{\partial r} dr + \frac{\partial y}{\partial \theta} d\theta + \frac{\partial y}{\partial z} dz = \sin \theta \, dr + r \cos \theta \, d\theta \qquad (6.4\text{-}3)$$

$$dz = \frac{\partial z}{\partial r} dr + \frac{\partial z}{\partial \theta} d\theta + \frac{\partial z}{\partial z} dz = dz$$

Substitution into Eq. (6.4-1) results in:

$$(ds)^2 = (dr)^2 + (r \, d\theta)^2 + (dz)^2 \qquad (6.4-4)$$

If the following superscript index notation is used for Cartesian and curvilinear coordinates:

$$x = x^1 \qquad r = z^1$$

$$y = x^2 \qquad \theta = z^2 \qquad\qquad (6.4-5)$$

$$z = x^3 \qquad z = z^3$$

all of the relations in Eq. (6.4-3) may be represented by the single expression:

$$dx^i = \frac{\partial x^i}{\partial z^j} \, dz^j \qquad\qquad (6.4-6)$$

where a summation in the repeated index j is implied.

A similar transformation applies to the relation between Cartesian base vectors $(\vec{i})$ and those of any other (curvilinear) system $(\vec{e})$. These vectors serve to define the components of a position vector, $\vec{r}$, with reference to these two systems:

$$\vec{r} = x^1 \vec{i}_1 + x^2 \vec{i}_2 + x^3 \vec{i}_3 = x^i \vec{i}_i \qquad \text{(Cartesian)} \qquad (6.4-7)$$

$$\vec{r} = z^1 \vec{e}_1 + z^2 \vec{e}_2 + z^3 \vec{e}_3 = z^i \vec{e}_i \qquad \text{(curvilinear)} \qquad (6.4-8)$$

Thus a differential vector, $d\vec{r}$, relative to the curvilinear system can be expressed as:

$$d\vec{r} = \vec{e}_1 dz^1 + \vec{e}_2 dz^2 + \vec{e}_3 dz^3 = \frac{\partial \vec{r}}{\partial z^1} \, dz^1 + \frac{\partial \vec{z}}{\partial z^2} \, dz^2 + \frac{\partial \vec{r}}{\partial z^3} \, dz^3 \quad (6.4-9)$$

where the latter form is again just the expression for the chain rule.

Hence by comparison of these two expressions, we see that

$$\vec{e}_j = \frac{\partial \vec{r}}{\partial z^j} \qquad\qquad (6.4\text{-}10)$$

Substitution for $\vec{r}$ from Eq. (6.4-7) into this expression gives:

$$\vec{e}_j = \frac{\partial (x^i \vec{i}_i)}{\partial z^j} = \frac{\partial x^i}{\partial z^j} \vec{i}_i \qquad\qquad (6.4\text{-}11)$$

which provides a transformation relation between base vectors, which may be compared with Eq. (6.4-6) for the transformation of the differential coordinate components.

——————————————— 0 ———————————————

Example 6.4 Determine expressions for the base vectors of a cylindrical coordinate system, starting with the relations between cylindrical and Cartesian coordinates, and use the result to show that these coordinates are orthogonal.

Solution. Equation (6.4-11), together with the transformations Eq. (6.4-2), provide the required relations:

$$\vec{e}_j = \frac{\partial x^i}{\partial z^j} \vec{i}_i$$

Hence

$$\vec{e}_1 = \frac{\partial x^1}{\partial z^1} \vec{i}_1 + \frac{\partial x^2}{\partial z^1} \vec{i}_2 + \frac{\partial x^3}{\partial z^1} \vec{i}_3 \; , \quad \text{etc.}$$

or

$$\vec{e}_1 = \vec{e}_r = \cos \theta \vec{i}_1 + \sin \theta \vec{i}_2 + 0$$

$$\vec{e}_2 = \vec{e}_\theta = -r \sin \theta \vec{i}_1 + r \cos \theta \vec{i}_2 + 0$$

$$\vec{e}_3 = \vec{e}_3 = 0 + 0 + \vec{i}_3$$

A coordinate system is orthogonal if its base vectors are mutually perpendicular. This requires that the scalar products of all combinations of dissimilar base vector pairs be zero. From Eq. (6.3-10):

$$\vec{e}_r \cdot \vec{e}_\theta = -r \cos \theta \sin \theta + r \sin \theta \cos \theta + 0 = 0 = \vec{e}_\theta \cdot \vec{e}_r$$

$$\vec{e}_r \cdot \vec{e}_z = 0 + 0 + 0 = 0 = \vec{e}_z \cdot \vec{e}_r$$

$$\vec{e} \cdot \vec{e}_z = 0 + 0 + 0 = 0 = \vec{e}_z \cdot \vec{e}_r$$

Therefore the coordinates (r, θ, z) must be orthogonal.

———————————————————— 0 ————————————————————

The expression for the invariant (scalar) quantity $(ds)^2$, Eq. (6.4-1), involves the quantities $(dx)^2$, $(dy)^2$, and $(dz)^2$. From Eq. (6.4-6), we see that:

$$(dx)^2 = \frac{\partial x}{\partial r} \frac{\partial x}{\partial r} dr \, dr + \frac{\partial x}{\partial r} \frac{\partial x}{\partial \theta} dr \, d\theta + \frac{\partial x}{\partial r} \frac{\partial x}{\partial z} dr \, dz$$

$$+ \frac{\partial x}{\partial \theta} \frac{\partial x}{\partial r} d\theta \, dr + \frac{\partial x}{\partial \theta} \frac{\partial x}{\partial \theta} d\theta \, d\theta + \frac{\partial x}{\partial \theta} \frac{\partial x}{\partial z} d\theta \, dz \qquad (6.4\text{-}12)$$

$$+ \frac{\partial x}{\partial z} \frac{\partial x}{\partial r} dz \, dr + \frac{\partial x}{\partial z} \frac{\partial x}{\partial \theta} dz \, d\theta + \frac{\partial x}{\partial z} \frac{\partial x}{\partial z} dz \, dz$$

which, using the index notation of Eq. (6.4-5), can be written:

$$(dx^1)^2 = \frac{\partial x^1}{\partial z^i} \frac{\partial x^1}{\partial z^j} dz^i \, dz^j \qquad (6.4\text{-}13)$$

Similar expressions can be written for $(dy)^2 = (dx^2)^2$ and

$(dz)^2 = (dx^3)^3$. If these are then summed to give an expression for
$(ds)^2 = (dx)^2 + (dy)^2 + (dz)^2$, the terms can be grouped as follows:

$$(ds)^2 = \left(\frac{\partial x}{\partial r}\frac{\partial x}{\partial r} + \frac{\partial y}{\partial r}\frac{\partial y}{\partial r} + \frac{\partial z}{\partial r}\frac{\partial z}{\partial r}\right) dr\ dr$$

$$+ \left(\frac{\partial x}{\partial r}\frac{\partial x}{\partial \theta} + \frac{\partial y}{\partial r}\frac{\partial y}{\partial \theta} + \frac{\partial z}{\partial r}\frac{\partial z}{\partial \theta}\right) dr\ d\theta$$

$$+ \left(\frac{\partial x}{\partial r}\frac{\partial x}{\partial z} + \frac{\partial y}{\partial r}\frac{\partial y}{\partial z} + \frac{\partial z}{\partial r}\frac{\partial z}{\partial z}\right) dr\ dz$$

$$+ \left(\frac{\partial x}{\partial \theta}\frac{\partial x}{\partial r} + \frac{\partial y}{\partial \theta}\frac{\partial y}{\partial r} + \frac{\partial z}{\partial \theta}\frac{\partial z}{\partial r}\right) d\theta\ dr$$

$$\text{(6.4-14)}$$

$$+ \left(\frac{\partial x}{\partial \theta}\frac{\partial x}{\partial \theta} + \frac{\partial y}{\partial \theta}\frac{\partial y}{\partial \theta} + \frac{\partial z}{\partial \theta}\frac{\partial z}{\partial \theta}\right) d\theta\ d\theta$$

$$+ \left(\right) d\theta\ dz$$

$$+ \left(\right) dz\ dr$$

$$+ \left(\right) dz\ d\theta$$

$$+ \left(\right) dz\ dz$$

Using the index notation and summation convention, this becomes:

$$(ds)^2 = \left(\frac{\partial x^k}{\partial z^i}\frac{\partial x^m}{\partial z^j}\delta_{km}\right) dz^i\ dz^j \qquad\qquad \text{(6.4-15)}$$

The four repeated (dummy) indices in this expression imply a sum of
$(3)^4 = 81$ terms. Note that each dummy index appears once as a subscript and once as a superscript. Many of the terms in the sum are
zero, however, as seen from the transformations in Eq. (6.4-2) and
the properties of δ_{km}. Equation (6.4-15) is valid for transformations between any two coordinate systems, x^i and z^i.

6.4.2 The Metric Tensor

If the x^i in Eq. (6.4-15) represent Cartesian coordinates and the z^i are any other system (linear or curvilinear, orthogonal or nonorthogonal), the quantity in brackets in Eq. (6.4-15) may be considered a characteristic of the z^i system. It is a second-order tensor, called the *metric tensor*, and is represented by g_{ij}:

$$g_{ij} \equiv \frac{\partial x^k}{\partial z^i} \frac{\partial x^m}{\partial z^j} \delta_{km} \qquad\qquad (6.4\text{-}16)$$

It should be evident from Eq. (6.4-11), that the components of the metric tensor are identical to the components of the scalar (dot) products of the base vectors $(\vec{e}_i \cdot \vec{e}_j)$. This, then, is consistent with our previous definition of the metric tensor, given by Eq. (6.3-33).

It is evident that g_{ij} is a symmetric second-order tensor with nine components, each of which involves a sum of nine terms. However, for many coordinate systems, a number of these components are zero. In fact, for all orthogonal systems only the three diagonal (i.e., i = j) components are nonzero, all others being identically zero.

Note that, by Eq. (6.4-15), g_{ij} may also be interpreted as a second-order tensor that relates the differential displacement between two points (ds) to the changes in the relative coordinate positions of the points (dz^i). As such, it may be considered to be a measure of infintesimal strain, and is often referred to in this context. This concept will be pursued further in the succeeding chapter, when more general concepts of deformation are considered.

For cylindrical coordinates, defined by the transformations in Eq. (6.4-2), the metric tensor components become:

$$g_{ij} = \begin{bmatrix} 1 & 0 & 0 \\ 1 & r^2 & 0 \\ 1 & 0 & 1 \end{bmatrix} \qquad \text{where} \qquad \begin{aligned} z^1 &= r \\ z^2 &= \theta \\ z^3 &= z \end{aligned} \qquad (6.4\text{-}17)$$

For this system, Eq. (6.4-15) reduces to

$$(ds)^2 = (dz^1)^2 + (z^1\ dz^2)^2 + (dz^3)^2$$

$$= (dr)^2 + (r\ d\theta)^2 + (dz)^2 \qquad (6.4\text{-}18)$$

If the coordinates z^i represent a Cartesian system, it is evident that

$$g_{ij} = \begin{bmatrix} 1 & 0 & 0 \\ 0 & 1 & 0 \\ 0 & 0 & 1 \end{bmatrix} \qquad \text{where} \qquad \begin{matrix} z^1 = x \\ z^2 = y \\ z^3 = z \end{matrix} \qquad (6.4\text{-}19)$$

and

$$(ds)^2 = (dz^1)^2 + (dz^2)^2 + (dz^3)^2$$

$$= (dx)^2 + (dy)^2 + (dz)^2 \qquad (6.4\text{-}20)$$

Another commonly employed orthogonal reference system is the spherical coordinate set, illustrated in Fig. 6.7. The transformation relations between the Cartesian (x^i = x, y, z) and spherical (z^i = r, θ, ϕ) coordinates are:

$$x = r \sin \theta \cos \phi\ , \qquad r = \sqrt{x^2 + y^2 + z^2}$$

$$y = r \sin \theta \sin \phi\ , \qquad \theta = \arccos \frac{z}{\sqrt{x^2 + y^2 + z^2}} \qquad (6.4\text{-}21)$$

$$z = r \cos \theta \qquad , \qquad \phi = \arctan \frac{y}{x}$$

The metric tensor components for spherical coordinates are:

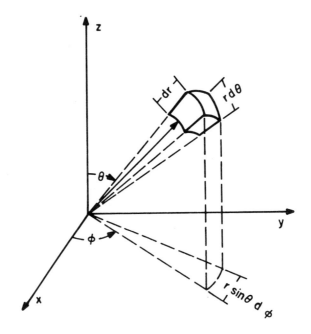

FIG. 6.7   Spherical coordinates.

$$g_{ij} = \begin{bmatrix} 1 & 0 & 0 \\ 0 & r^2 & 0 \\ 0 & 0 & \sin^2 \theta \end{bmatrix}$$

(6.4-22)

and Eq. (6.4-15) reduces to:

$$(ds)^2 = (dr)^2 + (r \, d\theta)^2 + (r \sin \theta \, d\theta)^2$$

(6.4-23)

In general, for any orthogonal coordinate system (i.e., one for which the base vectors are mutually perpendicular), the metric tensor is of the form:

$$g_{ij} = \begin{bmatrix} g_{11} & 0 & 0 \\ 0 & g_{22} & 0 \\ 0 & 0 & g_{23} \end{bmatrix}$$

(6.4-24)

and Eq. (6.4-15) reduces to the form:

$$(ds)^2 = (h_1 \; dz^1)^2 + (h_2 \; dz^2)^2 + (h_3 \; dz^3)^2 \qquad (6.4\text{-}25)$$

The h_is in Eq. (6.4-25) are functions of the coordinate directions, and are sometimes referred to as scale factors. They are related to the diagonal components of the metric tensor as follows:

$$(h_1)^2 = g_{11} \qquad (h_2)^2 = g_{22} \qquad (h_3)^2 = g_{33} \qquad (6.4\text{-}26)$$

As indicated by Eq. (6.3-33), the components of the metric tensor may also be expressed in terms of the scalar (dot) products of the base vectors $(\vec{e}_i \cdot \vec{e}_j)$.

For nonorthogonal coordinates, there will be, in general, six independent nonzero components of the metric tensor (since it is symmetric), for which case the equivalent of Eq. (6.9-25) is:

$$(ds)^2 = g_{11}(dz^1)^2 + g_{22}(dz^2)^2 + g_{33}(dz^3)^2$$

$$+ \; 2g_{12} \; dz^1 \; dz^2 + 2g_{13} \; dz^1 \; dz^3 + 2g_{23} \; dz^2 \; dz^3 \qquad (6.4\text{-}27)$$

——————————————————— 0 ———————————————————

Example 6.5 Determine the metric tensor for the nonorthogonal coordinate system, z^i, shown below

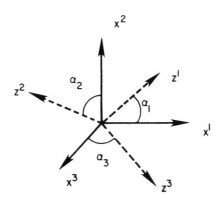

The z^1 coordinate lies in the $(x^1 - x^2)$ plane, z^2 in the $(z^2 - x^3)$ plane, and z^3 in the $(x^3 - x^1)$ plane.

Solution. Inspection of the geometry of the figure provides the transformation relations between the coordinates:

$$x^1 = z^1 \cos \alpha_1 + z^3 \sin \alpha_3$$

$$x^2 = z^2 \cos \alpha_2 + z^1 \sin \alpha_1$$

$$x^3 = z^3 \cos \alpha_3 + z^2 \sin \alpha_2$$

Hence, by Eq. (6.4-16), the metric tensor components are:

$$g_{11} = \frac{\partial x^1}{\partial z^1} \frac{\partial x^1}{\partial z^1} + \frac{\partial x^2}{\partial z^1} \frac{\partial x^2}{\partial z^1} + \frac{\partial x^3}{\partial z^1} \frac{\partial x^3}{\partial z^1}$$

$$= (\cos \alpha_1)^2 + (\sin \alpha_1)^2 + 0 = 1$$

$$g_{12} = \frac{\partial x^1}{\partial z^1} \frac{\partial x^1}{\partial z^2} + \frac{\partial x^2}{\partial z^1} \frac{\partial x^2}{\partial z^2} + \frac{\partial x^3}{\partial z^1} \frac{\partial x^3}{\partial z^2}$$

$$= (\cos \alpha_1)(0) + (\sin \alpha_1)(\cos \alpha_2) + (0)(\sin \alpha_2)$$

$$= (\sin \alpha_1)(\cos \alpha_2)$$

$$g_{13} = (\cos \alpha_1)(\sin \alpha_3) + (\sin \alpha_1)(0) + (0)(\cos \alpha_3) = (\cos \alpha_1)(\sin \alpha_3)$$

$$g_{22} = (0) + (\cos \alpha_2)^2 + (\sin \alpha_2)^2 = 1$$

$$g_{23} = (0)(\sin \alpha_3) + (\cos \alpha_2)(0) + (\sin \alpha_2)(\cos \alpha_3) + (\sin \alpha_2)(\cos \alpha_3)$$

$$g_{33} = (\sin \alpha_3)^2 + 0 + (\cos \alpha_3)^2 = 1$$

Therefore:

$$
g_{ij} = \begin{bmatrix} 1 & \sin \alpha_1 \cos \alpha_2 & \cos \alpha_1 \sin \alpha_3 \\ \sin \alpha_1 \cos \alpha_2 & 1 & \sin \alpha_2 \cos \alpha_3 \\ \cos \alpha_1 \sin \alpha_3 & \sin \alpha_2 \cos \alpha_3 & 1 \end{bmatrix}
$$

——————————————————— 0 ———————————————————

6.5. TENSOR RELATIONS

6.5.1. Contravariant, Covariant, and Mixed Tensors

Any quantity whose components transform from one coordinate system to another by a relation of the form of Eq. (6.4-6) is defined as a contravariant first-order tensor (i.e., a contravariant vector):

$$
\bar{v}^i(\bar{z}^1,\ \bar{z}^2,\ \bar{z}^3) = \frac{\partial \bar{z}^i}{\partial z^k}\, v^k(z^1,\ z^2,\ z^3) \tag{6.5-1}
$$

where the $\bar{v}^i$ are the vector components referred to the $\bar{z}^i$ coordinates, and the v^k are the components referred to the z^k coordinates. It is evident from Eq. (6.4-6) that coordinate differentials transform as contravariant vectors.

On the other hand, a quantity is defined as a covariant first-order tensor (covariant vector) if its components transform in accordance with a relation of the form

$$
\bar{v}_i(\bar{z}^1,\ \bar{z}^2,\ \bar{z}^3) = \frac{\partial z^k}{\partial z^i}\, v_k(z^1,\ z^2,\ z^3) \tag{6.5-2}
$$

It is evident from Eq. (6.4-11) that base vectors transform as covariant vectors.

The terms "contravariant" and "covariant" may be easily associated with the appropriate transformation relations by a simple device. If the expressions are cleared of fractions (treating the derivatives as a ratio of differentials), all quantities associated

with a given coordinate system appear on the same (i.e., "co-") side
of the equation in the covariant transformation, Eq. (6.5-2), while
in the contravariant definition, Eq. (6.5-1), the coordinate differentials are on opposite (i.e., "contra-") sides of the equation from
the corresponding vector components.

The extension of these definitions to higher order contravariant
and covariant tensors is straightforward. Thus, the components of a
contravariant second-order tensor transform according to:

$$\bar{A}^{ij} = \frac{\partial \bar{z}^i}{\partial z^m} \frac{\partial \bar{z}^j}{\partial z^n} A^{mn} \qquad\qquad (6.5\text{-}3)$$

while those of a covariant second-order tensor transform according to:

$$\bar{A}_{ij} = \frac{\partial z^m}{\partial \bar{z}^i} \frac{\partial z^n}{\partial \bar{z}^j} A_{mn} \qquad\qquad (6.5\text{-}4)$$

In addition, for second and higher order tensors we can define
mixed components, as those which transform according to:

$$\bar{A}^i_{\ j} = \frac{\partial \bar{z}^i}{\partial z^m} \frac{\partial z^n}{\partial \bar{z}^j} A^m_{\ n} \qquad\qquad (6.5\text{-}5)$$

Note that the order of indices must be preserved since, for example,
$A^i_{\ j}$ is not the same as $A_j^{\ i}$ unless the tensor is symmetric. Note,
also, that the double sum implied by the repeated indices in Eqs.
(6.5-3) to (6.5-5) indicates a sum of nine terms in each expression.
That is, all nine tensor components relative to a given coordinate
system contribute to each component when transformed to a different
coordinate system.

A given tensor quantity can be described in terms of its contravariant, covariant, or mixed components, and the relations between
these components will be discussed later.

The fact that the metric tensor components transform as a covariant tensor can be demonstrated as follows. Consider the expression for $(ds)^2$ in Eq. (6.4-15), for two different coordinate systems
(e.g., $\bar{z}^i$ and z^α):

$$(ds)^2 = \bar{g}_{ij} \, d\bar{z}^i \, d\bar{z}^j = g_{\alpha\beta} \, dz^\alpha \, dz^\beta \tag{6.5-6}$$

Substituting Eq. (6.4-6) for the transform relations for the coordinate differentials:

$$dz^\alpha = \frac{\partial z^\alpha}{\partial \bar{z}^i} \, d\bar{z}^i \tag{6.5-7}$$

$$dz^\beta = \frac{\partial z^\beta}{\partial \bar{z}^j} \, d\bar{z}^j \tag{6.5-8}$$

into Eq. (6.5-6) gives:

$$(ds)^2 = \bar{g}_{ij} \, d\bar{z}^i \, d\bar{z}^j = g_{\alpha\beta} \, \frac{\partial z^\alpha}{\partial \bar{z}^i} \, d\bar{z}^i \, \frac{\partial z^\beta}{\partial \bar{z}^j} \, d\bar{z}^j \tag{6.5-9}$$

It follows, therefore, that

$$\bar{g}_{ij} = g_{\alpha\beta} \, \frac{\partial z^\alpha}{\partial \bar{z}^i} \, \frac{\partial z^\beta}{\partial \bar{z}^j} \tag{6.5-10}$$

which, by Eq. (6.5-4) defines a covariant tensor.

6.5.2. Conservation of Indices

A convenient rule of thumb for confirming the consistent nature of the terms in a tensor equation may be described as the "conservation of indices." This states that every term in a tensor expression must be of the same net tensor character, having the same net (free) covariant and/or contravariant indices. Dummy or repeated indices are excluded, since they do not contribute to the order of the tensor, and can be assumed to "cancel out," inasmuch as they always occur in pairs as one convariant and one contravariant index. For this purpose, a contravariant index in a denominator is equivalent to a covariant index, and vice versa. For example each term in Eq. (6.5-10) has net covariant indices i and j, since the indices α and β are dummy

repeated indices and appear as both superscripts and subscripts.
Likewise, all terms in Eq. (6.5-9) have no net (free) indices (since
all indices are repeated), and hence are scalars. Note that the specific symbol used for a dummy index is immaterial, as long as each
one of a repeated pair is identical and they do not duplicate any
free index. However, the same covariant and contravariant free
indices must appear in each term of the equation.

───────────────────────────────── 0 ─────────────────────────────────

Example 6.6 The components of a velocity vector with respect to
Cartesian coordinates are:

$$v_x = 4 \qquad v_y = 7 \qquad v_z = 9$$

Determine the components of this vector with respect to cylindrical
coordinates.

Solution. Note that, since velocity is the time rate of change of a
coordinate position which transforms as a contravariant vector, the
velocity vector is also normally contravariant (although, as we shall
show, there is no difficulty in determining the covariant components
of any vector). Hence Eq. (6.5-1) applies, where covariant and
contravariant Cartesian components are identical:

$$v^r = \frac{\partial r}{\partial x} v^x + \frac{\partial r}{\partial y} v^y + \frac{\partial r}{\partial z} v^z$$

$$= \frac{x}{\sqrt{x^2 + y^2}} (4) + \frac{y}{\sqrt{x^2 + y^2}} (7) + 0 = 4 \cos \theta + 7 \sin \theta$$

$$v^\theta = \frac{\partial \theta}{\partial x} v^x + \frac{\partial \theta}{\partial y} v^y + \frac{\partial \theta}{\partial z} v^z$$

$$= - \frac{y}{x^2 + y^2} (4) + \frac{x(7)}{x^2 + y^2} + 0 = - \frac{4 \sin \theta}{r} + \frac{7 \cos \theta}{r}$$

$$v^z = \frac{\partial z}{\partial x} v^x + \frac{\partial z}{\partial y} v^y + \frac{\partial z}{\partial z} v^z$$

$$= 0 + 0 + 9 = 9$$

──────────────────────── 0 ────────────────────────

6.5.3. Tensor Multiplication

The operation of *outer multiplication* of two tensor quantities yields a third tensor of order equal to the sum of the orders of the initial tensors. For example:

$$A^i B^j = C^{ij} \tag{6.5-11}$$

This may be confirmed as follows. If A^i and B^j represent the tensor components referred to the z^i coordinate frame, and $\bar{A}^i$ and B^j are the components of the same tensors referred to the $\bar{z}^i$ coordinate frame, we have:

$$\bar{A}^i \bar{B}^j = \bar{C}^{ij} \tag{6.5-12}$$

Introducing the transformation properties of the contravariant vector from Eq. (6.5-1), this becomes:

$$\bar{C}^{ij} = \bar{A}^i \bar{B}^j = A^k \frac{\partial \bar{z}^i}{\partial z^k} B^m \frac{\partial \bar{z}^j}{\partial z^m} = A^k B^m \frac{\partial \bar{z}^i}{\partial z^k} \frac{\partial \bar{z}^j}{\partial z^m} \tag{6.5-13}$$

But from Eq. (6.5-11), $A^k B^m$ is equal to C^{km}, so that:

$$\bar{C}^{ij} = \frac{\partial \bar{z}^i}{\partial z^k} \frac{\partial \bar{z}^j}{\partial z^m} C^{km} \tag{6.5-14}$$

which, by Eq. (6.5-3), defines a second-order contravariant tensor. Thus the initial statement is proved. The operation of outer multiplication is general, and can be applied to any number of tensor quantities of any order or type.

If a mixed tensor is written with one covariant and one contravariant index equal, it is said to be contracted. The resulting tensor is of order two less than the uncontracted tensor. For example,
consider a fourth-order mixed tensor, whose components transform by

$$\bar{B}^{i}_{\cdot jk\ell} = B^{r}_{\cdot stu} \frac{\partial \bar{z}^{i}}{\partial z^{r}} \frac{\partial z^{s}}{\partial \bar{z}^{j}} \frac{\partial z^{t}}{\partial \bar{z}^{k}} \frac{\partial z^{u}}{\partial \bar{z}^{\ell}} \qquad (6.5\text{--}15)$$

If this tensor is contracted by equating i and k, the result is

$$\bar{B}^{i}_{\cdot ji\ell} = B^{r}_{\cdot stu} \frac{\partial \bar{z}^{i}}{\partial z^{r}} \frac{\partial z^{s}}{\partial \bar{z}^{j}} \frac{\partial z^{t}}{\partial \bar{z}^{i}} \frac{\partial z^{u}}{\partial \bar{z}^{\ell}} \qquad (6.5\text{--}16)$$

but

$$\frac{\partial \bar{z}^{i}}{\partial z^{r}} \frac{\partial z^{t}}{\partial \bar{z}^{i}} = \frac{\partial z^{t}}{\partial z^{r}} = \delta^{t}_{r} \qquad \text{(Kronecker delta)} \qquad (6.5\text{--}17)$$

so that

$$\bar{B}^{i}_{ji\ell} = B^{r}_{stu} \delta^{t}_{r} \frac{\partial z^{s}}{\partial \bar{z}^{j}} \frac{\partial z^{u}}{\partial \bar{z}^{\ell}} = B^{t}_{stu} \frac{\partial z^{s}}{\partial \bar{z}^{j}} \frac{\partial z^{u}}{\partial \bar{z}^{\ell}} \qquad (6.5\text{--}18)$$

But Eq. (6.5-18) defines a second-order covariant tensor, thus prov-
ing the initial statement.

It is evident that contraction of a second-order tensor yields
a scalar:

$$\text{Contr} (A^{j}_{i}) = A^{i}_{i} = A^{1}_{1} + A^{2}_{2} + A^{3}_{3} = \text{tr} (A^{j}_{i}) \qquad (6.5\text{--}19)$$

This is simply the trace (tr) of the tensor.

If the outer product of two tensors is contracted by equating
one index from each of the two tensors, the result is known as the
inner product:

$$\text{Contr} (A^{i}B_{jk\ell}) = A^{k}B_{jk\ell} = C_{j\ell} \qquad (6.5\text{--}20)$$

From the definition, it is immaterial which of the indices are involved in the contraction. This is determined by the physical implication of the operation in the context of its application.

Consider the inner product of two vectors, A^i and B^j:

$$A^i = \bar{A}^m \frac{\partial z^i}{\partial \bar{z}^m} \qquad B_j = \bar{B}_n \frac{\partial \bar{z}^n}{\partial z^j} \qquad (6.5\text{-}21)$$

The outer product is

$$A^i B_j = \bar{A}^m \bar{B}_n \frac{\partial z^i}{\partial \bar{z}^m} \frac{\partial \bar{z}^n}{\partial z^j} \qquad (6.5\text{-}22)$$

which, upon contraction, becomes

$$\text{Contr} (A^i B_j) = A^i B_i = \bar{A}^m \bar{B}_n \frac{\partial z^i}{\partial \bar{z}^m} \frac{\partial \bar{z}^n}{\partial z^i} = \bar{A}^m \bar{B}_n \delta^n_m = \bar{A}^n \bar{B}_n \qquad (6.5\text{-}23)$$

Thus the inner product of two vectors yields a scalar. This operation is identical to the scalar or dot product in Gibbs vector notation (e.g., $\vec{A} \cdot \vec{B}$).

Note that the inner product involves contraction of one covariant and one contravariant index. The scalar product of two tensors involves contraction of all indices, which must of necessity involve an equal number of covariant and contravariant indices.

6.6. TENSOR AND PHYSICAL COMPONENTS

The conversion of contravariant tensor components to covariant components, which is equivalent to lowering of the indices, can be accomplished by forming the inner product of the tensor with the metric tensor. The reverse process of transforming covariant components to contravariant components can similarly be accomplished by the inner product with the conjugate tensor, which is discussed below.

6.6.1. The Conjugate Tensor

As previously indicated (in Secs. 6.3.6 and 6.4.2) the components of the metric tensor, g_{ij}, for a given coordinate system are identical to the matrix of the scalar (dot) products of the base vectors defined by the coordinate axes. It was also shown that the scalar products of the base vectors defined by the reciprocal set of coordinates constitute the components of another second-order tensor, g^{ij}, called the *conjugate tensor*. The components of the metric and conjugate tensors are related by:

$$g^{ij}g_{jk} = \delta^i_k \qquad\qquad (6.6\text{-}1)$$

Thus the components of the conjugate tensor may be determined from the inverse matrix of the components of the metric tensor:

$$g^{ij} = \delta^i_k (g_{jk})^{-1} = (g_{ij})^{-1} \qquad\qquad (6.6\text{-}2)$$

since g_{ij} is symmetric. This may also be written:

$$g^{ij} = \frac{G^{ji}}{g} \qquad\qquad (6.6\text{-}3)$$

where

$$g \equiv |g_{ij}| = \det (g_{ij}) \qquad\qquad (6.6\text{-}4)$$

is the determinant of the components of g_{ij}, and

$$G^{ij} = \text{cofactor of the } g_{ij} \text{ element in } g$$

$$= (\text{minor of } g_{ij} \text{ element}) \times (-1)^{i+j} \qquad\qquad (6.6\text{-}5)$$

For orthogonal coordinate systems the metric tensor is diagonal (all off-diagonal components being identically zero). Thus the conjugate tensor will also be diagonal, with the nonzero components given by:

$$g^{ii} = \frac{1}{g_{ii}} \qquad \text{(no summation)} \qquad (6.6\text{-}6)$$

Note that both the metric and conjugate tensors are symmetric. For Cartesian coordinates, it is evident that the metric and conjugate tensors are identical, both being equal to the Kronecker delta, or unit tensor.

6.6.2. Raising and Lowering of Indices

A relation between covariant and contravariant vector components was established by Eqs. (6.3-40) and (6.3-41), namely,

$$A_j = A^i g_{ij} \qquad\qquad A^j = A_i g^{ij} \qquad (6.6\text{-}7)$$

This process is seen to be identical to the operation of inner multiplication between the given tensor and the metric or conjugate tensor, respectively. That the two expressions in Eq. (6.6-7) are consistent can be seen by forming the inner product of the first form with, say, g^{jk}:

$$A_j g^{jk} = A^i g_{ij} g^{jk} = A^i \delta_i^{\ k} = A^k \qquad (6.6\text{-}8)$$

which has resulted in raising of the index, as indicated by the second expression in Eq. (6.6-7).

This process is valid for a tensor of any order and kind. That is, the inner product of a tensor with the metric tensor is equivalent to lowering a contravariant index, while the inner product with the conjugate tensor is equivalent to raising a covariant index. For example:

$$g_{\ell i} A^i_{\ \cdot jk} = A_{\ell jk} \qquad (6.6\text{-}9)$$

and

$$g^{m\ell} A_{\ell jk} = g^{m\ell} g_{\ell i} A^i_{\ \ jk} = \delta^m_{\ i} A^i_{\ \ jk} = A^m_{\ \ jk} \qquad (6.6\text{-}10)$$

Since the inner product involves a repeated index, the operation of raising or lowering an index requires the sum of three terms.

6.6.3. Physical Components

In many coordinate systems, it often happens that neither the contravariant nor the covariant tensor components represent the actual physical components of the tensor.

To illustrate, consider the velocity vector, which is a first-order tensor. Velocity at a point is defined as the time rate of change of the coordinate position of the point. With respect to Cartesian coordinates, it is

$$v^i = v_i = \frac{dx^i}{dt}\left[\frac{length}{time}\right] \tag{6.6-11}$$

where the contravariant, covariant, and physical components are all identical. Now with respect to curvilinear coordinates, the contravariant components may be obtained by transformation of the Cartesian components to curvilinear coordinates:

$$\bar{v}^j = \frac{\partial \bar{z}^j}{\partial x^i}\, v^i = \frac{\partial \bar{z}^j}{\partial x^i}\frac{dx^i}{dt} = \frac{d\bar{z}^j}{dt} \tag{6.6-12}$$

If the $\bar{z}^j$ represent cylindrical coordinates, these components become:

$$\bar{v}^j = \left(\frac{dr}{dt}\,,\;\frac{d\theta}{dt}\,,\;\frac{dz}{dt}\right) \tag{6.6-13}$$

It is evident that these components are not all dimensionally consistent and, indeed, the $d\theta/dt$ components does not represent a physical velocity (with dimensions of length/time).

Now the covariant components of the velocity vector may be obtained by the inner product of the contravariant components with the metric tensor:

$$\bar{v}_j = \frac{\partial x^i}{\partial \bar{z}^j}\, v_i = \bar{g}_{ij}\bar{v}^j \tag{6.6-14}$$

Again with reference to cylindrical coordinates, these are:

$$\bar{v}_i = \left(\frac{dr}{dt} \,,\, r^2 \frac{d\theta}{dt} \,,\, \frac{dz}{dt}\right) \tag{6.6-15}$$

However, these components again are not dimensionally consistent, and do not all represent physical components.

The physical components of a vector are related to the magnitude of the vector as follows:

$$\bar{v} = \sqrt{v^i v_i} = \sqrt{v^1 v_1 + v^2 v_2 + v^3 v_3} = \sqrt{\bar{v}_1^2 + \bar{v}_2^2 + \bar{v}_3^2}$$

$$= \sqrt{\left(\frac{dr}{dt}\right)^2 + \left(r \frac{d\theta}{dt}\right)^2 + \left(\frac{dz}{dt}\right)^2} \tag{6.6-16}$$

Thus the physical components in cylindrical coordinates are:

$$v(i) = \left(\frac{dr}{dt} \,,\, r \frac{d\theta}{dt} \,,\, \frac{dz}{dt}\right) \tag{6.6-17}$$

For orthogonal coordinates, the relations between physical, co-variant, and contravariant components are given by:

$$A(i) = \frac{A_i}{\sqrt{g_{ii}}} = \sqrt{g_{ii}} \, A^i \qquad \text{(no summation)} \tag{6.6-18}$$

where g_{ii} here represents the iith component of g_{ij}, and no tensor multiplication is intended. In this and the following expressions, the indices all refer to a specific tensor component. Hence, repetition of a given index is not to be interpreted as a summation. Note that the physical components are not tensor components (by virtue of their transformation properties), and the index serves only as an identifying symbol.

For second-order tensors, the equivalent of Eq. (6.6-18) is:

$$A(ij) = \frac{A_{ij}}{\sqrt{g_{ii} g_{jj}}} = \sqrt{g_{ii} g_{jj}} \, A^{ij} = \sqrt{\frac{g_{jj}}{g_{ii}}} \, A^i_{\ j} \qquad \text{(no summation)} \tag{6.6-19}$$

These expressions can be written in the alternate form:

$$A(ij) = \frac{A_{ij}}{h_i h_j} = h_i h_j A^{ij} = \frac{h_j}{h_i} A^i_{\ j} \qquad \text{(no summation)} \qquad (6.6\text{-}20)$$

where the hs are the "scale factors," defined by Eq. (6.4-25), and are related to the metric tensor components by Eq. (6.4-26). It is emphasized that these relations apply only to components referred to orthogonal coordinate systems. Note that in Cartesian coordinates the covariant, contravariant, and physical components of any tensor are all identical, since the scale factors are all unity.

For any coordinate system (orthogonal as well as nonorthogonal), the general expression for the physical components of a second-order tensor is:

$$\sum_i \sum_j T(ij) = T_{ij} T^{ij} = T_i^{\ j} T_j^{\ i}$$

$$= g_{ik} g_{j\ell} T^{k\ell} T^{ij} \qquad\qquad (6.6\text{-}21)$$

$$= g^{ik} g^{j\ell} T_{k\ell} T_{ij}$$

where the terms on the right are the sum of the squares of the ij physical components

─────────────────────────── 0 ───────────────────────────

Example 6.7 Determine the physical and covariant components of the velocity vector of Example 6.6 in cylindrical coordinates.

Solution. For this we use the relations of Eq. (6.6-18):

$$v(i) = \frac{v_i}{\sqrt{g_{ii}}} = \sqrt{g_{ii}}\ v^i$$

for which we need the metric tensor for cylindrical coordinates:

$$g_{ij} = \begin{bmatrix} 1 & 0 & 0 \\ 0 & r^2 & 0 \\ 0 & 0 & 1 \end{bmatrix} \qquad \begin{aligned} z^1 &= r \\ z^2 &= \theta \\ z^3 &= z \end{aligned}$$

In Example 6.6, the contravariant components, v^i, were determined. Thus the physical components are:

$$v(r) = \sqrt{g_{rr}} \; v^r = v^r = 4 \cos \theta + 7 \sin \theta$$

$$v(\theta) = \sqrt{g_{\theta\theta}} \; v^\theta = rv^\theta = -4 \sin \theta + 7 \cos \theta$$

$$v(z) = \sqrt{g_{zz}} \; v^z = v^z = 9$$

and the covariant components are:

$$v_r = g_{rr} v^r = v^r = 4 \cos \theta + 7 \sin \theta$$

$$v_\theta = g_{\theta\theta} v^\theta = r^2 v^\theta = -4r \sin \theta + 7r \cos \theta$$

$$v_z = g_{zz} v^z = v^z = 9$$

---------------------------------- 0 ----------------------------------

6.7. DIFFERENTIATION OF TENSORS

Consider the partial derivative of an invariant (scalar) with respect to a spatial coordinate direction. A scalar, being independent of direction, is independent of any coordinate frame of reference (e.g., z^i or $\bar{z}^i$)

$$A = \bar{A} \qquad\qquad\qquad\qquad (6.7\text{-}1)$$

Differentiating with respect to z^j:

$$\frac{\partial A}{\partial z^j} = \frac{\partial \bar{A}}{\partial z^j} = \frac{\partial \bar{z}^k}{\partial z^j} \frac{\partial \bar{A}}{\partial \bar{z}^k} \qquad (6.7\text{-}2)$$

Since this transformation defines a covariant vector, it is evident that the spatial derivative (or gradient) of a zero-order tensor (scalar) is a first-order tensor.

Now consider a first-order tensor (vector):

$$A^j = \bar{A}^\alpha \frac{\partial z^j}{\partial \bar{z}^\alpha} \qquad (6.7\text{-}3)$$

The partial derivative of this vector with respect to the coordinate direction z^k is

$$\frac{\partial A^j}{\partial z^k} = \frac{\partial}{\partial z^k} \left(\bar{A}^\alpha \frac{\partial z^j}{\partial \bar{z}^\alpha} \right) = \frac{\partial \bar{A}^\alpha}{\partial z^k} \frac{\partial z^i}{\partial \bar{z}^\alpha} + \bar{A}^\alpha \frac{\partial^2 z^j}{\partial z^k \partial \bar{z}^\alpha}$$

$$= \frac{\partial \bar{A}^\alpha}{\partial \bar{z}^\beta} \frac{\partial \bar{z}^\beta}{\partial z^k} \frac{\partial z^j}{\partial \bar{z}^\alpha} + \bar{A}^\alpha \frac{\partial^2 z^j}{\partial \bar{z}^\alpha \partial \bar{z}^\gamma} \frac{\partial \bar{z}^\gamma}{\partial z^k} \qquad (6.7\text{-}4)$$

This transformation would define the components of a second-order mixed tensor if the last term were zero. However, this is not, in general, the case, except when the coordinate systems are Cartesian. Hence the partial spatial derivative of a tensor is not itself in general a tensor (except for Cartesian tensors), since it does not satisfy the transformation criterion for tensor components.

In the formation of equations relating tensor quantities, spatial gradients naturally arise. For the resulting equations to be valid tensor relations, the proper spatial gradient must also transform as a tensor, and thus must therefore be a more general operation than partial differentiation.

6.7.1. The Covariant Derivative

It can be shown that Eq. (6.7-4) may be rearranged in the form

$$
\left[\frac{\partial A^i}{\partial z^j} + \left\{\begin{matrix} i \\ k\ j \end{matrix}\right\} A^k\right] = \frac{\partial z^i}{\partial \bar{z}^\alpha} \frac{\partial \bar{z}^\beta}{\partial z^j}\left[\frac{\partial \bar{A}^\alpha}{\partial \bar{z}^\beta} + \left\{\begin{matrix} \alpha \\ \gamma\ \beta \end{matrix}\right\} \bar{A}^\gamma\right] \tag{6.7-5}
$$

where $\{{}^i_{m\ k}\}$ is called the *Christoffel symbol* (of the second kind), and is a function of the metric and conjugate tensors as follows:

$$
\left\{\begin{matrix} i \\ k\ j \end{matrix}\right\} = \frac{1}{2}\, g^{im}\left(\frac{\partial g_{km}}{\partial z^j} + \frac{\partial g_{jm}}{\partial z^k} - \frac{\partial g_{kj}}{\partial z^m}\right) \tag{6.7-6}
$$

Note the presence of a repeated (dummy) index in each term on the right of Eq. (6.7-6).

The quantity in square brackets in Eq. (6.7-5) is seen to transform as a second-order mixed tensor, and hence does represent a spatial derivative or gradient operator in a form which is independent of any specific coordinate system. It is called the *covariant derivative*, and is defined as follows:

$$
A^i_{,j} = \frac{\partial A^i}{\partial z^j} + \left\{\begin{matrix} i \\ m\ j \end{matrix}\right\} A^m \tag{6.7-7}
$$

For a covariant vector, the equivalent operation is:

$$
A_{i,j} = \frac{\partial A_i}{\partial z^j} - \left\{\begin{matrix} m \\ i\ j \end{matrix}\right\} A_m \tag{6.7-8}
$$

For a second-order tensor, the covariant derivative is given by:

$$A_{ij,k} = \frac{\partial A_{ij}}{\partial z^k} - \left\{ \begin{array}{c} m \\ i\ k \end{array} \right\} A_{mj} - \left\{ \begin{array}{c} m \\ j\ k \end{array} \right\} A_{im} \qquad (6.7\text{-}9)$$

$$A^{ij}_{\ ,k} = \frac{\partial A^{ij}}{\partial z^k} + \left\{ \begin{array}{c} i \\ k\ m \end{array} \right\} A^{mj} + \left\{ \begin{array}{c} j \\ k\ m \end{array} \right\} A^{im} \qquad (6.7\text{-}10)$$

$$A^i_{\ j,k} = \frac{\partial A^i_{\ j}}{\partial z^k} + \left\{ \begin{array}{c} i \\ k\ m \end{array} \right\} A^m_{\ j} - \left\{ \begin{array}{c} m \\ j\ k \end{array} \right\} A^i_{\ m} \qquad (6.7\text{-}11)$$

For any order tensor, the covariant derivative may be written:

$$A^{ij\cdots}_{\cdots rs.,P} = \frac{\partial A^{ij\cdots}_{\cdots rs.}}{\partial z^P} + \sum{}' \left\{ \begin{array}{c} i \\ m\ P \end{array} \right\} A^{mj\cdots}_{\cdots rs.} - \sum \left\{ \begin{array}{c} m \\ r\ P \end{array} \right\} A^{ij\cdots}_{\cdots ms.} \qquad (6.7\text{-}12)$$

Sum on contra-   Sum on covariant
variant indices   indices

The summation signs represent a sum of terms, one for each contra-variant index (Σ') and each covariant index (Σ).

For Cartesian coordinates (for which $g_{ij} \equiv \delta_{ij} = g^{ij}$), all components of the metric tensor are constants. Therefore, from Eq. (6.7-6), it is evident that all the Christoffel symbols are identically zero, thus the covariant derivative reduces to the partial derivative for Cartesian tensor components.

The covariant derivative of a tensor quantity is identical to the *gradient* of the tensor, while the contracted covariant derivative is the same as the *divergence* of the tensor.

6.7.2. Christoffel Symbols

The Christoffel symbols are defined by Eq. (6.7-6) for any coordinate system. It is evident that they are symmetric with respect to the two lower indices, that is,

$$\begin{Bmatrix} i \\ j\,k \end{Bmatrix} = \begin{Bmatrix} i \\ k\,j \end{Bmatrix} \tag{6.7-13}$$

The transformation relations for the Christoffel symbols are:

$$\begin{Bmatrix} i \\ j\,k \end{Bmatrix} = \frac{\partial z^i}{\partial \bar{z}^r} \frac{\partial \bar{z}^s}{\partial z^j} \frac{\partial \bar{z}^t}{\partial z^k} \begin{Bmatrix} \bar{r} \\ s\,t \end{Bmatrix} + \frac{\partial z^i}{\partial \bar{z}^r} \frac{\partial^2 \bar{z}^r}{\partial z^j \partial z^k} \tag{6.7-14}$$

which shows that they are not tensors, since they do not follow the transformation rules for tensor components.

For orthogonal coordinates, the nonzero Christoffel symbols may be expressed in simple form in terms of either the metric tensor components or the coordinate scale factors, as follows (no summation is to be implied in the following expressions):

$$\begin{Bmatrix} i \\ j\,k \end{Bmatrix} = 0 \qquad\qquad \text{for } i \neq j \neq k \tag{6.7-15}$$

$$\begin{Bmatrix} i \\ i\,i \end{Bmatrix} = \frac{1}{2g_{ii}} \frac{\partial g_{ii}}{\partial z^i} = \frac{1}{h_i} \frac{\partial h_i}{\partial z^i} \qquad \text{for } i = j = k \tag{6.7-16}$$

$$\begin{Bmatrix} i \\ j\,j \end{Bmatrix} = -\frac{1}{2g_{ii}} \frac{\partial g_{jj}}{\partial z^i} = -\frac{h_j}{h^2_i} \frac{\partial h_j}{\partial z^i} \qquad \text{for } j = k \neq i \tag{6.7-17}$$

$$\begin{Bmatrix} i \\ j\,i \end{Bmatrix} = \begin{Bmatrix} i \\ i\,j \end{Bmatrix} = \frac{1}{2g_{ii}} \frac{\partial g_{ii}}{\partial z^j} = \frac{1}{h_i} \frac{\partial h_i}{\partial z^j} \qquad \text{for } i = k \neq j \tag{6.7-18}$$

(Orthogonal coordinates)

The nonzero Christoffel symbols and other properties of a number of specific orthogonal coordinate systems are given in Appendix C.

-- 0 --

Example 6.8 Determine the physical components of the $\Delta_{r\theta}$ component of the rate of strain tensor in cylindrical coordinates from the general expression for Δ_{ij}

Solution. The general expression for Δ_{ij} is

$$\Delta_{ij} = v_{i,j} + v_{j,i}$$

so that

$$\Delta_{r\theta} = v_{r,\theta} + v_{\theta,r}$$

which requires the covariant derivatives of the covariant velocity components, as given by Eq. (6.7-8). For these we need the Christoffel symbols, which are functions of the scale factors, h_i. For cylindrical coordinates:

$$h_r = 1 \qquad h_\theta = r \qquad h_z = 1$$

from which, by Eqs. (6.7-15) through (6.7-18), it is easy to show that the only nonzero Christoffel symbols are

$$\left\{ \begin{matrix} \theta \\ \theta \ r \end{matrix} \right\} = \left\{ \begin{matrix} \theta \\ r \ \theta \end{matrix} \right\} = \frac{1}{r} \qquad\qquad \left\{ \begin{matrix} r \\ \theta \ \theta \end{matrix} \right\} = -r$$

(The Christoffel symbols for various coordinate systems are also tabulated in Appendix C.) Thus we have:

$$v_{r,\theta} = \frac{\partial v_r}{\partial \theta} - \left\{ \begin{matrix} r \\ r \ \theta \end{matrix} \right\}^{\nearrow 0} v_r - \left\{ \begin{matrix} \theta \\ r \ \theta \end{matrix} \right\} v_\theta - \left\{ \begin{matrix} z \\ r \ \theta \end{matrix} \right\}^{\nearrow 0} v_z$$

$$= \frac{\partial v_r}{\partial \theta} - \frac{v_\theta}{r}$$

$$v_{\theta,r} = \frac{\partial v_\theta}{\partial r} - \left\{\begin{matrix} r \\ \theta\ r \end{matrix}\right\}^{0} v_r - \left\{\begin{matrix} \theta \\ \theta\ r \end{matrix}\right\} v_\theta - \left\{\begin{matrix} z \\ \theta\ r \end{matrix}\right\}^{0} v_z$$

$$= \frac{\partial v_\theta}{\partial r} - \frac{v_\theta}{r}$$

so that

$$\Delta_{r\theta} = \frac{\partial v_r}{\partial \theta} + \frac{\partial v}{\partial r} - 2\frac{v_\theta}{r}$$

However, this result is in terms of the covariant tensor components, and we desire the result in terms of physical components. From Eq. (6.6-18), these are:

$$v_r = v(r)\sqrt{g_{rr}} = v(r) \qquad v_\theta = v(\theta)\sqrt{g_{\theta\theta}} = rv(\theta)$$

and from Eq. (6.6-19):

$$\Delta_{r\theta} = \sqrt{g_{rr}g_{\theta\theta}}\,\Delta(r\theta) = r\,\Delta(r\theta)$$

With these substitutions, we have:

$$\Delta_{r\theta} = \frac{\partial v(r)}{\partial \theta} + \frac{\partial rv(\theta)}{\partial r} - 2v(\theta)$$

or

$$\Delta(r\theta) = \frac{1}{r}\left[\frac{\partial v(r)}{\partial \theta} + r\frac{\partial v(\theta)}{\partial r} - v(\theta)\right] = \frac{1}{r}\left[\frac{\partial v(r)}{\partial \theta} + r\frac{\partial v(\theta)/r}{\partial r}\right]$$

in agreement with Table 3.2,2.

The physical components of the rate of strain tensor, in terms of physical velocity components, are tabulated in Appendix D for several coordinate systems

---------------------------------- 0 ----------------------------------

6.8.   TENSOR FORMS OF VECTOR NOTATION

The classical, or Gibbs, vector notation employs boldface or some other symbolic notation for vector quantities, and a variety of symbols representing the various vector operations. (We have used arrows in this volume.) This system is straightforward for first-order tensor (vector) quantities, but becomes quite cumbersome and often vague when extension to higher order tensors is required.

The tensorial index notation, on the other hand, is perfectly general and consistent for all orders of tensor quantities. It is thus very versatile, as well as being graphically descriptive of the tensorial nature and order of the terms involved, with the total number of components associated with a given term indicated explicitly. In addition, virtually all operations involving tensors can be described by utilizing the covariant derivative operator.

In this section, we present the tensor forms of some of the more common vector relations and operations with the equivalent Gibbs notation (Table 6.1).

TABLE 6.1

Tensor Equivalent of Some Common Vector Operations

Operation	Gibbs notation	Tensor notation
I. Operations Involving First-Order Tensors (Vectors)		
1. Scalar or dot product	$\vec{A} \cdot \vec{B}$	$A_i B^i = A^i B_i = g_{ij} A^i B^j$ $= g^{ij} A_i B_j$
2. Vector or cross product	$\vec{C} = \vec{A} \times \vec{B}$	$C^i = \varepsilon^{ijk} A_j B_k$ $C_i = \varepsilon_{ijk} A^j B^k$

TABLE 6.1 (continued)

Operation	Gibbs notation	Tensor notation
3. Vector triple product	$\vec{D} = \vec{A} \times (\vec{B} \times \vec{C})$	$D_i = (B_i A^m C_m - C_i A^m B_m)$ $D^i = (B^i A^m C_m - C^i A^m B_m)$ and other forms derived by raising or lowering indices
4. Scalar triple product	$\vec{A} \cdot (\vec{B} \times \vec{C})$	$\varepsilon_{ijk} A^i B^j C^k$ $= \varepsilon^{ijk} A_i B_j C_k$, etc.
5. Gradient of a scalar	$\nabla C = \vec{A}$	$C,_i = A_i$ $g^{ij} C,_j = A^i$
6. Gradient of a vector	$\nabla \vec{A}$	$A_{i,j},\ A^i,_j$ and other forms derived by raising or lowering indices
7. Divergence of a vector	$\nabla \cdot \vec{A}$	$A^i,_i,\ g^{ij} A_{j,i}$, etc.
8. Curl (rotation) of a vector	$\nabla \times \vec{A} = \vec{B}$	$\varepsilon^{ijk} A_{k,j} = B^i$ $g_{i\ell} \varepsilon^{\ell jk} A_{k,j} = B_i$, etc.

TABLE 6.1 (continued)

Operation	Gibbs notation	Tensor notation
9. Laplacian of a scalar	$\nabla^2 C$	$g^{ij}C,_{ij} = (g^{ij}C,_j),_i$
10. Laplacian of a vector	$\nabla^2 \vec{A} = \vec{B}$	$A^j,_{ij} = B_i,$
		$g^{ik}A^j,_{kj} = B^i$, etc.

II. Operations Involving Second-Order Tensors

1.	Dot product with a vector	$\vec{V} \cdot \vec{\vec{T}} = \vec{U}$	$U_k = V^j T_{jk} = V_j T^j{}_k$
		$(\vec{V} \cdot \vec{\vec{T}} = \vec{\vec{T}} \cdot \vec{V}$ <u>only</u>	$U_k = V^j T_j{}^k = V_j T^{jk}$
		if $\vec{\vec{T}}$ is symmetric)	
2.	Cross product with a vector	(a) $\vec{\vec{S}} = \vec{V} \times \vec{\vec{T}}$	$S_{ij} = \varepsilon_{ik\ell} V^k T^\ell{}_j$
			$S^{ij} = \varepsilon^{ik\ell} V_k T_\ell{}^j$, etc.
		(b) $\vec{\vec{U}} = \vec{\vec{T}} \times \vec{V}$	$U_{ij} = \varepsilon_{ik\ell} T^k{}_j V^\ell$
		(Note: $\vec{\vec{S}} \neq \vec{\vec{U}}$)	$U^{ij} = \varepsilon^{ik\ell} T_k{}^j V_\ell$, etc.
3.	Scalar, or double dot product	$S : T = T : S$	$S^{ij}T_{ij} = S_{ij}T^{ij} = S^i{}_j T_i{}^j$

TABLE 6.1 (continued)

Operation	Gibbs notation	Tensor notation
4. Divergence of a dyad	$\nabla \cdot \vec{\vec{T}} = \vec{V}$	$T_{k,j}^{\ j} = V_k$
		$T^{kj}_{\ ,j} = V^k$
		$g^{j\ell} T_{k\ell,j} = V_k$, etc.
5. Gradient of a dyad	$\vec{\vec{\nabla T}}$	$T^{ij}_{\ ,k}, \ T^i_{\ j,k}$
		$T_{ij,k}$, etc.

Note:

$$\varepsilon_{ijk} = \sqrt{g} \, e_{ijk} \qquad \varepsilon^{ijk} = \frac{e^{ijk}}{\sqrt{g}}$$

where $e_{ijk} = e^{ijk}$ = permutation symbol, and $g = \left| g_{ij} \right| = \det\left(g_{ij}\right)$.

6.9. SOME SPECIFIC PROPERTIES
OF SECOND-ORDER TENSORS

Since the basic quantities with which we are primarily concerned are second-order tensors (e.g., stress, strain, strain rate, etc.), it is pertinent at this point to discuss some specific properties of these quantities which are of particular concern to us.

As pointed out in Chap. 1, any second-order tensor can be expressed as the sum of a symmetric tensor and an antisymmetric tensor:

$$A_{ij} = \frac{1}{2}\left(A_{ij} + A_{ji}\right) + \frac{1}{2}\left(A_{ij} - A_{ji}\right) = B_{ij} + C_{ij} \qquad (6.9\text{-}1)$$

Because of its symmetry, only six of the nine total components of the symmetric tensor are independent. Also, since the diagonal elements of the antisymmetric tensor are identically zero, only three of its nine total components are independent.

We will consider some specific properties of both the symmetric and antisymmetric tensors.

6.9.1. Invariants

If T^i_j represents any symmetric second-order tensor, an orthogonal coordinate system (defined by three unit vectors, n^i) can always be found such that the only nonzero components of T^i_j in this system are the three normal (diagonal) components. These coordinates are referred to as the principle axes.

The condition for this statement to be true is that the vector formed by the inner product of T^i_j and the n^j must be parallel to n^j. That is,

$$T^i_j n^j = \lambda n^i \qquad (6.9\text{-}2)$$

where λ is a scalar constant, or scale factor. Equation (6.9-2) can be rearranged to

$$(T^i_j - \lambda \delta^i_j) n^j = 0 \qquad (6.9\text{-}3)$$

This expression represents three equations for the three vector components n^j. For the solution of these equations to yield other than the trivial solution $n^j = 0$, a necessary condition requires the vanishing of the determinant of the coefficients of the n^j. That is,

$$|T^i_j - \lambda \delta^i_j| = 0 \qquad (6.9\text{-}4)$$

or

$$
\begin{vmatrix}
(T^1_{\ 1} - \lambda) & T^1_{\ 2} & T^1_{\ 3} \\
T^2_{\ 1} & (T^2_{\ 2} - \lambda) & T^2_{\ 3} \\
T^3_{\ 1} & T^3_{\ 2} & (T^3_{\ 3} - \lambda)
\end{vmatrix} = 0
\tag{6.9-5}
$$

Expansion of the determinant yields the following cubic equation for λ, which is called the *characteristic equation* of the tensor $T^i_{\ j}$:

$$
\lambda^3 - I\lambda^2 + II\lambda - III = 0
\tag{6.9-6}
$$

where

$$
I = T^i_{\ i} = tr(T^i_{\ j}) = T^1_{\ 1} + T^2_{\ 2} + T^3_{\ 3}
\tag{6.9-7}
$$

$$
II = \begin{vmatrix} T^2_{\ 2} & T^2_{\ 3} \\ T^3_{\ 2} & T^3_{\ 3} \end{vmatrix} + \begin{vmatrix} T^1_{\ 1} & T^1_{\ 3} \\ T^3_{\ 1} & T^3_{\ 3} \end{vmatrix} + \begin{vmatrix} T^1_{\ 1} & T^1_{\ 2} \\ T^2_{\ 1} & T^2_{\ 2} \end{vmatrix}
\tag{6.9-8}
$$

$$
= \frac{1}{2} (T^i_{\ i} T^j_{\ j} - T^i_{\ j} T^j_{\ i}) = \frac{1}{2} (I^2 - T^i_{\ j} T^j_{\ i})
$$

$$
III = T^i_{\ j} = \det (T^i_{\ j}) = e_{ijk} T^i_{\ 1} T^j_{\ 2} T^k_{\ 3}
\tag{6.9-9}
$$

Note that while the development thus far has been presented in terms of mixed tensor components, equivalent expressions in terms of co-variant or contravarient components could have been used as well. However, Eqs. (6.9-7), (6.9-8) and (6.9-9) represent scalar quantities, which can be obtained only by contraction of one covariant and one contravarient index, so that mixed components are required in such expressions. The solution of Eq. (6.9-6) thus yields three values for the scalar (invariant) λ. Since these scalars are functions only of the quantities I, II, and III, these must also be scalars and are therefore independent of the frame of reference. They are known as the *scalar invariants* (first, second, and third, respectively) of the tensor $T^i{}_j$, and represent specific combinations of the components of $T^i{}_j$ which are scalars and hence independent of the coordinate system chosen to describe the components.

The three values of λ from the solution of Eq. (6.9-6), together with Eq. (6.9-2) or (6.9-3), they define the three unit vectors, n^j, which constitute the three principle axes. It can be shown that these three axes are mutually perpendicular (orthogonal), and serve to define a Cartesian coordinate system. Tensor components referred to the coordinate frame defined by the principle axes are diagonal, that is, all off-diagonal components are zero.

In order to determine the principle axes, and the tensor components referred to these axes, the procedure is as follows. For given values of the scalar components of a tensor T_{ij} or $(T^i{}_j$, etc.) relative to a specific coordinate system, the three roots of Eq. (6.9-6) may be determined, which correspond to three values of λ, i.e., $(\lambda_{(1)}, \lambda_{(2)}, \lambda_{(3)})$. These roots may be inserted, in turn, into the three component equations (6.9-3), i.e.,

$$(T^1{}_1 - \lambda)n^1 + T^1{}_2 n^2 + T^1{}_3 n^3 = 0 \qquad\qquad (6.9\text{-}10)$$

$$T^2{}_1 n^1 + (T^2{}_2 - \lambda)n^2 + T^2{}_3 n^3 = 0 \qquad\qquad (6.9\text{-}11)$$

$$T^3{}_1 n^1 + T^3{}_2 n^2 + (T^3{}_3 - \lambda)n^3 = 0 \qquad\qquad (6.9\text{-}12)$$

which, in turn, may be solved for the vector components n^1, n^2, n^3 for each value of λ. Since these three equations are not mutually independent, however, they define only two of the three values of n^i, in the form, say, (n^1/n^3) and (n^2/n^3) (or any two ratios). Since n^i is a unit Cartesian vector, the remaining relation for the third component is

$$(n^1)^2 + (n^2)^2 + (n^3)^2 = 1 \qquad\qquad (6.9\text{-}12a)$$

This process is repeated for each of the three values of λ successively in Eqs. (6.9-10) to (6.9-12). Hence, each value of λ determines a set of three components (n^1, n^2, n^3), which are the components of a unit vector relative to the original coordinate axes. The three unit vectors thus determined may be shown to be orthogonal, and define the Cartesian principle axes. Note that the vector components (n^1, n^2, n^3) are identical to the direction cosines of one of the base vectors of the principle axes. They also determine the transformation relations between the original axes (z^j) and the principle axes (x^j):

$$\vec{n}^j = \frac{\partial z^j}{\partial x^i} \vec{i}^i \tag{6.9-13}$$

Hence the nine scalar components of the three base vectors $\vec{n}^j$ are identical to the nine components of $\partial z^j / \partial x^i$ which define the coordinate transformation.

This transformation also determines the components of the tensor $T^i{}_j$ relative to the principle axes, $T^{i'}{}_j$:

$$T^{i'}{}_j = \frac{\partial x^i}{\partial z^k} \frac{\partial z^\ell}{\partial x^j} T^k{}_\ell \tag{6.9-14}$$

However, from Eq. (6.9-2) we see that

$$T^k{}_\ell n^\ell = \lambda n^k \tag{6.9-15}$$

or, using Eq. (6.9-13):

$$T^k \frac{\partial z^\ell}{\partial x^j} = \lambda_{(j)} \frac{\partial z^k}{\partial x^j} \tag{6.9-16}$$

where no summation is to be implied on the j index. Substituting this into Eq. (6.9-14):

$$T^{i'}_{j} = \frac{\partial x^i}{\partial z^k} \lambda_{(j)} \frac{\partial z^k}{\partial x^j} = \lambda_{(j)} \delta^i_j \tag{6.9-17}$$

That is,

$$T^{1'}_{1} = \lambda_{(1)} \qquad T^{2'}_{2} = \lambda_{(2)} \qquad T^{3'}_{3} = \lambda_{(3)} \tag{6.9-18}$$

all others = 0. Hence

$$T^{i'}_{j} = \begin{bmatrix} \lambda_{(1)} & 0 & 0 \\ 0 & \lambda_{(2)} & 0 \\ 0 & 0 & \lambda_{(3)} \end{bmatrix} \tag{6.9-19}$$

That is, the diagonal (nonzero) components of the tensor referred to the principle axes are identical to the three roots of Eq. (6.9-6).

Note that even though this development has been in terms of mixed tensor notation, it is just as valid for equivalent covariant or contravarient forms.

One of the virtues of a principle coordinate system is that certain tensor relationships can be proven quite easily with reference to this system. Then since (by their inherent nature) tensor relations which are valid in one coordinate system are valid in any other coordinate system, the generalization to any system follows directly.

─────────────────────────────── 0 ───────────────────────────────

Example 6.9 Find the principle axes for the tensor which has the following components relative to a given coordinate system

$$T_{ij} = \begin{bmatrix} 3 & 0 & 1 \\ 0 & 3 & -2 \\ 1 & -2 & 7 \end{bmatrix}$$

and determine the values of the components of this tensor relative to the principle axes.

Solution. First we must determine the three values of λ from Eq. (6.9-6), which results from the expansion of the determinant (6.9-5):

$$\begin{vmatrix} (3-\lambda) & 0 & 1 \\ 0 & (3-\lambda) & -2 \\ 1 & -2 & (7-\lambda) \end{vmatrix} = (3-\lambda)[(3-\lambda)(7-\lambda)-4] + \lambda - 3 = 0$$

The roots of this equation are:

$$\lambda_{(1)} = 3 \qquad \lambda_{(2)} = 8 \qquad \lambda_{(3)} = 2$$

The principle axis base vectors (n^i) are now determined from Eqs. (6.9-10) to (6.9-13):

$$(3-\lambda)n^1 + n^3 = 0$$

$$(3-\lambda)n^2 - 2n^3 = 0$$

$$n^1 - 2n^2 + (7-\lambda)n^3 = 0$$

$$(n^1)^2 + (n^2)^2 + (n^3)^2 = 0$$

For $\lambda = \lambda_{(1)} = 3$:

$$\left.\begin{array}{l} n^3 = 0 \\[2mm] n^1 = 2n^2 \\[2mm] (n^1)^2 + (n^2)^2 = 1 \end{array}\right\} \qquad n^1 = \frac{2}{\sqrt{5}} , \quad n^2 = \frac{1}{\sqrt{5}}$$

$$\therefore \ \vec{n}_{(1)} = \left[\frac{2}{\sqrt{5}} , \ \frac{1}{\sqrt{5}} , \ 0 \right]$$

For $\lambda = \lambda_{(2)} = 8$:

$$-5n^1 + n^3 = 0$$

$$-5n^2 - 2n^3 = 0$$

$$n^1 - 2n^2 - n^3 = 0$$

$$(n^1)^2 + (n^2)^2 + (n^3)^2 = 1$$

$$n^1 = \frac{1}{\sqrt{30}} \,, \quad n^2 = \frac{-2}{\sqrt{30}}$$

$$n^3 = \frac{5}{\sqrt{30}}$$

$$\therefore \; \vec{n}_{(2)} = \left(\frac{1}{\sqrt{30}} \,, \; \frac{-2}{\sqrt{30}} \,, \; \frac{5}{\sqrt{30}} \right)$$

For $\lambda = \lambda_{(3)} = 2$:

$$n^1 + n^3 = 0$$

$$n^2 - 2n^3 = 0$$

$$n^1 - 2n^2 + 5n^3 = 0$$

$$(n^1)^2 + (n^2)^2 + (n^3)^2 = 0$$

$$n^1 = \frac{-1}{\sqrt{6}} \,, \quad n^2 = \frac{2}{\sqrt{6}}$$

$$n^3 = \frac{1}{\sqrt{6}}$$

$$\therefore \; \vec{n}_{(3)} = \left(\frac{-1}{\sqrt{6}} \,, \; \frac{2}{\sqrt{6}} \,, \; \frac{1}{\sqrt{6}} \right)$$

The components of the resulting base vectors $\vec{n}_{(1)}, \vec{n}_{(2)}, \vec{n}_{(3)}$ are relative to the axes to which the original tensor components are referred. The magnitudes of the tensor components relative to the principle axes are:

$$T'_{ij} = \begin{bmatrix} \lambda_{(1)} & 0 & 0 \\ 0 & \lambda_{(2)} & 0 \\ 0 & 0 & \lambda_{(3)} \end{bmatrix} = \begin{bmatrix} 3 & 0 & 0 \\ 0 & 8 & 0 \\ 0 & 0 & 2 \end{bmatrix}$$

---------------------------------- 0 ----------------------------------

6.9.2. Dual Vector of Antisymmetric Tensor

As previously noted, an antisymmetric tensor has components of the form

$$W_{ij} = \begin{bmatrix} 0 & W_{12} & W_{13} \\ -W_{12} & 0 & W_{23} \\ -W_{13} & -W_{23} & 0 \end{bmatrix} \qquad (6.9\text{-}20)$$

so that only three of the nine components are independent. These same three components may serve to define a vector, w^i, which is known as the dual vector of the antisymmetric tensor, W_{ij}. The relation between the components of w_i and W_{ij} is:

$$w^i = \varepsilon^{ijk} W_{jk} \qquad (6.9\text{-}21)$$

where ε^{ijk} is the general permutation symbol. The inverse of Eq. (6.9-21) gives the components of W_{jk} in terms of those of w_i:

$$W_{jk} = \frac{1}{2} \varepsilon_{ijk} w^i \qquad (6.9\text{-}22)$$

If W_{jk} is taken to be the vorticity tensor:

$$\Omega_{ij} = v_{j,i} - v_{i,j} \qquad (6.9\text{-}23)$$

the dual vector of this tensor is:

$$w^i = 2[(v_{3,2} - v_{2,3}), (v_{1,3} - v_{3,1}), (v_{2,1} - v_{1,2})] \qquad (6.9\text{-}24)$$

These components are seen to be four times the components of the angular velocity tensor, $\vec{\omega}$:

$$\vec{\omega} = \frac{1}{2} \operatorname{curl} \vec{v} = \frac{1}{2} \nabla \times \vec{v} \qquad (6.9\text{-}25)$$

or

$$\omega^i = \frac{1}{2} \varepsilon^{ijk} v_{k,j} \qquad (6.9\text{-}26)$$

Thus, if the angular velocity vector is represented by ω^i, its components are related to those of the vorticity tensor by

$$\omega^i = \frac{1}{4} w^i = \frac{1}{4} \varepsilon^{ijk} \Omega_{jk} \qquad\qquad (6.9\text{-}27)$$

The inverse of this gives the vorticity tensor components in terms of the angular velocity vector components:

$$\Omega_{ij} = 2\varepsilon_{kji} \omega^k \qquad\qquad (6.9\text{-}28)$$

That is, the vorticity tensor Ω_{ij} provides a direct measure of the angular velocity, or rigid body rotation, at a point in any system.

6.9.3. Generalized Unit Tensor

We have had several occasions to employ a unit tensor in various tensor expressions and equations. For example, we have seen that the total stress tensor can be expressed as the sum of an isotropic (pressure) component and an anisotropic (shear) component:

$$\sigma_{ij} = -P\delta_{ij} + \tau_{ij} \qquad\qquad (6.9\text{-}29)$$

Since the pressure (P) is a scalar which contributes to the diagonal (normal) stress components only, it must be multiplied by the unit isotropic tensor δ_{ij} before it can be combined with other second-order tensor quantities. The notation for the unit tensor, δ_{ij}, implies identity with the Kronecker delta, and indeed this is so if all components are referred to Cartesian coordinates. Of course, δ_{ij} is also identical to the metric tensor, g_{ij}, for Cartesian coordinates.

In fact, in the process of defining the metric tensor in Sec. 6.4, the defining equation, Eq. (6.4-16), is also the transformation relation for the unit tensor or Kronecker delta:

$$g_{ij} = \frac{\partial x^k}{\partial z^i} \frac{\partial x^\ell}{\partial z^j} \delta_{k\ell} \qquad\qquad (6.9\text{-}30)$$

It follows, therefore, that the general unit tensor which is applicable in any coordinate system is identical to the metric tensor.

For contravariant forms, the corresponding unit tensor is, of course, the conjugate tensor.

The reader should confirm that the use of the metric tensor as the unit tensor in Eq. (6.9-29) ensures that P is always the physical pressure.

6.9.4. Generalized Permutation Symbol and Kronecker Delta

The concepts of the permutation symbol and Kronecker delta can be generalized to any number of indices.

The generalized permutation symbol, ($e^{ijk\cdots}$) is a special case of a general antisymmetric (or skew symmetric) tensor, and is defined to have the following properties:

(1) $e^{ijk}\cdots$ (or $e_{ijk\cdots}$) $\quad = 0$ if any two indices are equal

(2) $e^{ijk\cdots}$ (or $e_{ijk\cdots}$) $\quad = 1$ if the order of the indices is an *even* permutation of $1,2,3\ldots$

(3) $e^{ijk\cdots}$ (or $e_{ijk\cdots}$) $\quad = -1$ if the subscripts are an *odd* permutation of $1,2,3\ldots$

The generalized Kronecker delta ($\delta^{ijk\cdots}_{\alpha\beta\gamma\cdots}$) is closely related to the generalized permutation symbol, except that it has both subscripts and superscripts (the same number of each). It has the following properties:

(1) $\delta^{ij\cdots}_{\alpha\beta\cdots}$ $\quad = 0$ if any two subscripts *or* any two superscripts are equal, *or* if the set of subscripts ($\alpha,\beta\ldots$) is not the same set of numbers as the superscripts ($i,j\ldots$)

(2) $\delta^{ij\cdots}_{\alpha\beta\cdots}$ $\quad = 1$ if the subscripts are an *even* permutation of the superscripts

(3) $\delta^{ij\cdots}_{\alpha\beta\cdots}$ $\quad = -1$ if the subscripts are an *odd* permutation of the superscripts

Some useful specific properties of these quantities follow from these definitions:

$$e^{ijk}e_{\alpha\beta\delta} = \delta^{ijk}_{\alpha\beta\delta} \qquad\qquad (6.9\text{-}31)$$

$$e^{ijk} = \delta^{ijk}_{123} \qquad\qquad (6.9\text{-}32)$$

$$e_{ijk} = \delta^{123}_{ijk} \qquad\qquad (6.9\text{-}33)$$

Also, if $A_{ij}\ldots$ is a symmetric tensor of any order:

$$\delta^{ij\ldots}_{\alpha\beta\ldots}A_{ij\ldots} = 0 \qquad\qquad (6.9\text{-}34)$$

and equivalently for the contravariant case:

$$\delta^{\alpha\beta\ldots}_{ij\ldots}A^{ij\ldots} = 0 \qquad\qquad (6.9\text{-}35)$$

———————————————————— 0 ————————————————————

Example 6.10   Write the vector product

$$\vec{A} \times (\vec{B} \times \vec{C})$$

in index notation, and simplify the result to obtain the identity:

$$\vec{A} \times (\vec{B} \times \vec{C}) = (\vec{A} \cdot \vec{C})\vec{B} - (\vec{A} \cdot \vec{B})\vec{C}$$

Solution.   From Table 6.1, I, 2:

$$\vec{B} \times \vec{C} = \vec{D} \qquad \text{or} \qquad D^i = \varepsilon^{ijk}B_j C_k$$

Now we may write:

$$\vec{A} \times (\vec{B} \times \vec{C}) = \vec{A} \times \vec{D} = \vec{E}$$

From the covariant form of the above:

$$E_\ell = \varepsilon_{\ell mi} A^m D^i = \varepsilon_{\ell mi} \varepsilon^{ijk} A^m B_j C_k$$

Now

$$\varepsilon_{\ell mi} \varepsilon^{ijk} = \delta_{\ell m}^{\ jk} = \delta_\ell^{\ j} \delta_m^{\ k} - \delta_\ell^{\ k} \delta_m^{\ j}$$

So that

$$E_\ell = A^m B_j C_k \delta_\ell^{\ j} \delta_m^{\ k} - A^m B_j C_k \delta_\ell^{\ k} \delta_m^{\ j} = A^m B_\ell C_m - A^m B_m C_\ell$$

or

$$E_\ell = B_\ell A^m C_m - A^m B_m C_\ell$$

Now

$$A^m C_m = \vec{A} \cdot \vec{C} \qquad A^m B_m = \vec{A} \cdot \vec{B}$$

So that

$$\vec{E} = \vec{A} \times (\vec{B} \times \vec{C}) = \vec{B}(\vec{A} \cdot \vec{C}) - (\vec{A} \cdot \vec{B})\vec{C}$$

as was to be shown.

———————————————— 0 ————————————————

PROBLEMS

6-1. Show that the following vectors are perpendicular utilizing
index notation for vector components and operations:

(a) $\left\{ \begin{array}{l} \vec{A} = \vec{i}_1 + 4\vec{i}_2 + 3\vec{i}_3 \\ \\ \vec{B} = 4\vec{i}_1 + 2\vec{i}_2 + 4\vec{i}_3 \end{array} \right\}$ Cartesian coordinates

(b) $\begin{cases} \vec{A} = r \cos \theta \vec{e}_r + \sin \theta \vec{e}_\theta + r \vec{e}_z \\ \\ \vec{B} = r \cos \theta \vec{e}_r + \sin \theta \vec{e}_\theta - r \vec{e}_z \end{cases}$ Cylindrical coordinates

6-2. Prove that the following vectors are parallel utilizing index notation for vector components and operations:

$$\vec{A} = \frac{\sin 2\theta}{r^2} \vec{e}_r + \frac{2 \sin \theta}{r^2} \vec{e}_\theta$$

$$\vec{B} = r \cos \theta \vec{e}_r + r \vec{e}_\theta$$

6-3. Show that $(\vec{A} - \vec{B}) \times (\vec{A} + \vec{B}) = 2\vec{A} \times \vec{B}$ using index notation.

6-4. Show that:

$$\vec{A} \cdot (\vec{B} \times \vec{C}) = \vec{B} \cdot (\vec{C} \times \vec{A}) = \vec{C} \cdot (\vec{A} \times \vec{B})$$

$$= -\vec{C} \cdot (\vec{B} \times \vec{A}) = -\vec{A} \cdot (\vec{C} \times \vec{B})$$

$$= -\vec{B} \cdot (\vec{A} \times \vec{C})$$

using index notation.

6-5. Show that $\vec{A} \times (\vec{B} \times \vec{C}) = (\vec{A} \cdot \vec{C})\vec{B} - (\vec{A} \cdot \vec{B})\vec{C}$ by using index notation for the vectors and vector operations.

6-6. Show that the determinant of the matrix of the components of the second-order tensor A_{ij} can be written:

$$\left| A_{ij} \right| = \begin{vmatrix} A_{11} & A_{12} & A_{13} \\ A_{21} & A_{22} & A_{23} \\ A_{31} & A_{32} & A_{33} \end{vmatrix} = e^{ijk} A_{i1} A_{j2} A_{k3}$$

or

$$\left| A_i^{\ j} \right| = e^{ijk} A_i^{\ 1} A_j^{\ 2} A_k^{\ 3} = e_{ijk} A_1^{\ i} A_2^{\ j} A_3^{\ k}$$

6-7. Show that an antisymmetric third order tensor can be written:

$$A_{ijk} = A_{123}e_{ijk}$$

6-8. Show that $\delta_j{}^i \delta_k{}^j = \delta_k{}^i$ and that $\delta_i{}^i = 3$.

6-9. Show that $e_{ijk}e^{rst} = \delta_{ijk}{}^{rst}$

6-10. Find the cross product of $\vec{A}$ and $\vec{B}$ by application of Eq. (6.3-52), where:

(a) $\vec{A} = \vec{i}_1 - 2\vec{i}_2 + 3\vec{i}_3$

     $\vec{B} = 2\vec{i}_1 - 4\vec{i}_2 + 5\vec{i}_3$

(b) $\vec{A} = 2\vec{i}_2 + 3\vec{i}_3$

     $\vec{B} = \vec{i}_1$

(c) $\vec{A} = 4\vec{i}_1 + 3\vec{i}_2 + 2\vec{i}_3$

     $\vec{B} = \vec{i}_1 - \vec{i}_2 + \vec{i}_3$

6-11. Find the scalar product of $\vec{A}$ and $\vec{B}$, where:

(a) $\begin{cases} \vec{A} = 4\vec{i}_1 + 4\vec{i}_2 + 3\vec{i}_3 \\ \\ \vec{B} = 3\vec{i}_1 + 2\vec{i}_2 - 2\vec{i}_3 \end{cases}$

(b) $\begin{cases} \vec{A} = \vec{i}_1 \\ \\ \vec{B} = 2\vec{i}_2 + 3\vec{i}_3 \end{cases}$

(c) $\begin{cases} \vec{A} = \vec{i}_1 - 2\vec{i}_2 - \vec{i}_3 \\ \\ \vec{B} = \vec{i}_1 + 2\vec{i}_2 - 3\vec{i}_3 \end{cases}$

6-12.   If $V = \vec{e}_1 \cdot (\vec{e}_2 \times \vec{e}_3)$, show that also

$$V = \vec{e}_3 \cdot (\vec{e}_1 \times \vec{e}_2) = \vec{e}_2 \cdot (\vec{e}_3 \times \vec{e}_1) = e^{ijk}(\vec{e}_i \times \vec{e}_j) \cdot \vec{e}_k$$

6-13.   Derive Eq. (6.3-28) relating base vectors of a covariant set
        to those of the reciprocal contravariant set.

6-14.   Derive Eq. (6.3-49) relating the determinant of the components
        of the conjugate tensor to the volume of the parallelepiped
        defined by the base vectors (V).

6-15.   Write an expression analogous to Eq. (6.4-11) for the recip-
        rocal base vectors, $\vec{e}^j$. Use these expressions together with
        Eq. (6.4-2) to derive expressions for the base and reciprocal
        base vectors for cylindrical coordinates. Use these results
        in Eqs. (6.3-33) and (6.3-34) to determine g_{ij} and g^{ij}
        cylindrical coordinates.

6-16.   Consider the nonorthogonal coordinates $\bar{x}^i$.

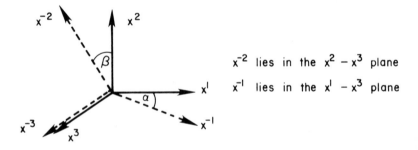

        $\bar{x}^2$ lies in the $x^2 - x^3$ plane

        $\bar{x}^1$ lies in the $x^1 - x^3$ plane

        Determine the components of the metric tensor for the $\bar{x}^i$ coor-
        dinates.

6-17.   If the components of a first-order covariant tensor function
        are $(xy, 2y - z^2, xz)$ in Cartesian coordinates, determine the
        covariant components relative to spherical coordinates and
        the contravariant components relative to cylindrical coordinates

6-18. If A_j is a covariant first-order tensor, establish whether $\partial A_j / \partial x^i$ is or is not a tensor.

6-19. If x_j is an arbitrary covariant vector and $(A^{ij} x_j)$ is a contravariant vector, show that A^{ij} is a contravariant second-order tensor.

6-20. A tensor equation which is valid for one coordinate system is also valid for all other coordinate systems. If the tensors A_{ij} and B_{ij} are equal in a given system, prove that they will be equal if transformed into any other coordinate system.

6-21. Using the basic transformation properties of tensor components [e.g., Eq. (6.5-4)], prove that the first and second invariants are indeed independent of any coordinate system. Show that this holds as well for covariant as for contravariant components.

6-22. Derive the continuity equation in cylindrical and spherical coordinates (Eqs. 2 and 3 of Table 3.1) starting with the general expression in general tensor form. Note that the equations in the tables in Chap. 3 are all written in terms of physical components.

6-23. Derive Eq. 12 of Table 3.1 for the ϕ component of the equation of motion in spherical coordinates starting with the general tensor expression. Note that all stress components in this table are physical components.

6-24. Derive each of the equations for the rate of strain tensor in Table 3.2 from the general tensor expression.

6-25. Derive the expressions for the second invariant of the rate of strain tensor for incompressible materials in Table 3.3.

6-26. Consider the steady laminar flow of an incompressible Newtonian fluid in a conical section, as illustrated in the

figure for Prob. 4.14. If the flow field is described relative to spherical coordinates centered in the centerline:

(a) Show that the physical velocity components and boundary
     conditions are

$$v_r = \frac{V(\theta)}{r^2} \qquad\qquad v_\theta = v_\phi = 0$$

B.C.: (1) $V(\theta) = 0$ at $\theta = \Theta$

       (2) $\dfrac{\partial V}{\partial \theta} = 0$ at $\theta = 0$

(b) Use the transformation properties of tensor components
     to derive expressions for the velocity components and
     boundary conditions relative to: (1) Cartesian,
     (2) cylindrical coordinates (with the z axis along the
     centerline), in terms of $V(\theta)$ and Θ.

6-27. Show that the double inner product (i.e., scalar product) of
       a symmetric tensor with an antisymmetric tensor is zero.

6-28. Consider the orthogonal coordinate system known as elliptical
       cylindrical coordinates, illustrated in Appendix C. The
       coordinates are z, u, and v, each of which define coordinate
       surfaces normal to these coordinate directions. On a plane
       of constant z, the curves of constant u are confocal ellipses
       with major axis of 2a, and the curves of constant v are
       hyperbolas.

       (a) What are the components of the metric and conjugate ten-
            sors in this system?

       (b) Write the continuity equation in this system.

       (c) Derive the z component of the equations of motion in
            this coordinate system.

       (d) Write the specific form of the equation in (c) which must
            be solved for the velocity distribution of a Newtonian
            fluid in steady laminar fully developed flow in a cylin-
            drical tube of elliptical cross section.

6-29. Derive expressions for the nonzero components of the metric
       tensor and Christoffel symbols for the following orthogonal
       coordinate systems, described in Appendix C:
       (a) Spherical
       (b) Eliptical cylindrical
       (c) Parabolic cylindrical
       (d) Parabolic

6-30. Show that $g^{ij}{}_{,k} = g_{ij,k} = g^{i}{}_{j,k} = 0$

6-31. Confirm Eq. (6.9-22) relating the components of an antisym-
       metric tensor and its dual vector.

6-32. Starting with the solution for the stress components in a
       Newtonian fluid in Poiseuille flow relative to cylindrical
       coordinates, $\tau_{ij}(r, \theta, z)$, apply the transformation rules for
       tensor components to determine expressions for the stress com-
       ponents in this flow field relative to a Cartesian reference
       frame.

6-33. Show that the diagonal components of a mixed tensor are iden-
       tical in all coordinate systems.

6-34. Prove that the Kronecker delta $\delta_i{}^j$ is a mixed second-order
       tensor.

6-35. Prove that the mixed components of the metric, $g^i{}_j$, transform
       as a mixed second-order tensor, and are identical to the
       Kronecker delta $\delta^i{}_j$.

6-36. Determine the principle axes for the stress tensor for a
       simple shear deformation in which the components of the
       stress tensor have the following magnitudes relative to the
       usual coordinates:

$$\tau_{ij} = \begin{bmatrix} 0 & 7 & 0 \\ 7 & 0 & 0 \\ 0 & 0 & 0 \end{bmatrix}$$

6-37. Repeat above for a stress tensor having the following component values.

$$\tau_{ij} = \begin{bmatrix} 8 & 7 & 0 \\ 7 & 2 & 0 \\ 0 & 0 & 5 \end{bmatrix}$$

Determine the magnitudes of the stress tensor components relative to the principle axes.

Chapter 7

GENERALIZED FLUID RESPONSE

7.1. INTRODUCTION

In this chapter, we make use of the mathematical properties of
general tensors presented in the previous chapter to illustrate the
formulation of generalized rheological equations of state (constitutive equations) for purely viscous and viscoelastic fluids. These
equations, which relate the total anisotropic stress and strain
tensors at any point in the material, are capable of describing all
measurable material functions which relate specific stress and strain
components in a given steady or unsteady deformation. We will show,
for example, that normal (deviatoric) stresses may arise from either
nonlinear viscous or from viscoelastic properties. In order to describe large or continuous deformations of time-dependent (viscoelastic) fluids, it will be necessary to define a suitable measure of
strain which is meaningful in such systems.

The formulation of a general rheological equation of state which
completely describes a given material is the ultimate objective of
the rheologist. This tensor equation is a completely general mathematical model for the rheological behavior of the material, and
may be used to predict a variety of specific material functions. The
test of validity of the model is the degree to which it can represent
measured material functions. If agreement between the model and

observed data is achieved, the constant parameters which appear in
the model equation, which constitute the rheological properties of
the material, may be evaluated. Of course, the number of different
material functions which must be determined in order to absolutely
confirm the validity of a given generalized model cannot be established a priori, and depends primarily upon the complexity of the
specific material which is being modeled, as well as the complexity
of the deformation in the system of interest.

7.2. PURELY VISCOUS FLUIDS

A purely viscous fluid has been defined as a material for which
the state of stress at a given point is a function only of the instantaneous rate of strain at that point. Special cases of the purely
viscous fluid include Newtonian, generalized Newtonian, and Reiner-
Rivlin fluids.

7.2.1. Newtonian Fluids

The general definition of a Newtonian fluid is one for which
the shear stress is directly proportional to the rate of strain.
Since the general description of such materials has been discussed
previously in some detail, only a brief review will be given here.

Since total strain may be resolved into volumetric and shear
strain components, the total stress in a Newtonian fluid will be
composed of components which resist both the rate of volumetric
strain and the rate of shear strain. If these effects are linearly
additive, an expression of the following form for the anisotropic
stress is implied:

$$\tau_{ij} = \mu\dot{\gamma}_{ij} + \kappa\dot{e}_v g_{ij} \tag{7.2-1}$$

where

$$\dot{\gamma}_{ij} = \Delta_{ij} - \bar{\Delta}g_{ij} = \Delta_{ij} - \frac{2}{3}\dot{e}_v g_{ij}$$

The constants of proportionality, μ and κ are the "shear viscosity" and the "bulk viscosity," and characterize the forces which resist the rate of change of shape and the rate of change of volume, respectively. The components of Eq. (7.2-2) are tabulated in Table 3.2 and also in Appendix D for Cartesian, cylindrical, and spherical coordinates.

Equations (7.2-1) and (7.2-2) can be combined to give:

$$\tau_{ij} = \mu \, \Delta_{ij} + (\kappa - \frac{2}{3}\mu)\dot{e}_v g_{ij} \qquad (7.2-3)$$

which is often presented as the general Newtonian equation of state. For an incompressible fluid $\dot{e}_v = 0$, so that these relations reduce to:

$$\tau_{ij} = \mu \, \Delta_{ij} = \mu\dot{\gamma}_{ij} \qquad (7.2-4)$$

This model is generally adequate for single-phase fluids of relatively simple molecular structure, but is inadequate for suspensions, slurries, polymers, or other complex fluids.

7.2.2. Generalized Newtonian Fluids

As discussed in Chap. 3, the generalized Newtonian fluid is an extension (by analogy) of the Newtonian fluid model, to account for the observed nonlinear shear stress-shear rate behavior of many complex fluids. The general form of this model is thus analogous to Eq. (7.2-4), namely,

$$\tau_{ij} = \eta \, \Delta_{ij} \qquad (7.2-5)$$

where η is the apparent viscosity function. Since η is assumed to be characteristic only of the material, it must be a scalar, but it also depends upon the state of deformation (i.e., shear rate or shear stress). This requires that η be, at most, of the form:

$$\eta = \eta(I, II, III) \qquad (7.2-6)$$

where I, II, and III are the three invariants of the rate of strain
(or stress) tensor. These were initially introduced in Chap. 3,
and their derivation is discussed in Chap. 6. Since for incompressible fluids the first invariant is zero, and for viscometric flows
the third invariant is also zero, it is generally assumed that Eq.
(7.2-6) reduces to the form:

$$\eta = \eta(II) \qquad\qquad\qquad (7.2-7)$$

The second invariant of the rate of strain tensor for an incompressible fluid is tabulated in Table 3.3 for Cartesian, cylindrical,
and spherical coordinates. Procedures for generalizing the simple
shear or viscometric forms of the apparent viscosity function to more
complex flows, in accordance with Eq. (7.2-7), have also been discussed in Chaps. 3 and 4.

Note that one consequence of the analogy between Eqs. (7.2-5)
and (7.2-4) is that only those components of stress which would be
nonzero for a Newtonian fluid in a given deformation are nonzero for
a generalized Newtonian fluid in the same deformation. However, as
has been previously noted, many fluids such as molten polymers and
polymer solutions, which exhibit nonlinear shear behavior, also
exhibit nonzero normal (deviatoric) stress components in deformations
in which these stresses would be absent for Newtonian or generalized
Newtonian fluids. Thus, such a model might be adequate for describing the flow behavior of an inelastic fluid in a variety of deformations, or the flow of an elastic fluid in a steady flow in which
only the consequences of viscous forces are of interest. However,
it would not be suitable for describing unsteady deformations of
viscoelastic fluids, or steady deformations of such fluids in situations where the effects of normal stresses may predominate.

7.2.3. Stokesian Fluids [7.1]

A Stokesian fluid is defined as a purely viscous isotropic fluid.
Thus the Newtonian and generalized Newtonian fluids may be considered
special cases of the Stokesian fluid. However, the more general

Stokesian fluid exhibits certain stress characteristics in steady
flows not exhibited by the special cases, as seen below.

One of the most general relations which can be written relating
stress to the rate of strain tensor is a polynomial of infinite
order:

$$\tau_{ij} = A_1 \Delta_{ij} + A_2 \Delta_{ik} \Delta^k_j + A_3 \Delta_{ik} \Delta^k_n \Delta^n_j + \cdots \qquad (7.2\text{-}8)$$

Using vector notation, this is equivalent to

$$\vec{\vec{\tau}} = \sum_{k=1}^{\infty} A_k \, (\vec{\vec{\Delta}})^k \qquad (7.2\text{-}9)$$

For an isotropic material, the A_K are scalars and may therefore
be (at most) functions of the scalar invariants of Δ_{ij}.

Now Eq. (7.2-8) or (7.2-9) can be simplified by use of the
Hamilton-Cayley theorem, which states that for any square matrix, the
cube of the matrix can be written in terms of its first and second
powers and its invariants, as follows:

$$\vec{\vec{\Delta}}^3 = I \, \vec{\vec{\Delta}}^2 - II \, \vec{\vec{\Delta}} + III \, \vec{\vec{\delta}} \qquad (7.2\text{-}10)$$

or

$$\Delta_{ik} \Delta^k_n \Delta^n_j = I(\Delta_{ik} \Delta^k_j) - II \, \Delta_{ij} + III \, g_{ij} \qquad (7.2\text{-}11)$$

where

$$\vec{\vec{\delta}} \equiv g_{ij} (= \delta_{ij} \text{ for Cartesian tensors})$$

That is, the matrix of tensor components satisfies its own characteristic equation (see Sec. 6.9.1).

It is thus obvious that $\vec{\vec{\Delta}}^3$ and all higher power of $\vec{\vec{\Delta}}$ in Eq.
(7.2-8) or (7.2-9) can be written in terms of $(\vec{\vec{\Delta}}^2, \vec{\vec{\Delta}}, I, II, III, \vec{\vec{\delta}})$
only. Hence Eq. (7.2-8) may be reduced to:

$$\tau_{ij} = \alpha_o g_{ij} + \alpha_1 \Delta_{ij} + \alpha_2 \Delta_{im} \Delta^m_j \qquad (7.2\text{-}12)$$

where $\alpha_o = 0$ if $\Delta_{ij} = 0$ and α_1 and α_2 are functions at most of the three invariants of Δ_{ij}.

Since pressure can only be determined to within an arbitrary constant (i.e., the magnitude of isotropic pressure has no effect upon the flow characteristics of an incompressible fluid), it is convenient to include α_o in P, so that the total stress tensor becomes:

$$\sigma_{ij} = -Pg_{ij} + \alpha_1 \Delta_{ij} + \alpha_2 \Delta_{im} \Delta^m_j \qquad (7.2-13)$$

The fluid described by this rheological equation of state is referred to as a Reiner-Rivlin fluid [7.2]. For viscometric flows, Eq. (7.2-12) reduces to

$$\tau_{ij} = \alpha_1 \dot{\gamma} \begin{bmatrix} 0 & 1 & 0 \\ 1 & 0 & 0 \\ 0 & 0 & 0 \end{bmatrix} + \alpha_2 \dot{\gamma}^2 \begin{bmatrix} 1 & 0 & 0 \\ 0 & 1 & 0 \\ 0 & 0 & 0 \end{bmatrix} \qquad (7.2-14)$$

Equation (7.2-14) shows that α_2 gives rise to nonzero anisotropic normal stresses in viscometric flows, and hence is sometimes called the cross viscosity or normal stress coefficient. From thermodynamic principles, and the fact that viscous dissipation of energy can only be positive, the following condition can be established [7.3]:

$$\alpha_1 \geq \left(\frac{3}{2} \frac{III}{II} \right) \alpha_2 \qquad (7.2-15)$$

For viscometric flows (for which III = 0), Eq. (7.2-15) simply requires that $\alpha_1 \geq 0$.

From Eq. (7.2-14), it is evident that the apparent viscosity and normal stress material functions for the Reiner-Rivlin fluid are:

$$\eta = \frac{\tau_{12}}{\dot{\gamma}} = \alpha_1 \qquad (7.2-16)$$

$$\theta_1 = \frac{\tau_{11} - \tau_{22}}{\dot{\gamma}^2} = 0 \qquad (7.2-17)$$

$$\theta_2 = \frac{\tau_{22} - \tau_{33}}{\dot{\gamma}^2} \tag{7.2-18}$$

Thus the Reiner-Rivlin parameter α_1 is identical to the apparent viscosity function, and the parameter α_2 is the ~~second~~ normal stress function. The ~~first~~ normal stress difference is zero for this model.

A. Poiseuille Flow of a Reiner-Rivlin Fluid

For fully developed steady laminar flow in a cylindrical tube (Poiseuille flow), Eq. (7.2-14) applies, where

$$\dot{\gamma} = \frac{dv_z}{dr} \tag{7.2-19}$$

and α_1 and α_2 are, at most, functions of $\dot{\gamma}^2$ (and hence vary in the r direction only). From Eq. (7.2-14), the nonzero physical components of stress are:

$$\tau_{zz} = \tau_{rr} = \alpha_2 \dot{\gamma}^2 \tag{7.2-20}$$

$$\tau_{rz} = \tau_{zr} = \alpha_1 \dot{\gamma} \tag{7.2-21}$$

all other $\tau_{ij} = 0$

and the r and z equations of motion are:

$$\frac{\partial P}{\partial r} = \frac{1}{r} \frac{\partial}{\partial r} (r\tau_{rr}) \tag{7.2-22}$$

$$\frac{\partial P}{\partial z} - \rho g_z = \frac{1}{r} \frac{\partial}{\partial r} (r\tau_{rz}) \tag{7.2-23}$$

As in previous analyses of these equations, integration of Eq. (7.2-23) leads to

$$\tau_{rz} = \frac{r\Phi}{2} = -\frac{r}{R} \tau_w \tag{7.2-24}$$

and

$$P = (\rho g_z + \Phi)z + f(r) \tag{7.3-25}$$

where Φ is a constant, being equal to the axial pressure gradient. The arbitrary function $f(r)$ results from the integration and the fact that, by Eq. (7.2-22), the pressure is not independent of r when τ_{rr} is nonzero. It can be evaluated from the derivative of Eq. (7.3-25) and Eq. (7.3-22) as follows:

$$\frac{\partial P}{\partial r} = \frac{\partial f}{\partial r} = \frac{1}{r}\frac{\partial}{\partial r}(r\tau_{rr}) = \frac{\partial \tau_{rr}}{\partial r} + \frac{\tau_{rr}}{r} \tag{7.2-26}$$

Integration from 0 to r provides an expression for $f(r)$:

$$f(r) = \tau_{rr} + \int_0^r \frac{\tau_{rr}}{r}\,dr = \alpha_2\dot{\gamma}^2 + \int_0^r \frac{\alpha_2\dot{\gamma}^2}{r}\,dr \tag{7.2-27}$$

Using Eqs. (7.2-20), (7.2-21), and (7.2-24), this can be rearranged to the form

$$f(r) = \frac{\Phi^2}{4}\left[\frac{\alpha_2 r^2}{\alpha_1^2} + \int_0^r \frac{\alpha_2 r}{\alpha_1^2}\,dr\right] \tag{7.2-28}$$

Note that if the material functions α_1 and α_2 are known functions of $\dot{\gamma}$, Eqs. (7.2-21) and (7.2-24) may be used to convert these to equivalent functions of r, and hence evaluate $f(r)$ from Eq. (7.2-28). It is evident that $f(r) = 0$ if $\alpha_2 = 0$.

Now the volumetric flow rate is given by:

$$Q = 2\pi \int_0^R v_z(r)r\,dr = \pi \int_0^R v_z(r)\,d(r^2) \tag{7.2-29}$$

or

$$Q = -\pi \int_{v_z(0)}^{v_z(R)} r^2\,dv_z = -\pi\Phi \int_0^R \frac{r^3}{2\alpha_1}\,dr \tag{7.2-30}$$

Thus the volumetric flow is dependent only on the viscous material function α_1 and is independent of α_2. If $\alpha_1 = \mu$ = constant (Newtonian viscosity), Eq. (7.2-30) reduces to the Hagen-Poiseuille equation.

Now the effect of the normal stresses may be seen as follows. From Eqs. (7.2-20) and (7.2-25), we see that

$$\sigma_{zz} = \sigma_{rr} = -P + \tau_{rr} = -(\rho g_z + \Phi)z - f(r) + \tau_{rr} + C_2 \qquad (7.3-31)$$

Equations (7.2-20), (7.2-21), and (7.2-24) may also be combined to give:

$$\tau_{rr} = \alpha_2 \dot\gamma^2 = \frac{\Phi^2}{4}\left[\frac{r^2 \alpha_2}{\alpha_1^2}\right] \qquad (7.2-32)$$

Substituting Eq. (7.2-32) for τ_{rr} and Eq. (7.2-28) for $f(r)$ into Eq. (7.2-31) leads to

$$\sigma_{zz} = \sigma_{rr} = -(\rho g_z + \Phi)z - \frac{\Phi^2}{4}\int_0^r \frac{\alpha_2 r}{\alpha_1^2}\, dr + C_2 \qquad (7.2-33)$$

If the functional dependence of the material functions α_1 and α_2 upon shear rate or shear stress (i.e., upon r) is known, the integral in Eq. (7.2-33) can be evaluated. However, even for constant values of α_1 and α_2, the results are informative. In this case Eq. (7.2-33) becomes:

$$\sigma_{zz} = \sigma_{rr} = -(\rho g_z + \Phi)z - \frac{\alpha_2 \Phi^2 r^2}{8\mu^2} + C_2 \qquad (7.2-34)$$

where

$$\mu = \alpha_1 = \text{constant} \qquad\qquad \alpha_2 = \text{constant}$$

The integration constant C_2 in Eq. (7.2-34) may be evaluated as follows. At the center of the tube (r = 0) the shear rate is zero,

so that all shear (dynamic) stresses should also be zero at this
point. Thus

$$\sigma_{zz}\Big|_{r=0} = -P = -(\rho g_z + \Phi)z + C_2 \qquad (7.2\text{-}35)$$

Now if z is measured from a point in the fluid just outside the end
of the tube where the jet exits into the atmosphere where the pressure
is P_o, the following condition determines the constant C_2:

$$@ \; z = 0: \quad P = P_o = -C_2 \qquad\qquad\qquad\qquad (7.2\text{-}36)$$

Inserting the value of C_2 from Eq. (7.2-36) into Eq. (7.2-34) gives:

$$\sigma_{zz} = \sigma_{rr} = -(\rho g_z + \Phi)z - \frac{\alpha_2 \Phi^2 r^2}{8\mu^2} - P_o \qquad (7.2\text{-}37)$$

Now $(-\sigma_{rr}$ at $r = R) = P$ is the stress (or "pressure") exerted by the
pipe wall on the fluid. Thus at the pipe wall at the exit (z = 0,
r = R) we have:

$$P - P_o = \frac{\alpha_2 \Phi^2 R^2}{8\mu^2} \qquad\qquad\qquad\qquad (7.2\text{-}38)$$

This represents the difference in pressure exerted on the fluid between two points just inside and just ouside the pipe exit.

If $\alpha_2 > 0$, Eq. (7.2-38) shows that the restraining pressure exerted by the pipe wall on the fluid inside the pipe at the exit is
greater than that just ouside the exit. Hence this excess pressure
or radial stress in the fluid will cause the fluid jet to swell as
it leaves the pipe. The Reiner-Rivlin fluid model is therefore
qualitatively consistent with the observed jet swell or die swell
characteristics of many complex fluids.

B. Couette Flow of a Reiner-Rivlin Fluid

For steady angular flow between concentric cylinders (Couette flow), the viscometric flow form of the Reiner-Rivlin model, Eq. (7.2-14), applies where:

$$\dot{\gamma} = r \frac{d\omega}{dr} \tag{7.2-39}$$

The nonzero components of τ_{ij} are, therefore:

$$\tau_{rr} = \tau_{\theta\theta} = \alpha_2 \dot{\gamma}^2 = \alpha_2 r^2 \left(\frac{d\omega}{dr}\right)^2 \tag{7.2-40}$$

$$\tau_{r\theta} = \tau_{\theta r} = \alpha_1 \dot{\gamma} = \alpha_1 r \left(\frac{d\omega}{dr}\right) \tag{7.2-41}$$

all others = 0

and the equations of motion reduce to:

r Eq:

$$-\rho r \omega^2 = - \frac{\partial P}{\partial r} + \frac{1}{r} \frac{\partial}{\partial r} (r\tau_{rr}) - \frac{\tau_{\theta\theta}}{r} \tag{7.2-42}$$

θ Eq:

$$0 = \frac{1}{r^2} \frac{\partial}{\partial r} (r^2 \tau_{r\theta}) \tag{7.2-43}$$

z Eq:

$$0 = \frac{\partial P}{\partial z} + \rho g_z \tag{7.2-44}$$

Integration of Eqs. (7.2-43) and (7.2-44) leads to:

$$\tau_{r\theta} = \frac{C_1}{r^2} \tag{7.2-45}$$

$$P = -\rho g_z z + f(r) \qquad\qquad (7.2\text{-}46)$$

The arbitrary function $f(r)$ may be obtained from Eqs. (7.2-46) and (7.2-40) as follows:

$$\frac{\partial f}{\partial r} = \frac{\partial P}{\partial r} = \rho r \omega^2 + \frac{1}{r}\frac{\partial}{\partial r}(r\alpha_2\dot{\gamma}^2) - \frac{\alpha_2}{r}\dot{\gamma}^2 \qquad\qquad (7.2\text{-}47)$$

$$= \rho r \omega^2 + \frac{d}{dr}(\alpha_2\dot{\gamma}^2)$$

Integration of Eq. (7.2-47) gives the following expression for $f(r)$:

$$f(r) = \alpha_2\dot{\gamma}^2 + \rho\int r\omega^2\,dr + C_3 \qquad\qquad (7.2\text{-}48)$$

An expression for the constant C_1 in Eq. (7.2-45) can be obtained from Eq. (7.2-41):

$$\tau_{r\theta} = \alpha_1\dot{\gamma} = \frac{C_1}{r^2}$$

thus

$$C_1 = \alpha_1 r^2\dot{\gamma} \qquad\qquad (7.2\text{-}49)$$

Expressions for the nonzero normal stresses can be obtained by combining Eqs. (7.2-40), (7.2-46), and (7.2-48) as follows:

$$\sigma_{\theta\theta} = \sigma_{rr} = -P + \tau_{rr} = \rho g_z z - f(r) + \alpha_2\dot{\gamma}^2$$

$$= \rho g_z z - \rho\int r\omega^2\,dr - C_3 \qquad\qquad (7.2\text{-}50)$$

$$\sigma_{zz} = -P + \tau_{zz} = \rho g_z z - \alpha_2\dot{\gamma}^2 - \rho\int r\omega^2\,dr - C_3 \qquad\qquad (7.2\text{-}51)$$

The velocity distribution in the gap can be obtained by integration of Eq. (7.2-49):

$$\dot{\gamma} = r\frac{d\omega}{dr} = \frac{C_1}{\alpha_1 r^2} \tag{7.2-52}$$

If the fluid is Newtonian, $\alpha_1 = \mu$ is a constant, and integration of Eq. (7.7-52) gives the velocity distribution of Sec. 4.3.2.A:

$$\omega = C_2 - \frac{C_1}{2\alpha_1 r^2} \tag{7.2-53}$$

where the constants C_1 and C_2 are evaluated from the boundary conditions.

It is evident that the velocity distribution is independent of the material properties if the fluid viscosity is constant. One consequence of this, as seen from Eqs. (7.2-50) and (7.2-51), is that the normal stress $\sigma_{\theta\theta}$ is also independent of the material rheological properties, whereas the stress component σ_{zz} does depend upon the rheological property α_2. For a fluid with a variable viscosity function (α_1), the velocity distribution and hence $\sigma_{\theta\theta}$ and σ_{zz} all depend on α_1.

Substituting Eq. (7.2-52) for $\dot{\gamma}$ and Eq. (7.2-53) for , Eq. (7.2-51) becomes

$$\sigma_{zz} = \rho g_z z - \left(\frac{C_1}{\alpha_1}\right)\frac{\alpha_2}{r^4} - \rho \int \left(C_2 r^2 - \frac{C_1}{2\alpha_1}\right)^2 \frac{dr}{r^3} - C_3 \tag{7.2-54}$$

At the free fluid surface $(z = z_o)$, which is assumed to be exposed to a uniform (atmospheric) pressure, we have $\sigma_{zz} = -P_o$. Inserting this into Eq. (7.2-54), and differentiating with respect to r gives an expression which may be solved for the slope of the free surface:

$$\frac{dz_o}{dr} = \frac{(C_2 r^2 - C_1/2\alpha_1)^2}{g_z r^3} - \frac{4\alpha_2}{\rho g_z r^5}\left(\frac{C_1}{\alpha_1}\right)^2 \tag{7.2-55}$$

where α_2 has been assumed constant, as well as α_1.

For a cylinder of radius R_i rotating at a rate Ω_i in a large volume of fluid (i.e., $R_o = \infty$, $\Omega_o = 0$), Eq. (7.2-55) becomes:

$$\frac{dz_o}{dr} = \frac{\Omega_i^2 R_i^4}{\rho g_z r^3}\left(\rho - \frac{16\alpha_2}{r^2}\right) \qquad (7.2\text{-}56)$$

If $\alpha_2 = 0$, the slope dz_o/dr is everywhere positive, so that the fluid surface is concave. However, if α_2 is finite and

$$\left(\frac{16\alpha_2}{r^2}\right) > \rho \qquad (7.2\text{-}57)$$

then the slope will be negative. Thus there will be a region near $r = 0$ where Eq. (7.2-57) holds (if R_i is sufficiently small), so that the fluid in this region appears to climb up the inner cylinder. The prediction of the Reiner-Rivlin model is therefore consistent with the Weissenberg effect, which is observed in many fluids.

It would seem that the Reiner-Rivlin model for a purely viscous fluid would be a most useful one, since its predictions are qualitatively consistent with observed jet swell and Weissenberg effects. Furthermore, complex shear dependent viscous and normal stress effects could be incorporated by taking the material functions α_1 and α_2 to be suitable functions of shear rate invariants. However, it should be noted that for viscometric flows, the normal stress character of the Reiner-Rivlin fluid is as follows:

$$\tau_{11} = \tau_{22}, \; \tau_{33} = 0$$

or

$$(\tau_{11} - \tau_{22}) = 0, \qquad (\tau_{22} - \tau_{33}) = \alpha_2 \qquad (7.2\text{-}58)$$

To date, rheological investigations of complex fluids which exhibit jet swell and the Weisenberg effect (e.g., molten polymers and polymer solutions) have not disclosed a material for which the first normal stress difference is zero. For this reason, the validity of the Reiner-Rivlin model is generally discounted. While it is granted that the probability of the existence of a fluid which follows this model is indeed quite small, the fact that one has not yet been found does not prove that one does not exist, especially in light of the fact that the fraction of all possible complex fluids for which reliable normal stress data exist is still quite small.

Inasmuch as a purely viscous Reiner-Rivlin fluid has not been proven to exist, and furthermore all fluids which have been observed to exhibit jet swell and the Weissenberg effect also exhibit elastic properties to varying degrees, these and other normal stress effects are commonly considered to be a manifestation of elastic forces. As we will see, a suitably generalized form of a linear viscoelastic model does indeed predict the existence of normal stresses in steady viscometric flows, of a form qualitatively consistent with observed jet swell, Weissenberg effect, etc.

7.3. DEFORMATION OF TIME-DEPENDENT FLUIDS

As previously illustrated, a unique property of viscoelastic fluids, in contrast with purely viscous fluids, is the time-dependence of the material response. Whereas the stresses developed within a purely viscous fluid are a function only of the instantaneous rate of deformation, those developed within a viscoelastic fluid are a function of the entire past history of deformation. This may be reflected in the rheological equation of state by additional "rate" terms; i.e., higher order time derivatives of stress and/or strain, or by a hereditary integral relation involving a time-dependent relaxation or memory function.

Now material functions and rheological equations of state are, by definition, a unique property only of the material to which they refer. Thus the values of stress and strain which serve to define these relations have meaning only when associated with a specific

element of material; i.e., a material point. For purely viscous
fluids or systems at steady state (i.e., independent of time), this
merely requires that stress and strain or strain rate both be evaluated at a given location in the system.

Now the classical definition of strain involves an infinitesimal
displacement between two material points, relative to their initial
separation. Such a strain measure is, obviously, strictly valid only
for infinitesimal, or very small, displacements of all material
points from their initial or reference positions. It follows, then,
that if we adopt the classical definition of strain as the basic measure of deformation for elastic or viscoelastic materials, we are
limited to systems in a "fixed state" in which all material points
are subject only to small or infinitesimal displacements from a reference configuration. For a purely viscous fluid, however, the instantaneous rate of strain is the only measure of deformation of
significance. Since this is independent of the initial or reference
positions of the material points, it is valid regardless of the magnitude of the deformation. Thus there are no restrictions on the
use of the rate of strain as a deformation variable, and consequently
constitutive equations for purely viscous fluids are valid for any
magnitude of deformation.

For a viscoelastic fluid, on the other hand, infinitesimal strain
may or may not be a suitable measure of deformation. For such materials it is not only the instantaneous strain or rate of strain, but
the entire past history of strain that is significant. Thus the
stress acting on a given material element at a given time is determined by the deformation history that the element has undergone at
all prior times. If the element has remained "fixed" in space at
all times (i.e., small displacements from a fixed location), then
the classical strain tensor is sufficient to define the state of
deformation, regardless of the time varying history. However, if
the material undergoes a large amplitude or continuous deformation,
the coordinate positions of a given material point (with reference
to a fixed origin) will not be "fixed." Hence any measure of deformation based on infinitesimal displacements of fixed coordinate

positions will be meaningless, since this would not always refer to
the same material element. Thus, in order to describe the deformation of a viscoelastic material under these circumstances, it is necessary that we be able to define deformation in a manner which allows
us to follow a given material element or point with time as it moves
from place to place in the system. Such a measure of deformation
would always refer to the same material element (or set of material
points) regardless of the time varying history of the element.

7.3.1. Convected Coordinates

One way in which we might follow the deformation of a material
element as it moves through a system is by means of a reference frame
which is defined by a set of base vectors which move and deform with
the material. That is, these base vectors must be "embedded" in the
material so that the coordinate axes which they define always pass
through the same material elements as they move through the system.
Such axes are referred to as "convected" coordinates, since they
move with the material. Any measure of deformation (strain) defined
relative to such a coordinate system should be independent of the
local translation or rotation of the material.

Once an appropriate convected coordinate system is eatablished,
and a suitable measure of deformation is defined relative to this
system, we can then formulate a rheological equation of state for a
given material in terms of stress and strain variables relative to
these convected coordinates. Since, by definition, these variables
will always refer to the same element of material, any variation
with time will be permissible regardless of the manner in which the
location of the element varies with time. These relations must then
be transformed from convected coordinates to a fixed coordinate frame,
however, since all physical observations are made relative to the
latter.

A set of embedded base vectors in a simple shear deformation is
illustrated in Fig. 7.1. The embedded base vectors are designated
by the $\hat{g}_i$, and the associated convected coordinates are denoted by

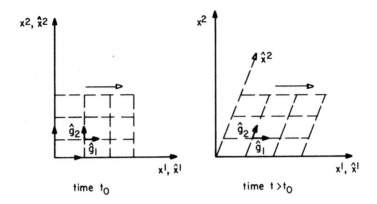

FIG. 7.1 Embedded base vectors in simple shear.

$\hat{x}^i$. Note that at time t_o (the reference or "undeformed" state) the
fixed and convected coordinates coincide and both are orthogonal.
However, at any later time, t, the convected coordinates are nonorthogonal. Note also that the convected coordinates, and hence any
quantities associated with them, are obviously a function of time
even in a steady flow situation, inasmuch as the coordinates follow
the material, which moves with time.

For fluids there is no unique preferred orientation or "undeformed" state, so that the reference state to which deformations are
referred is completely arbitrary. It is therefore sometimes desirable
to choose the present time, t, as the reference state so that states
at all previous times, t', represent deformed states. This situation
is illustrated in Fig. 7.2.

This system of convected coordinates is not the only one which
might serve as a reference frame which follows a given material element with time. For example we might define a set of orthogonal
coordinates in terms of base vectors, $\tilde{g}_i$, which are attached to a
fluid element such that they translate and rotate with the local
linear and angular velocity of the fluid, but remain orthogonal.
Such a system is illustrated in Fig. 7.3 for simple shear, where the
base vectors $\tilde{g}_i$ coincide with the vectors $\hat{g}_i$ at time t_o. Since the
local angular velocity is given by

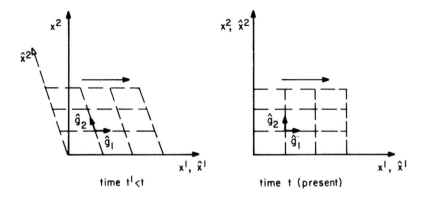

FIG. 7.2 Embedded base vectors relative to present state.

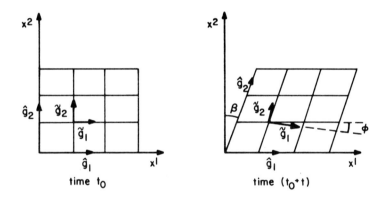

FIG. 7.3 Orthogonal embedded base vectors.

$$\vec{\omega} = \frac{1}{2} \nabla \times \vec{v}$$

or

$$\omega^i = \frac{1}{4} \varepsilon^{ijk} \Omega_{jk} \qquad (7.3\text{-}1)$$

it is seen that the angle ϕ through which the orthogonal vectors $\tilde{g}_1$, $\tilde{g}_2$ have rotated at any time is related to the angle β through which the embedded vector $\hat{g}_2$ has rotated, by

$$\phi = \frac{1}{2}\beta \tag{7.3-2}$$

The convected coordinates can also be described in terms of coordinate surfaces which are normal to the embedded base vectors. These surfaces must obviously move and deform with the fluid, with the requirement that a given coordinate surface must always pass through the same material points. As an illustration, the appropriate convected coordinate surfaces for a Newtonian fluid in laminar flow in a tube are shown in Fig. 7.4. In this diagram, the "undeformed state" is assumed to exist at time t' (t' < t), at which time the convected coordinate surfaces are orthogonal and coincide with conventional fixed cylindrical coordinates. Note that even though all three surfaces are convected, the $\hat{\zeta}^2$ and $\hat{\zeta}^3$ surfaces are not

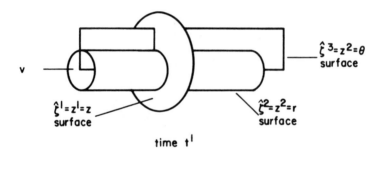

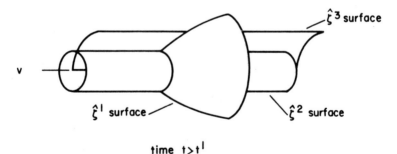

FIG. 7.4 Convected "material" surfaces for steady Poiseuille flow of a Newtonian fluid. Reprinted from Ref. 7.1, p. 34, by permission of Prentice-Hall.

deformed, since any given point in the system will have the same $\hat{\zeta}^2$ and $\hat{\zeta}^3$ coordinates at all times.

7.3.2. Deformation in Convected Coordinates [7.1]

A deformation occurs whenever the magnitude of the distance between any two (embedded) points in a material changes. Thus any
quantity which provides a quantitative measure of this can serve as
a measure of deformation (i.e., strain).

In Sec. 6.3.2, it was shown that the square of the differential
distance between any two points in a space described by the coordinates z^i is determined by the metric tensor of the coordinates, g_{ij},
and the differential coordinates separating the points:

$$(ds)^2 = g_{ij} \, dz^i \, dz^j \qquad (7.3-3)$$

For fixed coordinates, the metric tensor is a fixed characteristic of
the coordinate system, and so any change in the distance between the
two points (ds) is reflected by changes in the relative coordinate
positions (dz^is) of the points. Hence the appropriate definition of
strain (deformation) with reference to fixed coordinates requires
only a specification of the relative changes of the coordinate positions of the material points, as described in Chap. 1. Now this
same distance between any two material points may be described relative to a set of convected coordinates:

$$(ds)^2 = \hat{g}_{ij} \, d\hat{\zeta}^i \, d\hat{\zeta}^j \qquad (7.3-4)$$

where $\hat{g}_{ij}$ represents the metric tensor of the convected coordinates,
$\hat{\zeta}$. From the definition of convected coordinates, every material
point always has the same convected coordinate position at all
times, regardless of the extent of deformation of the medium. Thus
the relative convected coordinate displacements between any two
points ($d\hat{\zeta}^j$s) must be constant, so that any change in the distance
between the two points in convected space must be reflected by a

change in the metric $\hat{g}_{ij}$. That is, if the distance between two material points (ds) changes with time, the convected metric ($\hat{g}_{ij}$) must
change accordingly with time, since the convected coordinates ($\hat{\zeta}^i$)
of a material point are independent of time, by definition. It follows, then, that the convected metric tensor itself provides a suitable measure of deformation (i.e., strain), and hence is an appropriate kinematic variable applicable to any system regardless of the
magnitude of deformation.

To illustrate, consider the distance between two material points
at two different times t_o and $t(>t_o)$:

$$\text{at } t_o: \quad ds^2(t_o) = \hat{g}_{ij}(t_o) \, d\hat{\zeta}^i \, d\hat{\zeta}^j \tag{7.3-5}$$

$$\text{at } t: \quad ds^2(t) = \hat{g}_{ij}(t) \, d\hat{\zeta}^i \, d\hat{\zeta}^j \tag{7.3-6}$$

The change in the magnitude of the distance between the points from
t_o to t is then a measure of the strain or deformation occurring in
this time:

$$ds^2(t) - ds^2(t_o) = [\hat{g}_{ij}(t) - \hat{g}_{ij}(t_o)] \, d\hat{\zeta}^i \, d\hat{\zeta}^j \tag{7.3-7}$$

The quantity

$$E_{ij} \equiv [\hat{g}_{ij}(t) - \hat{g}_{ij}(t_o)] \tag{7.3-8}$$

is called the *convected covariant strain tensor* referred to time t_o.
Note that E_{ij} is a function of t, t_o, and ζ^i.

A *convected contravariant strain tensor* may similarly be defined as follows:

$$E^{ij} \equiv [\hat{g}^{ij}(t_o) - \hat{g}^{ij}(t)] \tag{7.3-9}$$

where

$$ds^2(t) - ds^2(t_o) = -E^{ij} \, d\hat{\zeta}_i \, d\hat{\zeta}_j \tag{7.3-10}$$

Although Eqs. (7.3-8) and (7.3-9) are not equivalent, it will be shown that they lead to equivalent definitions of the rate of strain tensor. The latter may be defined as the rate of change of deformation with time, with the convected coordinates held constant, that is, with reference to a given material element. It is evident that it represents a time derivative following the motion of the material, i.e., the material derivative:

$$\frac{D}{Dt} [ds^2(t) - ds^2(t_o)] = \frac{D}{Dt}(E_{ij}) \, d\hat{\zeta}^i \, d\hat{\zeta}^j \qquad (7.3\text{-}11)$$

It follows, then, that:

$$\left(\frac{DE_{ij}}{Dt}\right)_{\hat{\zeta}^i, t_o} = \frac{D}{Dt} [\hat{g}_{ij}(t) - \hat{g}_{ij}(t_o)] = \frac{D\hat{g}_{ij}(t)}{Dt} \qquad (7.3\text{-}12)$$

is the *convected covariant rate of strain tensor.* Using Eqs. (7.3-9) and (7.3-10), the contravariant equivalent of Eq. (7.3-11) is

$$\frac{D}{Dt} [ds^2(t) - ds^2(t_o)] = - \frac{DE^{ij}}{Dt} \, d\hat{\zeta}_i \, d\hat{\zeta}_j \qquad (7.3\text{-}13)$$

The quantity

$$- \frac{DE^{ij}}{Dt} = \frac{D}{Dt} [\hat{g}^{ij}(t) - \hat{g}^{ij}(t_o)] = \frac{D\hat{g}^{ij}(t)}{Dt} \qquad (7.3\text{-}14)$$

is the *convected contravariant rate of strain tensor.*

7.3.3. Finite Deformation Relative to Fixed Coordinates

We now have expressions representing strain and rate of strain in convected coordinates in terms of the convected metric ($\hat{g}_{ij}$ or $\hat{g}^{ij}$). It is necessary to transform these quantities to fixed coordinates, since physical quantities can only be measured relative to a fixed reference frame.

By definition of the metric tensor (in terms of the invariant ds^2), the fixed coordinate equivalent of the convected metric $\hat{g}_{ij}$ is just the fixed metric g_{ij}. However, the definition of the convected strain tensor, Eq. (7.3-8) or (7.3-9), involves the difference between two quantities associated with a given material element at different times, at the same point in convected space. Now in order to add or subtract quantities in a fixed coordinate reference frame, they must all refer to the same point in fixed space. Thus, we must transform the quantities $\hat{g}_{ij}(t)$ and $\hat{g}_{ij}(t_o)$ in such a manner that they both refer the same point in a fixed space before they can be combined by addition or subtraction. This can be done by making use of the transformation relations between fixed and convected coordinates, which can be derived as follows.

Consider a material point with *convected coordinates* ζ^i (which, by definition, are independent of time). Let the *fixed coordinates* of this at time t be denoted by $z^i(\zeta, t)$, and at some earlier time t' let the fixed coordinates of the same point be denoted by $Z^i(\zeta, t')$. The coordinates $z^i(\zeta, t)$ are termed the *current coordinates* (associating time t with "current" or present time), and the $Z^i(\zeta, t')$ are called *material coordinates*, being the fixed coordinates of the same material point at some earlier time.

Now the time rate of change of the current coordinates (z^i) are just the velocity components of the material point (v^i). Thus, for a steady flow system, the current and material coordinates are related by:

$$z^i(\zeta, t) = Z^i(\zeta, t') + u^i(z^j, t - t')$$

$$= Z^i(\zeta, t') + (t - t') \cdot v^i(z^j) \qquad (7.3\text{-}15)$$

or

$$Z^i(\zeta, t') = z^i(\zeta, t) - (t - t') \cdot v^i(z^j) \qquad (7.3\text{-}16)$$

where $u^i(z^i, t - t')$ is the displacement relative to fixed coordinates that the material point has undergone in time $(t - t')$. For unsteady flow (if the velocity components v^i are functions of time), the appropriate relation is

$$z^i(\zeta, t) = Z^i(\zeta, t') + \int_{t'}^{t} v^i(z^j, t) \, dt \qquad (7.3\text{--}17)$$

Now let us consider any tensor quantity, $b_i{}^j$, which is associated with the material. The components of this tensor with respect to the fixed coordinates z^i will be denoted $b_i{}^j(z, t)$ and the components relative to coordinates Z^i will be denoted $b_i{}^j(Z, t')$. Note that since both the coordinates z^i and Z^i are common to the same material point (at different times), so then are the tensor components $b_i{}^j(z, t)$ and $b_i{}^j(Z, t')$. These two sets of tensor components are distinct, however, as illustrated in Fig. 7.5.

Now in order to combine the tensor componets $b_i{}^j(Z, t')$ with the components $b_i{}^j(z, t)$, they must be transformed in such a manner that they both refer to the same point in fixed space. This can be done by recognizing that, since they both refer to the same material

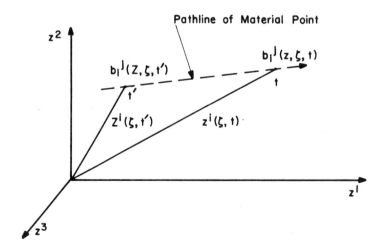

FIG. 7.5 Relation between current and material coordinates.

element, they may both be transformed directly to the same tensor
components in convected space. The transformation relation between
the fixed (material) components $b_i{}^j(Z, t')$ and convected components
$\beta_i{}^j(\zeta)$ is

$$\beta_k{}^\ell(\zeta) = \left| \frac{\partial \zeta^\ell}{\partial z^j} \frac{\partial z^i}{\partial \zeta^k} \right| b_i{}^j(Z, t') \qquad\qquad (7.3\text{-}18)$$

Now since the convected coordinates (ζ^i) are common to both the fixed
coordinates, z^i, and the material coordinates Z^i, and are independent
of time, i.e.,

$$\zeta^i(Z, t') = \zeta^i(z, t) \qquad\qquad (7.3\text{-}19)$$

we may transform any tensor components directly from convected coordinates to the fixed coordinates z^i. Thus, if the fixed (current)
components of the tensor $\beta_i{}^j(\zeta)$ referred to the coordinates $z^i(t)$
are denoted by $B_i{}^j(z, t, t')$, the transformation relation between
these components is

$$B_m{}^n(z, t, t') = \left| \frac{\partial z^n}{\partial \zeta^\ell} \frac{\partial \zeta^k}{\partial z^m} \right| \beta_k{}^\ell(\zeta) \qquad\qquad (7.3\text{-}20)$$

It is apparent, from Eqs. (7.3-18) and (7.3-20) that the components
$B_m{}^n(z, t, t')$ are the components of the tensor $b_i{}^j(Z, t')$ which have
been transformed to the fixed coordinates $z^i(t)$. These components
may then be combined with components of any other tensor associated
with the same fixed point and time, for example, the components
$b_i{}^j(z, t)$. Diagrammatically, the transformation has proceeded as
illustrated in Fig. 7.6. The convected components $\beta_k{}^\ell$ may be
eliminated by substitution of Eq. (7.3-18) into Eq. (7.3-20) to give:

$$B_m{}^n(z, t, t') = \left| \frac{\partial z^n}{\partial z^j} \frac{\partial z^i}{\partial z^m} \right| b_i{}^j(Z, t') \qquad\qquad (7.3\text{-}21)$$

The components $B_m{}^n(z, t, t')$ are called the *Eulerian components*
of the tensor $b_i{}^j(Z, t')$, with respect to the coordinates $z^i(t)$.

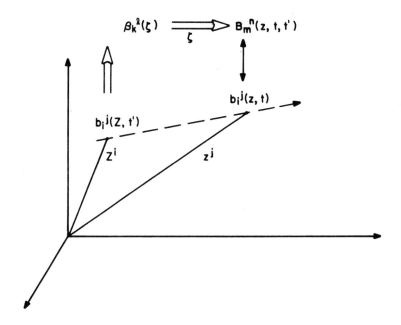

FIG. 7.6 Transformation of tensor components from material to current coordinates.

They are the components of the tensor $b_i{}^j$ (which represents any tensor quantity associated with the material) which have been transformed from the fixed coordinates of the material element at time t' (i.e., coordinates Z^j) to the corresponding fixed coordinates of the same element at later time t. Note they do not represent the values of the components of $b_i{}^j$ at time t, which are associated with the material point at coordinates z^j. The Eulerian components are determined entirely by the transformation between the current and material coordinates [Eq. (7.3-16)], the convected coordinates having been eliminated. Thus if any tensor quantity associated with a given material element or point at a given time (e.g., t') is to be combined with a tensor associated with the same material element at a later time (t), it is necessary to transform the former tensor into its Eulerian components before the two tensors can be combined.

Perhaps these relations can be further clarified by a simplified analogy. Suppose we desire to determine the contribution that the exhaust effluent from a particular car has made to the pollution index of the Dallas atmosphere at time t. However the car moves around with time, and at an earlier time t' was located in Ft. Worth. So, in order to determine the cumulative effect of the car's effluent on the Dallas atmosphere, we must determine that portion of the effluent discharged in Ft. Worth which drifts from Ft. Worth to Dallas, in order to combine this with that which is discharged in Dallas. The car is analogous to our material element, the tensor $\beta_k^{\ell}(\zeta)$ is analogous to the observed exhaust effluent as we follow the car around, $b_i^{\ j}(Z, t')$ is the effluent discharged in Ft. Worth (Z) at time t', $b_i^{\ j}(z, t)$ is the effluent discharged in Dallas (z) at time t, and $B_m^{\ n}(z, t, t')$ is the portion of the effluent released in Ft. Worth at time t' which ends up in the Dallas atmosphere (z) at the later time t.

It is thus apparent that transformation of the covariant convected strain tensor, Eq. (7.3-8), to fixed coordinates must involve the Eulerian components of the metric tensor, since it involves the difference between the metric tensor components which are associated with the same material point at different times (t, t_o). The Eulerian components of the metric g_{ij} are

$$c_{ij}(z, t, t_o) = \left(\frac{\partial Z^m}{\partial z^i} \frac{\partial Z^n}{\partial z^j}\right) g_{mn}(Z) \qquad (7.3-22)$$

where $Z^i = Z^i(z^j, t, t_o)$ are the material coordinates at time t_o of the point which has fixed coordinates z^j at time t. The tensor $c_{ij}(z, t, t_o)$ is called the *Cauchy deformation tensor*. It is this tensor which is the fixed component counterpart of the convected metric $\hat{g}_{ij}(t_o)$, referred to time t. Its components can thus be combined with those of the fixed coordinate equivalent of the convected metric $\hat{g}_{ij}(t)$, which is the fixed metric $g_{ij}(z)$. The fixed counterpart of the covariant convected strain tensor is, therefore, from Eqs. (7.3-8) and (7.3-22):

$$\Gamma_{ij}(z, t, t_o) = g_{ij}(z) - c_{ij}(z, t, t_o)$$

$$= g_{ij}(z) - \left|\frac{\partial Z^m}{\partial z^i} \frac{\partial Z^n}{\partial z^j}\right| g_{mn}(Z) \qquad (7.3-23)$$

The tensor $\Gamma_{ij}(z, t, t_o)$ is a *covariant finite strain tensor*, also known as the *Almansi strain tensor*. It represents the deformation that a material point located at point z at time t has experienced during the time period $(t - t_o)$, regardless of the magnitude of the deformation that has occurred during this time. This is in contrast to the infinitesimal strain tensor, e_{ij}, which is valid only for small amplitude (infinitesimal) deformation:

$$e_{ij} = \left|\frac{\partial u^k}{\partial z^i} g_{kj} + \frac{\partial u^k}{\partial z^j} g_{ki}\right| = u_{i,j} + u_{j,i} \qquad (7.3-24)$$

Comparison of Eqs. (7.3-23) and (7.3-24) shows that the strain tensors Γ_{ij} and e_{ij} are related by:

$$\Gamma_{ij} = e_{ij} - u_{n,i}u^n,_j \qquad (7.3-25)$$

The fixed counterpart of the contravariant convected strain tensor follows from Eq. (7.3-9):

$$\Gamma^{ij}(z, t, t_o) = c^{ij}(z, t, t_o) - g^{ij}(z)$$

$$= \left|\frac{\partial z^i}{\partial Z^m} \frac{\partial z^j}{\partial Z^n}\right| g^{mn}(Z) - g^{ij}(z) \qquad (7.3-26)$$

The contravariant tensor $c^{ij}(z, t, t_o)$ is also called the *Finger deformation tensor*, or sometimes the *left Cauchy-Green tensor*, and the tensor Γ^{ij} is the *Finger strain tensor*. Note that the Cauchy and Finger tensors are related by $c_{im}c^{mj} = \delta_i^{\ j}$, that is the matrix of the components of one is the inverse matrix of the other. As we shall demonstrate, the covariant and contravariant finite strain tensors Γ_{ij} and Γ^{ij} are not equivalent measures of deformation. The contravariant finite Finger strain tensor is related to the contravariant form of the infinitesimal strain tensor by:

$$\Gamma^{ij} = e^{ij} + u^i,_m u^j,_n g^{mn} \tag{7.3-27}$$

The transformations between current and material coordinates may also be used to define alternate covariant and contravariant finite strain tensors as follows:

$$G_{ij} = C_{ij} - g_{ij} \tag{7.3-28}$$

$$G^{ij} = g^{ij} - C^{ij} \tag{7.3-29}$$

where

$$C_{ij} = \frac{\partial z^m}{\partial z^i} \frac{\partial z^n}{\partial z^j} g_{mn} \tag{7.3-30}$$

is the *Green* (or sometimes the right Cauchy-Green) *deformation tensor*, and

$$C^{ij} = \frac{\partial z^i}{\partial z^m} \frac{\partial z^j}{\partial z^n} g^{mn} \tag{7.3-31}$$

is the *Piola deformation tensor*. The tensors G_{ij} and G^{ij} are the covariant and contravariant *Green strain tensors*, and are similar to the Cauchy and Finger tensors. The Green and Piola tensor component matrices are also the inverse of one another; i.e., $C_{im}C^{mj} = \delta_i{}^j$. Since the strain tensors Γ_{ij} and Γ^{ij} (as well as G_{ij} and G^{ij}) are functions of the transformation relations between the material and current coordinates, it should be evident they are dependent upon the flow or deformation configuration (i.e., the velocity components). As an example, we will illustrate the determination of the components of the finite strain tensors Γ_{ij} and Γ^{ij} for Poiseuille flow.

(The physical components of these tensors for steady simple shear, Poiseuille, Couette, and cone and plate flows are tabulated in Appendix E.)

———————————————————————— 0 ————————————————————————

Example 7.1 Determine the components of the finite covariant and contravariant strain tensors Γ_{ij} and Γ^{ij} for Poiseuille flow.

Solution. For Poiseuille flow, the tensor velocity components in cylindrical coordinates $(z, r, \Theta) = (z^1, z^2, z^3)$ are:

$$v_z(r) = v^1(z^2) \qquad v^2 = v^3 = 0$$

Hence, from Eq. (7.3-16), the material coordinates are:

$$z^1 = z^1 - (t - t_o)v^1(z^2) = z - (t - t_o)v_z(r)$$

$$z^2 = r$$

$$z^3 = \theta$$

since v_z is the only nonzero velocity component.

For fixed cylindrical coordinates, the metric tensor is:

$$g_{ij} = \begin{bmatrix} 1 & 0 & 0 \\ 0 & 1 & 0 \\ 0 & 0 & r^2 \end{bmatrix} = g_{ij}(r)$$

The Eulerian components of g_{ij}, by Eq. (7.3-22), are the components of the Cauchy tensor:

$$c_{ij}(z, t, t_o) = \left(\frac{\partial Z^m}{\partial z^i} \frac{\partial Z^n}{\partial z^j} \right) g_{mn}$$

or

$$c_{11} = \left(\frac{\partial z^1}{\partial z^1}\right)^2 g_{11} + \frac{\partial z^1}{\partial z^1}\frac{\partial z^2}{\partial z^1}\cancel{g_{12}}^{0} + \frac{\partial z^1}{\partial z^1}\frac{\partial z^3}{\partial z^1}\cancel{g_{13}}^{0}$$

$$+ \frac{\partial z^2}{\partial z^1}\frac{\partial z^1}{\partial z^1}\cancel{g_{21}}^{0} + + \left(\frac{\partial z^2}{\partial z^1}\right)^2 g_{22} + \frac{\partial z^2}{\partial z^1}\frac{\partial z^3}{\partial z^1}\cancel{g_{23}}^{0}$$

$$+ \frac{\partial z^3}{\partial z^1}\frac{\partial z^1}{\partial z^1}\cancel{g_{31}}^{0} + \frac{\partial z^3}{\partial z^1}\frac{\partial z^2}{\partial z^1}\cancel{g_{32}}^{0} + \cancel{\left(\frac{\partial z^3}{\partial z^1}\right)^2}^{0} g_{33} = 1$$

Following a similar procedure for the other 8 components, we find:

$$c_{ij} = \begin{bmatrix} 1 & -(t - t_o)\dfrac{dv}{dr} & 0 \\[2mm] -(t - t_o)\dfrac{dv}{dr} & 1 + (t - t_o)^2\left(\dfrac{dv}{dr}\right)^2 & 0 \\[2mm] 0 & 0 & r^2 \end{bmatrix}$$

By Eq. (7.3-23), the covariant finite strain tensor is:

$$\Gamma_{ij} = g_{ij} - c_{ij} = \begin{bmatrix} 0 & (t - t_o)\dfrac{dv}{dr} & 0 \\[2mm] (t - t_o)\dfrac{dv}{dr} & -(t - t_o)^2\left(\dfrac{dv}{dr}\right)^2 & 0 \\[2mm] 0 & 0 & 0 \end{bmatrix}$$

It should be noted that this differs from the infinitesimal strain
tensor (Eq. (7.3-24) by the normal strain term, where the displacements are the difference between the current and material coordinates.

The contravariant strain tensor, Eq. (7.3-26), is the difference between the Finger tensor and the conjugate metric. The latter is:

$$g_{ij} = \begin{bmatrix} 1 & 0 & 0 \\ 0 & 1 & 0 \\ 0 & 0 & \dfrac{1}{r^2} \end{bmatrix} = g^{ij}(r)$$

The former may be evaluated directly from the transformation between current and material coordinates, as before, to give

$$c^{ij} = \begin{bmatrix} 1 + (t - t_o)^2 \left(\dfrac{dv}{dr}\right)^2 & (t - t_o)\dfrac{dv}{dr} & 0 \\ (t - t_o)\dfrac{dv}{dr} & 1 & 0 \\ 0 & 0 & \dfrac{1}{r^2} \end{bmatrix}$$

so that the contravariant strain tensor is:

$$\Gamma^{ij} = c^{ij} - g^{ij} = \begin{bmatrix} (t - t_o)^2 \left(\dfrac{dv}{dr}\right)^2 & (t - t_o)\dfrac{dv}{dr} & 0 \\ (t - t_o)\dfrac{dv}{dr} & 0 & 0 \\ 0 & 0 & 0 \end{bmatrix}$$

Note that the covariant and contravariant forms are not equivalent, in that they contain different normal strain components.

The consequence of this difference is that Γ^{ij} and Γ_{ij} do not commute with the operation of raising or lowering indices, so that the physical process described by the contravariant form is not the same as that described by the covariant form. The same conclusions apply to the Green strain tensors G_{ij} and G^{ij}.

---------------------------------- 0 ----------------------------------

7.3.4. Deformation Rate--The Convected Derivative

We have deduced appropriate expressions for the covariant and contravariant forms of the rate of strain tensor with respect to the convected reference frame, Eqs. (7.3-12) and (7.3-14). It is necessary to transform these expressions from convected to fixed components if they are to be referred to physical systems. Note that we cannot simply replace the convected metric, $\hat{g}_{ij}$, by its fixed counterpart, g_{ij}, in these expressions since, in particular:

$$\frac{Dg_{ij}}{Dt} = 0 = \frac{\partial g_{ij}}{\partial t} + v^k g_{ij,k} \tag{7.3-32}$$

Specifically, we need to determine the general relations which permit us to express the fixed coordinate equivalent of the variation with time of some quantity associated with the material, as the material moves and deforms. That is, we need the fixed coordinate equivalent of the material derivative of a convected tensor.

To do this, let us consider the transformation of tensor components between a fixed and convected reference frame, at a given time. If the fixed components of a given tensor are b_{ij} and its convected components are β_{ij}, the transformation is:

$$\beta_{mn}(\zeta) = \left(\frac{\partial x^i}{\partial \zeta^m}\right)\left(\frac{\partial x^j}{\partial \zeta^n}\right) b_{ij}(x,\, t) \tag{7.3-33}$$

The material derivative of this tensor is:

$$\frac{D\beta_{mn}}{Dt} = \left(\frac{\partial x^i}{\partial \zeta^m}\right)\left(\frac{\partial x^j}{\partial \zeta^n}\right)\frac{Db_{ij}}{Dt} + \left(\frac{\partial x^i}{\partial \zeta^m}\right)\left[\frac{D}{Dt}\left(\frac{\partial x^j}{\partial \zeta^n}\right)\right] b_{ij}$$

$$+ \left[\frac{D}{Dt}\left(\frac{\partial x^i}{\partial \zeta^m}\right)\right]\left(\frac{\partial x^j}{\partial \zeta^n}\right) b_{ij} \tag{7.3-34}$$

where

$$\frac{Db_{ij}}{Dt} = \frac{\partial b_{ij}}{\partial t} + v^k b_{ij,k} \qquad (7.3\text{-}35)$$

Now we also have:

$$\frac{D}{Dt}\left(\frac{\partial x^j}{\partial \zeta^n}\right) = \frac{\partial}{\partial \zeta^n}\left(\frac{Dx^j}{Dt}\right) = \frac{\partial v^j}{\partial \zeta^n} \qquad (7.3\text{-}36)$$

since the material derivative, Dx^j/Dt, is just the rate of change of the fixed coordinate of a point following the motion of the medium, i.e., the velocity component of that point with reference to fixed coordinates. Thus, Eq. (7.3-34) can be written:

$$\frac{D\beta_{mn}}{Dt} = \left(\frac{\partial x^i}{\partial \zeta^m}\right)\left(\frac{\partial x^j}{\partial \zeta^n}\right)\frac{Db_{ij}}{Dt} + \left(\frac{\partial x^i}{\partial \zeta^m}\right)\left(\frac{\partial v^j}{\partial \zeta^n}\right)b_{ij} + \left(\frac{\partial v^i}{\partial \zeta^m}\right)\left(\frac{\partial x^j}{\partial \zeta^n}\right)b_{ij} \quad (7.3\text{-}37)$$

or, since $v^j = v^j(x^i)$:

$$\frac{D\beta_{mn}}{Dt} = \left(\frac{\partial x^i}{\partial \zeta^m}\right)\left(\frac{\partial x^j}{\partial \zeta^n}\right)\frac{Db_{ij}}{Dt} + \left(\frac{\partial x^i}{\partial \zeta^m}\right)\left(\frac{\partial x^r}{\partial \zeta^n}\right)\left(\frac{\partial v^j}{\partial \zeta^r}\right)b_{ij} + \left(\frac{\partial x^r}{\partial \zeta^m}\right)\left(\frac{\partial v^i}{\partial \zeta^r}\right)\left(\frac{\partial x^j}{\partial \zeta^n}\right)b_{ij}$$

$$(7.3\text{-}38)$$

Now the indices i, j, and r in Eq. (7.3-38) are repeated (dummy) indices, and may be replaced by any symbol. Thus if we replace r by j and j by k in the second term, on the right, and replace r by i and i by k in the last term, Eq. (7.3-38) becomes:

$$\frac{D\beta_{mn}}{Dt} = \left(\frac{\partial x^i}{\partial \zeta^m}\right)\left(\frac{\partial x^j}{\partial \zeta^n}\right)\left[\frac{Db_{ij}}{Dt} + \frac{\partial v^k}{\partial x^j}b_{ik} + \frac{\partial v^k}{\partial x^i}b_{kj}\right] \qquad (7.3\text{-}39)$$

The transformation Eq. (7.3-39) defines a covariant second-order tensor, so that the quantity in square brackets in Eq. (7.3-39) is the fixed coordinate equivalent of the material derivative of a second-order tensor referred to convected coordinates. This tensor is called the *convected derivative*, and will be denoted by:

$$\frac{\delta b_{ij}}{\delta t} = \frac{\partial b_{ij}}{\partial t} + v^k \frac{\partial b_{ij}}{\partial x^k} + \frac{\partial v^k}{\partial x^j} b_{ik} + \frac{\partial v^k}{\partial x^i} b_{kj} \tag{7.3-40}$$

Equation (7.3-40) is valid for any fixed coordinate system (z^i), not just for Cartesian coordinates. In fact, it can be readily demonstrated that Eq. (7.3-40) is identical to the result obtained by replacing the spatial derivatives by covariant derivatives, i.e.,

$$\frac{\delta b_{ij}}{\delta t} = \frac{\partial b_{ij}}{\partial t} + v^k b_{ij,k} + v^k,_j b_{ik} + v^k,_i b_{kj}$$

$$= \frac{D b_{ij}}{Dt} + v^k,_j b_{ik} + v^k,_i b_{kj} \tag{7.3-41}$$

Since Eqs. (7.3-40) and (7.3-41) are equivalent, it is usually more convenient to use the former when evaluating individual components of the convected derivative.

A similar procedure can be followed for a contravariant tensor, or for a mixed tensor of any order. The general result for the convected derivative of a tensor of any type or order can be written:

$$\frac{\delta b^{\cdots j \cdots}_{\cdots i \cdots}}{\delta t} = \frac{D b^{\cdots j \cdots}_{\cdots i \cdots}}{Dt} + \sum v^k,_i b^{\cdots j}_{\cdots k} \quad - \quad \sum^1 v^j,_k b^{\cdots k}_{\cdots i \cdots} \tag{7.3-42}$$

(Sum on covariant   (Sum on contra-
indices)   variant indices)

Note that Eq. (7.3-42) can also be written in terms of the rate of strain and vorticity tensors:

$$\frac{\delta b^{\cdots j}_{\cdots i}}{\delta t} = \frac{D b^{\cdots j}_{\cdots i}}{Dt} + \frac{1}{2} \left[\sum \Omega^{\cdot k}_{i \cdot} b^{\cdots j}_{\cdots k \cdot} + \sum' \Omega^{j \cdot}_{\cdot k} b^{\cdots k}_{\cdot \cdot i \cdot} \right]$$
Covariant   Contravariant

$$+ \frac{1}{2} \left[\sum \Delta^{\cdot k}_{i \cdot} b^{\cdots j}_{\cdots k} - \sum' \Delta^{j \cdot}_{\cdot k} b^{\cdots k}_{\cdot \cdot i} \right] \tag{7.3-43}$$
Covariant   Contravariant

since

$$v_{i,j} = (\Delta_{ij} + \Omega_{ji}) \tag{7.3-44}$$

The significance of each of the terms in Eq. (7.3-43) is as follows. The first term (material derivative) has been shown to be the rate of time variation while following the translational motion of a material element. The second term (in parentheses), follows the rotational motion of the element, while the third term follows its deformation. Note that the convected derivative of a scalar quantity reduces simply to the material derivative.

Returning, then, to the convected rate of strain tensor, Eqs. (7.3-12) and (7.3-14), the transformation from convected to fixed components involves simply replacing the convected metric by the fixed metric and the material derivative by the convected derivative:

$$\frac{D\hat{g}_{ij}}{Dt} \rightarrow \frac{\delta g_{ij}}{\delta t} \equiv \Delta_{ij} \tag{7.3-45}$$

Convected strain rate   Fixed strain rate

Evaluating the convected derivative of the metric tensor by means of Eq. (7.3-40) or (7.3-41) shows that:

$$\Delta_{ij} = \frac{\delta g_{ij}}{\delta t} = \underbrace{\frac{Dg_{ij}}{Dt}}_{0} + g_{ik}v^k{}_{,j} + g_{kj}v^k{}_{,i} = v_{i,j} + v_{j,i} \tag{7.3-46}$$

This obviously coincides with our original definition of the rate of strain tensor, based upon the concept of infinitesimal strain.

Similarly, the fixed components of the contravariant rate of strain tensor, Eq. (7.3-14), become:

$$\Delta^{ij} = -\frac{\delta g^{ij}}{\delta t} = -\left(\underbrace{\frac{Dg^{ij}}{Dt}}_{0} - v^i{}_{,k}g^{kj} - v^j{}_{,k}g^{ik}\right)$$

$$= v_{r,s}g^{ri}g^{sj} + v_{s,r}g^{sj}g^{ri} = \Delta_{rs}g^{ri}g^{sj} \tag{7.3-47}$$

It is thus evident that, even though our original definition of the covariant and contravariant finite strain tensors were not equivalent, they do lead to equivalent expressions for the covariant and contravariant rate of strain tensors.

Thus, in order to extend previous "small deformation" rheological equations for time-dependent (viscoelastic) materials to situations involving large amplitude or continuous deformations, all that is required is that the original equation be written in terms of the convected components of the tensor quantities involved, and that the result then transformed to fixed coordinates. The net result involves replacing all quantities associated with "prior" times (t') by their Eulerian components [Eq. (7.3-22)], and all time derivatives by convected derivatives. For example, an appropriate generalization of the rate equation for the Maxwell fluid might be written

$$
\tau_{ij} + \lambda \frac{\delta \tau_{ij}}{\delta t} = \mu \frac{\delta g_{ij}}{\delta t} = \mu \Delta_{ij}
\tag{7.3-48}
$$

and the equivalent integral or hereditary form would be:

$$
\tau_{ij} = \int_{-\infty}^{t} G e^{-(t-t')/\lambda} \frac{\partial Z^m}{\partial z^i} \frac{\partial Z^n}{\partial z^j} \Delta_{mn}(Z, t')\ dt'
\tag{7.3-49}
$$

The equivalent hereditary form in terms of the strain tensor and memory function could be written:

$$
\tau_{ij} = \int_{-\infty}^{t} \left(\frac{G}{\lambda}\right) e^{-(t-t')/\lambda} \Gamma_{ij}(t')\ dt'
\tag{7.3-50}
$$

where the state at time t is assumed to be the reference or undeformed state.

The appropriate definitions of convected strain and strain rate applicable to large amplitude (and continuous) deformations are summarized in Table 7.1, together with the corresponding expressions for fixed components and the limiting forms for small amplitude deformation, for reference.

TABLE 7.1

Kinematic Variables in Convected and Fixed Reference Frames

	Finite deformation (convected components)	Finite deformation (fixed components)	Infinitesimal deformation (fixed components)
Strain	$\hat{g}_{ij}(\hat{\zeta}, t) - \hat{g}_{ij}(\hat{\zeta}, t_o)$ $\hat{g}^{ij}(\hat{\zeta}, t_o) - \hat{g}^{ij}(\hat{\zeta}, t)$	$g_{ij}(z, t) - \left[\dfrac{\partial Z^m}{\partial z^i}\dfrac{\partial Z^n}{\partial z^j}\right] g_{mn}(Z, t_o) = \Gamma_{ij}$ $\left[\dfrac{\partial z^i}{\partial Z^m}\dfrac{\partial z^j}{\partial Z^n}\right] g^{mn}(Z, t_o) - g^{ij}(z, t) = \Gamma^{ij}$	$u_{i,j} + u_{j,i} = e_{ij}$ $(u_{r,s} + u_{s,r})g^{ri}g^{sj} = e^{ij}$
Strain rate	$\left(\dfrac{D\hat{g}_{ij}(\hat{\zeta}, t)}{Dt}\right) = \left(\dfrac{\partial \hat{g}_{ij}}{\partial t}\right)_{\hat{\zeta}}$ $\dfrac{D\hat{g}^{ij}(\hat{\zeta}, t)}{Dt} = -\left(\dfrac{\partial \hat{g}^{ij}}{\partial t}\right)_{\hat{\zeta}}$	$\dfrac{\delta g_{ij}}{\delta t} = v_{i,j} + v_{j,i} = \Delta_{ij}$ $-\dfrac{\delta g^{ij}}{\delta t} = (v_{r,s} + v_{s,r})g^{ri}g^{sj} = \Delta^{ij}$	$v_{i,j} + v_{j,i} = \Delta_{ij}$ $(v_{r,s} + v_{s,r})g^{ri}g^{sj} = \Delta^{ij}$
Second rate of strain	$\dfrac{D^2\hat{g}_{ij}(\hat{\zeta}, t)}{Dt^2} = \left(\dfrac{\partial^2 \hat{g}_{ij}}{\partial t^2}\right)_{\hat{\zeta}}$ $-\dfrac{D^2\hat{g}^{ij}(\hat{\zeta}, t)}{Dt^2} = -\left(\dfrac{\partial^2 \hat{g}_{ij}}{\partial t^2}\right)_{\hat{\zeta}}$	$\dfrac{\delta^2 g_{ij}}{\delta t^2} = \dfrac{\mathcal{D}\Delta_{ij}}{\mathcal{D}t} + \Delta_{ik}\Delta^k_{\ j}$ $-\dfrac{\delta^2 g^{ij}}{\delta t^2} = \dfrac{\mathcal{D}\Delta^{ij}}{\mathcal{D}t} + \Delta^{ik}\Delta_k^{\ j}$	$\dfrac{\partial \Delta_{ij}}{\partial t}$ $\dfrac{\partial \Delta^{ij}}{\partial t}$

7.3.5. Other "Convected" Time Derivatives

A major difficulty arises when applying the above generalization principles to various forms of tensor equations of state. This results from the fact that neither the formulation of Eulerian components, Eq. (7.3-21), nor the operation of convected differentiation, Eq. (7.3-40) or (7.3-42), commutes with the operation of raising and lowering indices. That is,

$$
\left.
\begin{array}{l}
\left(\dfrac{\partial z^m}{\partial z^i} \dfrac{\partial z^n}{\partial z^j} \right) b_{mn} = B_{ij} \\[3ex]
\left(\dfrac{\partial z^i}{\partial z^m} \dfrac{\partial z^j}{\partial z^n} \right) b^{mn} = B^{ij}
\end{array}
\right\}
\qquad B_{ij} \neq g_{ik} g_{j\ell} B^{k\ell}
\tag{7.3-51}
$$

and

$$
\frac{\delta b_{ij}}{\delta t} \neq g_{ik} g_{j\ell} \frac{\delta b^{k\ell}}{\delta t}
\tag{7.3-52}
$$

One consequence of Eq. (7.3-51) is that the Almansi and Finger tensors are not equivalent measures of finite strain, as has already been demonstrated. The primary consequence of Eq. (7.3-52) is that contravariant and covariant forms of a given tensor equation of state involving convected derivatives are not equivalent. For example, the corresponding contravariant form of Eqs. (7.3-48) to (7.3-50) predict different normal stress components than the covariant forms in many flows.

There are several ways to resolve this problem. For example, it is easily shown that there are other "time" derivative operators besides that defined by Eq. (7.3-42) which transform as a tensor from convected to fixed coordinates. One of these which does commute with the raising and lowering of indices is the *Jaumann derivative*, defined as follows:

$$\frac{\mathcal{D}b^{\cdots j}_{\cdot\cdot i\cdot}}{\mathcal{D}t} = \frac{Db^{\cdots j}_{\cdot\cdot i\cdot}}{Dt} + \frac{1}{2}\left[\sum \Omega_i{}^m b^{\cdots j}_{\cdot\cdot m\cdot} + \sum^1 b^{\cdots m}_{\cdot\cdot i\cdot} \Omega^j{}_m \right] \qquad (7.3\text{-}53)$$

Sum on covariant   Sum on contra-
indices   variant indices

where $\Omega_i{}^j$ is the vorticity tensor, which has been defined as:

$$\Omega_{ij} = (v_{j,i} - v_{i,j}) = -\Omega_{ji}$$

$$\Omega_i{}^j = \Omega_{ik}g^{kj} = -\Omega^j{}_i \qquad (7.3\text{-}54)$$

The components of the Jaumann derivative of a tensor are also related to the convected derivatives of the covariant and contravariant components of the tensor as follows:

$$\frac{\mathcal{D}b_{ji}}{\mathcal{D}t} = \frac{1}{2}\left(\frac{\delta b_{ij}}{\delta t} + g_{ir}g_{js}\frac{\delta b^{rs}}{\delta t} \right)$$

$$= \frac{Db_{ij}}{Dt} + \frac{1}{2}(\Omega_i{}^k b_{kj} + \Omega_j{}^k b_{ik})$$

$$= \frac{Db_{ij}}{Dt} + \frac{1}{2}(\Omega_i{}^k b_{kj} - b_{ik}\Omega^k{}_j) \qquad (7.3\text{-}55)$$

and

$$\frac{\mathcal{D}b^{ij}}{\mathcal{D}t} = \frac{1}{2}\frac{\delta b^{ij}}{\delta t} + g^{ir}g^{js}\frac{\delta b_{rs}}{\delta t}$$

$$= \frac{Db^{ij}}{Dt} + \frac{1}{2}(\Omega^i{}_k b^{kj} + b^{ik}\Omega^j{}_k)$$

$$= \frac{Db^{ij}}{Dt} + \frac{1}{2}(\Omega^i{}_k b^{kj} - b^{ik}\Omega_k{}^j) \qquad (7.3\text{-}56)$$

Comparison of Eqs. (7.3-53) and (7.3-43) shows that the Jaumann derivative is a measure of time variation while following the translation and rotation of a material element.

   The significance of the various time derivatives is illustrated
graphically in Fig. 7.7. Specific components of these derivatives
of a second-order tensor for the most common viscometric flow systems,
in terms of physical velocity components, are presented in Appendix E,
along with a tabulation of the components of the covariant and contravariant finite strain tensors for the same systems. Note that all of
the above time derivatives reduce to the partial derivative in the
limit of vanishingly small velocities and velocity gradients.

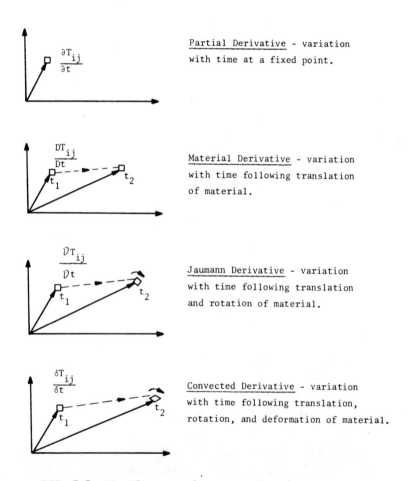

Partial Derivative - variation
with time at a fixed point.

Material Derivative - variation
with time following translation
of material.

Jaumann Derivative - variation
with time following translation
and rotation of material.

Convected Derivative - variation
with time following translation,
rotation, and deformation of material.

FIG. 7.7 Significance of various time derivatives.

A similar method can be used to formulate a measure for finite strain which commutes with the operation of raising and lowering indices. A suitable combination of the covariant and contravariant components of the finite strain tensors, Γ_{ij} and Γ^{ij}, is:

$$\frac{1}{2} (\Gamma_{ij} + g_{ir}g_{js}\Gamma^{rs}) \qquad\qquad (7.3\text{-}57)$$

or

$$\frac{1}{2} (\Gamma^{ij} + g^{ir}g^{js}\Gamma_{rs}) \qquad\qquad (7.3\text{-}58)$$

In the formulation of time-dependent equations of state for viscoelastic fluids, there are a number of possible measures of time variation and of finite strain that can be used in addition to those referred to here. There are no strict rules or standard methods which can be applied to determine which might be the best or most appropriate. The only true criterion for the validity of a given relation is whether or not the results it predicts agree with the observed deformation response of a given material in terms of all possible measurable material functions under a wide range of conditions. This includes the apparent viscosity and normal stresses as a function of shear rate, small amplitude (linearized) oscillatory response as a function of frequency, transient response as a function of time and amplitude of deformation, etc.

7.4. VISCOELASTIC FLUID MODELS

By proper application of the preceding principles, mathematical models or general rheological equations of state for viscoelastic fluids may be formulated which should be valid for any deformation, regardless of magnitude or time history. By employing these models to calculate the response (i.e., stress behavior) in various specific deformations such as steady simple shear, oscillatory shear, etc., analytical expressions for the corresponding material functions such

as apparent viscosity, normal stress functions complex modulus, etc.,
may be determined.

The validity of any model can only be judged by the degree to
which it represents actual observations. Thus, the validity of a
given rheological equation of state may be judged by the degree to
which the material functions which it predicts may be utilized to
represent measured values of these material functions, for a given
(fluid) material. In principle, a general rheological equation can
be used to predict the material response to any conceivable deformation. In practice, the data obtainable for a given material are invariably limited, so that it may be extremely difficult to absolutely
verify a given model for a complex material. The number of material
functions, and the required range of data for each, which are necessary to completely describe a given material depends largely upon the
complexity of the material. This may range from a very simple fluid
which has a Newtonian viscosity, no normal stress properties, and no
elastic characteristics for which the simple Newtonian model and hence
one datum point is adequate, to a complex polymer or polymer solution
which exhibits nonlinear apparent viscosity and normal stress behavior,
complex time-dependent response, etc. In the latter case, it may be
relatively easy to formulate a "generalized model" which represents
one of the measurable material functions over a limited range of
data, but which may not be adequate over an extended range or be consistent with other material functions. In such cases the model could
not be considered completely general, but may, nevertheless, be useful for predicting certain specific response behavior.

Materials and their generalized models or rheological equations
of state may be broadly classified as linear or nonlinear. One consequence of nonlinearity is shear dependent apparent viscosity and
normal stress coefficients. Essentially all real materials of complex structure are nonlinear except under conditions of very small
deformation. Nonlinearity may be incorporated in either of two ways:
by using linear operators (i.e., time derivatives) but including nonlinear terms (products of stress and/or strain or their derivatives)
in the equations; or by the use of nonlinear operators in otherwise

linear equations. In either case, the specific component equations will involve products of stress and/or velocity gradient components. The convected derivative is an example of a linear time derivative operator, while the Jaumann derivative is a nonlinear operator, as we shall demonstrate.

In this section, we present some examples of linear and nonlinear rheological equations or models, of both the differential and integral type. No attempt has been made to be exhaustive, inasmuch as a great many models have been proposed in the literature and none have been proven to be of sufficiently general validity as to represent the behavior of a large number of materials. A comparison and evaluation of a number of these models has been presented by Spriggs et al. [7.5] and by Bogue and Doughty [7.6]. Those selected for discussion here serve simply as representative examples of some of the various types of models which have been employed for viscoelastic fluids. In general, the materials which are of greatest rheological interest (e.g., polymers, polymer solutions, slurries, pastes, suspensions, etc.) are so complex that no single model has yet been found entirely adequate for any given material. Therefore, despite the rather large volume of literature devoted to this subject, the field of rheology from this point of view may still be said to be in its infancy.

7.4.1. Rate or Derivative Models

A. Linear Models

One possible generalization of the derivative form of the Maxwell fluid model has been given in Eq. (7.3-48). This employs the convected time derivative and covariant tensor components:

$$\tau_{ij} + \lambda \frac{\delta \tau_{ij}}{\delta t} = \mu \Delta_{ij} \qquad (7.4-1)$$

The steady flow material functions predicted by this model can be determined by considering the response to a simple shear deformation, defined by

$$v^1(x^2) \qquad v^2 = v^3 = 0 \tag{7.4-2}$$

$$\Delta_{ij} = \dot{\gamma} \begin{bmatrix} 0 & 1 & 0 \\ 1 & 0 & 0 \\ 0 & 0 & 0 \end{bmatrix} \qquad \dot{\gamma} = \frac{dv^1}{dx^2} = \text{constant} \tag{7.4-3}$$

In order to calculate the steady material functions for this model, we must evaluate the convected derivative of the stress tensor by Eq. (7.3-40) or (7.3-41). In expanded form, this becomes

$$\frac{\delta \tau_{ij}}{\delta t} = \cancel{\frac{\partial \tau_{ij}}{\partial t}}^{0} + v^1 \cancel{\frac{\partial \tau_{ij}}{\partial z^1}}^{0} + v^2 \cancel{\frac{\partial \tau_{ij}}{\partial z^2}}^{0} + v^3 \cancel{\frac{\partial \tau_{ij}}{\partial z^3}}^{0}$$

$$+ \frac{\partial v^1}{\partial z^j} \tau_{i1} + \cancel{\frac{\partial v^2}{\partial z^j}}^{0} \tau_{i2} + \cancel{\frac{\partial v^3}{\partial z^j}}^{0} \tau_{i3} \tag{7.4-4}$$

$$+ \frac{\partial v^1}{\partial z^i} \tau_{1j} + \cancel{\frac{\partial v^2}{\partial z^i}}^{0} \tau_{2j} + \cancel{\frac{\partial v^3}{\partial z^i}}^{0} \tau_{3j}$$

where the terms which are zero follow from Eq. (7.4-2). Note that, even though the flow is steady, the convected derivative contains nonzero terms. Taking into consideration Eq. (7.4-3), the covariant derivative of each stress component follows from above:

$$\frac{\delta \tau_{11}}{\delta t} = 0$$

$$\frac{\delta \tau_{12}}{\delta t} = \dot{\gamma} \tau_{11} = \frac{\delta \tau_{21}}{\delta t}$$

$$\tag{7.4-5}$$

$$\frac{\delta \tau_{22}}{\delta t} = 2 \dot{\gamma} \tau_{21}$$

$$\frac{\delta \tau_{33}}{\delta t} = 0$$

Substitution of Eqs. (7.4-3) and (7.4-5) into Eq. (7.4-1) results in
the following component equations for this model:

$$\tau_{11} = 0$$

$$\tau_{22} + 2\lambda\dot{\gamma}\tau_{12} = 0$$

$$\tau_{33} = 0 \qquad\qquad (7.4-6)$$

$$\tau_{12} + \lambda\tau_{11} = \mu\dot{\gamma}$$

These may be solved for the stress components in terms of the constant
shear rate to give

$$\tau_{12} = \mu\dot{\gamma}$$

$$\tau_{11} = 0$$

$$\tau_{22} = -2\mu\lambda\dot{\gamma}^2 \qquad\qquad (7.4-7)$$

$$\tau_{33} = 0$$

These stress components serve to define the steady flow material functions as follows:

$$\eta = \frac{\tau_{12}}{\dot{\gamma}} = \mu \text{ (constant)} \qquad\qquad (7.4-8)$$

$$\theta_1 = \frac{\tau_{11} - \tau_{22}}{\dot{\gamma}^2} = 2\mu\lambda \text{ (constant)} \qquad\qquad (7.4-9)$$

$$\theta_2 = \frac{\tau_{22} - \tau_{33}}{\dot{\gamma}^2} = -2\mu\lambda = -\theta_1 \qquad\qquad (7.4-10)$$

For unsteady flow, the equations to be solved for the stress
components are similar to Eq. (7.4-6), but with the nonzero time
derivatives included:

$$\tau_{11} + \lambda \frac{d\tau_{11}}{dt} = 0 \tag{7.4-11}$$

$$\tau_{22} + 2\lambda\dot{\gamma}\tau_{12} + \lambda \frac{d\tau_{22}}{dt} = 0 \tag{7.4-12}$$

$$\tau_{33} + \lambda \frac{d\tau_{33}}{dt} = 0 \tag{7.4-13}$$

$$\tau_{12} + \lambda\dot{\gamma}\tau_{11} + \lambda \frac{d\tau_{12}}{dt} = \mu\dot{\gamma} \tag{7.4-14}$$

Equations (7.4-11) and (7.4-13) yield

$$\tau_{11} = (\tau_{11})_o \, e^{-t/\lambda} \tag{7.4-15}$$

$$\tau_{33} = (\tau_{33})_o \, e^{-t/\lambda} \tag{7.4-16}$$

These stress components are transient and decay exponentially. For the case of steady oscillatory motion, Eq. (7.4-14) reduces to

$$\frac{d\tau_{12}}{dt} + \frac{\tau_{12}}{\lambda} = \frac{\mu\dot{\gamma}}{\lambda} = \frac{\mu\dot{\gamma}_o}{\lambda} \cos \omega t \tag{7.4-17}$$

where the strain rate has been assumed to have a real part only:

$$\dot{\gamma}(\omega) = \dot{\gamma}_o \cos \omega t = \text{Re } \dot{\gamma}_o \, e^{j\omega t} \tag{7.4-18}$$

Equation (7.4-17) can be readily solved to give:

$$\tau_{12}(\omega) = \frac{\mu_o \dot{\gamma}_o}{1 + \omega^2\lambda^2} (\cos \omega t + \omega\lambda \sin \omega t) \tag{7.4-19}$$

Since the cosine term represents the τ_{12} stress which is in phase with the strain rate, and the sine term is that which leads the strain rate by 90°, these terms define the real and imaginary components of the complex viscosity:

$$\eta' = \frac{\mu}{1 + \omega^2\lambda^2} \qquad\qquad \eta'' = \frac{\omega\lambda\mu}{1 + \omega^2\lambda^2} \qquad\qquad (7.4\text{-}20)$$

These are seen to be identical to the results derived in Chap. 2 for the Maxwell fluid.

There still remains the stress component τ_{22}, which is determined by Eq. (7.4-12). By substituting Eq. (7.4-18) for $\dot\gamma$ and Eq. (7.4-19) for τ_{12} into this equation, it can be solved for the steady oscillatory response of τ_{22} to give:

$$\tau_{22}(\omega) = -\frac{\mu\lambda\dot\gamma_o^2}{1 + \omega^2\lambda^2}\left[1 + \frac{3\omega\lambda \sin 2\omega t + (1 - 2\omega^2\lambda^2) \cos 2\omega t}{1 + 4\omega^2\lambda^2}\right]$$

$$(7.4\text{-}21)$$

$$= -(\tau_{11} - \tau_{22}) = (\tau_{22} - \tau_{33}) \qquad\qquad (7.4\text{-}22)$$

This normal stress component is seen to oscillate with twice the frequency of the applied strain. Furthermore, it has a nonzero steady component superimposed upon the oscillatory component. Just as for steady flow, the second normal stress difference is seen to be negative and equal in magnitude to the first normal stress difference.

We may also evaluate these material functions from the contravariant form of this model:

$$\tau^{ij} + \lambda\frac{\delta\tau^{ij}}{\delta t} = \mu\Delta^{ij} \qquad\qquad (7.4\text{-}23)$$

Employing Eq. (7.3-42) to evaluate the convected derivative of the contravariant stress components, a procedure equivalent to that outlined above leads to the following expressions for the steady flow material functions:

$$\eta = \frac{\tau^{12}}{\dot\gamma} = \mu \text{ (constant)} \qquad\qquad (7.4\text{-}24)$$

$$\theta_1 = \frac{\tau^{11} - \tau^{22}}{\dot{\gamma}^2} = \boxed{2\lambda\mu}\ (\text{constant}) \qquad\qquad (7.4\text{-}25)$$

$$\theta_2 = \frac{\tau^{22} - \tau^{33}}{\dot{\gamma}^2} = \boxed{0} \qquad\qquad (7.4\text{-}26)$$

and equivalent expressions for the oscillatory response functions.
It is evident that the covariant and contravariant forms of this
model do not predict the same second normal stress functions. As
discussed previously, most of the available data indicate that the
second normal stress difference is significantly smaller than the
first and negative in sign (see note 1). Thus neither the covariant
nor contravariant terms are entirely consistent with observations.
Whereas the former correctly predicts a negative value, it is equal
in magnitude to the first normal stress difference, while the latter
predicts a zero value.

Since simple shear deformation (which has been assumed for determination of the material functions) is described in Cartesian
coordinates, both covariant and contravariant components are identical and are the same as physical components. Hence the difference
in the two forms lies with the model (i.e., the derivative operator),
and not with the specific tensor components employed.

Note that these models are linear, since they predict a
Newtonian viscosity in steady shear, as well as constant normal
stress functions. This is not a generally desirable characteristic,
since fluids which exhibit elasticity inevitably exhibit non-
Newtonian viscosities, as well as shear dependent normal stress
functions. Hence various modifications of these rate equations have
been made in an attempt to reproduce qualitatively the observed nonlinear viscous shear and normal stress behavior of materials such
as molten polymers, and polymer solutions, suspensions, etc., as a
function of shear rate.

B. Nonlinear Models

An obvious, yet simple, modification of the preceding models involves the use of the Jaumann derivative in place of the convected derivative. The equivalent Maxwell model thus becomes:

$$\tau_{ij} + \lambda \frac{\mathcal{D}\tau_{ij}}{\mathcal{D}t} = \mu \, \Delta_{ij} \qquad\qquad covariant \qquad\qquad (7.4\text{-}27)$$

For simple shear deformation, the Jaumann derivative of the stress tensor, from Eq. (7.3-53), becomes

$$\frac{\mathcal{D}\tau_{ij}}{\mathcal{D}t} = \frac{\partial\tau_{ij}}{\partial t} + v^1 \overbrace{\frac{\partial\tau_{ij}}{\partial z^1}}^{0} + v^2 \overbrace{\frac{\partial\tau_{ij}}{\partial z^2}}^{0} + v^3 \overbrace{\frac{\partial\tau_{ij}}{\partial z^3}}^{0}$$

$$+ \frac{1}{2} [\Omega_i^{\,1}\tau_{1j} + \Omega_i^{\,2}\tau_{2j} + \overbrace{\Omega_i^{\,3}\tau_{3j}}^{0}$$

$$+ \Omega_j^{\,1}\tau_{i1} + \Omega_j^{\,2}\tau_{i2} + \overbrace{\Omega_j^{\,3}\tau_{i3}}^{0}] \qquad (7.4\text{-}28)$$

The components of the vorticity tensor for simple shear are

$$\Omega_{ij} = v_{j,i} - v_{i,j} = \dot{\gamma}\begin{bmatrix} 0 & -1 & 0 \\ 1 & 0 & 0 \\ 0 & 0 & 0 \end{bmatrix} \qquad (7.4\text{-}29)$$

$$\dot{\gamma} = \frac{dv_x}{dy}$$

Thus the component equations from Eq. (7.4-28) become:

$$\frac{\mathcal{D}\tau_{11}}{\mathcal{D}t} = \frac{\partial\tau_{11}}{\partial t} + \Omega_1^2 \tau_{21} = \frac{\partial\tau_{11}}{\partial t} - \dot{\gamma}\tau_{21}$$

$$\frac{\mathcal{D}\tau_{22}}{\mathcal{D}t} = \frac{\partial\tau_{22}}{\partial t} + \Omega_2^1 \tau_{21} = \frac{\partial\tau_{22}}{\partial t} + \dot{\gamma}\tau_{21}$$

$$\frac{\mathcal{D}\tau_{33}}{\mathcal{D}t} = \frac{\partial\tau_{33}}{\partial t} \tag{7.4-30}$$

$$\frac{\mathcal{D}\tau_{12}}{\mathcal{D}t} = \frac{\partial\tau_{12}}{\partial t} + \frac{1}{2} [\Omega_1^2 \tau_{22} + \Omega_2^1 \tau_{11}]$$

$$= \frac{\partial\tau_{12}}{\partial t} + \frac{1}{2} [-\dot{\gamma}\tau_{22} + \dot{\gamma}\tau_{11}]$$

Substitution of Eq. (7.4-30) into Eq. (7.4-27) gives the following simultaneous equations for the stress components at steady state:

$$\tau_{11} - \lambda \dot{\gamma} \tau_{21} = 0$$

$$\tau_{22} + \lambda \dot{\gamma} \tau_{21} = 0$$

$$\tau_{33} = 0 \tag{7.4-31}$$

$$\tau_{21} + \frac{1}{2} \lambda \dot{\gamma}(\tau_{11} - \tau_{22}) = \mu\dot{\gamma}$$

These may be solved for the steady state material functions to give:

$$\eta = \frac{\tau_{12}}{\dot{\gamma}} = \frac{\mu}{1 + \lambda^2\dot{\gamma}^2} \tag{7.4-32}$$

$$\theta_1 = \frac{\tau_{11} - \tau_{22}}{\dot{\gamma}^2} = \frac{2\mu\lambda}{1 + \lambda^2\dot{\gamma}^2} \tag{7.4-33}$$

$$\theta_2 = \frac{\tau_{22} - \tau_{33}}{\dot{\gamma}^2} = -\frac{\mu\lambda}{1 + \lambda^2\dot{\gamma}^2} \tag{7.4-34}$$

The contravariant form of Eq. (7.4-27) predicts these same material functions, and the predicted complex viscosity is identical to Eq. (7.4-20). This simple modification has resulted in a significant improvement in several ways. Not only has the discrepancy between covariant and contravariant forms been removed, but a shear dependent viscosity with a zero shear rate limiting viscosity of μ has been introduced, as well as shear dependent normal stress functions which decrease with shear rate. The prediction that the second normal stress difference is negative is also consistent with observation, although most data indicate that its magnitude is closer to 15% of the first, rather than 50% as predicted.

Note the similarity between the oscillatory functions, Eq. (7.4-20), and the steady shear functions, Eqs. (7.4-32) to (7.4-34). Many data on polymers show qualitative similarity between the functions $\eta(\dot{\gamma})$ and $\eta'(\omega)$, and also (but to a lesser extent) between $\dot{\gamma}\theta_1(\dot{\gamma})$ and $\eta''(\omega)$. This observation has been taken as the basis for predicting that an analogy should exist between these two sets of data, although the agreement is qualitative at best.

A simple but most useful extension of the two parameter Maxwell model involves the addition of a "retardation time" parameter. This model in its simplest form was apparently derived originally by Jeffreys [7.9], and later by Frohlich and Sack [7.10] for a suspension of elastic particles in a Newtonian fluid. The generalized form of this model incorporating the Jaumann derivative, often attributed to Oldroyd [7.11], is:

$$\tau_{ij} + \lambda_1 \frac{\mathcal{D}\tau_{ij}}{\mathcal{D}t} = \mu \left(\Delta_{ij} + \lambda_2 \frac{\mathcal{D}\Delta_{ij}}{\mathcal{D}t} \right) \tag{7.4-35}$$

The steady flow material functions predicted by this model are:

$$\eta = \frac{\tau_{12}}{\dot{\gamma}} = \frac{\mu(1 + \lambda_1\lambda_2\dot{\gamma}^2)}{1 + \lambda_1^2\dot{\gamma}^2} \tag{7.4-36}$$

$$\theta_1 = \frac{\tau_{11} - \tau_{22}}{\dot{\gamma}^2} = \frac{2\mu(\lambda_1 - \lambda_2)}{1 + \lambda_1^2 \dot{\gamma}^2} \qquad (7.4-37)$$

$$\theta_2 = \frac{\tau_{22} - \tau_{33}}{\dot{\gamma}^2} = -\frac{\theta_1}{2} \qquad (7.4-38)$$

and the complex viscosity components are:

$$\eta' = \frac{\mu(1 + \lambda_1\lambda_2\omega^2)}{1 + \lambda_1^2\omega^2} \qquad \eta'' = \frac{\omega\mu(\lambda_1 - \lambda_2)}{1 + \lambda_1^2\lambda^2} \qquad (7.4-39)$$

This model predicts a nonzero high shear rate limiting viscosity $(\mu\lambda_2/\lambda_1)$, which is more realistic than the value of zero predicted by Eq. (7.4-27). Note that the model reduces to a purely viscous Newtonian fluid if $\lambda_1 = \lambda_2$ (a much less restrictive condition than $\lambda_1 = \lambda_2 = 0$).

In order to predict more realistic normal stress functions, Oldroyd [7.1] introduced a number of complex modifications to these models. As a special case of these models, Williams and Bird [7.20] have proposed the following three constant form:

$$\tau_{ij} + \lambda_1 \mathcal{J}(\tau_{ij}) = \mu[\Delta_{ij} + \lambda_2 \mathcal{J}(\Delta_{ij})] \qquad (7.4-40)$$

where

$$\mathcal{J}(\tau_{ij}) \equiv \frac{\mathcal{D}\tau_{ij}}{\mathcal{D}t} - \frac{1}{2}(\Delta_i^{\ k}\tau_{jk} + \Delta_j^{\ k}\tau_{ik}) + \frac{1}{3}\tau_{k\ell}\Delta^{k\ell}g_{ij} \qquad (7.4-41)$$

is another nonlinear time derivative operator. The material functions predicted by this model in simple shear are:

$$\eta = \mu\frac{1 + (2/3)\lambda_1\lambda_2\dot{\gamma}^2}{1 + (2/3)\lambda_1^2\dot{\gamma}^2} \qquad (7.4-42)$$

$$\theta_1 = 2\mu \frac{\lambda_1 - \lambda_2}{1 + (2/3)\lambda_1^2 \dot{\gamma}^2} \qquad (7.4-43)$$

$$\theta_2 = 0 \qquad (7.4-44)$$

Note that this model predicts the Weissenberg hypothesis ($\theta_2 = 0$), which at the time of its conception was considered to be more realistic than, e.g., Eq. (7.4-38). However as previously noted, more recent considerations do not support this conclusion. The oscillatory response functions (complex viscosity) are identical to Eq. (7.4-39), and the model is otherwise similar to that of Eq. (7.4-35).

To account for deviations from the Weissenberg hypothesis, Spriggs [7.12] modified the operator of Eq. (7.4-41) by introduction of an additional parameter, ε, and applied it to a Maxwell-type model:

$$\tau_{ij} + \lambda \mathcal{J}_\varepsilon(\tau_{ij}) = \mu \Delta_{ij} \qquad (7.4-45)$$

where

$$\mathcal{J}_\varepsilon(\tau_{ij}) \equiv \frac{\mathcal{D}\tau_{ij}}{\mathcal{D}t} - (1 + \varepsilon)[\frac{1}{2}(\tau_i^{\ m}\Delta_{mj} + \tau_j^{\ m}\Delta_{mi}) - \frac{1}{3}\tau^{mn}\Delta_{mn}g_{ij}] \qquad (7.4-46)$$

This is a three-constant model, the parameters being μ, λ, and ε. The steady flow material functions predicted by this model in simple shear are:

$$\eta = \frac{\tau_{12}}{\dot{\gamma}} = \frac{\mu}{1 + (\lambda c \dot{\gamma})^2} \qquad (7.4-47)$$

$$\theta_1 = \frac{\tau_{11} - \tau_{22}}{\dot{\gamma}^2} = \frac{2\mu\lambda}{1 + (\lambda c \dot{\gamma})^2} \qquad (7.4-48)$$

$$\theta_2 = \frac{\tau_{22} - \tau_{33}}{\dot{\gamma}^2} = \frac{\varepsilon\mu\lambda}{1 + (\lambda c\dot{\gamma})^2} \qquad (7.4\text{-}49)$$

where

$$c^2 = \frac{2}{3}(1 - \varepsilon - \tfrac{1}{2}\varepsilon^2) \qquad (7.4\text{-}50)$$

The small amplitude oscillatory response functions (complex viscosity) are identical to Eq. (7.4-20), since the operator $\mathcal{J}_\varepsilon$ reduces to the partial time derivative for small deformations and deformation rates; i.e., in the limit of linear response. Note that the Weissenberg hypothesis requires $\varepsilon = 0$. This model also reduces to that of Eq. (7.4-27) if $\varepsilon = -1$. The factor c given by Eq. (7.4-50) is referred to as a "shift factor," since $\eta'(\omega)$ is the same function of ω as $\eta(\dot{\gamma})$ is of $(c\dot{\gamma})$. Also, $\eta''(\omega)$ is the same function of ω as $(c\theta_1\dot{\gamma}/2)$ is of $(c\dot{\gamma})$. If an analogy is assumed between these two material functions (i.e., steady shear and oscillatory response), the value of c may be determined by "shifting" the steady and/or oscillatory response curves to make them coincide.

There is a great variety of possible variations on the rate or derivative form of the viscoelastic model, generated by inclusion of higher order derivatives of stress or strain, modification of the time derivative operator, etc. A generalized rate model has been presented by Oldroyd [7.13] in the form:

$$\left[1 + \alpha_1 \frac{\mathcal{D}}{\mathcal{D}t} + \alpha_2 \frac{\mathcal{D}^2}{\mathcal{D}t^2} + \cdots + \alpha_N \frac{\mathcal{D}^N}{\mathcal{D}t^N}\right]\tau_{ij}$$

$$= \mu_o\left[1 + \beta_1 \frac{\mathcal{D}}{\mathcal{D}t} + \beta_2 \frac{\mathcal{D}^2}{\mathcal{D}t^2} + \cdots + \beta_N \frac{\mathcal{D}^N}{\mathcal{D}t^N}\right]\Delta_{ij} \qquad (7.4\text{-}51)$$

where the $\mathcal{D}^k/\mathcal{D}t^k$ are successive orders of the Jaumann derivative. The material functions in steady flow predicted by this model are:

$$\eta = \frac{\tau_{12}}{\dot\gamma} = \mu_o[(1 - \alpha_2\dot\gamma^2 + \alpha_4\dot\gamma^4 \ldots)(1 - \beta_2\dot\gamma^2 + \beta_4\dot\gamma^4 \ldots)$$

$$+ (\alpha_1\dot\gamma - \alpha_3\dot\gamma^3 + \alpha_5\dot\gamma^5 \ldots)(\beta_1\dot\gamma - \beta_3\dot\gamma^3 + \beta_5\dot\gamma^5)] \Big/$$

$$[(1 - \alpha_2\dot\gamma^2 + \alpha_4\dot\gamma^4 \ldots)^2 + (\alpha_1\dot\gamma - \alpha_3\dot\gamma^3 + \alpha_5\dot\gamma^5 \ldots)^2]$$

$$(7.4\text{-}52)$$

$$\theta_1 = \frac{\tau_{11} - \tau_{22}}{\dot\gamma^2} = 2\mu_o[(\alpha_1 - \alpha_3\dot\gamma^2 + \alpha_5\dot\gamma^4 \ldots)(1 - \beta_2\dot\gamma^2 + \beta_4\dot\gamma^4 \ldots)$$

$$- (\beta_1 - \beta_3\dot\gamma^2 + \beta_5\dot\gamma^4 \ldots)(1 - \alpha_2\dot\gamma^2 + \alpha_4\dot\gamma^4 \ldots)] \Big/$$

$$[(1 - \alpha_2\dot\gamma^2 + \alpha_4\dot\gamma^4 \ldots)^2 + (\alpha_1\dot\gamma - \alpha_3\dot\gamma^3 + \alpha_5\dot\gamma^5 \ldots)^2]$$

$$(7.4\text{-}53)$$

$$\theta_2 = \frac{\tau_{22} - \tau_{33}}{\dot\gamma^2} = -\frac{\theta_1}{2} \qquad\qquad (7.4\text{-}54)$$

The numerator and denominator of Eqs. (7.4-52) and (7.4-53) are polynomials of degree N in $\dot\gamma^2$. For small values of $\dot\gamma$, Eq. (7.4-53) is
insensitive to $\dot\gamma$, i.e., $(\tau_{11} - \tau_{22})$, and $(\tau_{22} - \tau_{33})$ are proportional
to $\dot\gamma^2$.

All of these models reduce to linear viscoelastic behavior at
small shear rates, but predict shear thinning apparent viscosity and
normal stress functions at larger shear rates. However, they are
implicit in the stress components, which makes them difficult to
apply to other than the simplest deformations.

———————————————————————— 0 ————————————————————————

Example 7.2   For a three parameter model, equivalent to the Jeffreys
model using the convected derivative and covariant components,

determine the transient buildup of stress with time after the instantaneous application of a constant uniform shear rate.

Solution. The model to be considered is

$$\tau_{ij} + \lambda_1 \frac{\delta \tau_{ij}}{\delta t} = \mu \left(\Delta_{ij} + \lambda_2 \frac{\delta \Delta_{ij}}{\delta t} \right)$$

where

$$\Delta_{ij} = \dot{\gamma} U(t) \begin{bmatrix} 0 & 1 & 0 \\ 1 & 0 & 0 \\ 0 & 0 & 0 \end{bmatrix}$$

The convected derivative of any tensor T_{ij} is, from Appendix E:

$$\frac{\delta T_{ij}}{\delta t} = \frac{\partial T_{ij}}{\partial t} + \dot{\gamma} \begin{bmatrix} 0 & T_{11} & 0 \\ T_{11} & 2T_{12} & 0 \\ 0 & 0 & 0 \end{bmatrix}$$

Using this in the above model, the component equations become:

$$\tau_{11} + \lambda_1 \frac{\partial \tau_{11}}{\partial t} = 0$$

$$\tau_{22} + \lambda_1 \left[\frac{\partial \tau_{22}}{\partial t} + 2\dot{\gamma}\, \tau_{12} \right] = 2\mu\lambda_2\dot{\gamma}^2$$

$$\tau_{33} + \lambda_1 \frac{\partial \tau_{33}}{\partial t} = 0$$

$$\tau_{12} + \lambda_1 \left[\frac{\partial \tau_{12}}{\partial t} + \dot{\gamma}\, \tau_{11} \right] = \mu\dot{\gamma}$$

no λ_2 term

Subject to the initial conditions:

$$\tau_{12} = \tau_{11} = \tau_{22} = \tau_{33} = 0 \quad \text{at} \quad t = 0$$

the solutions to these equations are:

$$\tau_{11} = 0$$

$$\tau_{33} = 0$$

$$\tau_{12} = \mu\dot{\gamma}(1 - e^{-t/\lambda_1})$$

$$\tau_{22} = 2\mu\dot{\gamma}^2[(\lambda_2 - \lambda_1) + (\lambda_1 - \lambda_2 + t)e^{-t/\lambda_1}]$$

Thus the relaxation time λ_1 is the characteristic time for stress buildup after imposition of a steady shear. Also note that τ_{22} rises to a maximum value at $t = \lambda_2$ and then falls, leveling off at a steady-state value of $2\mu\dot{\gamma}^2(\lambda_2 - \lambda_1)$.

$$\lambda_1 = (\eta_e + \eta_B)/G$$

_____ 0 ___ $\lambda_2 = \eta_B/G$ _____

7.4.2. Integral or Hereditary Models

A. Linear Models

It was shown in Chap. 2 how the memory property of a viscoelastic fluid requires that the state of stress at a given time be a function of the entire past history of deformation. This led directly to a rheological equation which is an integral function of time, of the form:

$$\tau(t) = \int_{-\infty}^{t} \psi(t - t')\dot{\gamma}(t') \, dt' \qquad (7.4\text{-}55)$$

where the relaxation function, $\psi(t)$, represents the complete time
dependent characteristics of a linear viscoelastic material. For a
linear material, the equivalent relaxation function for any rate
model can be determined directly by transform methods, as was shown
in Chap. 2. A major advantage of integral expressions of this sort
is that they are explicit in stress, and are thus easier to apply to
complex deformations than the rate models.

An equivalent integral expression involving strain instead of
strain rate, defines the memory function, $\phi(t)$. This results from
Eq. (7.4-55) by integration by parts:

$$\tau(t) = \psi(0)\gamma(t) + \int_{-\infty}^{t} \phi(t - t')\gamma(t')\,dt' \qquad (7.4\text{-}56)$$

where the relaxation and memory functions are related by:

$$\phi(t) = \frac{d\psi(t)}{dt} \qquad (7.4\text{-}57)$$

It is often convenient to take the state at time t (present time) as
the reference (i.e., undeformed) state so that the first term on the
right-hand side of Eq. (7.4-56) is identically zero.

Based upon the concept of a generalized Maxwell model, a spectrum
of relaxation times may be defined, which may be representative of the
molecular structure of the material. The distribution of these relaxation times can be characterized by the density of the corresponding
distribution of shear moduli, $F(\lambda)$, which is defined relative to the
generalized Maxwell model by the equation

$$\psi(t) = \int_{0}^{\infty} F(\lambda)e^{-t/\lambda}\,d\lambda \qquad (7.4\text{-}58)$$

Substitution of Eq. (7.4-58) into Eq. (7.4-55) provides an expression
for the shear stress in terms of the distribution function, $F(\lambda)$:

$$\tau(t) = \int_{-\infty}^{t} \int_{0}^{\infty} F(\lambda) e^{-(t-t')/\lambda} \, \dot{\gamma}(t') \, d\lambda \, dt' \tag{7.4-59}$$

The most direct way of generalized Eq. (7.4-55) to include all stress components and finite deformations would be to employ general tensor notation, and the Eulerian components of those tensor quantities associated with "prior" times (t'); i.e.,:

$$\tau_{ij}(z, t) = \int_{-\infty}^{t} \psi(t - t') \, \frac{\partial Z^m}{\partial z^i} \frac{\partial Z^n}{\partial z^j} \, \Delta_{mn}(Z, t') \, dt' \tag{7.4-60}$$

The contravariant equivalent of this expression is:

$$\tau^{ij}(z, t) = \int_{-\infty}^{t} \psi(t - t') \, \frac{\partial z^i}{\partial Z^m} \frac{\partial z^j}{\partial Z^n} \, \Delta^{mn}(Z, t') \, dt' \tag{7.4-61}$$

Equations (7.4-60) and (7.4-61) are not equivalent, however, as we may demonstrate for simple shear. For this deformation:

$$v^1 = v^1(x^2) = \dot{\gamma} x^2 \qquad v^2 = v^3 = 0$$

$$\Delta_{ij} = \dot{\gamma} \begin{bmatrix} 0 & 1 & 0 \\ 1 & 0 & 0 \\ 0 & 0 & 0 \end{bmatrix} \qquad \dot{\gamma} = \frac{dv^1}{dx^2} = \text{constant} \tag{7.4-62}$$

where the shear rate, $\dot{\gamma}$, is independent of position. The material coordinates for this flow are seen to be:

$$Z^3 = x^3$$

$$Z^2 = x^2$$

$$Z^1 = x^1 - \dot{\gamma} \cdot x^2 \cdot (t - t') \tag{7.4-63}$$

Hence the covariant form, Eq. (7.4-60), reduces to:

$$\tau_{ij} = \dot{\gamma} \int_{-\infty}^{t} \psi(t - t') \left[\frac{\partial z^2}{\partial x^i} \frac{\partial z^1}{\partial x^j} + \frac{\partial z^1}{\partial x^i} \frac{\partial z^2}{\partial x^j} \right] dt' \qquad (7.4-64)$$

The only nonzero stress components are, therefore,

$$\tau_{12} = \tau_{21} = \dot{\gamma} \int_{-\infty}^{t} \psi(t - t') \, dt' = \dot{\gamma} \int_{0}^{\infty} \psi(t) \, dt \qquad (7.4-65)$$

and

$$\tau_{22} = -2\dot{\gamma}^2 \int_{-\infty}^{t} (t - t')\psi(t - t') \, dt' = -2\dot{\gamma}^2 \int_{0}^{\infty} t\psi(t) \, dt \qquad (7.4-66)$$

All other $\tau_{ij} = 0$.

The material functions are thus:

$$\eta = \frac{\tau_{21}}{\dot{\gamma}} = \int_{-\infty}^{t} \psi(t - t') \, dt' = \int_{0}^{\infty} \psi(t) \, dt \quad \text{(const)} \qquad (7.4-67)$$

$$\theta_1 = \frac{\tau_{11} - \tau_{22}}{\dot{\gamma}^2} = 2 \int_{-\infty}^{t} (t - t')\psi(t - t') \, dt' = 2 \int_{0}^{\infty} t\psi(t) \, dt \text{(const)}$$

$$(7.4-68)$$

$$\theta_2 = \frac{\tau_{22} - \tau_{33}}{\dot{\gamma}^2} = -\theta_1 \qquad (7.4-69)$$

By using Eq. (7.4-58) relating $\psi(t)$ to the distribution function $F(\lambda)$, these expressions may be written in the alternate form:

$$\eta = \int_0^\infty \lambda F(\lambda) \ d\lambda \tag{7.4-70}$$

and

$$\theta_1 = -\theta_2 = 2 \int_0^\infty \lambda^2 F(\lambda) \ d\lambda \tag{7.4-71}$$

For the contravariant form, Eq. (7.4-61), the nonzero stress components are $\tau^{12} = \tau^{21}$ and τ^{11}. The first (τ^{12}) is identical to Eq. (7.4-65), while τ^{11} becomes:

$$\tau^{11} = 2\dot{\gamma}^2 \int_0^\infty t\psi(t) \ dt = 2\dot{\gamma}^2 \int_0^\infty \lambda^2 F(\lambda) \ d\lambda \ \text{(const)} \tag{7.4-72}$$

Hence a qualitative comparison of the two forms shows that the covariant form predicts:

$$0 = \tau_{33} = \tau_{11} > \tau_{22} \qquad \theta_2 = -\theta_1 \tag{7.4-73}$$

while the contravariant form predicts:

$$0 = \tau^{33} = \tau^{22} < \tau^{11} \qquad \theta_2 = 0 \tag{7.4-74}$$

Note that these results are equivalent to those predicted by Eqs. (7.4-1) and (7.4-23) for the respective convected derivative forms of the Maxwell model. Of course the integral forms in terms of the relaxation or distribution functions are not limited to a specific model but apply to any linear viscoelastic model. The results are identical if the relaxation function for the Maxwell model is employed in Eqs. (7.4-60) and (7.4-61), namely,

$$\psi(t) = Ge^{-t/\lambda} \tag{7.4-75}$$

Since these models are linear, they predict constant material functions, which are determined by the relaxation or distribution functions by Eqs. (7.4-70) and (7.4-71). This will be true for any linear model; that is, one for which the relaxation or memory functions are independent of strain or strain rate.

The above example employing the relaxation function and the Eulerian components of the rate of strian tensor is equivalent (and gives identical results) to the use of the corresponding memory function and the finite strain tensor Γ^{ij} or Γ_{ij}.

--------------------------------- 0 ---------------------------------

Example 7.3 Consider any linear viscoelastic fluid in steady simple shear. At time zero, the shear stress is removed and the memory properties of the material cause it to "recoil" or rebound. Determine an expression for the amount of strain recoil (γ_∞) as a function of the initial shear rate ($\dot{\gamma}_-$) and the relaxation function of the material, neglecting the mass of the fluid [7.14].

Solution. The shear stress, strain, and relaxation function are related by Eq. (7.4-55) or (7.4-65):

$$\tau_{12}(t) = \int_{-\infty}^{t} \psi(t - t')\dot{\gamma}(t') \, dt'$$

For all $t \geq 0$ the shear stress is zero, so that this equation becomes:

$$0 = \int_{-\infty}^{t} \psi(t - t')\dot{\gamma}(t') \, dt'$$

$$= \dot{\gamma}_- \int_{-\infty}^{0} \psi(t - t') \, dt' + \int_{0}^{t} \psi(t - t')\dot{\gamma}(t') \, dt'$$

Changing variables from t' to $t_1 = (t - t')$, this can be written:

$$-\dot{\gamma}_{-} \int_{t}^{\infty} \psi(t_1) \, dt_1 = \int_{0}^{t} \psi(t_1) \dot{\gamma}(t - t_1) \, dt_1$$

Integrating both sides over t from 0 to ∞:

$$-\dot{\gamma}_{-} \int_{0}^{\infty} \int_{t}^{\infty} \psi(t_1) \, dt_1 \, dt = \int_{0}^{\infty} \int_{t}^{\infty} \psi(t_1) \dot{\gamma}(t - t_1) \, dt_1 \, dt$$

and interchanging the order of integration, gives

$$-\dot{\gamma}_{-} \int_{0}^{\infty} \left[\int_{0}^{t_1} dt \right] \psi(t_1) \, dt_1 = \int_{0}^{\infty} \psi(t_1) \left[\int_{t_1}^{\infty} \dot{\gamma}(t - t_1) \, dt \right] dt_1$$

Changing variable from t_1 to $t^1 = t - t_1$ in the bracket on the right side, this becomes

$$-\dot{\gamma}_{-} \int_{0}^{\infty} t_1 \psi(t_1) \, dt_1 = \int_{0}^{\infty} \psi(t_1) \left[\int_{0}^{\infty} \dot{\gamma}(t^1) \, dt^1 \right] dt_1$$

The quantity in the bracket is a constant, and is the value of the ultimate strain recoil, γ_{∞}. Thus:

$$\frac{\gamma_{\infty}}{\dot{\gamma}_{-}} = - \frac{\displaystyle\int_{0}^{\infty} t\psi(t) \, dt}{\displaystyle\int_{0}^{\infty} \psi(t) \, dt}$$

Note that by Eqs. (7.4-67) and (7.4-68) this is identical to:

$$\frac{\gamma_{\infty}}{\dot{\gamma}_{-}} = - \frac{\theta_1}{2\eta}$$

That is, the ultimate recoil is directly related to the first normal stress and viscosity functions. Note that this derivation applies only for a linear fluid, but is independent of any specific model.

─────────────────────────────── 0 ───────────────────────────────

─────────────────────────────── 0 ───────────────────────────────

Example 7.4 Determine expressions for the complex viscosity of any linear viscoelastic fluid in terms of its relaxation function, and from these results determine an expression for [7.15]:

$$\lim_{\omega \to 0} \left(\frac{\eta''}{\omega \eta'} \right)$$

Solution. The equations needed were derived in Chap. 2, namely:

$$G'(\omega) = \omega \int_0^\infty G(t) \sin \omega t \, dt$$

$$G''(\omega) = \omega \int_0^\infty G(t) \cos \omega t \, dt$$

Noting that

$$G(t) \equiv \psi(t); \quad \eta' = \frac{G''}{\omega}, \quad \text{and} \quad \eta'' = \frac{G'}{\omega}$$

we find

$$\frac{\eta''}{\omega \eta'} = \frac{\displaystyle\int_0^\infty \psi(t) \sin \omega t \, dt}{\omega \displaystyle\int_0^\infty \psi(t) \cos \omega t \, dt}$$

The desired quantity is:

$$\lim_{\omega \to 0} \left(\frac{\eta''}{\omega\eta'}\right) = \lim_{\omega \to 0} \left[\frac{\dfrac{d}{d\omega} \displaystyle\int_0^\infty \psi(t) \sin \omega t \, dt}{\dfrac{d}{d\omega} \, \omega \displaystyle\int_0^\infty \psi(t) \cos \omega t \, dt}\right]$$

$$= \lim_{\omega \to 0} \left[\frac{\displaystyle\int_0^\infty t\psi(t) \cos \omega t \, dt}{-\omega \displaystyle\int_0^\infty t\psi(t) \sin \omega t + \displaystyle\int_0^\infty \psi(t) \cos \omega t \, dt}\right]$$

or

$$\lim_{\omega \to 0} \left(\frac{\eta''}{\omega\eta'}\right) = \frac{\displaystyle\int_0^\infty t\psi(t)}{\displaystyle\int_0^\infty \psi(t) \, dt}$$

Note that this is identical to the results of the previous example, that is,

$$\lim_{\omega \to 0} \frac{\eta''}{\omega\eta'} = -\frac{\gamma_\infty}{\dot{\gamma}_-} = \frac{\theta_1}{2\eta}$$

———————————————————— 0 ————————————————————

———————————————————— 0 ————————————————————

Example 7.5 Consider any linear viscoelastic fluid in steady simple shear. At time zero, the fluid is brought to a stop and held in position. Determine an expression for the stress required to maintain this condition, neglecting the fluid mass. From the result, determine an expression for

$$\int_0^\infty \frac{\tau(t)}{\tau_-} \, dt$$

where τ_- is the stress on the fluid at $t < 0$ [7.15].

Solution. Measuring strain relative to the position at time zero, we have

$$\tau(t) = \int_{-\infty}^t \psi(t - t')\dot{\gamma}(t') \, dt'$$

$$= \int_{-\infty}^0 \psi(t - t')\dot{\gamma}_- \, dt' + \int_0^t \psi(t - t')(0) \, dt'$$

or

$$\tau(t) = \dot{\gamma}_- \int_t^\infty \psi(t) \, dt$$

For $t < 0$, the stress is

$$\tau_- = \dot{\gamma}_- \int_0^\infty \psi(t) \, dt$$

Hence the desired relation is

$$\int_0^\infty \frac{\tau(t)}{\tau_-} \, dt = \frac{\int_0^\infty \left[\int_t^\infty \psi(t) \, dt \right] dt}{\int_0^\infty \psi(t) \, dt}$$

Interchanging the order of integration in the double integral term, this becomes

$$\int_0^\infty \frac{\tau(t)}{\tau_-} \, dt = \frac{\displaystyle\int_0^\infty t\psi(t) \, dt}{\displaystyle\int_0^\infty \psi(t) \, dt}$$

This is seen to be identical to the results of Examples 7.3 and 7.4, i.e.,

$$\int_0^\infty \frac{\tau(t)}{\tau_-} \, dt = \lim_{\omega \to 0} \left(\frac{\eta''}{\omega\eta'}\right) = -\frac{\gamma_\infty}{\dot{\gamma}_-} = \frac{\theta_1}{2\eta} = \frac{\displaystyle\int_0^\infty t\psi(t) \, dt}{\displaystyle\int_0^\infty \psi(t) \, dt}$$

This interesting result provides a direct relation between material functions from (a) stress relaxation, (b) oscillatory response, (c) creep recovery ("recoil"), and (d) steady normal and shear stress functions and the relaxation function, for a linear viscoelastic fluid. It is thus evident that the material properties represented by the relaxation function determine the response of the material in all of these situations.

———————————————————————— 0 ————————————————————————

An extensive treatment of the properties of linear integral viscoelastic models can be found in the book by Lodge [7.15].

There are several obvious objections to the integral models discussed so far. One of the most serious is the lack of correspondence between covariant and contravariant forms of the same equation. The result is that such models cannot be perfectly general. This difficulty can be resolved by employing a linear combination of the finite strain tensors Γ^{ij} and Γ_{ij} in place of just one or the other. For example:

$$(1 - \frac{\varepsilon}{2})\Gamma_{ij} + \frac{\varepsilon}{2} g_{im} g_{jn} \Gamma^{mn} \tag{7.4-78}$$

could be used for the covariant strain tensor. This is more general than Eq. (7.3-57), which is a special case of the above. Another problem is that these linear models predict constant viscosity and normal stress functions (a general consequence of linear models), whereas these functions are invariably nonlinear for real materials; i.e., they are dependent upon the magnitude of the deformation or deformation rate, except for small magnitude deformations.

B. Nonlinear Models

Nonlinear characteristics may be introduced into an integral model by incorporating a shear dependence into the relaxation or memory function. Since these are scalar functions (i.e., material functions), this dependence can only be in terms of the scalar invariants of the strain or rate of strain tensors.

There is a very extensive and rapidly expanding body of literature devoted to the formulation and testing of nonlinear rheological models, many of which are of the integral type. Most of the effort is centered around attempts to model the properties of polymeric fluids, both solutions and melts. A representative, but significant, portion of this literature is included in Refs. 7.1, 7.5, 7.6, and 7.11-7.34, and the interested reader is encouraged to consult these references for an appreciation of the variety of methods and approaches that have been tried. Because of the rapid and continually changing developments in this field, it is neither possible nor practical to attempt a comprehensive coverage or review here. Instead we will simply present two examples which are representative of nonlinear integral models.

A model proposed by Bird and Carreau [7.14, 7.16, 7.16] employs a memory function which is derived by empirically modifying the generalized Maxwell model as follows:

$$\tau_{ij} = \int_{-\infty}^{t} \left\{ \sum_{p=1}^{\infty} \frac{\mu_p}{\lambda_{2p}^2} \frac{e^{-(t-t')/\lambda_{2p}}}{[1 + \frac{1}{2} \lambda_{1p}^2 II(t')]} \right\} \left[(1 + \frac{\varepsilon}{2}) \Gamma_{ij} - \frac{\varepsilon}{2} g_{im} g_{jn} \Gamma^{mn} \right] dt'$$

7.4-78

(7.4-79)

where

$$\lambda_{np} = \lambda_n \left(\frac{2}{p+1} \right)^{\alpha_n} \qquad\qquad (7.4-80)$$

$$\mu_p = \frac{\lambda_{1p} \mu_o}{\sum_{p=1}^{\infty} \lambda_{1p}} \qquad\qquad (7.4-81)$$

This is a six constant model with the following parameters:

μ_o = zero shear rate viscosity

λ_1 = characteristic shear time constant

λ_2 = characteristic relaxation or elastic time constant

α_1, α_2 = dimensionless indices (order of 2)

ε = dimensionless weighting factor, which may be a function of $II(t')$, where $II(t')$ is the (negative) second invariant of Δ_{ij}

The normal stress characteristics of this model may be determined from the simple shear response, for constant $\dot{\gamma}$. The finite strain tensor components for this flow are (see Appendix E):

$$\Gamma_{ij} = \begin{bmatrix} 0 & (t - t')\dot{\gamma} & 0 \\ (t - t')\dot{\gamma} & -(t - t')^2 \dot{\gamma}^2 & 0 \\ 0 & 0 & 0 \end{bmatrix} \qquad\qquad (7.4-82)$$

$$\Gamma^{ij} = \begin{bmatrix} (t - t')^2\dot{\gamma}^2 & (t - t')\dot{\gamma} & 0 \\ (t - t')\dot{\gamma} & 0 & 0 \\ 0 & 0 & 0 \end{bmatrix} \qquad (7.4\text{-}83)$$

$$II(t') = 2\dot{\gamma}^2 \qquad (7.4\text{-}84)$$

The corresponding nonzero components are determined from Eq. (7.4-79), and are:

$$\tau_{12} = \tau_{21} = \sum_{p=1}^{\infty} \left\{ \frac{\mu_p}{\lambda_{2p}^2 [1 + (\lambda_{1p}\dot{\gamma})^2]} \int_{-\infty}^{t} e^{-(t-t')/\lambda_{2p}} (t - t')\dot{\gamma} \, dt' \right\}$$

$$(7.4\text{-}85)$$

$$\tau_{11} - \tau_{22} = \sum_{p=1}^{\infty} \left\{ \frac{\mu_p}{\lambda_{2p}^2 [1 + (\lambda_{1p}\dot{\gamma})^2]} \int_{-\infty}^{t} e^{-(t-t')\lambda_{2p}} (t - t')^2\dot{\gamma}^2 \, dt' \right\}$$

$$(7.4\text{-}86)$$

$$\tau_{22} - \tau_{33} = \sum_{p=1}^{\infty} \left\{ \frac{\mu_p}{\lambda_{2p}^2 [1 + (\lambda_{1p}\dot{\gamma})^2]} \int_{-\infty}^{t} e^{-(t-t')/\lambda_{2p}} \frac{\varepsilon}{2} (t - t')^2\dot{\gamma}^2 \, dt' \right\}$$

$$(7.4\text{-}87)$$

Evaluating the integral for constant $\dot{\gamma}$ (see note 2), the steady flow material functions result:

$$\eta = \sum_{p=1}^{\infty} \frac{\mu_p}{1 + (\lambda_{1p}\dot{\gamma})^2} \qquad (7.4\text{-}88)$$

$$\theta_1 = 2 \sum_{p=1}^{\infty} \frac{\mu_p \lambda_{2p}}{1 + (\lambda_{1p}\dot{\gamma})^2} \qquad \theta_2 = \frac{\varepsilon\theta_1}{2} \qquad (7.4\text{-}89)$$

(†)

For small deformations (in which terms of the order $\dot{\gamma}^2$ in the memory function are assumed negligible), this model reduces to the linear generalized Maxwell model, for which the complex viscosity components in oscillatory shear are:

$$\eta' = \sum_{p=1}^{\infty} \frac{\mu_p}{1 + (\lambda_{2p}\omega)^2} \qquad \eta'' = \sum_{p=1}^{\infty} \frac{\lambda_{2p}\mu_p\omega}{1 + (\lambda_{2p}\omega)^2} \qquad (7.4\text{-}90)$$

Note that the analogies between η and η', and between $\frac{1}{2}\dot{\gamma}\theta_1$ and η'' are not satisfied unless $\lambda_1 = \lambda_2$.

The relaxation of shear stress after sudden cessation of steady flow for this model is readily determined to be [7.14, 7.17]:

$$\frac{\tau(t)}{\tau_-} = \frac{\sum\limits_{p=1}^{\infty}\left\{\mu_p/[1 + (\lambda_{2p}\dot{\gamma}_-)^2]\right\}e^{-t/\lambda_{2p}}}{\sum\limits_{p=1}^{\infty}\mu_p/[1 + (\lambda_{1p}\dot{\gamma}_-)^2]} \qquad (7.4\text{-}91)$$

It is noted that this model predicts a non-Newtonian apparent viscosity function, nonlinear normal stresses, complex viscosity, and stress relaxation response identical to that of the generalized Maxwell equivalent of the Spriggs model [Eq. (7.4-45)], if $\lambda_{np} = \lambda_n(1/p)^n$, $\lambda_1 = c\lambda_2 = c\lambda$, and $\alpha_1 = \alpha_2 \neq 2$. However, the two models given different results for other material response such as stress buildup, elongational flow, and superimposed steady and oscillatory shear flow.

A somewhat similar integral model has been deduced by Meister [7.18] from a consideration of an interacting sphere model for concentrated polymer solutions, and the influence of the deformation rate on the rate of formation and breakage of molecular entanglements. The resulting model is:

$$\tau^{ij} = \int_{-\infty}^{t}\left\{\sum_{p=1}^{\infty}\frac{G}{\lambda_p}\exp\left[-\int_{t'}^{t}\frac{(1 + c\sqrt{II(\xi)}\,\lambda_p)d\xi}{\lambda_p}\right]\Gamma^{ij}(t')\ dt'\right\}$$

$$(7.4\text{-}92)$$

The parameter c represents a ratio of the center to center separation of two spheres in the direction of the shear gradient to the maximum extent of overlap or range of influence of the interacting spheres. It is taken to be a constant if there is no effect of orientation on the interaction. However, if orientation is significant, c is assumed to be shear dependent according to the following empirical formulation:

$$c = \frac{c'}{(1 + c'\sqrt{II(\xi)}\ \lambda_o)^n}$$

(7.4-93)

This, in effect, replaces the parameter c by two other parameters, c' and n. The constant c' is the key parameter of the model, and was found to vary from 0.20 to 0.30 for those polymer solutions studied. As before, II is the negative second invariant of the rate of strain tensor, while ξ represents the time of decay of entanglements, and t' is the time of interaction. The relaxation times, λ_p, and shear modulus G, are the same as those of the Bird-Carreau model:

$$\lambda_p = \lambda_o \left(\frac{2}{P + 1}\right)^{\alpha_1}$$

$$G = \frac{\mu_\infty}{\displaystyle\sum_{P=1}^{\infty} \lambda_p}$$

(7.4-95)

The model is thus a four or five constant model, depending upon whether or not c is assumed constant. The parameters are:

$$\lambda_o,\ \alpha_1,\ \mu_o,\quad c(\text{or } c' \text{ and } n)$$

(7.4-96)

For simple shear flow, the model predicts the following steady flow material functions:

$$\eta = \sum_{P=1}^{\infty} \frac{G\lambda_p}{(1 + c\dot{\gamma}\lambda_p)^2}$$

(7.4-97)

$$\theta_1 = \sum_{P=1}^{\infty} \frac{2G\lambda_P^2}{(1 + c\dot{\gamma}\lambda_P)^3} \qquad \theta_2 = 0 \qquad\qquad (7.4\text{-}98)$$

For stress relaxation after instantaneous cessation of steady shear (at time zero), the shear and first normal stress difference response is given by:

$$\tau_{12}(t) = \sum_{P=1}^{\infty} \frac{G\lambda_P \dot{\gamma}_-}{(1 + c\dot{\gamma}_-\lambda_P)^2} e^{-t/\lambda_P} \qquad\qquad (7.4\text{-}99)$$

$$(\tau_{11} - \tau_{22}) = \sum_{P=1}^{\infty} \frac{2G\lambda_P^2\dot{\gamma}^2}{(1 + c\dot{\gamma}_-\lambda_P)^3} e^{-t/\lambda_P} \qquad\qquad (7.4\text{-}100)$$

For small amplitude (linear) oscillatory response, the complex viscosity is identical to that of the Bird-Carreau model. Another unsteady response test which may be performed is stress growth, or the buildup of shear and normal stresses after sudden imposition of a constant step shear rate. For this model, the shear stress component is given by:

$$\tau_{12}(t) = \dot{\gamma} \left\{ \int_0^t \sum_{P=1}^{\infty} \frac{G}{\lambda_P} \exp\left[\frac{-\theta(1 + c\lambda_P\dot{\gamma})}{\lambda_P} \right] \theta \, d\theta \right.$$

$$\left. + \int_t^{\infty} \sum_{P=1}^{\infty} \left[\frac{G}{\lambda_P} \exp\left(-\frac{\theta}{\lambda_P} + c\dot{\gamma}t \right) \right] t \, d\theta \right\} \qquad (7.4\text{-}101)$$

which may be integrated to give:

$$\tau_{12}(t) = \sum_{P=1}^{\infty} \frac{G\lambda_P\dot{\gamma}}{(1 + c\dot{\gamma}\lambda_P)^2} \left\{ 1 - [1 - c\dot{\gamma}t(1 + c\dot{\gamma}\lambda_P)] \exp\left[\frac{-t(1 + c\lambda_P\dot{\gamma})}{\lambda_P} \right] \right\}$$

$$(7.4\text{-}102)$$

Likewise, the buildup of the first normal stress difference is predicted to be:

$$(\tau_{11} - \tau_{22}) = \sum_{P=1}^{\infty} \frac{G\lambda_P^2 \dot{\gamma}^2}{(1 + c\dot{\gamma}\lambda_P)^3}$$

$$\cdot \left\{ 2 - \left[2 + \frac{2t(1 + c\dot{\gamma}\lambda_P)}{\lambda_P} - \frac{c\dot{\gamma}^2 t^2 (1 + c\dot{\gamma}\lambda_P)^2}{2\lambda_P} \right] \right.$$

$$\left. \exp\left[\frac{-t(1 + c\lambda_P\dot{\gamma})}{\lambda_P} \right] \right\} \qquad (7.4\text{-}103)$$

Both of the stress growth expressions predict a maximum in the response curve, in qualitative agreement with observations

Meister experimentally evaluated each of the above material functions for a 2% polyacrylamide (see note 3) solution using a Weissenberg rheogoniometer and obtained excellent agreement with the predicted values over a range of 10^4 in shear rate using the following parameters:

$$c' = 0.20 \qquad\qquad n = 0.25$$

$$\alpha_1 = 2.9 \qquad\qquad \lambda_1 = 30 \text{ sec} \qquad\qquad (7.4\text{-}104)$$

$$\mu_o = 1600 \text{ P}$$

He also evaluated a number of other popular integral models, including the Bird-Carreau model, in light of these data. The results indicated this model to be superior, at least for the particular fluid tested and the range of data obtained.

Note that there is no direct method for converting a nonlinear derivative model into an equivalent nonlinear integral model, since neither the Laplace transform nor the Boltzmann superposition methods apply to nonlinear systems. A method of "inverting" the Jaumann

derivation to a corresponding integral expression has been given by
Goddard and Miller [7.35], but the method appears to be quite cumbersome to apply in practice.

7.5. CLOSURE

The models discussed in this chapter are presented only for purposes of illustration, and no implication as to their general usefulness is intended. The modern literature in rheology abounds with
reports of proposed models or constitutive equations for viscoelastic
fluids, and experimental tests of their validity with respect to com-
parisons with one or more measured material functions. Ideally, the
ultimate rheological model for a given material would be one which
reproduces all measurable response characteristics with a minimum
number of parameters or constants (material properties). It would
also be highly desirable that these parameters be easily related to,
or correlated with, the molecular properties of the material, an
aspect which is beyond the scope of this book.

Although considerable effort has been expended in the formulation and testing of viscoelastic fluid models (mostly for solutions
of high polymers), the present state of development is such that no
generalized model or models have been found for any complex material
which accurately represent all possible response characteristics of
the material. One of the simplest models which incorporates qualitatively the observed characteristics of most of the material functions for viscoelastic polymeric fluids is the generalized form of
the three parameter Jeffreys model employing the Jaumann derivative,
Eq. (7.4-35), although the more complex integral models have received
considerably more attention and have exhibited considerable success.

If a satisfactory explanation or quantitative description of
such complex flow phenomena as drag reduction in turbulent flow is
to be expected, it will be necessary to have a quantitative description of the appropriate rheological properties of the material.
Furthermore, it has not been unambiguously established just what

specific rheological material functions are necessary or sufficient
to completely define the response of a complex viscoelastic fluid in
complex deformations. Those which we have described in detail
(apparent viscosity, normal stress coefficients, complex moduli) are
those which are commonly measured and for which more-or-less routine
experimental and analytical procedures have been developed. However,
many other material functions, some of which have been mentioned only
briefly, may be defined and measured, many of which appear to be sensitive to properties which the above tests are not. These include
elongational viscosity, oscillatory response of normal stresses,
superimposed oscillatory strain on steady flow, transient growth and
relaxation of both shear and normal stresses to sudden application
or removal of a constant shear rate, etc. Indeed, a number of generalized models have been proposed which predict identical steady
and oscillatory material functions, but which differ in the predicted
superimposed and transient response. The reader interested in further pursuing these details should consult the modern periodical
literature.

It may be fairly stated, therefore, that we have but merely
scratched the surface of the subject of the rheology and continuum
mechanics of complex fluids. Indeed, our objective has not been to
produce an exhaustive and encompassing treatise, but only to provide
an introduction to the fundamentals which are required for an understanding and insight into the complex mechanical behavior of fluids
possessing both viscous and elastic properties. If we have succeeded
to the extent that the reader is now capable of reading, comprehend-
ing, and hopefully extending the modern literature and body of knowledge in this complex field, then our objective will have been well
satisfied.

PROBLEMS

7-1. Assuming the shear viscosity and cross viscosity of a Reiner-
      Rivlin fluid are constant, determine expressions for the nonzero
      stress components in the fluid in terms of velocity and veloc-
      ity gradients for:

(a) Steady laminar flow over a stationary sphere

(b) Helical flow, in which the fluid is contained in the an-
     nulus between concentric cylinders, the outer of which
     is stationary and the inner is rotating with an angular
     velocity Ω and is also moving axially with a constant
     velocity V

7-2. Determine the complex modulus and relaxation function for a
      Reiner-Rivlin fluid. Assume the shear viscosity and cross
      viscosity are constants.

7-3. Derive an expression for the total pressure required to force
      a Reiner-Rivlin fluid at a volumetric rate Q through a tube
      of length L which exits into the atmosphere if the fluid param-
      eters α_1 and α_2 are constants. Neglect irreversible losses due
      friction in the entrance region.

7-4. Plot a contour of the shape of the free surface of the fluid
      of Sec. 7.2.3B, for the following values of the system param-
      eters:

$$\rho = 1.0 \text{ g/cm}^3 \qquad R_i = 1 \text{ cm} \qquad \Omega_1 = 100 \text{ rpm}$$

$$m_2 = 6 \text{ dyn-sec}^2/\text{cm}^2$$

      Discuss the likelihood of observing a similar contour on a real
      fluid surface.

7-5. Derive a criteria for observation of the Weissenberg effect
      analogous to Eq. (7.2-57) for a Reiner-Rivlin fluid if the
      apparent viscosity and cross viscosity are expressed as "power-
      law" functions of shear rate.

7-6. Derive expressions for the components of the covariant and
      contravariant (Almansi and Finger) finite strain tensors in
      terms of velocity and velocity gradient components for steady
      laminar flow in

    (a)   Helical flow

    (b)   Flow over a stationary sphere

    (c)   Axial flow in a cylindrical tube with an elliptic cross section

    (d)   The field adjacent to a football (prolate spheroid) undergoing spiral flight through a stationary fluid

7-7.   Repeat Example 7.1 for the finite strain tensors defined by Eqs. (7.3-28) and (7.3-29) instead of Γ_{ij} and Γ^{ij}.

7-8.   Derive Eq. (7.3-25) relating the finite Almansi strain tensor Γ_{ij} to the infinitesimal strain e_{ij}.

7-9.   Derive an equation equivalent to Eq. (7.3-25) which relates the finite Finger strain tensor Γ^{ij} to the contravariant infinitesimal strain e^{ij}.

7-10.   Consider a cylinder of a viscoelastic solid which is held stationary at one end and is subject to an angular displacement about its axis at the other end. Determine the nonzero components of the finite Almansi and Finger strain tensors (Γ_{ij} and Γ^{ij}) for this deformation in terms of the applied displacement.

7-11.   Show that the material derivative of the metric tensor of a fixed coordinate system is zero.

7-12.   Show that Eq. (7.3-40) for the convected derivative is identical to Eq. (7.3-41), for any coordinate system ($x^i \equiv z^i$).

7-13.   Derive an expression for the convected derivative of a second-order contravariant tensor, equivalent to Eq. (7.3-41). Check your result by comparison with Eq. (7.3-42).

7-14.   Prove that the two expressions for the convected derivative, Eqs. (7.3-42) and (7.3-43), are identical.

7-15. Prove that the two forms of the Jaumann derivative given by Eq. (7.3-55) are identical, as are the two forms in Eq. (7.3-56).

7-16. Prove that the quantities defined by Eqs. (7.3-57) and (7.3-58) commute with the operation of raising and lowering indices, respectively.

7-17. Derive expressions for covariant and contravariant rate of strain tensors based upon a strain measure defined by Eq. (7.3-57) and by Eq. (7.3-58). Are these two forms of strain rate equivalent?

7-18. For the convected derivative model of Eq. (7.4-1), determine:
   (a) The "recoil" or strain recovery after removal of stress following a steady simple shear flow
   (b) The relaxation of shear and normal stresses as a function of time following sudden cessation of steady shear

7-19. Determine the stress relaxation as a function of time after cessation of steady flow for the two-parameter Jaumann derivative model of Eq. (7.4-27).

7-20. Derive the material functions given by Eqs. (7.4-36) to (7.4-39) for the three-parameter Jaumann derivative Jeffreys model of Eq. (7.4-35).

7-21. Consider the generalized form of the three-parameter Jeffreys model employing the Jaumann derivative, Eq. (7.4-35). For this fluid in helical flow, determine:
   (a) Expressions for each of the nonzero physical stress components as a function of the physical velocity components
   (b) The appropriate form of the equations of motion, with boundary conditions which would have to be solved with the expressions from (a) to determine the distribution of velocity and stress components in the system

7-22.   Derive expressions for the stress components in oscillatory
        deformation for the contravariant convected Maxwell model,
        Eq. (7.4-23), by utilizing complex notation for oscillatory
        stress and strain. Note that for any two quantities oscillat-
        ing at frequency ω, represented by complex notation such as

$$\tau(\omega t) = \tau^* e^{j\omega t}, \quad \dot{\gamma}(\omega t) = \dot{\gamma}^* e^{j\omega t}$$

their product may be expressed as

$$\tau(\omega t)\dot{\gamma}(\omega t) = \tfrac{1}{2}(\tau^* \dot{\gamma}^* e^{2j\omega t} + \tau^* \dot{\gamma}^*_c)$$

where $\dot{\gamma}^*_c$ is the complex conjugate of $\dot{\gamma}^*$ (i.e., $\dot{\gamma}^*_c = \dot{\gamma}' - j\dot{\gamma}''$).

7-23.   Derive the material functions given by Eqs. (7.4-42) to
        (7.4-44) for the nonlinear Oldroyd model of Eq. (7.4-40).

7-24.   Derive the material functions given by Eqs. (7.4-41) to
        (7.4-49) for the Spriggs model of Eq. (7.4-45).

7-25.   Derive the material functions given by Eqs. (7.4-52) to
        (7.4-54) and the small amplitude oscillatory response func-
        tions for the generalized Jaumann derivative model of Eq.
        (7.4-51).

7-26.   Consider the following three parameter derivative model:

$$\tau_{ij} + \lambda_1 \frac{\mathbb{D}\tau_{ij}}{\mathbb{D}t} = \mu\left(\Delta_{ij} + \lambda_2 \frac{\mathbb{D}\,\Delta_{ij}}{\mathbb{D}t}\right)$$

where

$$\frac{\mathbb{D}A_{ij}}{\mathbb{D}t} = \frac{\mathcal{D}A_{ij}}{\mathcal{D}t} - \frac{1}{2}(A_{ik}\Delta^k_{\ j} + A_{jk}\Delta^k_{\ i}) + \frac{1}{3}A_{k\ell}\Delta^{\ell k}g_{ij}$$

Determine the apparent viscosity and first and second normal
stress difference functions for this model.

7-27.   Derive Eqs. (7.4-70) and (7.4-71) for the viscosity and normal
        stress functions in terms of the distribution function, from
        preceding relations.

7-28.   Starting with the relaxation function for the three-parameter
        linear Jeffreys model, derive expressions for:
        (a) The ratio of first normal stress difference to the vis-
             cosity
        (b) The ratio of strain recovery (recoil) to steady shear
             rate after stress removal

7-29.   Derive the material functions of Eqs. (7.3-88) to (7.4-91)
        and also expressions for the stress buildup after sudden im-
        position of steady flow for the nonlinear Bird-Carreau model
        of Eq. (7.4-79).

7-30.   Derive the material functions of Eqs. (7.4-99) to (7.4-105)
        for the nonlinear Meister model of Eq. (7.4-92).

NOTES

1. A summary and comparison of first and second normal stress dif-
    ferences, including an evaluation of the various experimental
    methods employed for determining them, has been given by Ginn
    and Metzner [7.7] and by Tanner [7.8].

2. The following relation is employed in evaluating these integrals:

$$\int_{-\infty}^{t} e^{-(t-t')/\lambda_{2p}} (t - t')^{n}\, dt' = n!\,\lambda_{2p}^{n+1}$$

3. Note that a 2% polyacrylamide solution is considered quite con-
    centrated, the zero shear viscosity being 1600 P.

NOTATION

a_n	amplitude of nth damped wave (Fig. 5.14)
A	instrument constant, defined by Eq. (5.6-7)
A_{ij}	antisymmetric tensor
B	instrument constant, defined by Eq. (5.6-8)
B	parameter in Eyring model
$B_m^{\;n}$	Eulerian components of tensor $b_i^{\;j}$
c_{ij}	Cauchy deformation tensor
c^{ij}	Finger deformation tensor
C_{ij}	Green deformation tensor
C^{ij}	Piola deformation tensor
ds	differential line segment
$\bar{e}$	mean normal strain
$\vec{e}_i$	general (curvilinear) base vector

$\vec{e}^i$ base vectors reciprocal to $\vec{e}_i$ set

e_{ij} total strain tensor (Cartesian components)

$e_{ijk}, \ e^{ijk}$ permutation symbol

$e^{ijk\cdots}, \ e_{ijk}\cdots$ generalized permutation symbol

e_v volumetric strain

$\dot{e}_v$ volumetric strain rate

E   Young's modulus

E_{ij} covariant convected strain tensor

E^{ij} contravariant convected strain tensor

f( )   function

f(x)   general function of z; also specific function
                                    defined by Eq. (5.4-59) and Fig. 5.5

F   total normal thrust in cone plate or disc plate

F'   net normal thrust in cone plate or disc plate,
                                    in excess of force due to ambient pressure

F_c centrifugal force correction to measured normal
                                    thrust

$F_c(\omega)$ Fourier cosine transform

$F_s(\omega)$ Fourier sine transform

$F(\lambda)$ modulus of distribution of shear moduli

$F(\lambda)$ spectrum of shear moduli

F_z axial tube thrust from free jet expansion

g	determinant of components of g_{ij}
g_i	base vector for fixed coordinates
$\hat{g}_{ij}$	metric tensor for convected coordinates
g_{ij}	metric tensor
g^{ij}	conjugate tensor
g_j	j component of body force (e.g., gravity)
G	constant shear modulus
G_e	equilibrium modulus
G_{ij}	covariant Green strain tensor
G^{ij}	contravariant Green strain tensor
$G_1(t)$	time-dependent part of relaxation modulus
$G^*(j\omega)$	complex modulus
G'	storage modulus
G''	loss modulus
$G_o(t_1)$	gate function
$G(\gamma)$	shear-dependent shear modulus
$G(t)$	relaxation modulus
h	vertical distance above reference level
h	separation between plates
h	gap clearance in disc plate or concentric cylinder apparatus

Δh manometer head difference

h_i coordinate scale factor

$H(\lambda)$ spectrum of viscous moduli

$\vec{i}$ Cartesian unit base vector

I moment of inertia

I_o modified Bessel function

j unit imaginary number, $\sqrt{-1}$

J_e equilibrium compliance

J_o Bessel function of first kind, zero order

$J_1(t)$ time-dependent part of compliance function

J_1 Bessel function of first kind, first order

J_2 Bessel function of first kind, second order

$J^*(j\omega)$ complex compliance

$J(t)$ compliance function, creep function

J' real part of complex compliance

J'' imaginary part of complex compliance

K bulk modulus

K torsion spring constant

ℓ wavelength

L length of cylinder

L_e entrance length

L'	tube length in fully developed flow
$L(\lambda)$	spectrum of compliance moduli
m	slope of log-log plot of R vs. Ω for Couette flow
m	Power law consistency parameter
m'	slope of $1/m$ vs. $\ell n\ \tau_{Ri}$ plot for Couette flow
M	mass
n	general index; Power law flow index
n'	slope of log-log plot of τ_W vs. Γ for Poiseuille flow
N	grouping of normal stress components = $N_1 + 2N_2$
N_1	first normal stress difference, $\tau_{11} - \tau_{22}$
N_2	second normal stress difference, $\tau_{22} - \tau_{33}$
N_{De}	Deborah number
N_{Re}	Reynolds number, Newtonian fluid
N'_{Re}	Reynolds number, Power law fluid
p	parameter in Cross or Williams' model (not same in both)
p	material parameters in differential model
P	differential operator
P	fluid pressure
$\bar{P}$	negative mean normal stress
$P(0)$	pressure at r = 0

P_o ambient pressure

P_c pressure correction for centrifugal force in
                                        concentric cylinder apparatus

$\bar{P}_c$ centrifugal force pressure correction to stress
                                        distribution

P_o reference pressure, in undeformed state

ΔP total pressure drop in tube

ΔP_e extra pressure loss in entrance region

ΔP_L pressure drop in fully developed flow over length

P pressure in excess of hydrostatic head

P_v change in pressure associated with volumetric
                                        strain

q_i material parameters in differential model

Q differential operator

Q volumetric flow rate

Q^* oscillatory flow rate

r_i material parameters in differential model

r_{ij} rotation tensor (Cartesian components)

$r^*(\omega t)$ ratio of output to input in oscillatory motion

r' in-phase component of $r^*(\omega t)$

r'' out-of-phase component of $r^*(\omega t)$

r_n ratio of first to nth amplitude in damped wave

r_o	yield point for Bingham plastic
R	differential operator
R_o	outer cylinder radius
R_i	inner cylinder radius
R_j	radius of free jet
$R(\omega)$	in-phase (resistive) component of $Z^*(j\omega)$
s	Laplace transform variable
$\vec{S}$	position vector
S_{ij}	symmetric tensor
t	time
t'	time prior to time t
t_e	characteristic system time
t_1	characteristic time
t_1	parameter in Cross or Williams' models (not same in both)
t_2	parameter in non-Newtonian model
$\text{tr} \ (\ )$	trace of second-order tensor
T	temperature
T	torque in rotating apparatus
T	period in oscillatory wave
T	torque consistency variable in disc and plate system defined by Eq. (5.4-102)

T_{ij} any second-order tensor

$T(\omega t)$ oscillatory torque

T_o amplitude of oscillatory torque

T_o reference temperature

T_z axial thrust in tube flow

u_j, $\vec{u}$ displacement vector

$\dfrac{\partial u_i}{\partial x_j}$, $\dfrac{d\vec{u}}{d\vec{S}}$ displacement gradient tensor (Cartesian components)

u_s slip velocity

U coefficient of instrument friction

$U(t)$ unit step function

v flow velocity component

v_i, $\vec{v}$ velocity vector

$\dfrac{\partial v_i}{\partial x_j}$, $\dfrac{d\vec{v}}{d\vec{S}}$ velocity gradient tensor (Cartesian components)

v_o velocity of oscillating plate

V velocity component or volume

$\bar{V}_o$ velocity amplitude of oscillating plate

V volume change

$\bar{V}$ average velocity in tube

V_j velocity of free jet

V_o reference volume

x^i	Cartesian coordinate
$\hat{x}^i$	convected linear coordinates
x_o	displacement of oscillating plate
X	amplitude of oscillating plate displacement
$X(\omega)$	out-of-phase (reactive) component of $Z^*(j\omega)$
Y_1	Bessel function of second kind, first order
Y_2	Bessel function of second kind, second order
z	complex number
z^i	general (curvilinear) coordinate
$Z(\alpha)$	Riemann zeta function
Z^i	material coordinates
$Z^*(j\omega)$	mechanical or fluid impedance

Greek

α	parameter in Ellis, Meter models
α	rotation of material element
α	ratio R_o/R_i for Couette apparatus
α^*	complex fluid parameter equal to $(j\omega\rho/\eta^*)^{\frac{1}{2}}$
α_i	imaginary part of $\alpha^*(j\omega)$
α_o	real part of $\alpha^*(j\omega)$
$\bar{\alpha}(s)$	function of s defined by Eq. (4.4-35)
β	slip coefficient

β_k^{ℓ} convected components of tensor $b_i^{\ j}$

β_o compressibility

γ shear strain component

γ' real part of complex strain

γ'' imaginary part of complex strain

γ_∞ ultimate strain or "recoil" relative to time of stress removal

γ_{ij} shear strain tensor

γ_o magnitude of shear strain

$\dot{\gamma}$ shear rate component

$\dot{\gamma}_{ij}$ shear rate tensor

$\gamma^*(\omega t)$ complex (oscillatory) strain

$\dot{\gamma}_o$ referrence shear rate in Power law, $1 \ \text{sec}^{-1}$

$\dot{\gamma}_1$ parameter in truncated Power law model

$\dot{\gamma}_o$ magnitude of shear rate

$\dot{\gamma}_P$ reference shear rate

$\dot{\gamma}_w$ shear rate at tube wall

$\dot{\gamma}_-$ magnitude of constant shear rate prior to sudden removal of stress

Γ consistency flow variable equal to $4Q/\pi R^3$

Γ_{ij} covariant finite (Almansi) strain tensor

Γ^{ij} contravariant finite (Finger) strain tensor

δ_{ij}	Kronecker delta, unit Cartesian tensor
δ_{ij}, δ^{ij}, $\delta_i^{\ j}$	Kronecker delta
$\delta^{ij\cdots}_{\quad \alpha\beta\cdots}$	generalized Kronecker delta
$\delta(t)$	Dirac delta or impulse function
$\bar{\Delta}$	mean normal strain rate
Δ_{ij}	rate of strain tensor
ε	relative phase angle between input and output motions
ε	parameter in Spriggs model
ζ	ratio of jet to tube radius
ζ_d	damping factor for damped oscillatory wave
η	apparent viscosity function
η_o	zero-shear rate limiting Newtonian viscosity
η_∞	infinite shear rate-limiting Newtonian viscosity
η_P	viscosity parameter in Power law model
$\eta^*(j\omega)$	complex viscosity
η'	real part of complex viscosity
η''	negative imaginary part of complex viscosity
θ	angular displacement
Θ	amplitude of oscillatory angular deflection
$\theta_1(\dot{\gamma})$	first normal stress difference function
$\theta_2(\dot{\gamma})$	second normal stress difference function

θ_c cone angle

κ bulk viscosity

κ^* complex parameter equal to $(-\alpha^{*2})^{\frac{1}{2}} = (-j\omega\rho/\eta^*)^{\frac{1}{2}}$

λ relaxation time

λ' retardation time

λ_i ith time constant (defined separately for each model)

λ_{np} time constants in Bird-Carreau model

μ Newtonian viscosity

μ_e effective viscosity, defined by Eq. (5.4-20)

μ_o parameter in Bingham and Eyring models (not the same in both)

ν Poisson's ratio

ξ time of entanglement decay in Meister model

ξ ratio r/R

$\hat{\xi}^i$ general convected coordinates

ρ density

ρ_o density at reference temperature T_o

σ_{ij} total stress tensor

σ_n normal stress component

σ_s surface tension

$\bar{\sigma}_{zz}$ axial stress averaged over tube section

τ	component of shear stress tensor
τ'	real component of complex shear stress
τ''	imaginary component of complex shear stress
τ_-	shear stress in steady flow prior to stopping flow
$\tau_{\frac{1}{2}}$	parameter in Ellis model
$\tau(\omega t)$	complex (oscillatory) shear stress
τ_{ij}	shear stress tensor
τ_m	parameter in Meter model
τ_o	yield stress for Bingham plastic
τ_o	magnitude of shear stress component
τ_R	shear stress at r = R
τ_s	parameter in Reiner-Philippoff model
τ_w	wall shear stress
ϕ	angular deflection
$\phi(\omega t)$	oscillatory angular deflection
$\phi(t)$	memory function
Φ	pressure gradient in tube
Φ	amplitude of oscillatory angular deflection
Φ'	in-phase component of relative angular deflection
Φ''	out-of-phase component of relative angular deflection
Φ_o	amplitude of oscillatory pressure gradient

$\Phi(\omega t)$ oscillatory pressure gradient

ψ_- angle measured from plate toward cone

$\bar{\psi}(s)$ transform of relaxation function

$\psi(t)$ relaxation function

ω angular velocity, v_θ/r

ω_o natural frequency

Ω angular velocity of bounding surface

Ω_i angular velocity of inner cylinder

Ω_{ij} vorticity tensor (Cartesian components)

Ω_o angular velocity of outer cylinder

Other Symbols and Operators

D/Dt material derivative

$\mathcal{D}/\mathcal{D}t$ Jaumann derivative

$\mathcal{J}(\ )$ Oldroyd nonlinear time derivative

$\mathcal{J}_\varepsilon(\ )$ Spriggs nonlinear time derivative

$\begin{Bmatrix} i \\ j\ k \end{Bmatrix}$ Christoffel symbol of second kind

I, II, III   three invariants of second-order tensor

$\bar{T}(ij)$ physical components of tensor T_{ij}

$(\ )_{,j}$ covariant derivative of quantity $(\ )$ with respect to the j coordinate direction

$\dfrac{\delta}{\delta t}$ convected derivative

$\vec{\overset{\rightarrow}{\Delta}}:\vec{\overset{\rightarrow}{\Delta}}$	scalar self-product of rate of strain tensor
$\vec{\overset{\rightarrow}{\tau}}:\vec{\overset{\rightarrow}{\tau}}$	scalar self-product of stress tensor
Overbar ($^-$)	Laplace transform of variable
Overstar (*)	complex quantity
Overdot ($^\cdot$)	time derivative of variable

A SHORT TABLE OF
LAPLACE TRANSFORM PAIRS

I. Operations

Operation	Function $f(t)$	Transform $F(s) = \bar{f}(s)$ $= L[f(t)]$
1. Definition of transform	$f(t)$	$\int_{0}^{\infty} f(t)e^{-st}\,dt$
2. Definition of inverse	$\lim_{\sigma \to 0} \frac{1}{2\pi j} \int_{\sigma-j\infty}^{\sigma+j\infty} F(s)e^{st}\,ds$	$F(s)$
3. First derivative	$\dfrac{df(t)}{dt}$	$s\,F(s) - f(0)$
4. n^{th} derivative	$\dfrac{d^{n}f(t)}{dt^{n}}$	$s^{n}\,F(s) - s^{n-1}\,f(0)$ $- s^{n-2}\,f^{1}(0)\dots$ $\dots - f^{(n-1)}(0)$ where f^{k} is the kth derivative of $f(t)$

Operation	Function $f(t)$	Transform $F(s) = \bar{f}(s)$ $= L[f(t)]$
5. Integral	$\displaystyle\int_0^t f(t)\ dt$	$\dfrac{1}{2}\left[F(s) + (\int f(t)\ dt)\right]$ at $t = o$
6. Multiplication by t^n	$t^n f(t)$	$(-1)^n \dfrac{d^n F(s)}{ds^n}$
7. Division by t	$\dfrac{1}{t}\, f(t)$	$\displaystyle\int_s^\infty F(s)\ ds$
8. Time scale change	$f(at)$	$\dfrac{1}{a}\, F\!\left(\dfrac{s}{a}\right)$
9. Shift in t	$f(t - t_o)U(t - t_o)$	$e^{-t_o s}\, f(s)$
10. Shift in s	$e^{-at}\, f(t)$	$F(s + a)$
11. Scale factor	$\dfrac{1}{c}\, f\!\left(\dfrac{t}{c}\right)(c > o)$	$F(cs)$
12. Heaviside expansion formula	$\displaystyle\sum_{k=1}^{n} \dfrac{P(\alpha_k)}{Q'(\alpha_k)}\, e^{\alpha_k t}$ $\left[Q'(\alpha_k) = \left(\dfrac{dQ}{ds}\right)_{s=\alpha_k}\right]$	$\dfrac{P(s)}{Q(s)}$, where $Q(s) = (s - \alpha_1)(s - \alpha_2)$ $\ldots (s - \alpha_n)$ all αs distinct
13. Initial value theorem	$\lim_{t\to 0+} [f(t)]$ $=$	$\lim_{s\to\infty} [sF(s)]$
14. Final value theorem	$\lim_{t\to\infty} [f(t)]$ $=$	$\lim_{s\to 0} [sF(s)]$

		Transform
	Function	$F(s) = \bar{f}(s)$
Operation	$f(t)$	$= L[f(t)]$

15. Convolution $\displaystyle\int_0^t f_1(\tau)f_2(t - \tau)\, d\tau$ $\qquad F_1(s) \cdot F_2(s)$

$\displaystyle = \int_0^t f_1(t - \tau)f_2(\tau)\, d\tau$

16. n^{th} moment $\quad M_n(f) = \displaystyle\int_0^\infty t^n\, f(t)\, dt = (-1)^n \lim_{s\to 0}\left[\dfrac{d^n F(s)}{ds^n}\right]$

II. Functions

Function	Transform
$f(t)$	$F(s) = \bar{f}(s)$

1. Dirac delta, $\delta(t)$,

   $t = o$

   $\qquad\qquad 1$

2. Shifted Dirac delta, $\delta(t - a)$,

   $t = a$

   $\qquad\qquad e^{-as}$

3. Unit step, $U(t)$,

   1 $t = o$

   $\qquad\qquad \dfrac{1}{s}$

4. Shifted unit step, $U(t - a)$,

   1 $t = a$

   $\qquad\qquad \dfrac{e^{-as}}{s}$

| Function | Transform |
| f(t) | $F(s) = \bar{f}(s)$ |

5. Gate function, $G_a(T)$

   $= U(t - a) - U(t - a - T),$

   $t = a \quad a + T$

   $\dfrac{e^{-as}}{s}(1 - e^{-Ts})$

6. $\dfrac{t^{n-1}}{(n - 1)!},\qquad (n = 1, 2, 3\ \ldots)$

   $\dfrac{1}{s^n}$

7. $t^{k-1}\qquad (k > 0)$

   $\dfrac{\Gamma(k)}{s^k}$

   where $\Gamma(k) = \displaystyle\int_0^\infty x^k e^{-x}\,dx$

8. e^{-at}

   $\dfrac{1}{s + a}$

9. t

   $\dfrac{1}{s^2}$

10. $\dfrac{t^{n-1}e^{-at}}{(n - 1)!}\ (n = 1, 2, 3,\ \ldots)$

    $\dfrac{1}{(s + a)^n}$

11. $(1 - at)\,e^{-at}$

    $\dfrac{s}{(s + a)^2}$

12. $\dfrac{1}{a}(1 - e^{-at})$

    $\dfrac{1}{s(s + a)}$

13. $\dfrac{t}{a} - \dfrac{1}{a^2}(1 - e^{-at})$

    $\dfrac{1}{s^2(s + a)}$

14. $\dfrac{1}{a}\sin(at)$

    $\dfrac{1}{s^2 + a^2}$

Function $f(t)$	Transform $F(s) = \bar{f}(s)$
15. $\cos(at)$	$\dfrac{s}{s^2 + a^2}$
16. $\dfrac{1}{\sqrt{\pi t}}$	$\dfrac{1}{\sqrt{s}}$
17. $2\sqrt{\dfrac{t}{\pi}}$	$\dfrac{1}{s^{3/2}}$
18. $\dfrac{1}{a}\sinh(at)$	$\dfrac{1}{s^2 - a^2}$
19. $\cosh(at)$	$\dfrac{s}{s^2 - a^2}$
20. $\left(\dfrac{1}{b-a}\right)\left(be^{bt} - ae^{at}\right)$	$\dfrac{s}{(s-a)(s-b)} \quad a \neq b$
21. $\left(\dfrac{1}{b-a}\right)\left(e^{bt} - e^{at}\right)$	$\dfrac{s}{(s-a)(s-b)} \quad a \neq b$
22. $\dfrac{1}{ab}\left[1 + \dfrac{1}{a-b}\left(be^{-at} - ae^{-bt}\right)\right]$	$\dfrac{1}{s(s+a)(s+b)}$
23. $\dfrac{1}{(ab)^2}\left[\dfrac{1}{a-b}\left(a^2 e^{-bt} - b^2 e^{-at}\right)\right.$ $\left. + abt - a - b\right]$	$\dfrac{1}{s^2(s+a)(s+b)}$

Function f(t)	Transform $F(s) = \bar{f}(s)$

---

24. $\dfrac{e^{-at}}{(b-a)(c-a)} + \dfrac{e^{-bt}}{(a-b)(c-b)}$

     $+ \dfrac{e^{-ct}}{(a-c)(b-c)}$

$\qquad\qquad\qquad\qquad \dfrac{1}{(s+a)(s+b)(s+c)}$

25. $\dfrac{1}{a^2}\left(1 - e^{-at} - at e^{-at} \right)$

$\qquad\qquad\qquad\qquad \dfrac{1}{s(s+a)^2}$

26. $\dfrac{1}{a^3}\left(at - 2 + at e^{-at} + 2 e^{-at} \right)$

$\qquad\qquad\qquad\qquad \dfrac{1}{s^2(s+a)^2}$

GENERALIZED DERIVATION
OF CONSERVATION EQUATIONS

I. CONSERVATION OF MASS--CONTINUITY EQUATION

Consider an arbitrary fixed control volume V bounded by the surface S, designated locally by the unit normal vector n:

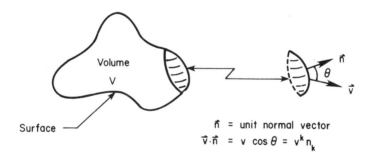

$\hat{n}$ = unit normal vector

$\vec{v} \cdot \hat{n}$ = v cos θ = $v^k n_k$

Here $\vec{v}$ represents the local velocity of the fluid crossing the surface S.

The conservation of mass principle can be expressed as:

$$\left\{ \begin{array}{c} \text{Rate of inflow} \\ \text{of mass} \\ \text{across S} \end{array} \right\} - \left\{ \begin{array}{c} \text{Rate of outflow} \\ \text{of mass} \\ \text{across S} \end{array} \right\} = \left\{ \begin{array}{c} \text{Rate of accumulation} \\ \text{of mass} \\ \text{in V} \end{array} \right\}$$

or, in vector form:

$$- \oint_S \rho v^k n_k \ ds = \frac{d}{dt} \oint_V \rho \ dv \qquad \text{(B-1)}$$

where $v^k n_k$ is the component of v^k normal to S in the outward direction.

Now Gauss' theorem provides the following relation between surface and volume integrals:

$$\oint_S \rho v^k n_k \ ds = \oint_V (\rho v^k),_k \qquad \text{(B-2)}$$

where $(\rho v^k),_k$ represents the divergence of the mass flux within volume V:

$$(\rho v^k),_k = \nabla \cdot (\rho \vec{v}) = \text{div} \ (\rho \vec{v})$$

$$= \frac{\partial (\rho v_1)}{\partial x_1} + \frac{\partial (\rho v_2)}{\partial x_2} + \frac{\partial (\rho v_3)}{\partial x_3} \qquad \text{(Cartesian)} \ \text{(B-3)}$$

where the right-hand side is the particular form with reference to rectangular coordinates.

Now since our control volume is fixed, the total rate of change of mass with V is given by the partial derivative, so that the right-hand side of (B-1) can be written:

$$\frac{d}{dt} \oint_V \rho \ dV = \int_V \frac{\partial \rho}{\partial t} \ dV \qquad \text{(B-4)}$$

Thus (B-1) becomes:

$$\oint_V \frac{\partial \rho}{\partial t} \ dV + \oint_V (\rho v^k),_k \ dV = 0 \qquad \text{(B-5))}$$

or

$$\frac{\partial \rho}{\partial t} + (\rho v^k)_{,k} = 0 \qquad\qquad\qquad (B-6)$$

which is one form of the continuity equation. Another form can be derived by expanding the $(\rho v^k)_{,k}$ term and rearranging:

$$(\rho v^k)_{,k} = \rho v^k_{,k} + v^k \rho_{,k} \qquad\qquad\qquad (B-7)$$

or

$$\nabla \cdot (\rho \vec{v}) = \rho \nabla \cdot \vec{v} + \vec{v} \cdot \nabla \rho$$

so that (B-6) becomes:

$$\frac{\partial \rho}{\partial t} + v^k \rho_{,k} + \rho v^k_{,k} = 0 \qquad\qquad\qquad (B-8)$$

Now the first two terms are identical to $\frac{D\rho}{Dt}$; so that (B-8) becomes:

$$\frac{D\rho}{Dt} = -\rho v^k_{,k} = -\rho \nabla \cdot \vec{v} \qquad\qquad\qquad (B-9)$$

For a constant density (isochoric) material, the continuity equation becomes:

$$v^k_{,k} = \nabla \cdot \vec{v} = 0 \qquad\qquad\qquad (B-10)$$

or

$$\frac{\partial v_1}{\partial x_1} + \frac{\partial v_2}{\partial x_2} + \frac{\partial v_3}{\partial x_3} = 0 \qquad \text{(Cartesian)}$$

II. CONSERVATION OF MOMENTUM--EQUATION OF MOTION

Consider now an arbitrary element of volume V moving with the fluid with the local velocity $\vec{v}$:

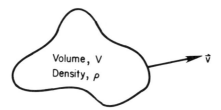

Now the rate of change of momentum associated with the material in the volume V is:

$$\frac{d}{dt} \oint_V \rho v^i \, dV \tag{B-11}$$

This can be written in an alternate way by making use of Leibnitz' formula for differentiating a multiple integral:

$$\frac{d}{dt} \oint_V \vec{A} \, dV = \oint_V \frac{\partial \vec{A}}{\partial t} \, dV + \oint_S \vec{A} \, \vec{v} \cdot \vec{n} \, dS \tag{B-12}$$

(This is also sometimes referred to as Reynolds' transport theorem.) Thus (B-11) becomes (substituting ρv^i for $\vec{A}$):

$$\frac{d}{dt} \oint_V \rho v^j \, dV = \oint_V \frac{\partial (\rho v^j)}{\partial t} \, dV + \oint_S \rho v^j v^k n_k \, dS \tag{B-13}$$

Now using Gauss' theorem to transform the surface integral to a volume integral:

$$\oint_S \rho v^j v^k n_k \, dS = \oint_V (\rho v^j v^k)_{,k} \, dV \tag{B-14}$$

(B-13) becomes:

$$\frac{d}{dt} \oint_V \rho v^j \; dV = \oint_V \left[\frac{\partial(\rho v^j)}{\partial t} + (\rho v^j v^k)_{,k} \right] dV$$

$$= \oint_V \left[\rho \frac{\partial v^j}{\partial t} + v^j \frac{\partial \rho}{\partial t} + \rho v^j v^k_{,k} + \rho v^j_{,k} v^k + \rho_{,k} v^j v^k \right] dV$$

$$= \oint_V \left[\rho \frac{Dv^j}{Dt} + v^j \frac{D\rho}{Dt} + \rho v^j v^k_{,k} \right] dV \qquad .$$

$$= \oint_V \left[\rho \frac{Dv^j}{Dt} + v^j \left(\frac{D\rho}{Dt} + \rho v^k_{,k} \right) \right] dV \qquad (B-15)$$

Now by the continuity equation, (B-9), the term in round brackets in (B-15) is zero. Thus:

$$\frac{d}{dt} \oint_V \rho v^j \; dV = \oint_V \rho \frac{Dv^j}{Dt} \; dV \qquad (B-16)$$

By Newton's second law, this rate of change of momentum must equal the total net force on the element:

$$\text{Net force} = F^j = \oint_S (\sigma^{jk} n_k) \; dS \qquad (B-17)$$

where $(\sigma^{jk} n_k \; dS)$ is the net force in the j direction resulting from the stress σ^{jk} acting on surface element $n_k \; dS$. Including the total net body force G^j (e.g., gravity):

$$\text{Body force} = G^j = \int_V \rho g^j \; dV \qquad (B-18)$$

Newton's law becomes:

$$\oint_V \rho \frac{Dv^j}{Dt} \, dV = \oint_S \sigma^{jk} n_k \, dS + \oint_V \rho g^j \, dV \tag{B-19}$$

Again employing Gauss' theorem to transform the surface integral to the equivalent volume integral gives:

$$\oint_V \rho \frac{Dv^j}{Dt} \, dV = \oint_V \sigma^{jk}{}_{,k} \, dV + \oint_V \rho g^j \, dV \tag{B-20}$$

or

$$\rho \frac{Dv^j}{Dt} = \sigma^{jk}{}_{,k} + \rho g^j \tag{B-21}$$

which is the general form of the fluid momentum equations of motion, applicable to any fluid.

SOME ORTHOGONAL COORDINATE SYSTEMS

I. Cartesian

$$z^1 = x \qquad z^2 = y \qquad z^3 = z$$

$$(ds)^2 = (dx)^2 + (dy)^2 + (dz)^2 \qquad h_x = h_y = h_z = 1$$

$$g_{ij} = g^{ij} = \begin{bmatrix} 1 & 0 & 0 \\ 0 & 1 & 0 \\ 0 & 0 & 1 \end{bmatrix}$$

all $\left\{ \begin{matrix} i \\ j\ k \end{matrix} \right\} = 0$

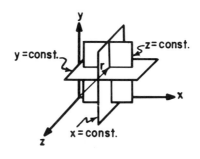

CARTESIAN COORDINATES

II. Cylindrical

$$z^1 = r \qquad z^2 = \theta \qquad z^3 = z$$

$$(ds)^2 = (dr)^2 + (r\, d\theta)^2 + (dz)^2$$

$$h_r = 1 \qquad h_\theta = r \qquad h_z = 1$$

$$g_{ij} = \begin{bmatrix} 1 & 0 & 0 \\ 0 & r^2 & 0 \\ 0 & 0 & 1 \end{bmatrix} \qquad g^{ij} = \begin{bmatrix} 1 & 0 & 0 \\ 0 & \dfrac{1}{r^2} & 0 \\ 0 & 0 & 1 \end{bmatrix}$$

$$\left\{ \begin{matrix} \theta \\ \theta\ r \end{matrix} \right\} = \left\{ \begin{matrix} \theta \\ r\ \theta \end{matrix} \right\} = \frac{1}{r} \qquad \left\{ \begin{matrix} r \\ \theta\ \theta \end{matrix} \right\} = -r$$

$$x = r \cos \theta \qquad\qquad r = \sqrt{x^2 + y^2}$$

$$y = r \sin \theta \qquad\qquad \theta = \tan^{-1}\left(\frac{y}{x}\right)$$

$$z = z \qquad\qquad\qquad z = z$$

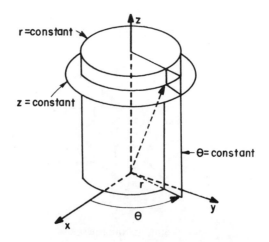

Cylindrical   Coordinates

III. Spherical

$$z^1 = \phi \qquad z^2 = \theta \qquad z^3 = r$$

$$(ds)^2 = (r \sin \theta \, d\phi)^2 + (r \, d\theta)^2 + (dr)^2$$

$$h_\phi = r \sin \theta \qquad h_\theta = r \qquad h_r = 1$$

$$g_{ij} = \begin{bmatrix} r^2 \sin^2 \theta & 0 & 0 \\ 0 & r^2 & 0 \\ 0 & 0 & 1 \end{bmatrix} \qquad g^{ij} = \begin{bmatrix} \dfrac{1}{r^2 \sin^2 \theta} & 0 & 0 \\ 0 & \dfrac{1}{r^2} & 0 \\ 0 & 0 & 1 \end{bmatrix}$$

$$x = r \sin \theta \cos \phi \qquad r = \sqrt{x^2 + y^2 + z^2}$$

$$y = r \sin \theta \sin \phi \qquad \theta = \cos^{-1}\left(\frac{z}{\sqrt{x^2 + y^2 + z^2}}\right) = \tan^{-1}\left(\frac{\sqrt{x^2 + y^2}}{z}\right)$$

$$z = r \cos \theta \qquad \phi = \tan^{-1}\left(\frac{y}{x}\right)$$

$$\left\{ \begin{matrix} r \\ \theta\ \theta \end{matrix} \right\} = -r \qquad \left\{ \begin{matrix} \theta \\ \phi\ \phi \end{matrix} \right\} = -\sin \theta \cos \theta \qquad \left\{ \begin{matrix} r \\ \phi\ \phi \end{matrix} \right\} = -r \sin^2 \theta$$

$$\left\{ \begin{matrix} \phi \\ \phi\ \theta \end{matrix} \right\} = \left\{ \begin{matrix} \phi \\ \theta\ \phi \end{matrix} \right\} = \cot \theta \qquad \left\{ \begin{matrix} \theta \\ \theta\ r \end{matrix} \right\} = \left\{ \begin{matrix} \theta \\ r\ \theta \end{matrix} \right\} = \frac{1}{r}$$

$$\left\{ \begin{matrix} \phi \\ \phi\ r \end{matrix} \right\} = \left\{ \begin{matrix} \phi \\ r\ \phi \end{matrix} \right\} = \frac{1}{r}$$

$$(0 \le r \le \infty \qquad 0 \le \theta \le \pi \qquad 0 \le \phi \le 2\pi)$$

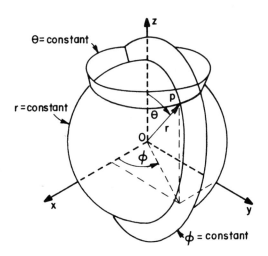

Spherical Coordinates

IV. Elliptic cylindrical

$$z^1 = u \qquad z^2 = v \qquad z^3 = z$$

Coordinate surfaces are:

1. Elliptic cylinders parallel to the z axis, with major axis 2a ($u = z^1$ = constant)

2. Hyperbolic cylinders parallel to the z axis with foci on the ellipse major axis ($v = z^2$ = constant). $0 \le v \le 2\pi$

3. Planes perpendicular to the z axis ($z = z^3$ = constant)

$$x = a \cosh u \cos v \qquad\qquad (u \ge 0)$$

$$y = z \sinh u \sin v \qquad\qquad (0 \le v \le 2\pi)$$

$$z = z \qquad\qquad\qquad\qquad (-\infty < z < \infty)$$

$$h_u = h_v = a(\sinh^2 u + \sin^2 v)^{\frac{1}{2}} \qquad h_z = 1$$

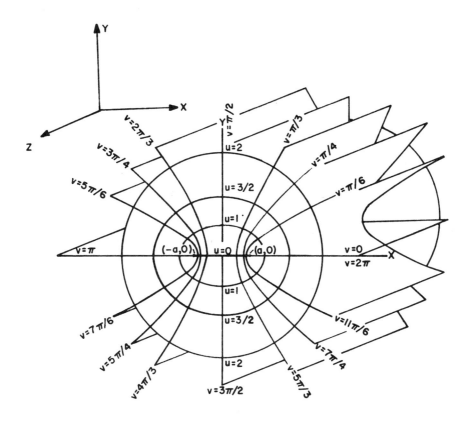

Elliptic Cylindrical Coordinates

$$\left\{\begin{matrix} u \\ u\ u \end{matrix}\right\} = \left\{\begin{matrix} v \\ u\ u \end{matrix}\right\} = \left\{\begin{matrix} v \\ u\ v \end{matrix}\right\} = \left\{\begin{matrix} v \\ v\ u \end{matrix}\right\} = -\left\{\begin{matrix} u \\ v\ v \end{matrix}\right\} = \frac{\sinh u \cosh u}{\sinh^2 u + \sin^2 v}$$

$$\left\{\begin{matrix} u \\ v\ u \end{matrix}\right\} = \left\{\begin{matrix} v \\ v\ v \end{matrix}\right\} = \left\{\begin{matrix} u \\ u\ v \end{matrix}\right\} = -\left\{\begin{matrix} v \\ u\ u \end{matrix}\right\} = -\frac{\sin v \cos v}{\sinh^2 u + \sin^2 v}$$

V. Parabolic cylindrical

$$z^1 = u \qquad z^2 = v \qquad z^3 = z$$

Coordinate surfaces are:

1. Parabolic cylinders ($v = z^2$ = constant)
2. Parabolic cylinders ($u = z^1$ = constant)
3. Planes perpendicular to the z axis ($z = z^3$ = constant)

$$x = \frac{u^2 - v^2}{2}$$

$$y = uv$$

$$z = z$$

$$h_u = h_v = (u^2 + v^2)^{\frac{1}{2}} \qquad h_z = 1$$

$$\left\{ \begin{matrix} u \\ u\ u \end{matrix} \right\} = \left\{ \begin{matrix} v \\ v\ u \end{matrix} \right\} = \left\{ \begin{matrix} v \\ u\ v \end{matrix} \right\} = -\left\{ \begin{matrix} u \\ v\ v \end{matrix} \right\} = \frac{u}{u^2 + v^2}$$

$$\left\{ \begin{matrix} u \\ u\ v \end{matrix} \right\} = \left\{ \begin{matrix} u \\ v\ u \end{matrix} \right\} = \left\{ \begin{matrix} v \\ v\ v \end{matrix} \right\} = -\left\{ \begin{matrix} v \\ u\ u \end{matrix} \right\} = \frac{v}{u^2 + v^2}$$

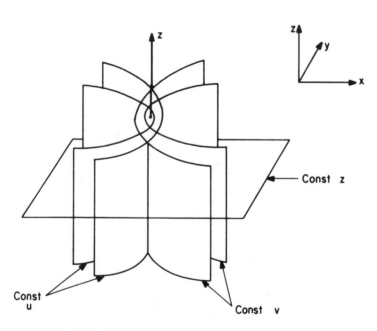

Parabolic Cylindrical Coordinates

VI.   Parabolic

$$z^1 = \zeta \qquad z^2 = \eta \qquad z^3 = \phi$$

Coordinate surfaces are generated by rotating the parabolas in the z plane of parabolic cylindrical coordinates about the x axis, which is renamed the z axis. The surfaces are:

1.   Paraboloids of revolution in +z direction with vertex at $-\zeta^2/2$ and focus at origin (ζ = constant)
2.   Paraboloids of revolution in -z direction with vertex at $\zeta^2/2$ and focus at origin (η = constant)
3.   Planes through the z axis (ϕ = constant)

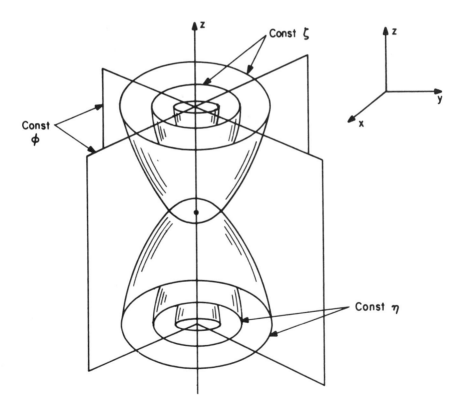

Parabolic Coordinates

$$x = \zeta\eta \cos \phi$$

$$y = \zeta\eta \sin \phi$$

$$z = \frac{\eta^2 - \zeta^2}{2}$$

$$h_\zeta = h_\eta = (\zeta^2 + \eta^2)^{\frac{1}{2}} \qquad h_\phi = \zeta\eta$$

A variety of other orthogonal coordinate systems are described in the following references:

H. Margenau and G. M. Murphy, <u>The Mathematics of Physics and Chemistry</u>, Chap. 5, D. Van Nostrand, New York, 1956.

M. R. Spiegel, <u>Vector Analysis</u>, Schaum, New York, 1959.

J. Happel and H. Brenner, <u>Low Reynolds Number Hydrodynamics</u>, Appendix A, Prentice-Hall, Englewood-Cliffs, N.J., 1965.

SPECIFIC COMPONENTS OF SOME FREQUENTLY ENCOUNTERED QUANTITIES

This Appendix tabulates all components of the following quantities, with respect to Cartesian, cylindrical, and spherical coordinate systems.

1. Covariant derivative of a covariant vector:

$$v_{i,j} = \frac{\partial v_i}{\partial z^j} - \left\{ \begin{matrix} m \\ i\ j \end{matrix} \right\} v_m$$

2. Covariant rate of strain tensor:

$$\Delta_{ij} = v_{i,j} + v_{j,i}$$

3. Vorticity tensor:

$$\Omega_{ij} = v_{j,i} - v_{i,j}$$

4. Material derivative of a vector

$$\frac{Dv^i}{Dt} = \frac{\partial v^i}{\partial t} + v^k v^i,_k$$

5. Covariant derivative of a second-order tensor:

$$T_{ij,k} = \frac{\partial T_{ij}}{\partial z^k} - \left\{ \begin{matrix} m \\ i\ k \end{matrix} \right\} T_{mj} - \left\{ \begin{matrix} m \\ j\ k \end{matrix} \right\} T_{im}$$

6. Material derivative of a second-order tensor:

$$\frac{DT_{ij}}{Dt} = \frac{\partial T_{ij}}{\partial t} + v^k T_{ij,k}$$

7. Jaumann derivative of a second-order tensor:

$$\frac{\mathcal{D}T_{ij}}{\mathcal{D}t} = \frac{DT_{ij}}{Dt} + \frac{1}{2} (\Omega_i{}^k T_{kj} - T_{ik}\Omega^k{}_j)$$

All tabulated quantities are physical components. These can be transformed into appropriate tensor components by applying the following relations:

$$\bar{v}(i) = \frac{v_i}{h_i} = h_i v^i \qquad \text{(all velocities in the following tables are physical components)}$$

$$\bar{T}(ij) = \frac{T_{ij}}{h_i h_j} = h_i h_j T^{ij} = \frac{h_i}{h_j} T^i{}_j$$

TABLE D.1

Covariant Derivative of a Vector

$$v_{i,j} = \frac{\partial v_i}{\partial z^j} - \begin{Bmatrix} m \\ i\ j \end{Bmatrix} v_m$$

I.　Cartesian coordinates: $(x = z^1,\ y = z^2,\ z = z^3)$

$$\bar{v}_{i,j} = \begin{bmatrix} \dfrac{\partial v_x}{\partial x} & \dfrac{\partial v_x}{\partial y} & \dfrac{\partial v_x}{\partial z} \\[2mm] \dfrac{\partial v_y}{\partial x} & \dfrac{\partial v_y}{\partial y} & \dfrac{\partial v_y}{\partial z} \\[2mm] \dfrac{\partial v_z}{\partial x} & \dfrac{\partial v_z}{\partial y} & \dfrac{\partial v_z}{\partial z} \end{bmatrix}$$

II.　Cylindrical coordinates: $(r = z^1,\ \theta = z^2,\ z = z^3)$

$$\bar{v}_{i,j} = \begin{bmatrix} \dfrac{\partial v_r}{\partial r} & \dfrac{1}{r}\left(\dfrac{\partial v_r}{\partial \theta} - v_\theta\right) & \dfrac{\partial v_r}{\partial z} \\[2mm] \dfrac{\partial v_\theta}{\partial r} & \dfrac{1}{r}\left(\dfrac{\partial v_\theta}{\partial \theta} + v_r\right) & \dfrac{\partial v_\theta}{\partial z} \\[2mm] \dfrac{\partial v_z}{\partial r} & \dfrac{1}{r}\left(\dfrac{\partial v_z}{\partial \theta}\right) & \dfrac{\partial v_z}{\partial z} \end{bmatrix}$$

III.　Spherical coordinates: $(\phi = z^1,\ \theta = z^2,\ r = z^3)$

$$\bar{v}_{i,j} = \begin{bmatrix} \dfrac{1}{r\sin\theta}\left(\dfrac{\partial v_\phi}{\partial \phi} + v_r\sin\theta + v_\theta\cos\theta\right) & \dfrac{1}{r}\dfrac{\partial v_\phi}{\partial \theta} & \dfrac{\partial v_\phi}{\partial r} \\[2mm] \dfrac{1}{r\sin\theta}\left(\dfrac{\partial v_\theta}{\partial \phi} - v_\phi\cos\theta\right) & \left(\dfrac{1}{r}\dfrac{\partial v_\theta}{\partial \theta} + v_r\right) & \dfrac{\partial v_\theta}{\partial r} \\[2mm] \dfrac{1}{r\sin\theta}\left(\dfrac{\partial v_r}{\partial \phi} - v_\phi\sin\theta\right) & \left(\dfrac{1}{r}\dfrac{\partial v_r}{\partial \theta} - v_\theta\right) & \dfrac{\partial v_r}{\partial r} \end{bmatrix}$$

TABLE D.2

Rate of Strain Tensor

$$\Delta_{ij} = v_{i,j} + v_{j,i}$$

I.   Cartesian coordinates: $(x = z^1, \quad y = z^2, \quad z = z^3)$

$$\bar{\Delta}_{ij} = \begin{bmatrix} 2\dfrac{\partial v_x}{\partial x} & \left(\dfrac{\partial v_x}{\partial y} + \dfrac{\partial v_y}{\partial x}\right) & \left(\dfrac{\partial v_x}{\partial z} + \dfrac{\partial v_z}{\partial x}\right) \\[3ex] \left(\dfrac{\partial v_y}{\partial x} + \dfrac{\partial v_x}{\partial y}\right) & 2\dfrac{\partial v_y}{\partial y} & \left(\dfrac{\partial v_y}{\partial z} + \dfrac{\partial v_z}{\partial y}\right) \\[3ex] \left(\dfrac{\partial v_z}{\partial x} + \dfrac{\partial v_x}{\partial z}\right) & \left(\dfrac{\partial v_x}{\partial y} + \dfrac{\partial v_y}{\partial z}\right) & 2\dfrac{\partial v_z}{\partial z} \end{bmatrix}$$

II. Cylindrical coordinates: $(r = z^1, \quad \theta = z^2, \quad z = z^3)$

$$\bar{\Delta}_{ij} = \begin{bmatrix} 2\dfrac{\partial v_r}{\partial r} & \left[\dfrac{1}{r}\dfrac{\partial v_r}{\partial \theta} + r\dfrac{\partial}{\partial r}\left(\dfrac{v_\theta}{r}\right)\right] & \left(\dfrac{\partial v_r}{\partial z} + \dfrac{\partial v_z}{\partial r}\right) \\[3ex] \left[\dfrac{1}{r}\dfrac{\partial v_r}{\partial \theta} + r\dfrac{\partial}{\partial r}\left(\dfrac{v_\theta}{r}\right)\right] & \dfrac{2}{r}\left(\dfrac{\partial v_\theta}{\partial \theta} + v_r\right) & \left(\dfrac{\partial v_\theta}{\partial z} + \dfrac{1}{r}\dfrac{\partial v_z}{\partial \theta}\right) \\[3ex] \left(\dfrac{\partial v_r}{\partial z} + \dfrac{\partial v_z}{\partial r}\right) & \left(\dfrac{\partial v_\theta}{\partial z} + \dfrac{1}{r}\dfrac{\partial v_z}{\partial \theta}\right) & 2\dfrac{\partial v_z}{\partial z} \end{bmatrix}$$

TABLE D.2 (continued)

III. Spherical coordinates: $(\phi = z^1, \quad \theta = z^2, \quad r = z^3)$

$$\bar{\Delta}_{ij} = \begin{bmatrix} \dfrac{2}{r \sin\theta}\left(\dfrac{\partial v_\phi}{\partial\phi} + v_r \sin\theta + v_\theta \cos\theta\right) & \dfrac{1}{r}\left[\dfrac{1}{\sin\theta}\dfrac{\partial v_\theta}{\partial\phi} + \sin\theta\dfrac{\partial}{\partial\theta}\left(\dfrac{v_\phi}{\sin\theta}\right)\right] & \left[r\dfrac{\partial}{\partial r}\left(\dfrac{v_\phi}{r}\right) + \dfrac{1}{r\sin\theta}\dfrac{\partial v_r}{\partial\phi}\right] \\[4ex] \dfrac{1}{r}\left[\dfrac{1}{\sin\theta}\dfrac{\partial v_\theta}{\partial\phi} + \sin\theta\dfrac{\partial}{\partial\theta}\left(\dfrac{v_\phi}{\sin\theta}\right)\right] & \dfrac{2}{r}\left(\dfrac{\partial v_\theta}{\partial\theta} + v_r\right) & \left[r\dfrac{\partial}{\partial r}\left(\dfrac{v_\theta}{r}\right) + \dfrac{1}{r}\dfrac{\partial v_r}{\partial\theta}\right] \\[4ex] \left[r\dfrac{\partial}{\partial r}\left(\dfrac{v_\phi}{r}\right) + \dfrac{1}{r\sin\theta}\dfrac{\partial v_r}{\partial\phi}\right] & \left[r\dfrac{\partial}{\partial r}\left(\dfrac{v_\theta}{r}\right) + \dfrac{1}{r}\dfrac{\partial v_r}{\partial\theta}\right] & 2\dfrac{\partial v_r}{\partial r} \end{bmatrix}$$

TABLE D.3

Vorticity Tensor

$$\Omega_{ij} = v_{j,i} - v_{i,j}$$

I. Cartesian coordinates: $(x = z^1, \quad y = z^2, \quad z = z^3)$

$$\bar{\Omega}_{ij} = \begin{bmatrix} 0 & \left(\dfrac{\partial v_y}{\partial x} - \dfrac{\partial v_x}{\partial y}\right) & \left(\dfrac{\partial v_z}{\partial x} - \dfrac{\partial v_x}{\partial z}\right) \\[2em] \left(\dfrac{\partial v_x}{\partial y} - \dfrac{\partial v_y}{\partial x}\right) & 0 & \left(\dfrac{\partial v_z}{\partial y} - \dfrac{\partial v_y}{\partial z}\right) \\[2em] \left(\dfrac{\partial v_x}{\partial z} - \dfrac{\partial v_z}{\partial x}\right) & \left(\dfrac{\partial v_y}{\partial z} - \dfrac{\partial v_z}{\partial y}\right) & 0 \end{bmatrix}$$

II. Cylindrical coordinates: $(r = z^1, \quad \theta = z^2, \quad z = z^3)$

$$\bar{\Omega}_{ij} = \begin{bmatrix} 0 & \dfrac{1}{r}\left(\dfrac{\partial (rv_\theta)}{\partial r} - \dfrac{\partial v_r}{\partial \theta}\right) & \left(\dfrac{\partial v_z}{\partial r} - \dfrac{\partial v_r}{\partial z}\right) \\[2em] \dfrac{1}{r}\left(\dfrac{\partial v_r}{\partial \theta} - \dfrac{\partial}{\partial r}(rv_\theta)\right) & 0 & \dfrac{1}{r}\left(\dfrac{\partial v_z}{\partial \theta} - \dfrac{\partial v_\theta}{\partial z}\right) \\[2em] \left(\dfrac{\partial v_r}{\partial z} - \dfrac{\partial v_z}{\partial r}\right) & \left(\dfrac{\partial v}{\partial z} - \dfrac{1}{r}\dfrac{\partial v_z}{\partial \theta}\right) & 0 \end{bmatrix}$$

TABLE D.3 (continued)

III. Spherical coordinates: ($\phi = z^1$, $\theta = z^2$, $r = z^3$)

$$\bar{\Omega}_{ij} = \begin{bmatrix} 0 & \dfrac{1}{r \sin \theta}\left(\dfrac{\partial v_\theta}{\partial \phi} - \dfrac{\partial (v_\phi \sin \theta)}{\partial \theta}\right) & \left(\dfrac{1}{r \sin \theta}\dfrac{\partial v_r}{\partial \phi} - \dfrac{1}{r}\dfrac{\partial (rv_\phi)}{\partial r}\right) \\[4ex] \dfrac{1}{r \sin \theta}\left(\dfrac{\partial (v_\phi \sin \theta)}{\partial \theta} - \dfrac{\partial v_\theta}{\partial \phi}\right) & 0 & \dfrac{1}{r}\left(\dfrac{\partial v_r}{\partial \theta} - \dfrac{\partial (rv_\theta)}{\partial r}\right) \\[4ex] \left(\dfrac{1}{r}\dfrac{\partial (rv_\phi)}{\partial r} - \dfrac{1}{r \sin \theta}\dfrac{\partial v_r}{\partial \phi}\right) & \dfrac{1}{r}\left(\dfrac{\partial (rv_\theta)}{\partial r} - \dfrac{\partial v_r}{\partial \theta}\right) & 0 \end{bmatrix}$$

TABLE D.4

Material Derivative of a Vector

$$\frac{Dv^i}{Dt} = \frac{\partial v^i}{\partial t} + v^k v^i{}_{,k}$$

I.   Cartesian coordinates: $(x = z^1,\ y = z^2,\ z = z^3)$

$$\overline{v^k v^i{}_{,k}} = \begin{bmatrix} v_x \dfrac{\partial v_x}{\partial x} + v_y \dfrac{\partial v_x}{\partial y} + v_z \dfrac{\partial v_x}{\partial z} \\[2ex] v_x \dfrac{\partial v_y}{\partial x} + v_y \dfrac{\partial v_y}{\partial y} + v_z \dfrac{\partial v_y}{\partial z} \\[2ex] v_x \dfrac{\partial v_z}{\partial x} + v_y \dfrac{\partial v_z}{\partial y} + v_z \dfrac{\partial v_z}{\partial z} \end{bmatrix}$$

II. Cylindrical coordinates: $(r = z^1,\ \theta = z^2,\ z = z^3)$

$$\overline{v^k v^i{}_{,k}} = \begin{bmatrix} v_r \dfrac{\partial v_r}{\partial r} + \dfrac{v_\theta}{r} \left(\dfrac{\partial v_r}{\partial \theta} - v_\theta \right) + v_z \dfrac{\partial v_r}{\partial z} \\[3ex] v_r \dfrac{\partial v_\theta}{\partial r} + \dfrac{1}{r} \left(v_\theta \dfrac{\partial v_\theta}{\partial \theta} + v_r v_\theta \right) + v_z \dfrac{\partial v_\theta}{\partial z} \\[3ex] v_r \dfrac{\partial v_z}{\partial r} + \dfrac{v_\theta}{r} \dfrac{\partial v_z}{\partial \theta} + v_z \dfrac{\partial v_z}{\partial z} \end{bmatrix}$$

III. Spherical coordinates: $(\phi = z^1,\ \theta = z^2,\ r = z^3)$

$$\overline{v^k v^i{}_{,k}} = \begin{bmatrix} v_r \dfrac{\partial v_\phi}{\partial r} + \dfrac{v_\theta}{r} \dfrac{\partial v_\phi}{\partial \theta} + \dfrac{v_\phi}{r \sin \theta} \dfrac{\partial v_\phi}{\partial \phi} + \dfrac{v_\phi v_r}{r} + \dfrac{v_\theta v_\phi}{r} \cot \theta \\[3ex] v_r \dfrac{\partial v_\theta}{\partial r} + \dfrac{v_\theta}{r} \dfrac{\partial v_\theta}{\partial \theta} + \dfrac{v_\phi}{r \sin \theta} \dfrac{\partial v_\theta}{\partial \phi} + \dfrac{v_\theta v_r}{r} - \dfrac{v_\phi^2 \cot \theta}{r} \\[3ex] v_r \dfrac{\partial v_r}{\partial r} + \dfrac{v_\theta}{r} \dfrac{\partial v_r}{\partial \theta} + \dfrac{v_\phi}{r \sin \theta} \dfrac{\partial v_r}{\partial \phi} - \dfrac{v_\theta^2 + v_\phi^2}{r} \end{bmatrix}$$

TABLE D.5

Covariant Derivative of a Symmetric Second-Order Tensor

$$T_{ij,k} = \frac{\partial T_{ij}}{\partial z^k} - \left\{ \begin{matrix} m \\ i\ k \end{matrix} \right\} T_{mj} - \left\{ \begin{matrix} m \\ j\ k \end{matrix} \right\} T_{im} = T_{ji,k}$$

I. Cartesian coordinates: $(x = z^1,\ y = z^2,\ z = z^3)$

$$\bar{T}_{ij,x} = \begin{bmatrix} \dfrac{\partial T_{xx}}{\partial x} & \dfrac{\partial T_{xy}}{\partial x} & \dfrac{\partial T_{xz}}{\partial x} \\[2em] \dfrac{\partial T_{yx}}{\partial x} & \dfrac{\partial T_{yy}}{\partial x} & \dfrac{\partial T_{yz}}{\partial x} \\[2em] \dfrac{\partial T_{zx}}{\partial x} & \dfrac{\partial T_{zy}}{\partial x} & \dfrac{\partial T_{zz}}{\partial x} \end{bmatrix}$$

$$\bar{T}_{ij,y} = \begin{bmatrix} \dfrac{\partial T_{xx}}{\partial y} & \dfrac{\partial T_{xy}}{\partial y} & \dfrac{\partial T_{xz}}{\partial y} \\[2em] \dfrac{\partial T_{yx}}{\partial y} & \dfrac{\partial T_{yy}}{\partial y} & \dfrac{\partial T_{yz}}{\partial y} \\[2em] \dfrac{\partial T_{zx}}{\partial y} & \dfrac{\partial T_{zy}}{\partial y} & \dfrac{\partial T_{zz}}{\partial y} \end{bmatrix}$$

$$\bar{T}_{ij,z} = \begin{bmatrix} \dfrac{\partial T_{xx}}{\partial z} & \dfrac{\partial T_{xy}}{\partial z} & \dfrac{\partial T_{xz}}{\partial z} \\[2em] \dfrac{\partial T_{yx}}{\partial z} & \dfrac{\partial T_{yy}}{\partial z} & \dfrac{\partial T_{yz}}{\partial z} \\[2em] \dfrac{\partial T_{zx}}{\partial z} & \dfrac{\partial T_{zy}}{\partial z} & \dfrac{\partial T_{zz}}{\partial z} \end{bmatrix}$$

TABLE D.5 (continued)

II.   Cylindrical coordinates: $(r = z^1, \quad \theta = z^2, \quad z = z^3)$

$$\overline{T_{ij,r}} = \begin{bmatrix} \dfrac{\partial T_{rr}}{\partial r} & \dfrac{\partial T_{r}}{\partial r} - \dfrac{T_{r\theta}}{r} & \dfrac{\partial T_{rz}}{\partial r} \\[3ex] \dfrac{\partial T_{\theta r}}{\partial r} - \dfrac{T_{\theta r}}{r} & \dfrac{\partial T_{\theta\theta}}{\partial r} - \dfrac{2T_{\theta\theta}}{r} & \dfrac{\partial T_{\theta z}}{\partial r} \\[3ex] \dfrac{\partial T_{zr}}{\partial r} & \dfrac{\partial T_{z\theta}}{\partial r} & \dfrac{\partial T_{zz}}{\partial r} \end{bmatrix}$$

$$\overline{T_{ij,\theta}} = \begin{bmatrix} \dfrac{1}{r}\left(\dfrac{\partial T_{rr}}{\partial \theta} - T_{r\theta} - T_{\theta r}\right) & \dfrac{1}{r}\left(\dfrac{\partial T_{r\theta}}{\partial \theta} - T_{\theta\theta} + T_{rr}\right) & \dfrac{1}{r}\left(\dfrac{\partial T_{rz}}{\partial \theta} - T_{\theta z}\right) \\[3ex] \dfrac{1}{r}\left(\dfrac{\partial T_{\theta r}}{\partial \theta} - T_{\theta\theta} + T_{rr}\right) & \dfrac{1}{r}\left(\dfrac{\partial T_{\theta\theta}}{\partial \theta} + T_{r\theta} + T_{\theta r}\right) & \dfrac{1}{r}\left(\dfrac{\partial T_{\theta z}}{\partial \theta} + T_{rz}\right) \\[3ex] \dfrac{1}{r}\left(\dfrac{\partial T_{zr}}{\partial \theta} - T_{z\theta}\right) & \dfrac{1}{r}\left(\dfrac{\partial T_{z}}{\partial \theta} + T_{zr}\right) & \dfrac{1}{r}\dfrac{\partial T_{zz}}{\partial \theta} \end{bmatrix}$$

$$\overline{T_{ij,z}} = \begin{bmatrix} \dfrac{\partial T_{rr}}{\partial z} & \dfrac{\partial T_{r\theta}}{\partial z} & \dfrac{\partial T_{rz}}{\partial z} \\[3ex] \dfrac{\partial T_{\theta r}}{\partial z} & \dfrac{\partial T_{\theta\theta}}{\partial z} & \dfrac{\partial T_{\theta z}}{\partial z} \\[3ex] \dfrac{\partial T_{zr}}{\partial z} & \dfrac{\partial T_{z\theta}}{\partial z} & \dfrac{\partial T_{zz}}{\partial z} \end{bmatrix}$$

TABLE D.5 (continued)

III. Spherical coordinates: $(\phi = z^1, \quad \theta = z^2, \quad r = z^3)$

$$\bar{T}_{ij,\phi} = \begin{bmatrix} \left(\dfrac{1}{r \sin \theta} \dfrac{\partial T_{\phi\phi}}{\partial \phi} + T_{r\phi} \right. & \left(\dfrac{1}{r \sin \theta} \dfrac{\partial T_{\phi\theta}}{\partial \phi} + \dfrac{T_{r\theta}}{r} \right. & \left(\dfrac{1}{r \sin \theta} \dfrac{\partial T_{\phi r}}{\partial \phi} \right. \\[2mm] + \, T_{\phi r} + \dfrac{\cot \theta}{r} & + \dfrac{\cot \theta}{r} \left[T_{\theta\theta} - T_{\phi\phi} \right] \Big) & + \dfrac{1}{r} \left[T_{rr} - T_{\phi\phi} \right] \\[2mm] \left[T_{\theta\phi} + T_{\phi\theta} \right] \Big) & & + \dfrac{\cot \theta}{r} \, T_{\theta r} \Big) \\[5mm] \left(\dfrac{1}{r \sin \theta} \dfrac{\partial T_{\theta\phi}}{\partial \phi} + \dfrac{T_{\theta r}}{r} \right. & \left(\dfrac{1}{r \sin \theta} \dfrac{\partial T_{\theta\theta}}{\partial \phi} \right. & \left(\dfrac{1}{r \sin \theta} \dfrac{\partial T_{\theta r}}{\partial \phi} \right. \\[2mm] + \dfrac{\cot \theta}{r} \left[T_{\theta\theta} - T_{\phi\phi} \right] \Big) & - \dfrac{\cot \theta}{r} \left[T_{\theta\phi} + T_{\phi\theta} \right] \Big) & - \dfrac{\cot \theta}{r} \, T_{\theta r} \\[2mm] & & - \dfrac{1}{r} \, T_{\theta\phi} \Big) \\[5mm] \left(\dfrac{1}{r \sin \theta} \dfrac{\partial T_{r\phi}}{\partial \phi} \right. & \left(\dfrac{1}{r \sin \theta} \dfrac{\partial T_{r\theta}}{\partial \phi} \right. & \left(\dfrac{1}{r \sin \theta} \dfrac{\partial T_{rr}}{\partial \phi} \right. \\[2mm] + \dfrac{1}{r} \left[T_{rr} - T_{\phi\phi} \right] & - \dfrac{\cot \theta}{r} \, T_{r\phi} & - \dfrac{1}{r} \left[T_{\phi r} + T_{r\phi} \right] \Big) \\[2mm] + \dfrac{\cot \theta}{r} \, T_{r\theta} \Big) & - \dfrac{1}{r} \, T_{\phi\theta} \Big) & \end{bmatrix}$$

TABLE D.5 (continued)

$$\bar{T}_{ij,\theta} = \begin{bmatrix} \dfrac{1}{r}\dfrac{\partial T_{\phi\phi}}{\partial\theta} & \dfrac{1}{r}\left(\dfrac{\partial T_{\phi\theta}}{\partial\theta} + T_{\phi r}\right) & \dfrac{1}{r}\left(\dfrac{\partial T_{\phi r}}{\partial\theta} - T_{\theta\phi}\right) \\[2em] \dfrac{1}{r}\left(\dfrac{\partial T_{\phi\theta}}{\partial\theta} + T_{\phi r}\right) & \dfrac{1}{r}\left(\dfrac{\partial T_{\theta\theta}}{\partial\theta} + T_{r\theta} + T_{\theta r}\right) & \dfrac{1}{r}\left(\dfrac{\partial T_{\theta r}}{\partial\theta} + T_{rr} - T_{\theta\theta}\right) \\[2em] \dfrac{1}{r}\left(\dfrac{\partial T_{\phi r}}{\partial\theta} - T_{\theta\phi}\right) & \dfrac{1}{r}\left(\dfrac{\partial T_{\theta r}}{\partial\theta} + T_{rr} - T_{\theta\theta}\right) & \dfrac{1}{r}\left(\dfrac{\partial T_{rr}}{\partial\theta} - T_{r\theta} - T_{\theta r}\right) \end{bmatrix}$$

$$\bar{T}_{ij,r} = \begin{bmatrix} \dfrac{\partial T_{\phi\phi}}{\partial r} & \dfrac{\partial T_{\theta\phi}}{\partial r} & \dfrac{\partial T_{\phi r}}{\partial r} \\[2em] \dfrac{\partial T_{\phi\theta}}{\partial r} & \dfrac{\partial T_{\theta\theta}}{\partial r} & \dfrac{\partial T_{\theta r}}{\partial r} \\[2em] \dfrac{\partial T_{r\phi}}{\partial r} & \dfrac{\partial T_{r\theta}}{\partial r} & \dfrac{\partial T_{rr}}{\partial r} \end{bmatrix}$$

TABLE D.6

Material Derivative of Second-Order Tensor

$$\frac{DT_{ij}}{Dt} = \frac{\partial T_{ij}}{\partial t} + v^{k}T_{ij,k}$$

I. Cartesian coordinates

$$v^{k}T_{xx,k} = v_{x}\frac{\partial T_{xx}}{\partial x} + v_{y}\frac{\partial T_{xx}}{\partial y} + v_{z}\frac{\partial T_{xx}}{\partial z}$$

$$v^{k}T_{xy,k} = v_{x}\frac{\partial T_{xy}}{\partial x} + v_{y}\frac{\partial T_{xy}}{\partial y} + v_{z}\frac{\partial T_{xy}}{\partial z}$$

TABLE D.6 (continued)

$$v^k T_{xz,k} = v_x \frac{\partial T_{xz}}{\partial x} + v_y \frac{\partial T_{xz}}{\partial y} + v_z \frac{\partial T_{xz}}{\partial z}$$

$$v^k T_{yx,k} = v_x \frac{\partial T_{yx}}{\partial x} + v_y \frac{\partial T_{yx}}{\partial y} + v_z \frac{\partial T_{yx}}{\partial z}$$

$$v^k T_{yy,k} = v_x \frac{\partial T_{yy}}{\partial x} + v_y \frac{\partial T_{yy}}{\partial y} + v_z \frac{\partial T_{yy}}{\partial z}$$

$$v^k T_{yz,k} = v_x \frac{\partial T_{yz}}{\partial x} + v_y \frac{\partial T_{yz}}{\partial y} + v_z \frac{\partial T_{yz}}{\partial z}$$

$$v^k T_{zx,k} = v_x \frac{\partial T_{zx}}{\partial x} + v_y \frac{\partial T_{zx}}{\partial y} + v_z \frac{\partial T_{zx}}{\partial z}$$

$$v^k T_{zy,k} = v_x \frac{\partial T_{zy}}{\partial x} + v_y \frac{\partial T_{zy}}{\partial y} + v_z \frac{\partial T_{zy}}{\partial z}$$

$$v^k T_{zz,k} = v_x \frac{\partial T_{zz}}{\partial x} + v_y \frac{\partial T_{zz}}{\partial y} + v_z \frac{\partial T_{zz}}{\partial z}$$

II. Cylindrical coordinates

$$v^k T_{rr,k} = v_r \frac{\partial T_{rr}}{\partial r} + \frac{v_\theta}{r}\left(\frac{\partial T_{rr}}{\partial \theta} - T_{r\theta} - T_{\theta r}\right) + v_z \frac{\partial T_{rr}}{\partial z}$$

$$v^k T_{r\theta,k} = v_r \frac{\partial T_{r\theta}}{\partial r} + \frac{v_\theta}{r}\left(\frac{\partial T_{r\theta}}{\partial \theta} - T_{\theta\theta} + T_{rr}\right) + v_z \frac{\partial T_{r\theta}}{\partial z}$$

$$v^k T_{rz,k} = v_r \frac{\partial T_{rz}}{\partial r} + \frac{v_\theta}{r}\left(\frac{\partial T_{rz}}{\partial \theta} - T_{\theta z}\right) + v_z \frac{\partial T_{rz}}{\partial z}$$

$$v^k T_{\theta r,k} = v_r \frac{\partial T_{\theta r}}{\partial r} + \frac{v_\theta}{r}\left(\frac{\partial T_{\theta r}}{\partial \theta} - T_{\theta\theta} + T_{rr}\right) + v_z \frac{\partial T_{\theta r}}{\partial z}$$

TABLE D.6 (continued)

$$v^k T_{\theta\theta,k} = v_r \frac{\partial T_{\theta\theta}}{\partial r} + \frac{v_\theta}{r} \left(\frac{\partial T_{\theta\theta}}{\partial \theta} + T_{r\theta} + T_{\theta r} \right) + v_z \frac{\partial T_{\theta\theta}}{\partial z}$$

$$v^k T_{\theta z,k} = v_r \frac{\partial T_{\theta z}}{\partial r} + \frac{v_\theta}{r} \left(\frac{\partial T_{\theta z}}{\partial \theta} + T_{rz} \right) + v_z \frac{\partial T_{\theta z}}{\partial z}$$

$$v^k T_{zr,k} = v_r \frac{\partial T_{zr}}{\partial r} + \frac{v_\theta}{r} \left(\frac{\partial T_{zr}}{\partial \theta} - T_{z\theta} \right) + v_z \frac{\partial T_{zr}}{\partial z}$$

$$v^k T_{z\theta,k} = v_r \frac{\partial T_{z\theta}}{\partial r} + \frac{v_\theta}{r} \left(\frac{\partial T_{z\theta}}{\partial \theta} + T_{zr} \right) + v_z \frac{\partial T_{z\theta}}{\partial z}$$

$$v^k T_{zz,k} = v_r \frac{\partial T_{zz}}{\partial r} + \frac{v_\theta}{r} \left(\frac{\partial T_{zz}}{\partial \theta} \right) + v_z \frac{\partial T_{zz}}{\partial z}$$

III. Spherical coordinates

$$v^k T_{\phi\phi,k} = v_\phi \left[\frac{1}{r \sin\theta} \frac{\partial T_{\phi\phi}}{\partial \phi} + \frac{1}{r} (T_{r\phi} + T_{\phi r}) + \frac{\cot\theta}{r} (T_{\theta\phi} + T_{\phi\theta}) \right]$$

$$+ \frac{v_\theta}{r} \frac{\partial T_{\phi\phi}}{\partial \theta} + v_r \frac{\partial T_{\phi\phi}}{\partial r}$$

$$v^k T_{\phi\theta,k} = v_\phi \left[\frac{1}{r \sin\theta} \frac{\partial T_{\phi\theta}}{\partial \phi} + \frac{T_{r\theta}}{r} + \frac{\cot\theta}{r} (T_{\theta\theta} - T_{\phi\phi}) \right]$$

$$+ \frac{v_\theta}{r} \left[\frac{\partial T_{\phi\theta}}{\partial \theta} + T_{\phi r} \right] + v_r \frac{\partial T_{\phi\theta}}{\partial r}$$

$$v^k T_{\phi r,k} = v_\phi \left[\frac{1}{r \sin\theta} \frac{\partial T_{\phi r}}{\partial \phi} + \frac{1}{r} (T_{rr} - T_{\phi\phi}) + \frac{\cot\theta}{r} T_{\theta r} \right]$$

$$+ \frac{v_\theta}{r} \left[\frac{\partial T_{\phi r}}{\partial \theta} - T_{\theta\phi} \right] + v_r \frac{\partial T_{\phi r}}{\partial r}$$

TABLE D.6 (continued)

$$v^k T_{\theta\phi,k} = v_\phi \left[\frac{1}{r \sin \theta} \frac{\partial T_{\theta\phi}}{\partial \phi} + \frac{T_{\theta r}}{r} + \frac{\cot \theta}{r} (T_{\theta\theta} - T_{\phi\phi}) \right]$$

$$+ \frac{v_\theta}{r} \left[\frac{\partial T_{\theta\phi}}{\partial \theta} + T_{r\phi} \right] + v_r \frac{\partial T_{\theta\phi}}{\partial r}$$

$$v^k T_{\theta\theta,k} = v_\phi \left[\frac{1}{r \sin \theta} \frac{\partial T_{\theta\theta}}{\partial \phi} - \frac{\cot \theta}{r} T_{\theta\phi} \right]$$

$$+ \frac{v_\theta}{r} \left[\frac{\partial T_{\theta\theta}}{\partial \theta} + T_{r\theta} + T_{\theta r} \right] + v_r \frac{\partial T_{\theta\theta}}{\partial r}$$

$$v^k T_{\theta r,k} = v_\phi \left[\frac{1}{r \sin \theta} \frac{\partial T_{\theta r}}{\partial \phi} - \frac{\cot \theta}{r} T_{\phi r} - \frac{1}{r} T_{\theta\phi} \right]$$

$$+ \frac{v_\theta}{r} \left[\frac{\partial T_{\theta r}}{\partial \theta} + T_{rr} - T_{\theta\theta} \right] + v_r \frac{\partial T_{\theta r}}{\partial r}$$

$$v^k T_{r\phi,k} = v_\phi \left[\frac{1}{r \sin \theta} \frac{\partial T_{r\phi}}{\partial \phi} + \frac{1}{r} (T_{rr} - T_{\phi\phi}) + \frac{\cot \theta}{r} T_{r\theta} \right]$$

$$+ \frac{v_\theta}{r} \left[\frac{\partial T_{r\phi}}{\partial \theta} - T_{\phi\theta} \right] + v_r \frac{\partial T_{r\theta}}{\partial r}$$

$$v^k T_{r\theta,k} = v_\phi \left[\frac{1}{r \sin \theta} \frac{\partial T_{r\theta}}{\partial \phi} - \frac{\cot \theta}{r} T_{r\phi} - \frac{1}{r} T_{\phi\theta} \right]$$

$$+ \frac{v_\theta}{r} \left[\frac{\partial T_{r\theta}}{\partial \theta} + T_{rr} - T_{\theta\theta} \right] + v_r \frac{\partial T_{r\theta}}{\partial r}$$

$$v^k T_{rr,k} = v_\phi \left[\frac{1}{r \sin \theta} \frac{\partial T_{rr}}{\partial \phi} - \frac{1}{r} (T_{\phi r} + T_{r\phi}) \right]$$

$$+ \frac{v_\theta}{r} \left[\frac{\partial T_{rr}}{\partial \theta} - T_{\theta r} - T_{r\theta} \right] + v_r \frac{\partial T_{rr}}{\partial r}$$

TABLE D.7

Jaumann Derivative of Second-Order Tensor

$$\frac{\mathcal{D}T_{ij}}{\mathcal{D}t} = \frac{DT_{ij}}{Dt} + \frac{1}{2} \left(\Omega_i{}^k T_{kj} - T_{ik} \Omega^k{}_j \right) = \frac{DT_{ij}}{Dt} + \frac{1}{2} J_{ij}$$

I.   Cartesian coordinates

$$J_{xx} = \left(\frac{\partial v_y}{\partial x} - \frac{\partial v_x}{\partial y} \right) \left(T_{yx} + T_{xy} \right) + \left(\frac{\partial v_z}{\partial x} - \frac{\partial v_x}{\partial z} \right) \left(T_{zx} + T_{xz} \right)$$

$$J_{xy} = \left(\frac{\partial v_y}{\partial x} - \frac{\partial v_x}{\partial y} \right) \left(T_{yy} - T_{xx} \right) + \left(\frac{\partial v_z}{\partial x} - \frac{\partial v_x}{\partial z} \right) T_{zy} + \left(\frac{\partial v_z}{\partial y} - \frac{\partial v_y}{\partial z} \right) T_{xz}$$

$$J_{xz} = \left(\frac{\partial v_y}{\partial x} - \frac{\partial v_x}{\partial y} \right) T_{yz} + \left(\frac{\partial v_z}{\partial x} - \frac{\partial v_x}{\partial z} \right) \left(T_{zz} - T_{xx} \right) + \left(\frac{\partial v_y}{\partial z} - \frac{\partial v_z}{\partial y} \right) T_{xy}$$

$$J_{yx} = \left(\frac{\partial v_y}{\partial x} - \frac{\partial v_x}{\partial y} \right) \left(T_{yy} - T_{xx} \right) + \left(\frac{\partial v_z}{\partial x} - \frac{\partial v_x}{\partial z} \right) T_{yz} + \left(\frac{\partial v_z}{\partial y} - \frac{\partial v_y}{\partial z} \right) T_{zx}$$

$$J_{yy} = \left(\frac{\partial v_y}{\partial x} - \frac{\partial v_x}{\partial y} \right) \left(T_{xy} + T_{yx} \right) + \left(\frac{\partial v_z}{\partial y} - \frac{\partial v_y}{\partial z} \right) \left(T_{zy} + T_{yz} \right)$$

$$J_{yz} = \left(\frac{\partial v_x}{\partial y} - \frac{\partial v_y}{\partial x} \right) T_{xz} + \left(\frac{\partial v_z}{\partial y} - \frac{\partial v_y}{\partial z} \right) \left(T_{zz} - T_{yy} \right) + \left(\frac{\partial v_x}{\partial z} - \frac{\partial v_z}{\partial x} \right) T_{yx}$$

$$J_{zx} = \left(\frac{\partial v_x}{\partial z} - \frac{\partial v_z}{\partial x} \right) \left(T_{xx} - T_{zz} \right) + \left(\frac{\partial v_y}{\partial z} - \frac{\partial v_z}{\partial y} \right) T_{yx} + \left(\frac{\partial v_y}{\partial x} - \frac{\partial v_x}{\partial y} \right) T_{zy}$$

$$J_{zy} = \left(\frac{\partial v_x}{\partial z} - \frac{\partial v_z}{\partial x} \right) T_{xy} + \left(\frac{\partial v_z}{\partial y} - \frac{\partial v_y}{\partial z} \right) \left(T_{zz} - T_{yy} \right) + \left(\frac{\partial v_x}{\partial y} - \frac{\partial v_y}{\partial x} \right) T_{zx}$$

$$J_{zz} = \left(\frac{\partial v_x}{\partial z} - \frac{\partial v_z}{\partial x} \right) \left(T_{xy} + T_{zx} \right) + \left(\frac{\partial v_y}{\partial z} - \frac{\partial v_z}{\partial y} \right) \left(T_{yz} + T_{zy} \right)$$

TABLE D.7 (continued)

II. Cylindrical coordinates

$$
J_{rr} = \frac{1}{r}\left[\frac{\partial(rv_\theta)}{\partial r} - \frac{\partial v_r}{\partial \theta}\right]\left(T_{\theta r} + T_{r\theta}\right) + \left(\frac{\partial v_z}{\partial r} - \frac{\partial v_r}{\partial z}\right)\left(T_{zr} + T_{rz}\right)
$$

$$
J_{r\theta} = \frac{1}{r}\left[\frac{\partial(rv_\theta)}{\partial r} - \frac{\partial v_r}{\partial \theta}\right]\left(T_{\theta\theta} - T_{rr}\right) + \left(\frac{\partial v_z}{\partial r} - \frac{\partial v_r}{\partial z}\right)T_{z\theta} + \left(\frac{1}{r}\frac{\partial v_z}{\partial \theta} - \frac{\partial v_\theta}{\partial z}\right)T_{rz}
$$

$$
J_{rz} = \frac{1}{r}\left[\frac{\partial(rv_\theta)}{\partial r} - \frac{\partial v_r}{\partial \theta}\right]T_{\theta z} + \left(\frac{\partial v_z}{\partial r} - \frac{\partial v_r}{\partial z}\right)\left(T_{zz} - T_{rr}\right) + \left(\frac{\partial v_\theta}{\partial z} - \frac{1}{r}\frac{\partial v_z}{\partial \theta}\right)T_{r\theta}
$$

$$
J_{\theta r} = \frac{1}{r}\left[\frac{\partial(rv_\theta)}{\partial r} - \frac{\partial v_r}{\partial \theta}\right]\left(T_{\theta\theta} - T_{rr}\right) + \left(\frac{\partial v_z}{\partial r} - \frac{\partial v_r}{\partial z}\right)T_{\theta z} + \frac{1}{r}\left(\frac{\partial v_z}{\partial \theta} - \frac{\partial v_\theta}{\partial z}\right)T_{zr}
$$

$$
J_{\theta\theta} = \frac{1}{r}\left[\frac{\partial v_r}{\partial \theta} - \frac{\partial(rv_\theta)}{\partial r}\right]\left(T_{r\theta} + T_{\theta r}\right) + \left(\frac{1}{r}\frac{\partial v_z}{\partial \theta} - \frac{\partial v_\theta}{\partial z}\right)\left(T_{z\theta} + T_{\theta z}\right)
$$

$$
J_{\theta z} = \frac{1}{r}\left[\frac{\partial v_r}{\partial \theta} - \frac{\partial(rv_\theta)}{\partial r}\right]T_{rz} + \left(\frac{1}{r}\frac{\partial v_z}{\partial \theta} - \frac{\partial v_\theta}{\partial z}\right)\left(T_{zz} - T_{\theta\theta}\right) + \left(\frac{\partial v_r}{\partial z} - \frac{\partial v_z}{\partial r}\right)T_{\theta r}
$$

$$
J_{zr} = \frac{1}{r}\left[\frac{\partial(rv_\theta)}{\partial r} - \frac{\partial v_r}{\partial \theta}\right]T_{z\theta} + \left(\frac{\partial v_z}{\partial r} - \frac{\partial v_r}{\partial z}\right)\left(T_{zz} - T_{rr}\right) + \left(\frac{\partial v_\theta}{\partial z} + \frac{1}{r}\frac{\partial v_z}{\partial \theta}\right)T_{\theta r}
$$

$$
J_{z\theta} = \frac{1}{r}\left[\frac{\partial v_r}{\partial \theta} - \frac{\partial(rv_\theta)}{\partial r}\right]T_{zr} + \left(\frac{1}{r}\frac{\partial v_z}{\partial \theta} - \frac{\partial v_\theta}{\partial r}\right)\left(T_{zz} - T_{\theta\theta}\right) + \left(\frac{\partial v_r}{\partial z} - \frac{\partial v_z}{\partial r}\right)T_{r\theta}
$$

$$
J_{zz} = \left(\frac{\partial v_r}{\partial z} - \frac{\partial v_z}{\partial r}\right)\left(T_{rz} + T_{zr}\right) + \left(\frac{\partial v_\theta}{\partial z} - \frac{1}{r}\frac{\partial v_z}{\partial \theta}\right)\left(T_{\theta z} + T_{z\theta}\right)
$$

III. Spherical coordinates

$$
J_{\phi\phi} = \frac{1}{r\sin\theta}\left[\frac{\partial v_\theta}{\partial \theta} - \frac{\partial(v_\phi\sin\theta)}{\partial \phi}\right]\left(T_{\theta\phi} + T_{\phi\theta}\right) + \left(\frac{1}{r\sin\theta}\frac{\partial v_r}{\partial \phi} - \frac{1}{r}\frac{\partial(rv_\phi)}{\partial r}\right)T_{r\phi}
$$

TABLE D.7 (continued)

$$J_{\phi\theta} = \frac{1}{r \sin \theta}\left(\frac{\partial v_\theta}{\partial\theta} - \frac{\partial(v_\phi \sin \theta)}{\partial\theta}\right)\left(T_{\theta\theta} - T_{\phi\phi}\right)$$

$$+ \left(\frac{1}{r \sin \theta}\frac{\partial v_r}{\partial\phi} - \frac{1}{r}\frac{\partial(rv_\phi)}{\partial r}\right)T_{r\theta} + \frac{1}{r}\left(\frac{\partial v_r}{\partial\theta} - \frac{\partial(rv_\theta)}{\partial r}\right)T_{\phi r}$$

$$J_{\phi r} = \frac{1}{r \sin \theta}\left(\frac{\partial v_\theta}{\partial\phi} - \frac{\partial(v_\phi \sin \theta)}{\partial\theta}\right)T_{\theta r} + \left(\frac{1}{r \sin \theta}\frac{\partial v_r}{\partial\phi} - \frac{1}{r}\frac{\partial(rv_\phi)}{\partial r}\right)$$

$$\cdot \left(T_{rr} - T_{\phi\phi}\right) + \frac{1}{r}\left(\frac{\partial(rv_\theta)}{\partial r} - \frac{\partial v_r}{\partial\theta}\right)T_{\phi\theta}$$

$$J_{\theta\phi} = \frac{1}{r \sin \theta}\left(\frac{\partial v_\theta}{\partial\phi} - \frac{\partial(v_\phi \sin \theta)}{\partial\theta}\right)\left(T_{\theta\theta} - T_{\phi\phi}\right)$$

$$+ \left(\frac{1}{r \sin \theta}\frac{\partial v_r}{\partial\phi} - \frac{1}{r}\frac{\partial(rv_\phi)}{\partial r}\right)T_{\theta r} + \frac{1}{r}\left(\frac{\partial v_r}{\partial\theta} - \frac{\partial(rv_\theta)}{\partial r}\right)T_{r\phi}$$

$$J_{\theta\theta} = \frac{1}{r \sin \theta}\left(\frac{\partial(v_\phi \sin \theta)}{\partial\theta} - \frac{\partial v_\theta}{\partial\phi}\right)\left(T_{\theta\phi} + T_{\phi\theta}\right) + \frac{1}{r}\left(\frac{\partial v_r}{\partial\theta} - \frac{\partial(rv_\theta)}{\partial r}\right)$$

$$\cdot \left(T_{r\theta} + T_{\theta r}\right)$$

TABLE D.7 (continued)

$$
J_{\theta r} = \frac{1}{r \sin \theta}\left(\frac{\partial(v_\phi \sin \theta)}{\partial \theta} - \frac{\partial v_\theta}{\partial \phi}\right)T_{\phi r} + \frac{1}{r}\left(\frac{\partial v_r}{\partial \theta} - \frac{\partial(rv_\theta)}{\partial r}\right)\left(T_{rr} - T_{\theta\theta}\right)
$$

$$
+ \frac{1}{r}\left(\frac{\partial(rv_\phi)}{\partial r} - \frac{1}{r \sin \theta}\frac{\partial v_r}{\partial \phi}\right)T_{\theta\phi}
$$

$$
J_{r\phi} = \frac{1}{r \sin \theta}\left(\frac{\partial v_\theta}{\partial \phi} - \frac{\partial(v_\phi \sin \theta)}{\partial \theta}\right)T_{r\theta} + \left(\frac{1}{r \sin \theta}\frac{\partial v_r}{\partial \phi} - \frac{1}{r}\frac{\partial(rv_\phi)}{\partial r}\right)
$$

$$
\cdot \left(T_{rr} - T_{\phi\phi}\right) + \frac{1}{r}\left(\frac{\partial(rv_\theta)}{\partial r} - \frac{\partial v_r}{\partial \theta}\right)T_{\theta\phi}
$$

$$
J_{r\theta} = \frac{1}{r \sin \theta}\left(\frac{\partial(v_\phi \sin \theta)}{\partial \theta} - \frac{\partial v_\theta}{\partial \phi}\right)T_{r\phi} + \frac{1}{r}\left(\frac{\partial v_r}{\partial \theta} - \frac{\partial(rv_\theta)}{\partial r}\right)\left(T_{rr} - T_{\theta\theta}\right)
$$

$$
+ \frac{1}{r}\left(\frac{\partial(rv_\phi)}{\partial r} - \frac{1}{r \sin \theta}\frac{\partial v_r}{\partial \phi}\right)T_{\phi\theta}
$$

$$
J_{rr} = \frac{1}{r}\left(\frac{\partial(rv_\phi)}{\partial r} - \frac{1}{r \sin \theta}\frac{\partial v_r}{\partial \phi}\right)\left(T_{\phi r} + T_{r\phi}\right) + \frac{1}{r}\left(\frac{\partial(rv_\theta)}{\partial r} - \frac{\partial v_r}{\partial \theta}\right)\left(T_{\theta r} + T_{r\theta}\right)
$$

SPECIAL RELATIONS
FOR VISCOMETRIC FLOW

This Appendix presents tables of the nonzero components of the following quantities:

E.1 Rate of Strain Tensor, Δ_{ij}

E.2 Vorticity Tensor, Ω_{ij}

E.3 Material Derivative of T_{ij} – DT_{ij}/Dt

E.4 Convected Derivative of T_{ij} – $\delta T_{ij}/\delta t$

E.5 Jaumann Derivative of T_{ij} – $\mathcal{D}T_{ij}/\mathcal{D}t$

E.6 Spriggs Derivative of T_{ij} – $\mathcal{J}_e T_{ij}$

E.7 Covariant Finite (Almansi) Strain Tensor, Γ_{ij}

E.8 Contravariant Finite (Finger) Strain Tensor, Γ^{ij}

for each of the following viscometric flows:

I. Simple Shear: $v_x = v_x(y) = \bar{v}_x$, $v_y = v_z = 0$

II. Poiseuille Flow: $v^z = v^z(r) = \bar{v}_z$, $v_r = v_\theta = 0$

III. Couette Flow: $v^{\theta} = \omega(r)$, $\bar{v}_{\theta} = r\omega$, $v_r = v_z = 0$

IV. Cone and Plate Flow: $v^{\phi} = \omega(\theta)$, $\bar{v}_{\phi} = r\omega \sin \theta$, $v^{\theta} = v^r = 0$

The tensor T_{ij} is assumed to have the following nonzero components:

$$T_{ij} = \begin{bmatrix} T_{11} & T_{12} & 0 \\ T_{12} & T_{22} & 0 \\ 0 & 0 & T_{33} \end{bmatrix} = T_{ij}(v^1)$$

All tensor quantities are written in terms of physical components. All velocity components represent physical velocity components.

TABLE E.1

Rate of Strain Tensor

$$\bar{\Delta}(ij) = (v_{i,j} + v_{j,i}) \frac{1}{h_i h_j} \qquad v_i = h_i \bar{v}(i)$$

I. Simple Shear: $(x = z^1, \quad y = z^2, \quad z = z^3)$

$$\bar{\Delta}(ij) = \frac{\partial v_x}{\partial y} \begin{bmatrix} 0 & 1 & 0 \\ 1 & 0 & 0 \\ 0 & 0 & 0 \end{bmatrix}$$

II. Poiseuille Flow: $(z = z^1, \quad r = z^2, \quad \theta = z^3)$

$$\bar{\Delta}(ij) = \frac{\partial v_z}{\partial r} \begin{bmatrix} 0 & 1 & 0 \\ 1 & 0 & 0 \\ 0 & 0 & 0 \end{bmatrix}$$

III. Couette Flow: $(\theta = z^1, \quad r = z^2, \quad z = z^3)$

$$\bar{\Delta}(ij) = r \frac{\partial}{\partial r} \left(\frac{v_\theta}{r}\right) \begin{bmatrix} 0 & 1 & 0 \\ 1 & 0 & 0 \\ 0 & 0 & 0 \end{bmatrix}$$

IV. Cone and Plate Flow: $(\phi = z^1, \quad \theta = z^2, \quad r = z^3)$

$$\bar{\Delta}(ij) = \frac{\sin\theta}{r} \frac{\partial}{\partial\theta} \left(\frac{v_\phi}{\sin\theta}\right) \begin{bmatrix} 0 & 1 & 0 \\ 1 & 0 & 0 \\ 0 & 0 & 0 \end{bmatrix}$$

TABLE E.2

Vorticity Tensor

$$\bar{\Omega}(ij) = \frac{\Omega_{ij}}{h_i h_j} = \frac{1}{h_i h_j} (v_{j,i} - v_{i,j}) \qquad v_i = h_i \bar{v}(i)$$

I. Simple Shear: $(x = z^1, \quad y = z^2, \quad z = z^3)$

$$\bar{\Omega}(ij) = \frac{\partial v_x}{\partial y} \begin{bmatrix} 0 & -1 & 0 \\ 1 & 0 & 0 \\ 0 & 0 & 0 \end{bmatrix}$$

II. Poiseuille Flow: $(z = z^1, \quad r = z^2, \quad \theta = z^3)$

$$\bar{\Omega}(ij) = \frac{\partial v_z}{\partial r} \begin{bmatrix} 0 & -1 & 0 \\ 1 & 0 & 0 \\ 0 & 0 & 0 \end{bmatrix}$$

III. Couette Flow: $(\theta = z^1, \quad r = z^2, \quad z = z^3)$

$$\bar{\Omega}(ij) = \frac{1}{r} \frac{\partial(rv_\theta)}{\partial r} \begin{bmatrix} 0 & -1 & 0 \\ 1 & 0 & 0 \\ 0 & 0 & 0 \end{bmatrix}$$

TABLE E.2 (continued)

IV. Cone and Plate: $(\phi = z^1, \quad \theta = z^2, \quad r = z^3)$

$$\bar{\Omega}(ij) = \begin{bmatrix} 0 & -\dfrac{1}{r \sin \theta} \dfrac{\partial}{\partial \theta}(v_\phi \sin \theta) & -\dfrac{v_\phi}{r} \\[3ex] \dfrac{1}{r \sin \theta} \dfrac{\partial}{\partial \theta}(v_\phi \sin \theta) & 0 & 0 \\[3ex] \dfrac{v_\phi}{r} & 0 & 0 \end{bmatrix}$$

TABLE E.3

Material Derivative

$$\frac{D\bar{T}_{ij}}{Dt} = \frac{\partial \bar{T}_{ij}}{\partial t} + \frac{1}{h_i h_j}\left(\frac{\bar{v}_k}{h_k}\right)\left(T_{ij}h_i h_j\right),_k = \frac{\bar{v}_1}{h_i h_j h_1}(T_{ij}h_i h_j),_1$$

I. Simple Shear $(x = z^1, \quad y = z^2, \quad z = z^3)$

$$\frac{D\bar{T}_{ij}}{Dt} = v_x \frac{\partial T_{ij}}{\partial x} = 0$$

II. Poiseuille Flow: $(z = z^1, \quad r = z^2, \quad \theta = z^3)$

$$\frac{D\bar{T}_{ij}}{Dt} = v^z \frac{\partial \bar{T}_{ij}}{\partial z} = 0$$

III. Couette Flow: $(\theta = z^1, \quad r = z^2, \quad z = z^3)$

$$\frac{D\bar{T}_{ij}}{Dt} = v^\theta \bar{T}_{ij,\theta} = \frac{v_\theta}{r}\begin{bmatrix} 2T_{r\theta} & T_{rr} - T_{\theta\theta} & 0 \\[2ex] T_{rr} - T_{\theta\theta} & -2T_{r\theta} & 0 \\[2ex] 0 & 0 & 0 \end{bmatrix}$$

TABLE E.3 (continued)

IV.   Cone and Plate Flow: $(\phi = z^1,\ \theta = z^2,\ r = z^3)$

$$\frac{D\bar{T}_{ij}}{Dt} = \frac{v_\phi}{r\sin\theta}\begin{bmatrix} 2\cos\theta\,T_{\theta\phi} & (T_{\theta\theta} - T_{\phi\phi})\cos\theta & (T_{rr} - T_{\phi\phi})\sin\theta \\ (T_{\theta\theta} - T_{\phi\phi})\cos\theta & -2T_{\theta\phi}\cos\theta & -T_{\theta\phi}\sin\theta \\ (T_{rr} - T_{\phi\phi})\sin\theta & -T_{\theta\phi}\sin\theta & 0 \end{bmatrix}$$

TABLE E.4

Convected Drivative of a Covariant Tensor

$$\frac{\delta T_{ij}}{\delta t} = \frac{\partial T_{ij}}{\partial t} + v^k\frac{\partial T_{ij}}{\partial z^k} + \frac{\partial v^k}{\partial z^j}T_{ik} + \frac{\partial v^k}{\partial z^i}T_{kj}$$

$$\frac{\overline{\delta T}_{ij}}{\delta t} = h_i h_j\left[\frac{\partial}{\partial z^j}\left(\frac{v_1}{h_1}\right)\left(\bar{T}_{i1}h_i h_1\right) + \frac{\partial}{\partial z^i}\left(\frac{v_1}{h_1}\right)\left(\bar{T}_{ij}h_1 h_j\right)\right]$$

I.   Simple Shear: $(x = z^1,\ y = z^2,\ z = z^3)$

$$\frac{\overline{\delta T}_{ij}}{\delta t} = \frac{\partial v_x}{\partial y}\begin{bmatrix} 0 & T_{xx} & 0 \\ T_{xx} & 2T_{yx} & 0 \\ 0 & 0 & 0 \end{bmatrix}$$

II.   Poiseuille Flow: $(z = z^1,\ r = z^2,\ \theta = z^3)$

$$\frac{\overline{\delta T}_{ij}}{\delta t} = \frac{\partial v_z}{\partial r}\begin{bmatrix} 0 & T_{zz} & 0 \\ T_{zz} & 2T_{rz} & 0 \\ 0 & 0 & 0 \end{bmatrix}$$

$$\text{TABLE E.4 (continued)}$$

III. Couette Flow: $(\theta = z^1, \quad r = z^2, \quad z = z^3)$

$$\frac{\overline{\delta T}_{ij}}{\delta t} = r \frac{\partial}{\partial r} \left(\frac{v_\theta}{r} \right) \begin{bmatrix} 0 & T_{\theta\theta} & 0 \\ T_{\theta\theta} & 2T_{r\theta} & 0 \\ 0 & 0 & 0 \end{bmatrix}$$

IV. Cone and Plate Flow: $(\phi = z^1, \quad \theta = z^2, \quad r = z^3)$

$$\frac{\overline{\delta T}_{ij}}{\delta t} = \frac{\sin \theta}{r} \frac{\partial}{\partial \theta} \left(\frac{v_\phi}{\sin \theta} \right) \begin{bmatrix} 0 & T_{\phi\phi} & 0 \\ T_{\phi\phi} & 2T_{\theta\phi} & 0 \\ 0 & 0 & 0 \end{bmatrix}$$

$$\text{TABLE E.5}$$

$$\text{Jaumann Derivative}$$

$$\frac{\mathcal{D}T_{ij}}{\mathcal{D}t} = \frac{DT_{ij}}{Dt} + \frac{1}{2} \left(\Omega_{ik}T^k_{\ j} - T_i^{\ k}\Omega_{kj} \right)$$

I. Simple Shear: $(z = z^1, \quad y = z^2, \quad z = z^3)$

$$\frac{\overline{\mathcal{D}T}_{ij}}{\mathcal{D}t} = -\frac{1}{2} \frac{\partial v_x}{\partial y} \begin{bmatrix} 2T_{yx} & T_{yy} - T_{xx} & 0 \\ T_{yy} - T_{xx} & -2T_{yx} & 0 \\ 0 & 0 & 0 \end{bmatrix}$$

II. Poiseuille Flow: $(z = z^1, \quad r = z^2, \quad \theta = z^3)$

$$\frac{\overline{\mathcal{D}T}_{ij}}{\mathcal{D}t} = -\frac{1}{2} \frac{\partial v_z}{\partial r} \begin{bmatrix} 2T_{rz} & T_{rr} - T_{zz} & 0 \\ T_{rr} - T_{zz} & -2T_{rz} & 0 \\ 0 & 0 & 0 \end{bmatrix}$$

TABLE E.5 (continued)

III. Couette Flow: $(\theta = z^1, \quad r = z^2, \quad z = z^3)$

$$\frac{\overline{\mathcal{D}T}_{ij}}{\mathcal{D}t} = -\frac{1}{2} r \frac{\partial}{\partial r} \left(\frac{v_\theta}{r}\right) \begin{bmatrix} 2T_{r\theta} & T_{rr} - T_{\theta\theta} & 0 \\ T_{rr} - T_{\theta\theta} & -2T_{r\theta} & 0 \\ 0 & 0 & 0 \end{bmatrix}$$

IV. Cone and Plate Flow: $(\phi = z^1, \quad \theta = z^2, \quad r = z^3)$

$$\frac{\overline{\mathcal{D}T}_{ij}}{\mathcal{D}t} = -\frac{\sin\theta}{2r} \frac{\partial}{\partial\theta} \left(\frac{v_\phi}{\sin\theta}\right) \begin{bmatrix} 2T_{\theta\phi} & T_{\theta\theta} - T_{\phi\phi} & 0 \\ T_{\theta\theta} - T_{\phi\phi} & -2T_{\theta\phi} & 0 \\ 0 & 0 & 0 \end{bmatrix}$$

TABLE E.6

Spriggs Derivative

$$\mathcal{J}_\varepsilon T_{ij} = \frac{\mathcal{D}T_{ij}}{\mathcal{D}t} - \left(\frac{1+\varepsilon}{2}\right)\left[T_i^{\ m} \Delta_{mj} + T_j^{\ m} \Delta_{mi} - \frac{2}{3} T^{mn} \Delta_{mn} g_{ij}\right]$$

I. Simple Shear: $(x = z^1, \quad y = y^2, \quad z = z^3)$

$$\overline{\mathcal{J}_\varepsilon T}_{ij} = \frac{\partial v_x}{\partial y} \begin{bmatrix} -\left(\frac{4+\varepsilon}{3}\right)T_{yx} & -\left[\frac{\varepsilon}{2}(T_{yy} + T_{xx}) + T_{yy}\right] & 0 \\ -\left[\frac{\varepsilon}{2}(T_{yy} + T_{xx}) + T_{yy}\right] & \left(\frac{2-\varepsilon}{3}\right)T_{yx} & \\ 0 & 0 & 2\left(\frac{1+\varepsilon}{3}\right)T_{yx} \end{bmatrix}$$

TABLE E.6 (continued)

II. Poiseuille Flow: $(z = z^1, \quad r = z^2, \quad \theta = z^3)$

$$\overline{\mathcal{J}_\varepsilon T_{ij}} = \frac{\partial v_z}{\partial r} \begin{bmatrix} -\left(\dfrac{4+\varepsilon}{3}\right)T_{rz} & -\left[\dfrac{\varepsilon}{2}\,(T_{rr} + T_{zz}) + T_{rr}\right] & 0 \\[3ex] -\left[\dfrac{\varepsilon}{2}\,(T_{rr} + T_{zz}) + T_{rr}\right] & \left(\dfrac{2-\varepsilon}{3}\right)T_{rz} & 0 \\[3ex] 0 & 0 & 2\left(\dfrac{1+\varepsilon}{3}\right)T_{rz} \end{bmatrix}$$

III. Couette Flow: $(\theta = z^1, \quad r = z^2, \quad z = z^3)$

$$\overline{\mathcal{J}_\varepsilon T_{ij}} = r\,\frac{\partial}{\partial r}\left(\frac{v_\theta}{r}\right) \begin{bmatrix} -\left(\dfrac{4+\varepsilon}{3}\right)T_{r\theta} & -\left[\dfrac{\varepsilon}{2}\,(T_{rr} + T_{\theta\theta}) + T_{rr}\right] & 0 \\[3ex] -\left[\dfrac{\varepsilon}{2}\,(T_{rr} + T_{\theta\theta}) + T_{rr}\right] & \left(\dfrac{2-\varepsilon}{3}\right)T_{r\theta} & 0 \\[3ex] 0 & 0 & 2\left(\dfrac{1+\varepsilon}{3}\right)T_{r\theta} \end{bmatrix}$$

IV. Cone and Plate Flow: $(\phi = z^1, \quad \theta = z^2, \quad r = z^3)$

$$\overline{\mathcal{J}_\varepsilon T_{ij}} = \frac{\sin\theta}{r}\,\frac{\partial}{\partial\theta}\,\frac{v_\phi}{\sin\theta} \begin{bmatrix} -\left(\dfrac{4+\varepsilon}{3}\right)T_{\theta\phi} & -\left[\dfrac{\varepsilon}{2}(T_{\theta\theta} + T_{\phi\phi}) + T_{\theta\theta}\right] & 0 \\[3ex] -\left[\dfrac{\varepsilon}{2}(T_{\theta\theta} + T_{\phi\phi}) + T_{\theta\theta}\right] & \left(\dfrac{2-\varepsilon}{3}\right)T_{\theta\phi} & 0 \\[3ex] 0 & 0 & 2\left(\dfrac{1+\varepsilon}{3}\right)T_{\theta\phi} \end{bmatrix}$$

TABLE E.7

Covariant Finite (Almansi) Strain Tensor

$$\Gamma_{ij} = g_{ij} - \left(\frac{\partial z^m}{\partial z^i}\right)\left(\frac{\partial z^n}{\partial z^j}\right)g_{mn}; \quad z^i = z^i - (t - t')v^i$$

I. Simple Shear: $z^1 = x - (t - t')v_x(y), \quad z^2 = y, \quad z^3 = z$

$$\overline{\Gamma_{ij}} = (t - t')\frac{\partial v_x}{\partial y}\begin{bmatrix} 0 & 1 & 0 \\ 1 & -(t - t')\frac{\partial v_x}{\partial y} & 0 \\ 0 & 0 & 0 \end{bmatrix}$$

II. Poiseuille Flow: $z^1 = z - (t - t')v^z(r), \quad z^2 = r, \quad z^3 = \theta$

$$\overline{\Gamma_{ij}} = (t - t')\frac{\partial v_z}{\partial r}\begin{bmatrix} 0 & 1 & 0 \\ 1 & -(t - t')\frac{\partial v_z}{\partial r} & 0 \\ 0 & 0 & 0 \end{bmatrix}$$

III. Couette Flow: $z^1 = \theta - (t - t')v^\theta(r), \quad z^2 = r, \quad z^3 = z$

$$\overline{\Gamma_{ij}} = (t - t')r\frac{\partial}{\partial r}\left(\frac{v_\theta}{r}\right)\begin{bmatrix} 0 & 1 & 0 \\ 1 & -(t - t')r\frac{\partial}{\partial r}\left(\frac{v_\theta}{r}\right) & 0 \\ 0 & 0 & 0 \end{bmatrix}$$

TABLE E.7 (continued)

IV. Cone and Plate Flow: $z^1 = \phi - (t - t')v^\phi(\theta)$, $z^2 = \theta$, $z^3 = r$

$$\overline{\Gamma_{ij}} = (t - t') \frac{\sin \theta}{r} \frac{\partial}{\partial \theta}\left(\frac{v_\phi}{\sin \theta}\right) \begin{bmatrix} 0 & 1 & 0 \\ 1 & -(t - t') \frac{\sin \theta}{r} \frac{\partial}{\partial \theta} \frac{v_\phi}{\sin \theta} & 0 \\ 0 & 0 & 0 \end{bmatrix}$$

TABLE E.8

Contravariant Finite (Finger) Strain Tensor

$$\Gamma^{ij} = \left(\frac{\partial z^i}{\partial Z^m}\right)\left(\frac{\partial z^j}{\partial Z^n}\right) g^{mn} - g^{ij}, \quad z^i = Z^i + (t - t')v^i$$

I.   Simple Shear: $x = Z^1 + (t - t')v_x(y)$, $y = Z^2$, $z = Z^3$

$$\overline{\Gamma^{ij}} = (t - t') \frac{\partial v_x}{\partial y} \begin{bmatrix} (t - t') \dfrac{\partial v_x}{\partial y} & 1 & 0 \\ 1 & 0 & 0 \\ 0 & 0 & 0 \end{bmatrix}$$

II.   Poiseuille Flow: $z = Z^1 + (t - t')v^z(r)$, $r = Z^2$, $\theta = Z^3$

$$\overline{\Gamma^{ij}} = (t - t') \frac{\partial v_z}{\partial r} \begin{bmatrix} (t - t') \dfrac{\partial v_z}{\partial r} & 1 & 0 \\ 1 & 0 & 0 \\ 0 & 0 & 0 \end{bmatrix}$$

TABLE E.8 (continued)

III. Couette Flow: $\theta = z^1 + (t - t')v^\theta(r)$, $r = z^2$, $z = z^3$

$$
\Gamma^{ij} = (t - t')r \frac{\partial}{\partial r}\left(\frac{v_\theta}{r}\right)
\begin{bmatrix}
(t - t')r \frac{\partial}{\partial r}\left(\frac{v_\theta}{r}\right) & 1 & 0 \\[12pt]
1 & 0 & 0 \\[12pt]
0 & 0 & 0
\end{bmatrix}
$$

IV. Cone and Plate Flow: $\phi = z^1 + (t - t')v^\phi(\theta)$, $\theta = z^2$, $r = z^3$

$$
\overline{\Gamma_{ij}} = (t - t')\frac{\sin\theta}{r}\frac{\partial}{\partial\theta}\left(\frac{v_\phi}{\sin\theta}\right)
\begin{bmatrix}
(t - t')\frac{\sin\theta}{r}\frac{\partial}{\partial\theta}\left(\frac{v_\phi}{\sin\theta}\right) & 1 & 0 \\[12pt]
1 & 0 & 0 \\[12pt]
0 & 0 & 0
\end{bmatrix}
$$

REFERENCES

Chapter 1

1.1. M. Reiner, *Lectures on Theoretical Rheology*, North-Holland Publishing, Amsterdam, 1960.

1.2. L. M. Milne-Thompson, *Theoretical Hydrodynamics*, Macmillan, New York, 1955, p. 542.

1.3. W. H. Michener, *Physics for Students of Science and Engineering*, Wiley, New York, 1947.

1.4. C. Truesdell, Elasticity and fluid dynamics, *J. Rational Mech. Anal.*, *1*:125 (1952).

1.5. A. G. Fredrickson, *Principles and Applications of Rheology*, Prentice-Hall, Englewood-Cliffs, N.J., 1964.

1.6. R. Aris, *Vectors, Tensors, and the Basic Equations of Fluid Mechanics*, Prentice-Hall, Englewood-Cliffs, N.J., 1962.

1.7. A. Sommerfeld, *The Mechanics of Deformable Bodies*, Academic Press, New York, 1964.

Chapter 2

2.1. J. G. Savins, in *Encyclopedia of Industrial Chemical Analysis*, Vol. 3, Wiley, New York, 1966, pp. 408–463.

2.2. R. B. Bird, W. E. Stewart, and E. N. Lightfoot, *Transport Phenomena*, Wiley, New York, 1960.

2.3. W. L. Wilkinson, *Non-Newtonian Fluids*, Pergamon, New York, 1960.

2.4.   M. Reiner, *Deformation, Strain, and Flow*, Lewis, London, 1960.

2.5.   D. M. Meter and R. B. Bird, Tube flow of non-Newtonian polymer solutions: Part I. Laminar flow and rheological models, *A.I.Ch.E. J.*, 10:878 (1964).

2.6.   M. M. Cross, in *Polymer Systems--Deformation and Flow* (R. E. Wetton and R. M. Whorlow, eds.), Macmillan, London, 1968.

2.7.   M. C. Williams, *A.I.Ch.E. J.*, 12:1064 (1966).

2.8.   M. Reiner, *Lectures on Theoretical Rheology*, North-Holland Publishing, Amsterdam, 1960.

2.9.   M. Reiner, The Deborah number, *Phys. Today*, 17(1):61 (1964).

2.10.   T. Alfrey, *Mechanical Behavior of High Polymers*, Interscience, New York, 1948, p. 533.

2.11.   B. Gross, *Mathematical Structures of the Theories of Viscoelasticity*, Hermann, Paris, 1953.

2.12.   J. D. Ferry and M. L. Williams, *J. Colloid Sci.*, 7:347 (1952).

2.13.   J. D. Ferry, *Viscoelastic Properties of Polymers*, Wiley, New York, 1961.

2.14.   T. L. Smith, *Trans. Soc. Rheol.*, 2:131 (1958).

2.15.   B. Zimm, *J. Chem. Phys.*, 24:269 (1956).

2.16.   P. E. Rouse, *J. Chem. Phys.*, 21:1272 (1953).

2.17.   T. W. Spriggs, *Chem. Eng. Sci.*, 20:931 (1965).

2.18.   T. W. Spriggs and R. B. Bird, *Ind. Eng. Chem. Fundamentals*, 4:182 (1965).

2.19.   R. F. Ginn and A. B. Metzner, *Trans. Soc. Rheol.*, 13:429 (1969).

2.20.   R. I. Tanner, *Trans. Soc. Rheol.*, 17:365 (1973).

2.21.   R. Darby, *Trans. Soc. Rheol.*, 14:185 (1970).

2.22.   A. G. Fredrickson, *Principles and Applications of Rheology*, Prentice-Hall, Englewood-Cliffs, N.J., 1964.

Chapter 3

3.1.   J. S. Dahler and L. E. Scriven, *Nature*, 192:36 (1961).

3.2.   R. B. Bird, W. E. Stewart, and E. N. Lightfoot, *Transport Phenomena*, Wiley, New York, 1960.

3.3.   S. Whitaker, *Introduction to Fluid Mechanics*, Prentice-Hall, Englewood-Cliffs, N.J., 1968.

3.4.   W. H. Corcoran, J. B. Opfell, and B. H. Sage, *Momentum Transfer in Fluids*, Academic Press, New York, 1956.

3.5. A. G. Fredrickson, *Principles and Applications of Rheology*, Prentice-Hall, Englewood-Cliffs, N.J., 1964.

3.6. A. Sommerfeld, *Mechanics of Deformable Bodies: Lectures on Theoretical Physics*, Vol. 2, Academic Press, New York, 1964.

3.7. Y. C. Fung, *A First Course in Continuum Mechanics*, Prentice-Hall, Englewood-Cliffs, N.J., 1969.

3.8. L. R. Calcote, *Introduction to Continuum Mechanics,* Van Nostrand, New York, 1969.

3.9. J. G. Knudsen and D. L. Katz, *Fluid Dynamics and Heat Transfer*, McGraw-Hill, New York, 1958.

3.10. B. D. Coleman, H. Markovitz, and W. Noll, *Viscometric Flows of Non-Newtonian Fluids,* Springer Verlag, New York, 1966.

Chapter 4

4.1. R. B. Bird, W. F. Stewart, and E. N. Lightfoot, *Transport Phenomena*, Wiley, New York, 1960.

4.2. J. M. McKelvey, *Polymer Processing*, Wiley, New York, 1962.

4.3. A. H. P. Skelland, *Non-Newtonian Flow and Heat Transfer*, Wiley, New York, 1967.

4.4. A. B. Fredrickson, *Principles and Applications of Rheology*, Prentice-Hall, Englewood-Cliffs, N.J., 1964.

4.5. J. R. A. Pearson, *Mechanical Principles of Polymer Melt Processing*, Pergamon, New York, 1966.

4.6. B. D. Coleman, H. Markovitz, and W. Noll, *Viscometric Flows of Non-Newtonian Fluids*, Springer Verlag, New York, 1966.

4.7. W. L. Wilkinson, *Non-Newtonian Fluids*, Pergamon, New York, 1960.

4.8. R. J. Hansen, Drag reduction in polymer solutions, *A.I.Ch.E. Symp. Ser. 130*, 69 (1973).

4.9. J. M. McKelvey, *Polymer Processing*, Wiley, New York, 1962, p. 21.

4.10. L. J. F. Broer, *Appl. Sci. Res.*, *A6*:266 (1957).

4.11. A. S. Lodge, *Elastic Liquids*, Academic Press, New York, 1964, p. 219.

4.12. C. D. Han, M. Charles, and W. Philippoff, *Trans. Soc. Rheol.*, *14*(3):393 (1970).

4.13. C. D. Han and M. Charles, *Trans. Soc. Rheol.*, *14*(3):409 (1970).

4.14. C. D. Han and M. Charles, *Trans. Soc. Rheol.*, *15*(2):371 (1971).

4.15. R. I. Tanner, *Trans. Soc. Rheol.*, *17*(2):365 (1973).

4.16.   R. F. Ginn and A. B. Metzner, *Proc. 4th Int. Cong. Rheol.*,
        Part 2 (1965).

4.17.   R. L. Powell and S. Middleman, *Trans. Soc. Rheol.*, *13*(1):111
        (1969).

4.18.   W. W. Graessley, S. D. Glasscock, and R. L. Crawley, *Trans.
        Soc. Rheol.*, *14*(4):519 (1970).

4.19.   R. I. Tanner, *J. Polymer Sci.*, *A-2*, *8*:2067 (1970).

4.20.   J. Vlachopoulos, M. Horie, and S. Lidorikis, *Trans. Soc.
        Rheol.*, *16*(4):669 (1972).

4.21.   E. B. Bagley and H. J. Duffey, *Trans. Soc. Rheol.*, *14*(4):545
        (1970).

4.22.   S. Middleman and J. Gavis, *Phys. Fluids*, *4*:355, 1450 (1961).

4.23.   D. R. Oliver, *Can. J. Chem. Eng.*, *44*:100 (1966).

4.24.   H. L. LaNieve, III, and D. C. Bogue, *J. Appl. Polymer Sci.*,
        12:353 (1968).

4.25.   A. Ram and M. Narkis, *J. Appl. Polymer Sci.*, *10*:361 (1966).

4.26.   T. W. McHugh, E. R. Harrell, J. W. Powell, and R. P. Chartoff,
        Trans. Soc. Rheol., *16*(2):331 (1972).

Chapter 5

5.1.   B. Rabinowitsch, *Z. Phys. Chem.*, *A145*:1 (1929).

5.2.   M. Mooney, *J. Rheol.*, *2*:210 (1931).

5.3.   H. Schlichting, *Boundary Layer Theory*, McGraw-Hill, New York,
        1955, p. 218.

5.4.   E. B. Bagley, *J. Appl. Phys.*, *28*:624 (1957).

5.5.   A. G. Fredrickson, *Principles and Applications of Rheology*,
        Prentice-Hall, Englewood-Cliffs, N.J., 1964, p. 197.

5.6.   J. G. Oldroyd, in *Rheology*, Chap. 16 (F. R. Eiric, ed.),
        Academic Press, New York, 1957.

5.7.   J. R. Van Wazer, J. W. Lyons, K. Y. Kim, and R. E. Colwell,
        Viscosity and Flow Measurement, Interscience, New York, 1963.

5.8.   I. M. Krieger and H. Elrod, *J. Appl. Phys.*, *24*:134 (1953).

5.9.   I. M. Krieger, *Trans. Soc. Rheol.*, *12*:5 (1968).

5.10.   I. M. Krieger and S. H. Maron, *J. Appl. Phys.*, *23*:147 (1952).

5.11.   K. Walters and N. D. Waters, in *Polymer Systems, Deformation
        and Flow*, Chap. 17 (R. E. Wetton and R. W. Whorlow, eds.),
        Macmillan, 1968.

5.12.   O. Olabisi and M. C. Williams, *Trans. Soc. Rheol.*, *16*:727 (1972).

5.13. K. Walters, *Basic Concepts and Formulae for the Rheogoniometer*, Sagamo Controls, Ltd., North Bersted, Begnor Regis, Sussex, England, 1968.

5.14. A. S. Lodge, *Elastic Liquids*, Academic Press, New York, 1964.

5.15. R. I. Tanner, *Trans. Soc. Rheol.*, *14*:483 (1970).

5.16. N. Adams and A. S. Lodge, *Phil. Trans. Roy. Soc. London*, *A256*:149 (1964).

5.17. H. W. Greensmith and R. S. Rivlin, *Trans. Roy. Soc. London*, *A245*:399 (1953).

5.18. M. C. Williams, *Chem. Eng. Sci.*, *20*:693 (1965).

5.19. M. J. Miller and E. B. Christiansen, *A.I.Ch.E. J.*, *18*:600 (1972).

5.20. R. F. Ginn and A. B. Metzner, *Proc. Fourth Internat. Congr. Rheol.* (E. H. Lee, ed.), Interscience, 1965, p. 583.

5.21. R. F. Ginn and A. B. Metzner, *Trans. Soc. Rheol.*, *13*:429 (1969).

5.22. T. Kotaka, M. Kurata, and M. Tamura, *J. Appl. Phys.*, *30*:1705 (1959).

5.23. F. J. Padden and T. W. DeWitt, *J. Appl. Phys.*, *25*:1086 (1954).

5.24. H. Markowitz, *J. Polymer Sci.*, *B3*:3 (1965).

5.25. B. D. Coleman, H. Markovitz, and W. Noll, *Viscometric Flows of Non-Newtonian Fluids*, Springer Verlag, New York, 1966, p. 82.

5.26. J. M. Davies, J. F. Hutton and K. Walters, *J. Phys. D.: Appl. Phys.*, *6*:2259 (1973).

5.27. C. D. Han, *A.I.Ch.E. J.*, *18*:116 (1972).

5.28. A. B. Metzner, W. T. Houghton, R. A. Sailor, and J. L. White, *Trans. Soc. Rheol.*, *5*:133 (1961).

5.29. W. W. Graessley, S. D. Glascock, and R. J. Grawley, *Trans. Soc. Rheol.*, *14*:519 (1970).

5.30. R. L. Powell and S. Middleman, *Trans. Soc. Rheol.*, *13*:111 (1969).

5.31. E. B. Bagley and H. J. Duffey, *Trans. Soc. Rheol.*, *14*:5.45 (1970).

5.32. R. I. Tanner, *J. Poly. Sci.*, *A-2*, *8*:2067 (1970).

5.33. J. Vlachopoulos, M. Horie, and S. Lidorikis, *Trans. Soc. Rheol.*, *16*:669 (1972).

5.34. J. D. Ferry, *Viscoelastic Properties of Polymers*, Chap. 5 and references therein, Wiley, New York, 1970.

5.35. K. Walters, *Basic Concepts and Formulae for the Rheogoniometer*, Sagamo Controls, Ltd., Bognor Regis, Sussex, England, 1968.

5.36. K. Walters, *Quart. J. Mech. Appl. Math.*, *13*:444 (1960).

5.37. K. Walters, *Quart. J. Mech. Appl. Math.*, *14*:431 (1961).

5.38. K. Walters and R. A. Kemp, in *Polymer Systems*, Chap. 18, Proc. 1966 Ann. Conf. of Br. Soc. Rheol. (R. E. Wetton and R. M. Whorlow, eds.), Macmillan, New York, 1968.

5.39. K. Walters and R. A. Kemp, *Rheol. Acta*, 7:1 (1968).

5.40. M. H. Birnboim and J. D. Ferry, *J. Appl. Phys.*, *32*:2305 (1961).

5.41. N. W. Tschoegl and J. D. Ferry, *Kolloid Zeit.*, *189*:37 (1963).

5.42. J. G. Oldroyd, *Quart. J. Mech. Appl. Math.*, 4:271 (1951).

5.43. A. G. Fredrickson, *Quart. J. Mech. Appl. Math.*, 4:139 (1951).

5.44. R. Darby, *Trans. Soc. Rheol.*, *14*:185 (1970).

5.45. S. Middleman, *The Flow of High Polymers*, Wiley, New York, 1968.

5.46. R. I. Tanner and A. C. Pipkin, *Trans. Soc. Rheol.*, *13*:471 (1969).

5.47. A. C. Pipkin and R. I. Tanner, *Mechanics Today*, *1*:272 (1972).

Chapter 6

6.1. G. A. Hawkins, *Multilinear Analysis for Students in Engineering and Science*, Wiley, New York, 1963.

6.2. R. Aris, *Vectors, Tensors, and the Basic Equations of Fluid Mechanics*, Prentice-Hall, Englewood-Cliffs, N.J., 1962.

6.3. A. J. McConnel, *Applications of Tensor Analysis*, Dover, New York, 1957.

6.4. M. R. Spiegel, *Vector Analysis*, Shaum's Outline, McGraw-Hill, New York (1959).

6.5. I. S. Sokolnikoff, *Tensor Analysis*, Wiley, New York, 1964.

6.6. L. Brand, *Vector and Tensor Analysis*, Chapman and Hall, London, 1947.

6.7. S. Middleman, *The Flow of High Polymers*, Part A, Interscience, New York, 1968.

Chapter 7

7.1. A. G. Fredrickson, *Principles and Applications of Rheology*, Prentice-Hall, Englewood-Cliffs, N.J., 1964, p. 68ff.

7.2. M. Reiner, *Am. J. Math.*, *67*:350 (1945).

7.3. A. G. Fredrickson, *Principles and Applications of Rheology*, Prentice-Hall, Englewood-Cliffs, N.J., 1964, p. 70.

7.4. E. A. Uebler, *Ind. Eng. Chem. Fundamentals*, *10*:250 (1971).

7.5. T. W. Spriggs, J. D. Huppler, and R. B. Bird, *Trans. Soc. Rheol.*, *10*:191 (1966).

7.6. D. C. Bogue and J. O. Doughty, *Ind. Eng. Chem. Fundamentals*, *5*:243 (1966).

7.7. R. F. Ginn and A. B. Metzner, *Trans. Soc. Rheol.*, *13*:429 (1969).

7.8. R. I. Tanner *Trans. Soc. Rheol.*, *17*(2):365 (1973).

7.9. H. Jeffreys, *The Earth*, 2nd ed., Cambridge University Press, London, 1929, p. 265.

7.10. H. Frohlich and R. Sack, *Proc. Roy. Soc. London*, *A218*:122 (1953).

7.11. J. G. Oldroyd, *Proc. Roy. Soc. London*, *A245*:278 (1958).

7.12. T. W. Spriggs, *Chem. Eng. Sci.*, *20*:931 (1965).

7.13. J. G. Oldroyd, in *Second Order Effects in Elasticity, Plasticity, and Fluid Dynamics* (M. Reiner and D. Abir eds.), Macmillan, New York, 1964.

7.14. R. B. Bird, W. E. Stewart, E. N. Lightfoot, and T. W. Chapman, Lectures in transport phenomena, Chap. 1, *A.I.Ch.E. Continuing Educ. Ser.*, *4* (1969).

7.15. A. S. Lodge, *Elastic Liquids*, Academic Press, New York, 1964.

7.16. R. B. Bird and P. J. Carreau, *Chem. Eng. Sci.*, *23*:427 (1968).

7.17. P. J. Carreau, I. F. MacDonald, and R. B. Bird, *Chem. Eng. Sci.*, *23*:901 (1968).

7.18. B. J. Meister, *Trans. Soc. Rheol.*, *15*:63 (1971).

7.19. M. C. Williams and R. B. Bird, *A.I.Ch.E. J.*, *8*:378 (1962).

7.20. M. C. Williams and R. B. Bird, *Phys. Fluids*, *5*:1867 (1963).

7.21. J. D. Hyppler, I. F. MacDonald, E. Ashare, T. W. Spriggs, R. B. Bird, and L. A. Holmes, *Trans. Soc. Rheol.*, *11*:181 (1962).

7.22. T. W. Spriggs and R. B. Bird, *Ind. Eng. Chem. Fundamentals*, *4*:182 (1965).

7.23. I. F. MacDonald and R. B. Bird, *J. Phys. Chem.*, *70*:2068 (1966).

7.24. J. D. Hyppler, E. Ashare, and L. A. Holmes, *Trans. Soc. Rheol.*, *11*:159 (1967).

7.25. E. Ashare, *Trans. Soc. Rheol.*, *12*:535 (1968).

7.26. R. B. Bird and E. K. Harris, Jr., *A.I.Ch.E. J.*, *14*:758 (1968).

7.27.   I. F. MacDonald, B. D. Marsh, and E. Ashare, *Chem. Eng. Sci.*, *24*:1615 (1969).

7.28.   J. L. White and A. B. Metzner, *J. Appl. Polymer Sci.*, 7:1867 (1963).

7.29.   A. B. Metzner, J. L. White, and M. M. Denn, *A.I.Ch.E. J.*, *12*:863 (1966).

7.30.   A. B. Metzner, E. A. Uebler, and C. F. Chan Man Fong, *A.I.Ch.E. J.*, *15*:750 (1969).

7.31.   B. Bernstein, E. A. Kearsley, and L. J. Zapas, *Trans. Soc. Rheol.*, 7:391 (1963).

7.32.   R. I. Tanner and J. M. Simmons, *Chem. Eng. Sci.*, *22*:1803 (1967).

7.33.   D. C. Bogue, *Ind. Eng. Chem. Fundamentals*, *5*:253 (1966).

7.34.   E. B. Adams and D. C. Bogue, *A.I.Ch.E. J.*, *16*:53 (1970).

7.35.   J. D. Goddard and C. Miller, *Rheol. Acta*, *5*:177 (1966).

INDEX

168494